Illustrated Encyclopedia of

Applied and Engineering Physics

Volume II

H–O

Illustrated Encyclopedia of

Applied and Engineering Physics

Volume II

H–O

Robert Splinter, PhD

CRC Press
Taylor & Francis Group
Boca Raton London New York

CRC Press is an imprint of the
Taylor & Francis Group, an **informa** business

CRC Press
Taylor & Francis Group
6000 Broken Sound Parkway NW, Suite 300
Boca Raton, FL 33487-2742

Printed and bound in India by Replika Press Pvt. Ltd.

Printed on acid-free paper
Version Date: 20160831

International Standard Book Number-13: 978-1-4987-4082-1 (Hardback)

Library of Congress Cataloging-in-Publication Data

Names: Splinter, Robert, author.
Title: Illustrated encyclopedia of applied and engineering physics / Robert Splinter.
Description: Boca Raton, FL : CRC Press, Taylor & Francis Group, [2016] | "2016 | Includes bibliographical references and index.
Identifiers: LCCN 2015040711| ISBN 9781498740784 (alk. paper : v. 1) | ISBN 1498740782 (alk. paper : v. 1) | ISBN 9781498740821 (alk. paper : v. 2) | ISBN 9781498740838 (alk. paper : v. 3) | ISBN 1498740839 (alk. paper : v. 3)
Subjects: LCSH: Physics--Dictionaries.
Classification: LCC QC5 .S65 2016 | DDC 530.03--dc23
LC record available at http://lccn.loc.gov/2015040711

Visit the Taylor & Francis Web site at
http://www.taylorandfrancis.com

and the CRC Press Web site at
http://www.crcpress.com

Contents

Preface

The purpose of this *encyclopedia* is to provide a single, concise reference that contains terms and expressions used in the study, practice, and applications of physical sciences. The reader will be able to quickly identify critical information about professional jargon, important people, and events. This encyclopedia gives self-contained definitions with essentials regarding the technical terms and their usages and information about important people in the following areas of physics:

- Acoustics
- Astronomy/astrophysics
- Atomic physics
- Biomedical physics
- Chemical physics
- Computational physics
- Condensed matter
- Dynamics
- Electromagnetism
- Electronics
- Energy
- Engineering
- Fluid dynamics
- General
- Geophysics
- High-energy physics
- Imaging
- Instrumentation
- Materials sciences
- Mechanics
- Meteorology
- Nanotechnology
- Nuclear physics
- Optics
- Quantum physics
- Relativistic physics
- Rheology
- Sensing
- Signal processing
- Solid-state physics
- Theoretical physics
- Thermodynamics
- Ultrafast phenomena

This reference differs from the standard dictionaries in its inclusion of numerous illustrations, including photographs, micrographs, diagrams, graphs, and tables, which support the textual definitions and draw the reader into the explanation to enhance didactic value. Together, these over 2500 entries will educate the reader about the current practice of physics and its applications in biomedicine, materials sciences, chemical engineering, electrical engineering, mechanical engineering, geology, astronomy, meteorology, and energy.

It is envisioned that novices and trainees, in addition to seasoned professionals, will find this resource useful, both for sustained reading and for taking a dip into the topics periodically. The contents are also designed to help the professionals who are new to a work environment and recently enrolled students who need to become more familiar with terminology and nuances relevant to certain research and applications. Moreover, it will assist in understanding the primary literature as well as technical reports and proposals. Finally, any student from the high school to graduate levels should be able to benefit from the broad and applied emphasis of this concise encyclopedia, which may support undergraduate courses in applied sciences for nonscience majors.

AUTHOR

Robert Splinter MSc PhD—University of North Carolina at Charlotte, North Carolina

Author

Robert Splinter, PhD, obtained his master of science degree in applied physics from the Eindhoven University of Technology, Eindhoven, the Netherlands, and his PhD from the VU University of Amsterdam. Dr. Splinter built his career as a scientist and technology manager in biomedical engineering. His work is dedicated to resolving issues in device development with a particular focus on medicine and biology through the development of novel diagnostic techniques and treatment methods using all multidisciplinary aspects of engineering and applied physics.

He cofounded several companies in biomedical engineering and worked for several established metrology and medical device companies. In addition, Dr. Splinter worked in clinical settings, prototyping, and validating devices using the full practical and theoretical knowledge of physics, engineering, electrical engineering, chemistry, and biology. He is an associate professor (Adj.) in the Department of Physics at the University of North Carolina at Charlotte.

H

[atomic, chemical] HYDROGEN ATOM $[(^2_1)H]$, most elementary ELEMENT known. The hydrogen excitation spectra are described by the BALMER SERIES, discovered by JOHANN JAKOB BALMER (1825–1898) in 1885 with the FREQUENCY (ν) spectrum defined as $\nu = cR\left[\left(1/2^2\right)+\left(1/n^2\right)\right]$, where $R = 10{,}967{,}758\,\text{m}^{-1}$ is the RYDBERG CONSTANT, $c = 299{,}792{,}458$ m/s is the speed of light, and $n = 3, 4, 5, \ldots$ is an integer depicting the excitation levels. The Balmer series emission lines (i.e., ATOMIC LINE SPECTRA) are all in the visible spectrum.

H_2 problem

[atomic, computational, condensed matter, energy, mechanics, solid-state] The SCATTERING of electrons of hydrogen forms an interesting computational problem with respect to the theoretical observations. The electron scattering process is apparently a function of the electron density based on the acting strong and weak forces on atomic level. The electron velocity (i.e., momentum) distribution is non-Gaussian, providing an INELASTIC SCATTERING model. The ENERGY configuration of the hydrogen MOLECULE creates an interesting format due to the fact that the protons can have identical SPIN and this leads to DEGENERACY. While the electrons are energetically forced to be antiparallel (PAULI EXCLUSION PRINCIPLE), this does not apply to the protons since they are not in the same ATOM, whereas the electrons are shared between the atoms. The PROTON spins form both a SINGLET and a TRIPLET.

Haas, Arthur Erich (1884–1941)

[atomic, nuclear, quantum] A physicist and scientist from Austria. Arthur Haas defined that electrons orbit around, then still undefined, the NUCLEUS of the atomic structure in uniform circular orbit with "fixed" radius in 1910, predating the atomic model developed by NIELS HENRIK DAVID BOHR (1885–1962) by three years. This was a substantiated contribution to the QUANTUM principles (see Figure H.1).

Figure H.1 Arthur Erich Haas (1884–1941). (Courtesy of Universitätsarchiv Leipzig, Leipzig, Germany.)

Haas, Georg (1886–1971)

[biomedical] A physician from Germany that is known to perform the first human KIDNEY dialysis in 1926, following in the footsteps of THOMAS GRAHAM (1805–1869), ADOLF EUGEN FICK (1829–1901) [also known for FICK'S LAW], and JOHN JACOB ABEL (1857–1938). Even though all of his patients eventually died either from the procedure or from the consequences of the disease, the process was later perfected by WILLEM JOHAN KOLFF (1911–2009) and is still in use (see Figure H.2).

Figure H.2 Georg Haas (1886–1971).

Hadron

[atomic, general, high-energy, nuclear] The generic name of a PARTICLE class with a strong inter-particle attraction. Hadrons are, for instance, protons (subclass: BARYON), neutrons (subclass: baryon), as well as the ð, K, and D mesons, and their respective antiparticles. The known constituents of ordinary nuclei, PROTON and NEUTRON, are members of a hadron subclass called BARYONS. Other baryons are "strange" ($\overline{s}$) and "charmed" ($\overline{c}$), for example, 0 s and 0 c. Baryons obey FERMI–DIRAC STATISTICS, have half-integral SPIN, and are also known as FERMIONS. Another subclass of hadrons: MESONS obey BOSE–EINSTEIN STATISTICS, have zero or integral spin, and are known as BOSONS. The ELECTRIC CHARGES of baryons and mesons have three options: either zero or a charge equivalent to the electron in either positive or negative value.

Hagen, Gotthilf Heinrich Ludwig (1797–1884)

[engineering, fluid dynamics] A hydraulic engineer and physicist from Germany (Prussian Empire). Gotthilf Hagan provided a significant theoretical description with respect to hydraulic displacement and FLOW. Specifically, the HAGEN–POISEUILLE LAW summarizes the combined efforts by Gotthilf Hagan and JEAN LÉONARD MARIE POISEUILLE (1799–1869) (see Figure H.3).

Figure H.3 Gotthilf Heinrich Ludwig Hagen (1797–1884).

Hagen–Poiseuille law

[biomedical, fluid dynamics, rheology] A viscous flow rate for a NEWTONIAN FLUID flowing through a tube is described by the correlation between the rate of flow (Q) of a fluid (Q/t, over time t) with respect to the WALL stress ($\sigma_r = Pr/2\ell = F_{xy}/A_{xy} = \eta\left[d(dx/dy)/dt\right]$, for the force: F_{xy} over an area A_{xy}) and the radius of the tube (r) and the length of the flow (l), all in relation to the VISCOSITY (η) when a PRESSURE (P) is applied, expressed as $Q/t = \pi Pr^4/8\eta\ell$. This FLOW dynamic description was defined independently by both JEAN LÉONARD MARIE POISEUILLE (1799–1869) in 1838 and GOTTHILF HEINRICH LUDWIG HAGEN (1797–1884) in 1839.

Hahn, Otto (1879–1968)

[general, nuclear] A German chemist and scientist who, working with LISE MEITNER (1878–1968), a Jew under Hitler's directive, and FRIEDRICH WILHELM "FRITZ" STRASSMANN (Straßmann, 1902–1980), verified the predictions of ENRICO FERMI (1901–1954) followed by IDA NODDACK (1896–1978) regarding the splitting of uranium by bombardment with thermal NEUTRON in 1938. Hahn described the principle of FISSION of heavy nuclei and received the Nobel Prize in Chemistry in 1944 on this work. The Hahn–Meitner–Strassmann experiment revealed the uranium was split into isotopes of the ELEMENT barium $^{138}_{56}Ba$ and $^{95}_{36}Kr$ (krypton ISOTOPE) and three neutrons with the difference in mass expressed as energy 216 MeV for splitting one MOLECULE, the equivalent of the ENERGY released resulting from the combustion of approximately 1 million molecules of gasoline (approximately 1×10^{16} l of GAS at standard pressure [P] and standard temperature [T]; from $PV = nRT$, where n is the number of moles [$1\,\text{mole} = 6.022 \times 10^{23}$ molecules, i.e., Avogadro's number $N_A = 6.022 \times 10^{23}$], and $R = 8.3145\,\text{J/molK}$ the universal gas constant), as derived and concluded by LISE MEITNER (1878–1968) and her nephew Otto Robert Frisch (1904–1979) in late 1938 while working at the Bohr Institute in Copenhagen (see Figure H.4).

Figure H.4 Otto Hahn (1879–1968) in 1944.

Hale, George Ellery (1868–1938)

[astronomy/astrophysics, optics] An astronomer and physicist from the United States. In 1908, Hale discovered the MAGNETIC effects of sunspots associated with their inherent vorticity under examination with the spectroheliscope of his own design (see Figure H.5).

Figure H.5 George Ellery Hale (1868–1938). (Courtesy of *The World's Work: A History of Our Time*, Vol. XXV, Doubleday, Page & Company, Garden City, NY, 1913.)

Hale's law

[astronomy/astrophysics] A description of the symmetry in MAGNETIC polarity in correlation with sunspot cycles from northern to southern hemisphere.

Hale–Bopp comet

[astronomy/astrophysics] A COMET discovered in 1995 by Alan Hale (1958–) and amateur astronomer Thomas Bopp (1949–), remaining visible for more than 18 months. The trajectory of the Hale–Bopp comet has a period of approximately 4200 years (see Figure H.6).

Figure H.6 Picture of Hale–Bopp comet with the separate gas trail and the ion tail visible.

Half thickness ($d_{1/2}$)

[atomic, biomedical, computational, general, nuclear] The thickness of absorbing material necessary to reduce the intensity of RADIATION to one-half (50%) of its incident value.

Half-cell

[biomedical, chemical, electromagnetism, energy, general, solid-state] Two cells in contact but separated by a semipermeable BARRIER allowing for a slow and controlled chemical reaction. One CELL has an ELECTROLYTE with cations and the other cell has an electrolyte that produces anions. The connection between the two cells indices a FLOW of electrons that reduces the cations and oxidizes the anions. The connection between the two half-cells can be made by means of a wire where the ELECTRODE in the CATION solute is the CATHODE and the electrode in the electrolyte with anions is the ANODE. In biology, half-cells generate electric potentials that can be measured externally while performing electric communications and inducing actions in the biology, such as the formation of the NERNST POTENTIAL, and inducing muscular contraction and neutral transmission of sensations and delivery of triggers to instigate actions. The half-cell potential in batteries provides the ENERGY for operation of electrical devices, whereas in biology this is measured by means of electrodes on the SKIN or needle electrode based on the respective mechanism of action resulting from ELECTROMYOGRAM for MUSCLE action, ELECTROENCEPHALOGRAM for brain ACTIVITY, and ELECTROCARDIOGRAM for cardiac contraction to name a few (see Figure H.7).

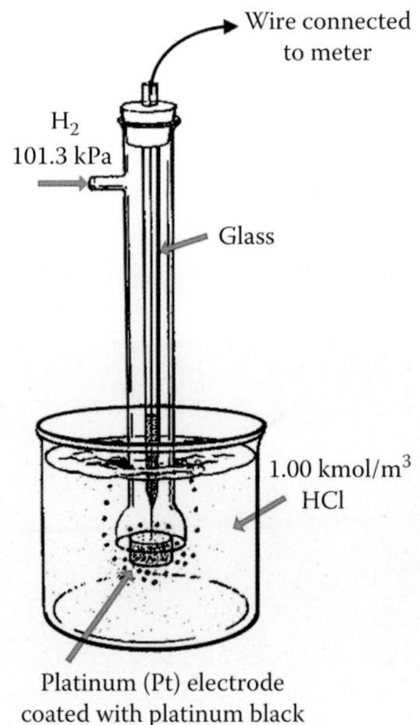

Figure H.7 Electrochemical design of the half-cell concept.

Half-life ($\tau_{1/2}$)

[atomic, biomedical, computational, general, nuclear] The time required for one-half of the atoms of the substance originally present to DECAY by RADIOACTIVITY $\tau_{1/2} = 1/\lambda_{1/2}$, where the decay constant $\lambda_{1/2} = (\Delta N/\Delta t)/N$ represents the change in the number of isotopes of reactive atoms N over time with respect to the original quantity by half, which is a fixed number for any specific element or ISOTOPE. For radioactive isotopes, the half-life ranges from 10^{-22}s to 10^{21}year. ERNEST RUTHERFORD (1871–1937) introduced this term representing the period in which the decay rate R drops to $(1/2)R_0$ (see Figure H.8).

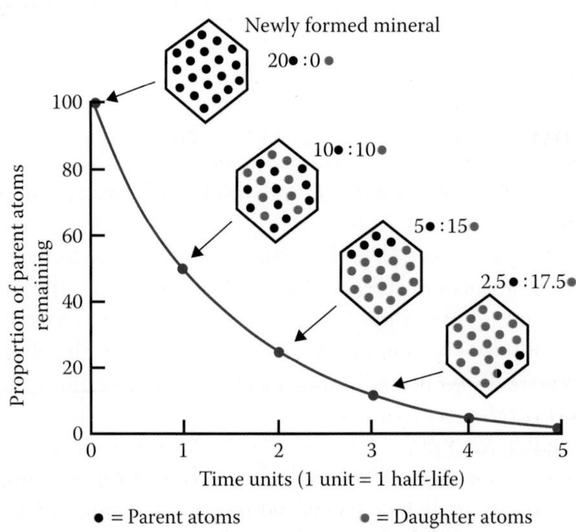

Figure H.8 How the half-life represents the time to reduce the quantity of seed atoms by half.

Halley, Edmund (1656–1742)

[astronomy/astrophysics, general] An astronomer, mathematician, and physicist from the United Kingdom/Great Britain. Halley used prior data and his own observations to describe a recurring COMET (in 1682), now named HALLEY'S COMET. Halley defined the trajectory and axes of the orbit (see Figure H.9).

Figure H.9 Edmond Halley engraved by W. T. Fry.

Halley's comet

[astronomy/astrophysics, general] A COMET that is described in various books and transcripts dating back to the early Greek astronomy researchers (minimally 240 BC), but is named after the scientific contributions by EDMUND HALLEY (1656–1742) from his 1682 observation, also described by JOHANNES KEPLER (1571–1630) in 1607. The comet has a trajectory that makes it pass EARTH every 75–76 years (depending on the earth's position and the accuracy of early recordings) with two observations, before reaching the Sun and after returning from its orbit around the Sun. Initially considered as two independent comets, as described by SIR ISAAC NEWTON (1642–1727), but corrected by Edmund Halley. The Halley's comet has the shortest period of all known comets that are visible from the Earth, specifically with the rudimentary telescopes available over the past several centuries.

Hamilton, William Rowan, Sir (1805–1865)

[computational, general] A mathematician and physicist who formalized the concepts introduced by PIERRE DE FERMAT (1601–1665) (with respect to light in his case) that actions take the path of least RESISTANCE. In Fermat's case, this led to SNELL'S LAW of refraction, whereas PIERRE LOUIS MOREAU DE MAUPERTUIS (1698–1759) in 1747 described the same principle for any action or FLOW of ENERGY, much later formalized by Hamilton as $\sum \vec{p}\Delta q \downarrow$ minimum, where $\vec{p} = m\vec{v}$ is the momentum (MASS (m) times VELOCITY ($\vec{v}$), but can also be angular momentum $\vec{L} = I\vec{\omega} = r_{\perp}mv$, $I = \sum mr^2$ the MOMENT OF INERTIA of a body with mass m in motion with $r_{\perp}$ the DISTANCE in perpendicular direction from the MOTION to the center of symmetry of the motion and ω the ANGULAR VELOCITY) and q is a spatial indicator (for instance, $q_1 = x$), also referred to as conjugate space variable, which for angular momentum translate into ANGLE in space instead of location in CARTESIAN COORDINATES. The description of Hamilton involves the introduction of spatial surfaces on which the action of the motion of the system is constant. The surfaces of constant action, as they are referenced, traverse space in the same fashion as how Fermat described the propagation of the PHASE of electromagnetic wave fronts in OPTICS.

In energetic format, the Hamilton equation uses the total energy ($KE + U = E$, the sum of kinetic ($KE = (1/2)mv^2 = p^2/2m$) and potential (U) energy) as $(1/2m)p^2 + U = E$. This concept was adapted by ERWIN SCHRÖDINGER (1887–1961) into a differential equation, the WAVE EQUATION. The EQUATIONS OF MOTION in Hamiltonian space are now $\dot{p}_j = -(\partial H/\partial q_j)$ and $\dot{q}_j = +(\partial H/\partial p_j)$, with $H(p,q) = \sqrt{(m^2 + p^2)}$ the Hamiltonian function of energy for a PARTICLE (see Figure H.10).

Figure H.10 William Rowan Hamilton (1805–1865).

Hamiltonian energy

[computational, energy, mechanics] $H(p,q) = \sqrt{(m^2 + p^2)}$ is the Hamiltonian function of ENERGY for a PARTICLE with mass m and momentum $p = mv$, where v is the velocity of the moving system.

Hamiltonian mechanics

[computational, energy, fluid dynamics, mechanics] In kinetics, there is acceleration, constant speed, ENERGY, and momentum with respect to either linear, curved (~Coriolis), or rotational displacement. In Hamiltonian mechanics, the energy is depicted through PHASE and spatial orientation and location. The HAMILTONIAN ENERGY is $H(q,p)$.

Hamiltonian operator

[atomic] Also Hamiltonian (H), the ENERGY operator belonging to the Hamilton energy: $H = KE + U = (p^2/2m) + U$, the sum of kinetic ($KE = (1/2)mv^2 = p^2/2m$) and potential ($U$) energy, expressed as $H^{op} = -(\hbar^2/2m)\nabla^2 + U = -(\hbar^2/2m)[(\partial^2/\partial x^2) + (\partial^2/\partial y^2) + (\partial^2/\partial z^2)] + U$, where $\hbar = h/2\pi$, $h = 6.626076$ Js Planck's constant, for a PARTICLE with mass m and momentum $p = mv$, where v is the velocity of the moving system. The Hamiltonian operator was introduced by SIR WILLIAM ROWAN HAMILTON (1805–1865) over the period 1823–1828. The Hamiltonian can be a matrix with a considerably large number of matrix ELEMENTS $H^{op}{}_{ts}(\vec{k}) = \int \Phi_t^*(\vec{k},\vec{r}) H \Phi_s(\vec{k},\vec{r}) d^3r$, where $\Phi_t^*(\vec{k},\vec{r})$ is the complex conjugate of the general number of base sets $\Phi_t(\vec{k},\vec{r})$ with respect to a previously specified set of functions $\Phi_s(\vec{k},\vec{r} + \vec{R_i}) = \exp(i\vec{k} \cdot \vec{R_i})\Phi_s(\vec{k},\vec{r})$, with LATTICE vector $\vec{R_i} = n_{i1}\vec{a_1} + n_{i2}\vec{a_2} + n_{i3}\vec{a_3}$, using three primitive lattice vectors a_j and n_{ij} integers; r is the location in three-dimensional space and $\vec{k}$ is the WAVE vector that can be equated to a QUANTUM number defining the electron states.

Hankel function

[computational] A function series, designed in an approximation of complex mathematical functions. Hankel functions are some of the solutions that apply to the Helmholtz equation, in the form of cylinder harmonics. One kind of Hankel functions is the BESSEL FUNCTIONS of the third kind (also known as Weber functions). The Hankel functions of the first kind are combinations of Bessel functions of the first ($J_n(z)$) and second ($Y_n(z)$) kind $H_n^{(1)}(z) \equiv J_n(z) + iY_n(z)$, also known as spherical Hankel functions. The Hankel functions of the first kind can be represented by contour integration over the upper half-plane $H_n^{(1)}(z) = (1/i\pi)\int_{0\,(\text{upper half plane})}^{\infty} e^{(z/2)(1-(1/t))}/t^{n+1}\,dt$. The second class of Hankel functions is defined by a specific contour (C_e, Hankel contour) integral, defined by $H_e(z) = \int_{C_e} (-w)^{z-1} e^{-w}/(1-e^{-w})\,dw$.

Harmonic motion

[acoustics, fluid dynamics, general, mechanics] Sinusoidal oscillation, rhythmic vibration with fixed frequency. Generally, in harmonic motion the restoring force is proportional to the displacement, as found for HOOKE'S LAW with respect to a spring. When any form of DAMPING is applied, FRICTION or FLOW, the harmonic motion becomes a damped HARMONIC OSCILLATION (*see* DAMPED OSCILLATION *and* OSCILLATION). A simple harmonic oscillation can be represented as the projection of a circular motion. The generalized description of the periodic displacement (y) with AMPLITUDE A_0 and ANGULAR FREQUENCY ω for the harmonic motion is a sinusoidal function, which includes a phase offset (φ) $y(t) = A_{1,0}\sin(\omega t) + A_{2,0}\cos(\omega t) = A_0\cos(\omega t - \varphi) = A_0\cos(2\pi\nu t - \varphi)$ as a function of time (t), with frequency ν. A forced harmonic motion can result in RESONANCE under the appropriate boundary conditions (see Figure H.11).

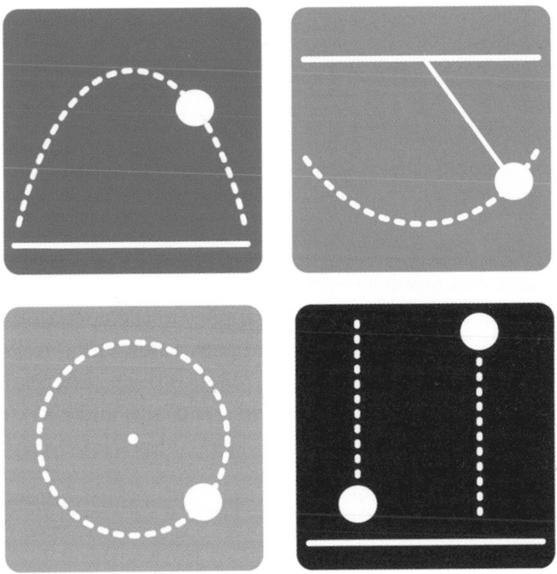

Figure H.11 Examples of harmonic motion.

Harmonic oscillation

[acoustics, atomic, fluid dynamics, general, mechanics, thermodynamics] Periodic OSCILLATION, HARMONIC MOTION. Sound is an acoustic harmonic pressure fluctuation with a specific frequency. Harmonic oscillations generally are the spectrum starting out with the base FREQUENCY (ν_0, also referred to as FUNDAMENTAL frequency ν_1) and associated higher harmonics, at respective frequency $\nu_n = n\nu_0$, $n = 1, 2, \ldots$. In atomic PHYSICS, the electron orbit in the Bohr model performs a harmonic oscillation that is a perfect match to the orbit, a QUANTUM harmonic oscillator (classical physics) with ENERGY $E_n = [n + (1/2)]h\nu$, where $h = 6.62606957 \times 10^{-34}\ \text{m}^2\text{kg/s}$ is the Planck's constant (*also see* **OSCILLATION, QUANTUM OSCILLATOR,** *and* **NATURAL FREQUENCY**) (see Figure H.12).

Figure H.12 Musical notes are a prime example of harmonic oscillation, each with a specific base frequency. The harmonic motion for sound is longitudinal pressure waves in fluids or solids.

H-bomb

[atomic, nuclear] A hydrogen fusion bomb ${}_1^1\text{H} + {}_1^1\text{H} \rightarrow {}_1^2\text{H} + \text{e}^+ + \nu_e$, emitting a DEUTERON (${}_1^2\text{H}$) and a NEUTRINO ($\nu_e$) as well as ENERGY. This principle also applies to the operations of stars and our Sun. The deutron ("deuterium", also presented as ${}_1^2\text{D}$) immediately fuses with another hydrogen nucleus, emitting gamma radiation (γ) and energy ${}_1^1\text{H} + {}_1^2\text{H} \rightarrow {}_2^3\text{He} + \gamma + \textit{energy}$. Alternatively, ${}_1^2\text{H} + {}_1^2\text{H} \rightarrow {}_2^3\text{He} + n + 3.3\,MeV$, releasing tritium (${}_2^3\text{T}$ and a PROTON) and a NEUTRON (n). The final stage in the FUSION process is the formation of helium ${}_2^3\text{H} + {}_2^3\text{H} \rightarrow {}_2^4\text{He} + 2{}_1^1\text{H} + \textit{energy}$, alternatively

$^2_1H + ^3_2H \rightarrow ^4_2He + proton + 18.3\,MeV$, or $^2_1H + ^3_1T \rightarrow ^4_2He + neutron + 17.6\,MeV$. H-bomb is also known as the ATOMIC BOMB (*see* **FUSION**) (see Figure H.13).

Figure H.13 Recovered hydrogen bomb, lost during a midair collision of B-52 bomber plane and a refueling plane in their path over Palomares, Spain, in 1966.

He4, 4Helium (^{4}He)

[astronomy/astrophysics, biomedical, chemical, general] The ELEMENT helium.

Head loss

[fluid dynamics] Loss in the equivalence of ENERGY expressed as the loss in height of a column of LIQUID (representative of the local Bernoulli pressure), expressed as $h_s = (P_1 - P_2)/\rho g$, where the pressure prior to the segment under consideration is P_1 and after the segment P_2, with g the GRAVITATIONAL ACCELERATION and ρ the FLUID density (see Figure H.14).

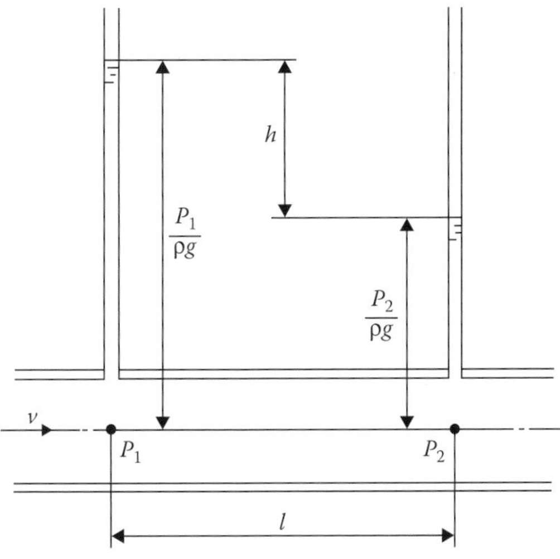

Figure H.14 Head loss in pipe flow with pressure drop over distance.

Head loss, Borda–Carnot

[fluid dynamics] Head loss due to an EXPANSION in fluid flow, expressed as the "Borda–Carnot head loss" $h_s = (v_1 - v_2)/g$, where the average flow velocity prior to the expansion is v_1 and after the expansion v_2, with g the GRAVITATIONAL ACCELERATION (see Figure H.15).

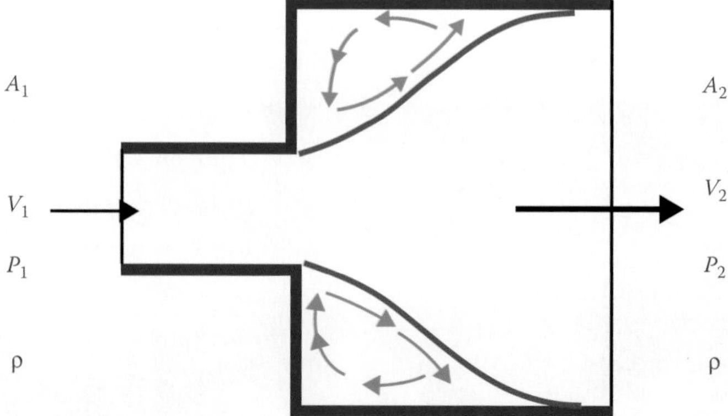

Figure H.15 Illustration of the concept of Borda–Carnot head loss.

Head-on collisions

[general, mechanics] Two objects with respective opposite velocity vectors, which are perfectly aligned, reach a position where they make physical contact (see Figure H.16).

Figure H.16 Head-on collision example.

Health physics

[atomic, biomedical, general, imaging, solid-state] A designation of professional field in MEDICINE, often specifically geared to RADIATION controls and imaging accuracy. The major responsibility of the health physicist is often in NUCLEAR MEDICINE. The health physicist role varies from country to country, based on traditional role and academic involvement. In most cases, the work effort involves a multitude of PHYSICS, ENGINEERING, and biology as well as chemistry knowledge, related to quality control of diagnostic and safety issues next to basic science and device development (see Figure H.17).

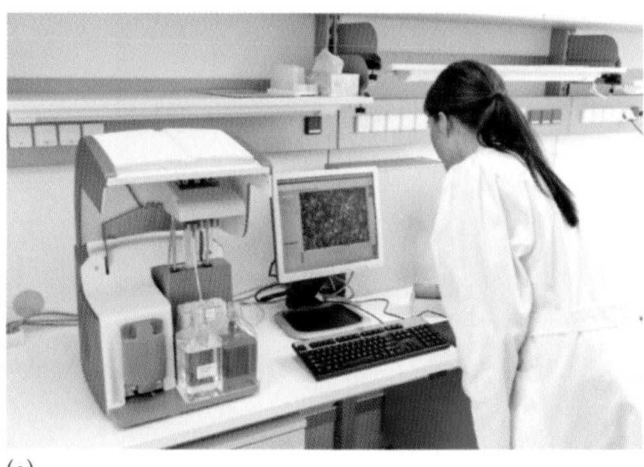

(a)

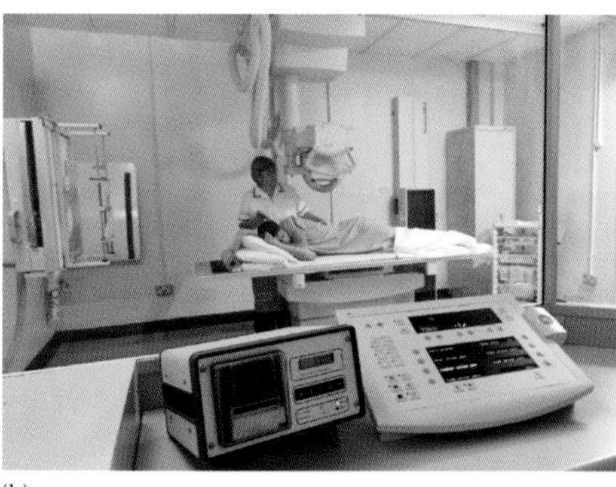

(b)

Figure H.17 Example of a health physics aspect involving the diagnostic and therapeutic modalities for clinical care: in vivo examination of equipment (a) and application (b).

Hearing

[acoustics, general] The conversion of mechanical waves in electronic pulse train by a biological device such as an EAR. The human ear has three anatomical components: OUTER EAR, MIDDLE EAR, and INNER EAR. In the outer ear, the pressure waves are guided into the middle ear by means of the horn-shaped exterior shell leading into the auditory meatus (ear canal). At the tympanic membrane of the middle ear, the pressure waves are converted into mechanical waves on a solid. The oval window connects to the liquid-filled inner ear, where the mechanical waves are passing through the COCHLEA. The human ear due to its cochlear construction performs a mechanical FOURIER TRANSFORM of the SOUND impacting on the oval window of the eardrum, splitting the pressure wavelengths out from short near the entrance (high frequencies are converted into electronic pulses, i.e., ACTION POTENTIAL spikes, close to the oval window) to long toward the end of the coil, which is actually near the point of entry since the design of the cochlea allows the WAVE propagation to double over at the tip of the coil. Each location on the inner design of the cochlea hence responds to a narrow wave band and the resulting electronic pulse train indicating the AMPLITUDE of the locally detected sound wave to be encoded for neural processing in the brain by binary processing (i.e., digitized). A variety of conversions take place in the ear, ranging from conversion of pressure changes in mechanical momentum of MOTION at the tympanic membrane $P(t) = mv(t)/tA = F/A$, where $P(t)$ is the time modulated pressure (sound), m the mass of the tympanic membrane, A the area of the tympanic membrane, $v(t)$ the time varying velocity of motion of the MEMBRANE, and F the force. In this situation with kinetic transfer, there will be a need for impedance matching to ensure transfer of ENERGY with maximum efficiency and without frequency filtering. Generally, the human ear can detect sound waves with a frequency range of roughly 20 Hz to 20 kHz (approximately 8 octaves, as a rule diminishing with AGE), which changes with age due to degradation of the elastic modulus of a variety of the components involved: tympanic membrane, muscular suspension of the malleus, incus, and stapes as well as the ORGAN OF CORTI. Additionally, nerve degeneration also affects the hearing. Animals have a different spectral range depending on the specific functional use. For instance, certain bats are reported to have hearing extending into the 400 kHz range with lower limit of approximately 20 Hz (generally, the upper limit is 120 kHz for the average BAT), dogs are sensitive from 60 to 40,000 Hz and for cats it is generally higher, whereas bottlenose dolphins are sensitive in the range 200 Hz to 150 kHz and certain whales have a 12-octave range of detection starting as low as 16 Hz (*see* **EAR**) (see Figure H.18).

(a)

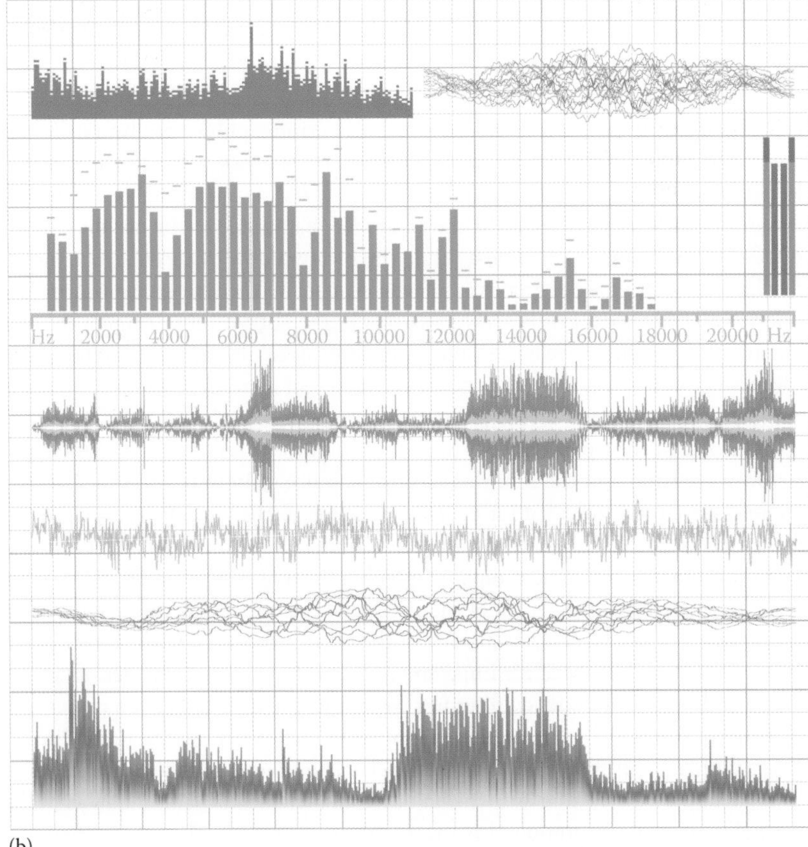

(b)

Figure H.18 Spectral profile span for a frequency spectrum (b) of an equalizer recording display (a).

Heart

[biomedical, chemical, fluid dynamics, mechanics] A hollow MUSCLE designed to pump BLOOD through a biological system when contraction takes place. The HEART acts with two pumps in series, one to circulate blood through the body and the other through the lungs. The arteries are providing the outflow tubes for the heart connected to the ventricles. The arteries in general carry oxygen-rich blood, except for the pulmonary artery leaving from the right ventricle to the lungs. The FLOW system is mediated by mechanical valves that open under applied pressure and close when specific components of the heart muscle are relaxing. The left atrium is separated from the left ventricle by means of the mitral VALVE, leading into the AORTA closed off by the aortic valve. The right atrium is prevented from receiving backflow from the right ventricle as a result of the tricuspid valve, and subsequent at the outflow into the pulmonary artery, the system has one-way flow only by means of the pulmonary valve. The atria (left and right atrium) collect blood on return from the body and lungs, respectively, and provide a windkessel SOLUTION in temporary storage for before transferring the content to the respective ventricles. The COMPLIANCE (C_{compl}) of the vascular system is defined by the ability to change the VOLUME (V) under influence of a change in pressure (P): $C_{compl} = \Delta V/\Delta P$. The TENSION ($T$) in the cardiac muscle wall of the heart is defined through the LAPLACE LAW, based on the PRESSURE (P) in the ventricle (primary muscle segment of the heart) and the radius (R) of the ventricular volume (assumed as a cylinder), divided by the WALL thickness (h): $T = (P \times R)/h$. The vascular compliance mediates the forced outflow from the ventricles into a resistive flow system of arteries, arterioles, and capillaries, flowing out into the venules and finally the veins, leading back to the respective left and right atrium. The myocardial muscle is a special muscle, unlike any other muscle in the body, human or other animal. The average power output of the human heart per contraction beat (averaged over AGE and gender) is $1.33\,\mathrm{W}$ (*Note:* $1\,\mathrm{W} = 1\,\mathrm{J/s} = 1\,\mathrm{Nm/s}$, compare to a refrigerator on average 615 Watt and the SOLAR POWER incident on a square meter 1380 Watt—the work per unit time), which can be calculated from the pressure produced by the heart multiplied by the flow rate (Φ), using $P = 1.33\,\mathrm{N/m^2}$ and $\Phi = 1.05 \times 10^{-4}\,\mathrm{m^3/s}$: $P_{power} = P \times \Phi$. The heart pumps based on an autonomic system that depolarized the atrium in order to stimulate for contraction by means of the sinoatrial node (SA node), followed by the DEPOLARIZATION of the atrioventricular node (AV node) on the ventricle for ventricular contraction. Both the SA node and AV node can be modified in their depolarization rate based on several chemical, neurochemical, and mechanical factors, hence increasing the heart rate under exercise. Since all the components of the cardiac flow system have very different parameters: number of vessel, diameter, compliance, and flow RESISTANCE, the system can be treated as a cascade of systems that are continuous at the connecting points, which is generally represented by means of Bond graphs (see Figure H.19).

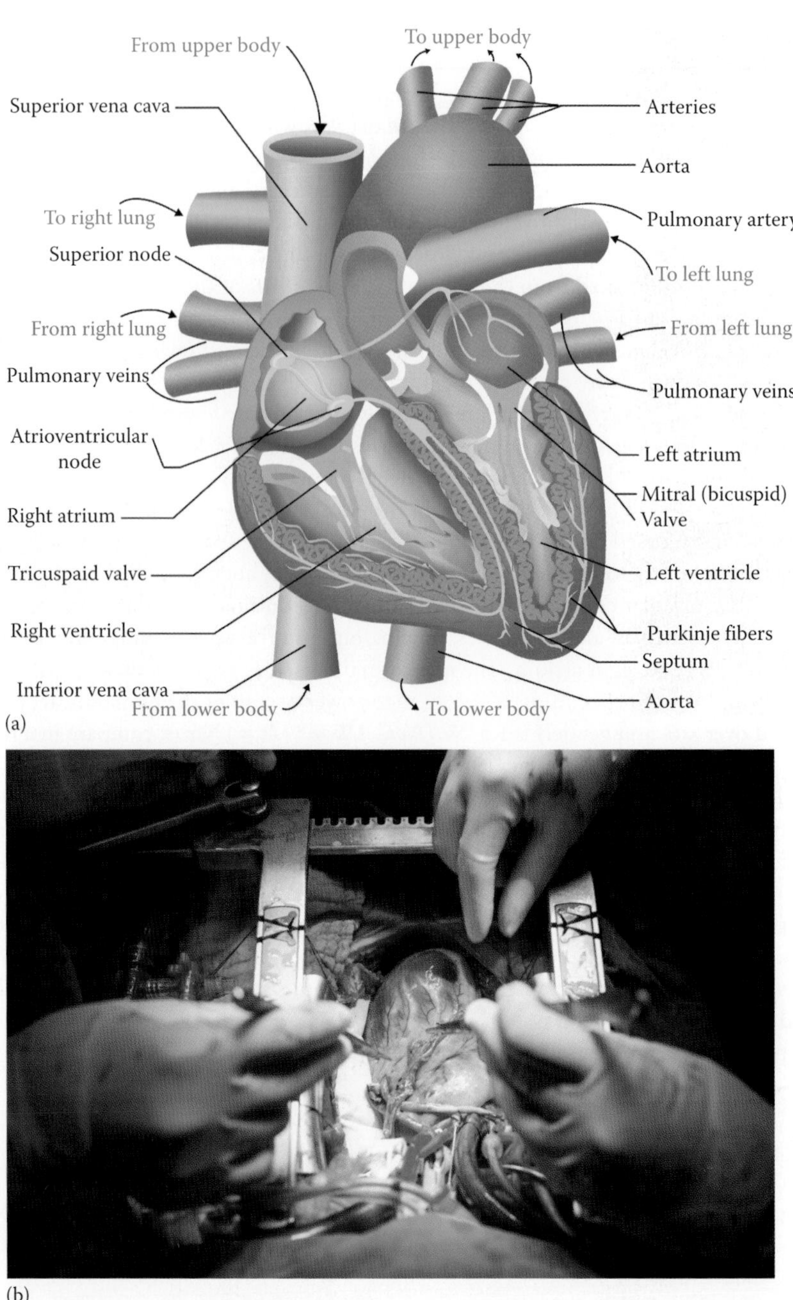

Figure H.19 (a) Anatomy of the heart and (b) open chest surgery, exposing the heart.

Heat (Q)

[energy, general, nuclear, thermodynamics] An indication of the thermal process of transfer of ENERGY. This is not equivalent to the definition of temperature, which is the indication of the ability to transfer heat; not equivalent to THERMAL ENERGY: the energy of random MOTION in kinetic energy as well as stored in potential energy on atomic and molecular scale. Heat and work both represent the specific phenomenological description of energy in motion. One specific application of heat is in CALORIMETRY, which is used to indicate the interchange of energy (see Figure H.20).

H

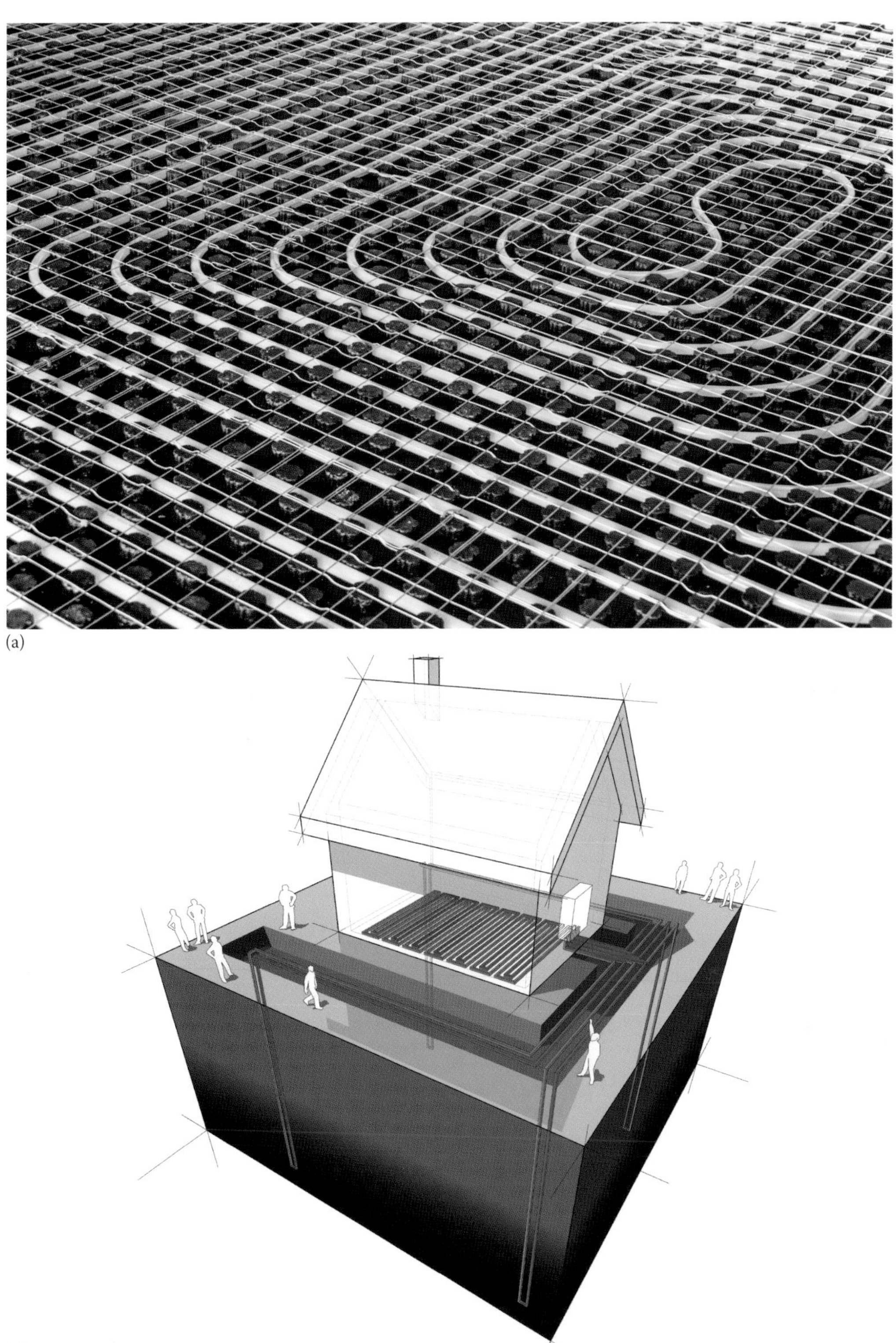

(a)

(b)

Figure H.20 (a) Illustration of a geothermal heating arrangement, explaining (b) the heat exchange with a volume at constant temperature (subterranean Earth).

Heat, mechanical equivalent

[thermodynamics] In 1842, the German physician JULIUS ROBERT VON MAYER (1814–1878) hypothesized that the MECHANICS of expanding gasses could be coupled to the transfer of ENERGY in the form of heat and introduced the mechanical equivalence of heat (Q), or rather the relationship between work (W) and heat as $W = Q$; this was corroborated by the paper of JAMES PRESCOTT JOULE (1818–1889) in 1843.

Heat capacity (*c*)

[thermodynamics] The amount of HEAT (Q) necessary to raise the temperature of a substance by 1 K, in a specific PHASE, indicated by a subscript for the specific medium when used in heat exchange and establishing THERMAL EQUILIBRIUM as described by the ZEROTH LAW OF THERMODYNAMICS or in any heat exchange between two or more bodies with respective mass (m_i) and of unlike temperature resulting in a respective temperature change (ΔT_i) for each based on the heat exchange $-Q_3 = Q_1 + Q_2 = -m_3c_3\Delta T_3 = m_1c_1\Delta T_1 + m_2c_2\Delta T_2$. Unit: J/kgK. In popular scientific terms, this relates to the capacity of a body to maintain its temperature or rather exchange the heat resulting from the temperature gradient with respect to a body in contact, for instance, comparing a block of cork to a GLASS ball of equal mass and elevated temperature (*also see* CALORIE).

Heat of dissociation

[thermodynamics] *See* HEAT OF FUSION.

Heat of fusion (L_f)

[general, thermodynamics] The quantity of heat per unit mass required to liquefy a solid object while at its melting temperature $Q = \pm mL_f$ (*see also* LATENT HEAT OF FUSION).

Heat of vaporization (L_v)

[general, thermodynamics] The quantity of heat per unit mass required to vaporize a LIQUID substance while at its condensation temperature $Q = \pm mL_v$, characteristic for each material. For instance, water at 100°C (the BOILING POINT), under ATMOSPHERIC PRESSURE, has a heat of vaporization of $L_v = 2.259 \times 10^3$ J/g (*see also* LATENT HEAT OF FUSION) (see Figure H.21).

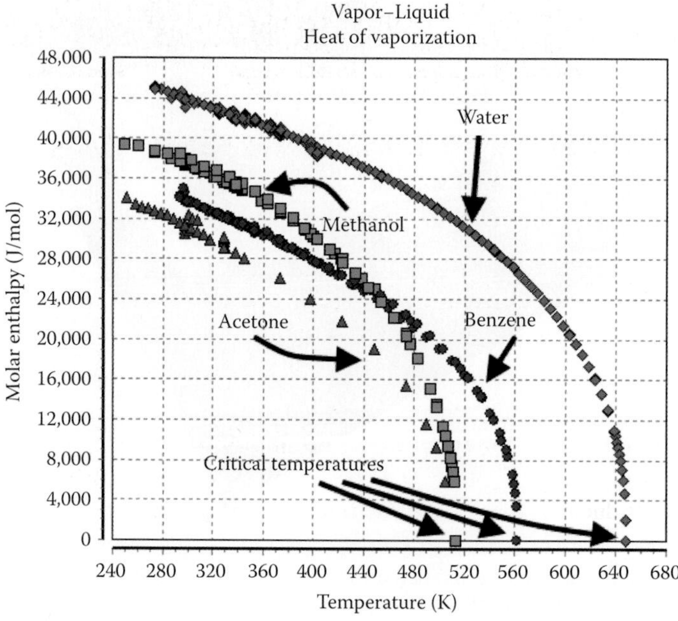

Figure H.21 Diagram of the temperature dependence of the heat of vaporization for several media.

Heat transfer

[thermodynamics] Using the EQUATION-OF-STATE the HEAT TRANSFER between two states of a system is defined as $dQ = C_v dT + (RT/V)dV$, where Q is the heat, C_v the SPECIFIC HEAT, T temperature, V the volume of the phenomenon, and R the universal GAS constant; R = 0.082057 liter atm/mol K, R = 8.314472 J/mol K, R = 8.205745 m^3 atm/mol K, R = 62.36367 liter Torr/mol K (alt. liter mmHg/mol K).

Heavy water

[general] The popular name for water, which is composed of two atoms of deuterium and one ATOM of oxygen.

Heisenberg, Werner Karl (1901–1976)

[atomic, computational, general, nuclear] A physicist and mathematician from Germany known for the introduction of the UNCERTAINTY PRINCIPLE in 1927; the location (y) of a phenomenon with momentum $p = h/\lambda$ ($h = 6.62606957 \times 10^{-34}$ m^2kg/s the Planck's constant and λ the wavelength associated with the phenomenon), specifically applied to measure the atomic configuration. Alternatively, object with mass m and velocity v has a momentum $p = mv$. The object/phenomenon can only be defined with limited confidence $\Delta p_y \Delta y \geq h/2\pi$ (see Figure H.22).

Figure H.22 (a) Werner Karl Heissenberg (1901–1976) and (b) Werner Heisenberg at the 1927 Solvay conference. (Courtesy of Friedrich Hund.)

Heisenberg's uncertainty principle

[computational, general, nuclear, quantum] *See* UNCERTAINTY PRINCIPLE.

Heliocentric

[astronomy/astrophysics, general] A description of the organization of our planetary system placing the Sun in the center of the orbiting 8, respectively, 9 planets. The International Astronomical Union may decide to exclude Pluto as a PLANET due to the fact that is too small and there is additional debris in its orbit that is significant in size to reclassify Pluto as a dwarf planet, thus reducing the number of planets from 9 to 8. The HELIOCENTRIC system was developed by NICOLAUS COPERNICUS (1473–1543) and published in 1543 as *De revolutionibus orbium coelestium libri sex*, in contrast with the GEOCENTRIC model, assuming the EARTH as the center of the planetary system, described by PTOLEMAEUS (third century BC–~130 BC), and most likely dating back even farther (see Figure H.23).

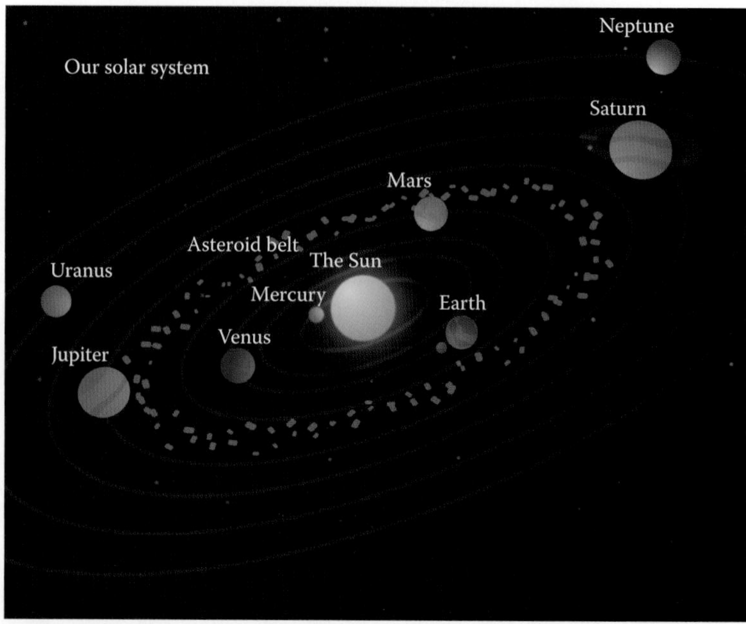

Figure H.23 The solar system with the Sun as the center and the planets in orbit around the Sun.

Heliographic latitude

[astronomy/astrophysics, general, geophysics] The solar LATITUDE. The angular DISTANCE from the solar geographic equator with respect to the reference frame of the SOLAR SYSTEM (average plane of all PLANETARY ORBITS), based on the SPIN and PRECESSION.

Helmholtz, Hermann Ludwig Ferdinand von (1821–1894)

[acoustics, electromagnetism, energy, fluid dynamics, optics, thermodynamics] A mathematician, physicist, physiologist, and anatomist from the Prussian Empire: Germany. A German scientist with a broad range of contributions in science and technology. Apart from being a theorist, Helmholtz was also an inventor. In 1850, Helmholtz introduced the design for an ophthalmoscope, and in 1856, he published the MECHANICS of reshaping the LENS for accommodation of the EYE in his *Handbuch der Physiologischen Optik*. Helmholtz's scientific career was quite prolific and presented, for instance, his theoretical review of rotational MOTION (e.g., vortices) in 1858, next to his experimental work and theoretical proof of electric induction with the HELMHOLTZ COILS in addition to an elaborate analysis of acoustical phenomena, including the HELMHOLTZ RESONATOR. Helmholtz's primary contribution to science and engineering is the fact that he provided the proof that EUCLIDEAN GEOMETRY is not the only theoretical approach to the description of conceptual and physical space. His second most noteworthy influence is in field theory, moving away from PARTICLE interaction. He also formulated ENERGY CONSERVATION, as well as the VORTEX equations for fluid dynamics. Additional work by Helmholtz is in the area of thermodynamics with his parametric description of free energy (i.e., Helmholtz free energy) (see Figure H.24).

Figure H.24 Hermann Ludwig Ferdinand von Helmholtz (1821–1894).

Helmholtz coil

[energy, thermodynamics] A combination of two or more identical small cross section annular coils with common axis, lined up at variable distance connected in series. This design is intended to produce a more uniform magnetic field than a single coil without the specific need for a solenoid, which is significantly larger. In the optimal arrangement, the distance separating the two coils is equal to the radius of the coils, with negligible fluctuations in the virtually uniform magnetic field measured in the core (see Figure H.25).

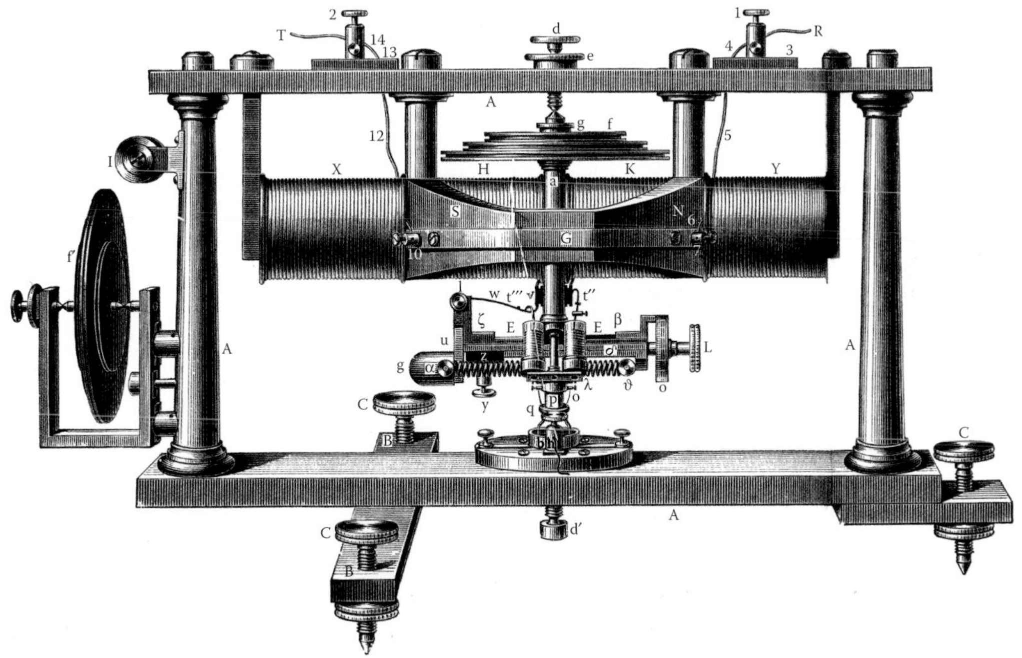

Figure H.25 Drawing of the Helmholtz coil design.

Helmholtz decomposition

[computational, fluid dynamics] A fundamental part of vector calculus. In three-dimensional space, the vector field composed of sufficiently smooth, rapidly decaying vectors can be decomposed into the sum of two "orthogonal" components, one consisting of an IRROTATIONAL (CURL-FREE) VECTOR FIELD and the second segment composed of rotational (divergence-free) or solenoidal vector field. The vector ($\vec{V}$) decomposition is formulated as follows: $\vec{V} = -\nabla\mathbb{C} + \nabla \times \mathbb{D}$, with the curl-free component $\mathbb{C}$ and divergence-free component $\mathbb{D}$.

Helmholtz energy

[acoustics, energy, thermodynamics] Work involved in isothermal irreversible processes. It was introduced by HERMANN LUDWIG FERDINAND VON HELMHOLTZ (1821–1894) in 1882. It was defined by $A_\sigma = U_\sigma - TS_\sigma$, where U_σ is the surface excess ENERGY, T is the thermodynamic temperature, and S_σ is the surface excess entropy. It is also known as HELMHOLTZ FREE ENERGY (*also see* **GIBBS FREE ENERGY**).

Helmholtz free energy (*F*)

H

[thermodynamics] $F = U - TS$, where U is the internal ENERGY, T is the temperature, and S is the entropy of the system, respectively. In an isothermal process, the internal energy does not change for an IDEAL GAS, which makes the Helmholtz free energy most appropriate to work within the energy balance.

Helmholtz resonator

[acoustics, energy, thermodynamics] A rigid acoustic apparatus with a minimum of one ORIFICE. The design of the device results in specific RESONANCE frequencies due to the material selection, dimensions, and placement of the openings. The design was developed by HERMANN LUDWIG FERDINAND VON HELMHOLTZ (1821–1894) for spectral analysis of musical tones. The natural frequency that the device can support is a function of the respective dimensions and properties and is described in detail under NATURAL FREQUENCY.

Henry, Joseph (1797–1878)

[electromagnetism, general] An electrical engineer and physicist from the United States. The work of Henry on electromagnetic induction lends his name to the MAGNETIC FIELD strength as the Henry (H). Joseph Henry described the relationship between electric fields and magnetic fields in the 1820s. Simultaneously in the United Kingdom, MICHAEL FARADAY (1791–1867) discovered and described similar correlations. Based on the work of both Joseph Henry and Michael Faraday, the integral theories of electromagnetic WAVE propagation were developed by JAMES CLERK MAXWELL (1831–1879) (see Figure H.26).

Figure H.26 Joseph Henry (1797–1878).

Henry, William (1774–1836)

[biomedical, chemical, fluid dynamics, thermodynamics] A chemist from the United Kingdom/Great Britain, also a mechanical engineer. William Henry is known for his description with respect to the solubility of substances (see Figure H.27).

Figure H.27 William Henry (1774–1836). (Courtesy of the trustees of the British Museum, London.)

Henry, unit (*H*)

[general] Unit for the inductance of a MAGNETIC coil, that is, SOLENOID based on the definition that one Henry provides a magnetic flux of 1 Weber under the influence of a current of 1 AMPÈRE.

Henry's constant

[chemical, thermodynamics] The solubility α_{sol} for the SOLUTE (*also* **HENRY'S LAW COEFFICIENT**), representing the concentration of dissolved gas ($[C_{Dissolved}]$) in a LIQUID proportional to the partial pressure of the GAS (P_{gas}), expressed by $[C_{Dissolved}] = \alpha_{sol} P_{gas}$.

Henry's law

[biomedical, chemical, fluid dynamics, thermodynamics] The solubility of substances expressed by WILLIAM HENRY (1774–1836) in 1803. Henry's law is a representation of the concentration of dissolved gas ($[C_{Dissolved}]$) in a liquid in proportion to the partial pressure of the gas (P_{gas}), expressed by $[C_{Dissolved}] = \alpha_{sol} P_{gas}$. The DIFFUSION coefficient in LIQUID phase is related to this by the Krogh diffusion for liquid phase solutes $K_{Diff} = \alpha_{sol} D_{diff}$, where α_{sol} is the solubility for the SOLUTE (Henry's law coefficient), and D_{diff} is the diffusion coefficient in GAS PHASE. One example of Henry's law is the dissolved carbon dioxide in carbonated drinks (i.e., soda's). Another interpretation is in the representation of the CHEMICAL POTENTIAL ($\mu_{i\chi}$, where i indicates the constituent within a SOLUTION and χ the PHASE; gas: g or liquid: ℓ) of a solution providing Henry's law $\mu_{1g} P_{gas} = \mu_{1\ell} \mathcal{H}_{1\ell}(T,P)$, where $\mathcal{H}_{1\ell}(T,P) = P_{sat,11}(T) \exp\{[\lambda_{1\ell}(T,P) - \mu_{11,\ell}(T, P_{sat,11}(T))]/RT\}$ is the HENRY'S CONSTANT for the SOLUTION of solute 2 in liquid phase under pressure P and temperature T, with $\lambda_{1\ell}(T,P)$ a constant that defines the boundary conditions of the integration over the partial pressure of the potential equivalent gas equation $\left(\partial \mu_{1\ell} / \partial \ln(\mathcal{Y}_{1\ell})\right)_{T,P} = RT$, where $R = 8.3145\ \mathrm{J/molK}$ is the universal GAS constant and $\mathcal{Y}_k = n_k/n = (x_k/M_k)/\left(\sum_{\ell=1}^{r} x_\ell / M_\ell\right)$ is the MOLE fraction of the dissolved constituent k, with M_ξ the mean MOLECULAR WEIGHT of solute ξ, for the amount of constituent n_k summing to a total of solutes $n = \sum_{k=1}^{r} n_k$, x_ξ

the fractional mass for constituent ξ (*Note:* $\sum x_\xi = 1$), P_{jj} the molar partial pressure of constituent j in solution (*also see* **VAN'T HOFF, JACOBUS HENDRICUS,** *and* **OSMOTIC PRESSURE**).

Herschel, Friedrich Wilhelm (Frederick William), Sir (1738–1822)

[astronomy, fluid dynamics, general] A scientist and astronomer from Germany. Friedrich Herschel was a musician interested in scientific exploration. He examined RADIATION with the assistance of a THERMOMETER, thus eluding to the heat properties of infrared radiation in the early concept stage around 1800. He discovered that longer wavelengths (RED and beyond the red) induce higher temperatures and as such discovered infrared light, indicating that the solar radiation consists approximately 50% of invisible (INFRARED) radiation. He also discovered the neighboring Splinter Galaxy at approximately 5×10^7 lightyears from our SOLAR SYSTEM. He primarily acquired fame for his discovery of the PLANET Uranus. He investigated the effect of various bandwidths of the ELECTROMAGNETIC SPECTRUM with respect to induced temperature rise by exposing a thermometer to sunlight filtered by colored GLASS and other OPTICS.

Herschel, Winslow Hobart (1873–1940)

H

[fluid dynamics, general, mechanics] Because of the steady-state flow, the phenomenon can be described with a model that is spatially nonlinear as well as temperature and location dependent. The shear stress resulting from BLOOD flow through a vessel can be described using the Herschel–Bulkley approximation to model blood as a flow medium. This gives the SHEAR STRESS (τ_s) as a function of flow with flow velocity $u(r,t)$ as a function of time t and radius r as $\tau_s = \mu_\gamma'^{1/n} \left(\partial u(r,t)/\partial r\right)^{1/n} + \mu_\gamma'$ under the condition $\tau_s \geq \tau_\gamma$, while $\partial u(r,t)/\partial r = 0$ for $\tau_s < \tau_\gamma$, τ_γ' is the HERSCHEL–BULKLEY YIELD STRESS and μ_γ' is the HERSCHEL–BULKLEY COEFFICIENT OF FRICTION. The shear rate is also dependent on the vessel diameter, the FLOW velocity itself, next to the flow pulsation frequency along with other system condition parameters. These dependencies can be defined either by means of the mechanical COMPLIANCE of the vessel or by the mechanical impedance as a function of the time-dependent flow traversing a compliant vessel.

Herschel–Bulkley coefficient of friction

[biomedical, fluid dynamics, mechanics] Generally the Herschel–Bulkley flow describes the situation of a nonlinear VISCOSITY that is associated with the movement of a medium that is a plasticide, with a threshold that needs to be exceeded before flow is initiated introduced by Ronald Bulkley (1895–1985), based on the work of, and in collaboration with, WINSLOW HOBART HERSCHEL (1873–1940).

Herschel–Bulkley fluid

[biomedical, fluid dynamics, mechanics] Non-Newtonian fluid (colloid SOLUTION) that is defined by a threshold yield stress (τ_γ) before flow can be established. Examples of this type of media are jelly and jam and other food products, cement, mud sludge encountered during drilling for OIL, magma/lava, mud, toothpaste, composites (PLASTICS), pulp, and paint to name a few. The concept was introduced in 1926 by Ronald Bulkley (1895–1985) and WINSLOW HOBART HERSCHEL (1873–1940). The Herschel–Bulkley model is especially useful in the formation of a model for a dampener such as found in a SHOCK ABSORBER, mainly due to the inherent HYSTERESIS of the FLOW. Since APPARENT VISCOSITY (η_{app}) is a function of the relationship between shear stress and shear rate, the VISCOSITY will change depending on the shear rate (see Figure H.28).

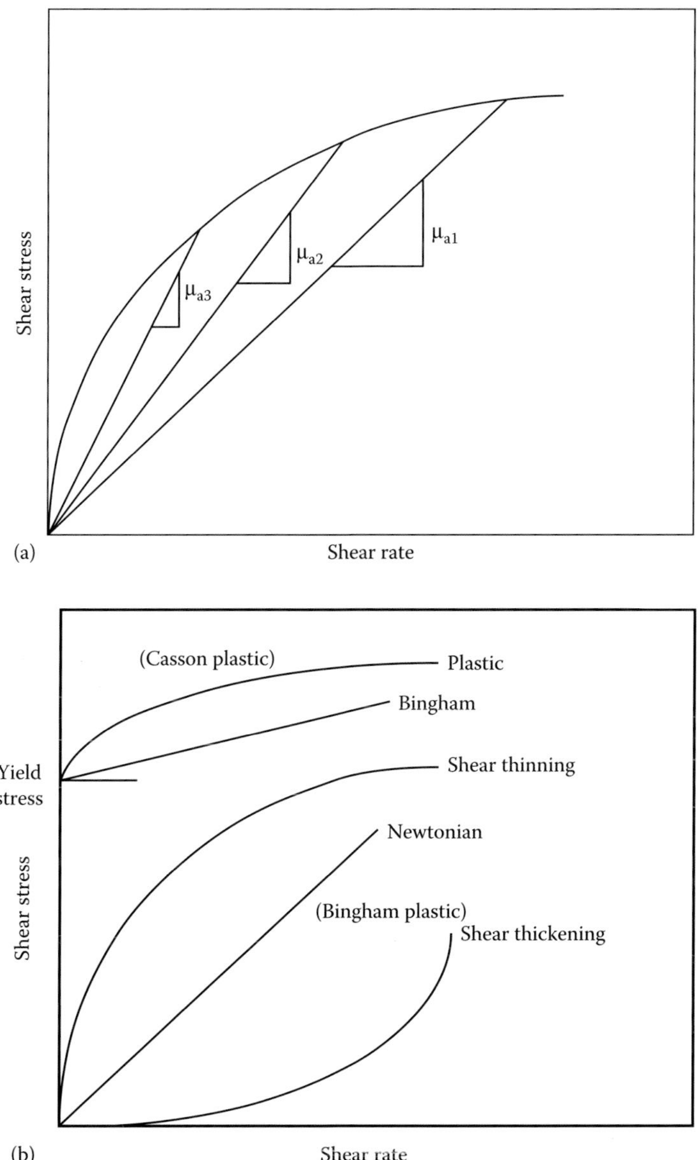

Figure H.28 (a) Illustration of the change in viscosity with applied shear rate under the Herschel–Buckley model and (b) various viscous models, in comparison to the Herschel–Buckley model.

Herschel–Bulkley yield stress (σ_{yield})

[biomedical, fluid dynamics, mechanics] The threshold for stress below which no FLOW is possible for a "plastic" fluid. This is a dynamic phenomenon, since the stress is influenced by the applied force (i.e., pressure). Its applications are specifically in RHEOLOGY. Below this threshold, the FLUID can be suspended, such as ketchup not willing to flow from a bottle held upside down; in this manner, the fluid can support its own weight by shear stress to the WALL.

Hertz, Heinrich Rudolf (1857–1894)

[acoustics, computational, electromagnetism, general] A German physicist and experimentalist. As one of the pioneers in the transmission and reception of RADIO waves, his name became attached to the WAVE phenomenon. His experiments illustrated the commonality between radio waves and light waves in REFLECTION, REFRACTION, and transmission, tying all together as ELECTROMAGNETIC RADIATION. Hertz's theoretical work confirmed his experimental model after reinterpreting the Maxwell's wave equations, pertaining to electromagnetic waves, eliminating the notion of the ETHER proposed by JAMES CLERK MAXWELL (1831–1879) (see Figure H.29).

Figure H.29 Heinrich Rudolf Hertz (1857–1894).

Hertz (Hz), unit

[general] Unit for number of fluctuations per SECOND. The unit Hertz was named after the contributions to RADIO wave and experimental verification of the MAXWELL EQUATIONS by HEINRICH RUDOLF HERTZ (1857–1894).

Hertzsprung–Russell diagram

[astronomy/astrophysics] An evolutionary log–log plot of the luminosity of a STAR (L_s) against the effective surface temperature of a star, specifically in reference to our solar parameters: solar luminosity ($L_\odot$) and solar radius ($R_\odot$), and solar mass ($M_\odot$; also expressed in density $\rho_\odot$). The diagram was designed by Ejnar Hertzsprung (1873–1967) from Denmark and HENRY NORRIS RUSSELL (1877–1957) from the United States in 1923. The implied ENERGY configuration will indicate the "locations" for ignition of hydrogen, helium, and carbon, respectively, and the relative effects in comparison to NEUTRINO energy loss based on the

FISSION processes (*see* **H-BOMB** *and* **FISSION**). Specifically low-mass stars, including the Sun ($0.08M_{\odot} < M < 8M_{\odot}$), experience hydrogen and helium burning stages (see Figure H.30).

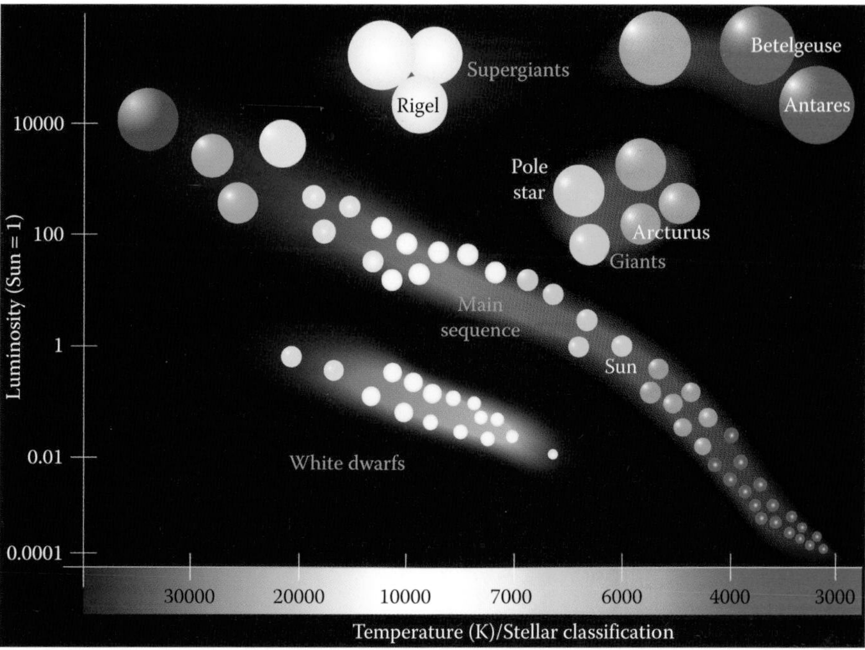

Figure H.30 Hertzsprung–Russell diagram.

Hessian

[computational] A mathematical tool in spectral function analysis. The second-order gradient of a real function that is twice differentiable with respect to its vector domain in κ-dimensional space:

$$\mathbb{S}^{\kappa}:\nabla^2 f(x) \equiv \begin{matrix} \dfrac{\partial^2 f(x)}{\partial x_1^{\,2}} & \dfrac{\partial^2 f(x)}{\partial x_1 \partial x_2} & \cdots & \dfrac{\partial^2 f(x)}{\partial x_1 \partial x_k} \\ \dfrac{\partial^2 f(x)}{\partial x_2 \partial x_1} & \dfrac{\partial^2 f(x)}{\partial x_2^{\,2}} & & \dfrac{\partial^2 f(x)}{\partial x_2 \partial x_k} \\ \vdots & \vdots & \ddots & \vdots \\ \dfrac{\partial^2 f(x)}{\partial x_k \partial x_1} & \dfrac{\partial^2 f(x)}{\partial x_k \partial x_2} & \cdots & \dfrac{\partial^2 f(x)}{\partial x_k^{\,2}} \end{matrix}$$

Applications are found particularly in spectral analysis. The second-order derivative provides significant RESOLUTION enhancement, particularly with respect to the identification of the slope of a curve as well as locating extremes based on experimental data. The use of the Hessian transforms the analysis from an absolute algorithm to a relative algorithm with increase in sensitivity up to an order of MAGNITUDE.

Hexagonal closed packed (hcp) structure

[condensed matter, solid-state] Hexagonal LATTICE structure, for example, cobalt (Co).

Higgs, Peter Ware (1929–)

[atomic, computational, energy, general, solid-state] A physicist from Great Britain. Peter Higgs is known for his work on the ELECTROWEAK FORCE, specifically the discontinuities or broken symmetry in this theoretical concept. Other work of Higgs was on ELEMENTARY PARTICLES, in particular the elusive HIGGS BOSON and the description of the mass of the W and Z bosons (see Figure H.31).

Figure H.31 Peter Ware Higgs (1929–). (Courtesy of Gert-Martin Greuel—Mathematisches Institut Oberwolfach, Oberwolfach, Germany.)

Higgs boson

[atomic, general, solid-state] An elementary particle that has been introduced from a theoretical standpoint in 1964. The Higgs boson is a particle that conforms to the GAUGE THEORY concepts. The PARTICLE was named after PETER WARE HIGGS (1929–), one of the theoretical physicists involved in the development of the concept. Peter Higgs' work was in collaboration with Gerald Stanford Guralnik (1936–2014), and in parallel with the works of Robert Brout (1928–2011) and François Englert (1932–) in Belgium, next to Carl Richard Hagen (1937–) in the United States and Sir Thomas Walter Bannerman Kibble (1932–) in the United Kingdom. The Higgs boson in principle has zero SPIN and positive PARITY. The particle has been tentatively verified as recent as 2013.

Higgs mechanism

[atomic, computational, energy, general, solid-state] A gauge transformation applied to massless bosons with SPIN 0. The gauge transformation rectifies the loss of symmetry in the Lagrangian describing the WEAK INTERACTION in the BOSE CONDENSATE, consisting of SCALAR fields.

High-energy physics

[computational, electromagnetism, energy, general, thermodynamics] With the increasing elementary structure of the ATOM unfolding, there was a growing need for a description that could capture the phenomena in the ELEMENTARY PARTICLES. The quarks forming the elementary PARTICLE that under STRONG FORCE form NEUTRON, pions, protons, and the like in contrast to the complementary subnuclear group of leptons that do not form strong force ties such as electrons and the NEUTRINO among others. These subnuclear particles will be described by the QUANTUM ELECTRODYNAMIC theory in only limited cases, but it forms a general basis. In addition to the WEAK FORCE, which is described by QUANTUM electrodynamic theory as outlined by ENRICO FERMI (1901–1954) in 1932, HIDEKY YUKAWA (1907–1981) postulated that the STRONG FORCE relies on the exchange of a VIRTUAL BOSON around 1934. The fact that SUBATOMIC structures are high ENERGY is conveyed by the fact that second- and third-generation ELEMENTARY PARTICLES: LEPTONS and QUARKS can have energy in excess of 11GeV = 2μJ.

Hilbert, David (1862–1943)

[computational] A mathematician from Germany (Prussian Empire). David Hilbert was instrumental in documenting and verifying a broad range of elementary mathematical concepts and provided a foundation for modern mathematical analysis (see Figure H.32).

Figure H.32 David Hilbert (1862–1943) in 1886.

Hilbert space (H_X)

[quantum, theoretical] The dot product of the continuous set of function in SOLUTION to the WAVE EQUATION that is in COMPLIANCE with the equivariance condition, designed by DAVID HILBERT (1862–1943). The equivariance condition assumes equivalence of gravitational and inertial mass. This defines the vectors of the QUANTUM mechanical state density matrices (see Figure H.33).

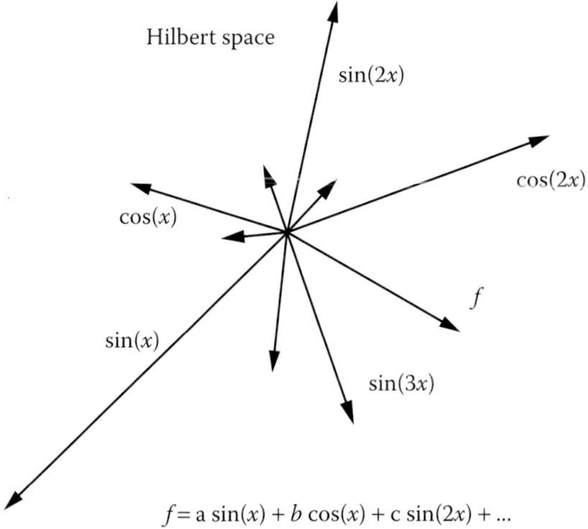

Figure H.33 Illustration of the Hilbert space concept.

Hill, Archibald Vivian (1886–1977)

[biomedical, chemical, mechanics] A physiologist and scientist from Great Britain. Archibald Hill contributed significant insight into the ENERGY exchange, kinetics, and work performed by muscles.

Hill coefficient "n_H"

[biomedical, chemical] Probabilistic number of LIGAND molecules binding sites in the chemical reaction. It is also defined as an interaction coefficient for a chemical reaction. The quantitative number of bindings is based on the chemical structure and VALENCE of the constituents of the reaction, rather than the estimated number of binding sites (see Figure H.34).

Figure H.34 Archibald Vivian Hill (1886–1977) in 1925. (Courtesy of the History of Medicine [NLM], Bethesda, Maryland.)

H

Hill equation

[biomedical, chemical] The ratio of protein that is in a complex chemical bond with a LIGAND, for instance, the protein hemoglobin bound to oxygen to form oxyhemoglobin, introduced by ARCHIBALD VIVIAN HILL (1886–1977) in 1910. This process will reach a certain SATURATION based on the oxygen supply during exposure in the lung during inhalation. In (bio-)chemical reactions, the equilibrium is described by a rate constant ($K_d = [P][L]^{nH} / [P : L_{nH}]$, where $[P]$ is the protein concentration, $[L]$ is the ligand concentration {in biology often oxygen (O_2)}, and $[P : L_{nH}]$ is the protein:ligand complex concentration; for instance, oxygen bound to hemoglobin (Hb)), with the HILL COEFFICIENT: "n_H" representing the number of ligand molecules binding sites in the chemical reaction (for instance, n_H can be as high as 4 for oxygen binding to hemoglobin: $\mathrm{Hb} + 4\mathrm{O}_2 \rightleftarrows \mathrm{Hb}(\mathrm{O}_2)_4$. Note that the oxyhemoglobin reduces to hemoglobin when flowing through the tissue where the partial pressure for oxygen is lower (depleted from metabolic action). The ratio of ligand binding is defined as $Y = \text{protein : ligand complex/total protein} = [P : L_{nH}] / \{[P] + [P : L_{nH}]\} = [L]^{nH} / \{K_d + [L]^{nH}\}$, which represents, for instance, $Y = 0.3$ for 30% saturation.

Hipparchus (190–125 BC)

[astronomy, general] An astronomer and mathematician from Turkey/Greece. Hipparchus collected an impressive amount of critical astronomical observations that he subjected to geometric calculations. Hipparchus is by some considered to be the "father of trigonometry." He calculated and determined the eccentricity of the MOON orbit and its "long axis" of the elliptical orbit. He documented 1025 bright stars and named them; however, some may be attributed to Naburiannu (~500 BC) and Kidinnu (~400 BC). In his time, he calculated the DISTANCE to the Sun to be roughly 1200 times the radius of the Earth and the distance to the Moon (relatively accurately) to be 59 times the radius of Earth (see Figure H.35).

(a) (b)

Figure H.35 (a) Picture of stamp commemorating Hipparchus (190–125 BC) with an impression of his likeness, and (b) picture of the armillary sphere designed by Hipparchus, celestial sphere model of objects in the sky with the Earth as center.

Hippocrates of Cos (460–377 BC)

[biomedical, general] A Greek physician who introduced that credo that a doctor shall not harm a person based on the knowledge acquired in experimental observation and anatomical studies. He proposed as one of the first that a disease is an environmental factor, not a punishment of god/the gods. Hippocrates introduced traction to treat chiropractic ailments, using a mechanical bed. His philosophy is now recognized under the Hippocratic Oath, a promise physician still take upon completion of their medical university training (see Figure H.36).

Figure H.36 Chest sculpture with impression of what Hippocrates of Cos (460–377 BC) may have looked like.

Hoar frost

[general, thermodynamics] Frozen ADHESION of water vapor. Hoarfrost often creates a fine mesh of water crystal tentacles, in appearance resembling a forest of minuscule pine trees on the surface of the cold object (see Figure H.37).

Figure H.37 Hoar frost, freezing water vapor. Sometimes also known as Rime frost. (Courtesy of Tony Garramone.)

Hodgkin, Alan Lloyd, Sir (1914–1998)

[biophysics, chemical, computational, electromagnetism, energy] A physicist and biomedical engineer from Great Britain. His work with SIR ANDREW FIELDING HUXLEY (1917–2012) and supporting efforts on the neural transmitter interface by JOHN CAREW ECCLES (1903–1997) revealed the mathematical/chemical description of the ACTION POTENTIAL in a depolarizing CELL (e.g., MUSCLE cell or nerve cell [NEURON]). Their work resulted in the Nobel Prize in Physiology in 1963 (see Figure H.38).

Figure H.38 Sir Alan Lloyd Hodgkin (1914–1998).

Hodgkin, Dorothy Mary (1910–1994)

[chemical, imaging] A chemist from Egypt. She was also known as Dorothy Crowfoot Hodgkin. Dorothy Hodgkin received the Nobel Prize in Chemistry in 1964 for her development of the process and technique of protein crystallography (see Figure H.39).

Figure H.39 Dorothy Mary Hodgkin (1910–1994).

Hodgkin–Huxley model

[biomedical, computational, electronics] A time-dependent membrane potential equation used to describe the construction of the ACTION POTENTIAL for a depolarizing CELL MEMBRANE. The Hodgkin–Huxley model is a variation on the steady-state multi-ion Goldman equation. The Hodgkin–Huxley model is the result of the work by ALAN LLOYD HODGKIN (1914–1998) and ANDREW FIELDING HUXLEY (1917–2012) in 1952. The Goldman equation in turn was an EXPANSION to the single-ion steady-state ion potential described by WALTHER HERMANN NERNST (1864–1941), the NERNST POTENTIAL, which was based on the DONNAN EQUILIBRIUM, introduced around 1905. In general, the steady-state and time-dependent membrane potential is based on the ION concentration in the intracellular and extracellular space for sodium (Na^+), POTASSIUM (K^+), and chlorine (Cl^-), with additional contributions from calcium (Ca^{2+}) and magnesium (Mg^{2+}). Alan Hodgkin and Andrew Huxley derived their model from the experiments they performed on the giant squid axon. The giant squid axon is a large nerve cell (diameter 1 mm [100 times the diameter of any mammalian nerve cell]; length 10 cm) that can easily be probed and measured for ion concentration and localized electrochemical potential. The giant squid axon in the mantle of the North Atlantic squid was discovered by Leonard Worcester Williams (1875–1912) in 1909, but John Zachary Young (1907–1997) made the scientific community aware of its experimental importance in 1936. The model describes the ion migration through three channels, one for each of the main ions (Na^+, K^+, and Cl^-), leading up to the ACTION POTENTIAL. The ion transport is mediated by gap junctions. Based on existing electrical parameters, specifically OHM'S LAW, the ion currents were defined as $I_{\mathrm{Na}} = g_{\mathrm{Na}}\left(V - V_{\mathrm{Na}}\right)$, $I_{\mathrm{K}} = g_{\mathrm{K}}\left(V - V_{\mathrm{K}}\right)$, and $I_{\mathrm{Cl}} = g_{\mathrm{Cl}}\left(V - V_{\mathrm{Cl}}\right)$, where the chlorine current is generally represented as a combined ion leakage current (of predominantly negative ions) $I_\ell = g_i\left(V - V_i\right)$, where g_i the "conductance" for the ion is a representation of the ION MOBILITY, inversely related to the RESISTANCE. In this, V_i is the Nernst potential for the respective ion(s) and V is the MEMBRANE potential. The conductance was modeled by Hodgkin and Huxley represented by the theoretical maximum ($\mathcal{G}_i$) multiplied by rate factors (α_n and β_n) that were all based on heuristic determination. For instance, for potassium: $\mathcal{G}_K = \overbrace{\mathcal{G}_K}\, n^4$, where $0 \le n \le 1$ is a scaling factor with boundary condition $dn/dt = \alpha_n\left(1-n\right) - \beta_n n$, where $\alpha_n = 0.01\left\{\left(V+10\right)/\left[\exp\left((V+10)/10\right)-1\right]\right\}$ and $\beta_n = 0.125\exp\left(V/10\right)$. Equivalently for sodium $g_{\mathrm{Na}} = \overbrace{g_{\mathrm{Na}}}\, m^3 h$, with boundary conditions $dm/dt = \alpha_m\left(1-m\right) - \beta_m m$, and $dh/dt = \alpha_m\left(1-h\right) - \beta_m h$; $0 \le m \le 1$, $0 \le h \le 1$ scaling factors, with best fit: $\alpha_m = 0.1\{(V+25)/[\exp((V+25)/10)-1]\}$ and $\beta_m = 4\exp\left(V/18\right)$, respectively, $\alpha_h = 0.07\exp\left(V/20\right)$

and $\beta_m = [\exp((V+30)/10)11]^{-1}$. The total Kirchhoff current summation for all respective ion-currents is now $I = I_K + I_{Na} + I_\ell = C_m(dV/dt) + \overbrace{\mathcal{G}_K} n^4 (V - V_K) + \overbrace{\mathcal{G}_{Na}} m^3 h(V - V_{Na}) + \overbrace{\mathcal{G}_\ell}(V - V_\ell)$, where C_m is the MEMBRANE CAPACITANCE. The individual ion FLOW current density (J_i) across the gates in the membrane is based on the NERNST–PLANCK DIFFUSION EQUATION, using the DIFFUSION coefficient of the respective ions D_i, expressed as $\vec{J_i} = -D_i\left(\vec{\nabla} C_{m,i} + \left(C_{m,i}/\gamma_i^{\text{charge}}\right)\vec{\nabla} V\right)$, incorporating the ionic charge distribution by means of $\gamma_i^{\text{charge}} = RT/FZ_i$ (R the universal GAS constant, F the Faraday's constant, Z_i the ion VALENCE, and T the ABSOLUTE TEMPERATURE). The action potential is derived from the Crank–Nicholson differential equation $(1/r_a)\nabla^2 V = C_m(dV/dt) + I_K + I_{Na} + I_{Ca} + I_\ell + I_{\text{stimulus}}$, where r_a is the electrical resistance for the intracellular medium (ion migration) and I_{stimulus} is the stimulation current (originating from an influence on the membrane). The stimulant current can result from the chemical imbalance induced, for instance, by means of the interaction of light on BACTERIORHODOPSIN, pressure applied to a pressure sensing cell, chemicals on taste buds, and so on.

Hodgson number ($H = fV\Delta P/Q\bar{P}$)

[fluid dynamics, thermodynamics] A dimensionless time for a system in alternating MOTION, describing the time constant during pulsation period for the system, where f is the frequency, V the characteristic volume, ΔP the pressure gradient, Q the volumetric flow rate, and $\bar{P}$ the average static pressure. The Hodgson number applies specifically to unsteady pulsating gas FLOW and generally to momentum transfer. The Hodgson number can provide a useful means of predicting errors in metered flow recordings, for instance, at a pulsating compressor, at the location of the meter such as a venture or ORIFICE.

Holography

[general, optics] An interference IMAGE that is constructed by means of laser scanning of two images on layers of photographic plates that will provide the same three-dimensional appearance when illuminated with a small, narrow ANGLE emission light source. The mechanism to capture the image consists of a three-dimensional open weave grid coated with photographic emulsion (e.g., silver chloride, as found on regular photographic film). The image is formed by means of INTERFERENCE, retaining the PHASE information of the electromagnetic OSCILLATION next to the AMPLITUDE information based on the "reflectiveness" of the object. The scanning and object illuminating LIGHT SOURCE is by requirement coherent and as such requires the use of laser light. The laser beam is split by a beam splitter in a reference beam and a probing/imaging beam, which are recombined in the three-dimensional PHOTOGRAPHIC PLATE, writing an image in three dimensions. The viewing of the hologram can be performed in several different ways, one is looking at the plate itself from where the image is appearing as outlined by the frame only, not anchored to the plate itself. The image formation itself performs an interference scheme that appeals to the stereoscopic VISION aspect of our two eyes and subsequent cerebral interpretation. In theory, every cubic millimeter of the photographic mesh contains an angular view of the entire object, providing a wealth of redundancy. Alternatively, a holographic projection can be produced free from the photographic film mesh, appearing in free space. The requirements for the viewing light source do not include coherence *per se*, nor does it need to be monochromatic. However, the crispness of the image in free-space will be more well defined when the source is more tightly defined. The concept of holography was invented by the physicist Dennis Gabor (1900–1979) from Hungary in 1947 for which he received the Nobel Prize in Physics in 1971 (see Figure H.40).

(a)

(b)

Figure H.40 (a,b) Artist rendering of the future of holography.

Homeostasis

[biomedical] Refers to the maintenance of the parameters with respect to all aspects of the internal cellular environment within tolerable limits. Cells carefully regulate their intracellular ionic concentrations, as well as the water level, to ensure that no osmotic pressures arise. As a consequence, the major ions Na^+, K^+, Cl^-, and Ca^{2+} have different concentrations in the extracellular and intracellular environments. Additionally, the energy consumption of the cell with respect to survival as well as providing a function (e.g., muscle) requires a balance of nutrients, oxygen, waste, energy, and water, reducing down to maintaining the ATP level. The homeostasis regulates the energy, chemical, and fluid balance within a cell, between similar cells, between different cells, between different organs, and across the cell membrane.

Hooke, Robert (1635–1703)

[biomedical, general, mechanics, optics, solid-state] A physicist, scientist, and engineer from Great Britain. In 1660, Robert Hooke investigated the phenomenon of COLOR separation on thin transparent films, such as the colorful soap BUBBLE. This study provided him with the rudimentary theoretical conviction that light is a WAVE. SIR ISAAC NEWTON (1642–1727) used Hooke's information and proposed a dual nature for light, both with PARTICLE (mechanical) properties as well as with wave properties. Furthermore, both THOMAS YOUNG (1773–1829) and AUGUSTIN-JEAN FRESNEL (1788–1827) confirmed the hypothesis of Robert Hooke not until the early 1800s. In 1665, Robert Hooke proposed the atomic model of MATTER, based on crystalline structures and apparent transparence, indicating holes between the SOLID-STATE nature. This observation was confirmed by his description of MIXING one GLASS of ALCOHOL and one glass of water, which form less than two glasses of mixture, apparently the one is slipping between the other. The full context of the atomic model was not confirmed until JOHN DALTON (1766–1844) in the early 1800s provided a detailed description of chemical reactions. In 1676, Robert Hooke published his SPRING FORCE theory, proportional to the displacement, known as HOOKE'S LAW (see Figure H.41).

Figure H.41 Robert Hooke (1635–1703); no known surviving images of Robert Hooke are in existence. (Artist rendering; Courtesy of Rita Greer.)

Hooke's law

[biomedical, general] The mathematical relation between stress (S_n) and STRAIN (ϵ_n) resulting from an axial force. This concept was introduced in 1676 by ROBERT HOOKE (1635–1703). Graphically, this is represented in the slope of the linear part of the stress–strain curve, defined as the YOUNG'S MODULUS (Y_n) of that material under stress $S_n = Y_n\epsilon_n$, as defined by Hooke's law of linear ELASTICITY. More generally, Hooke's law of elasticity defines the force ($\vec{F}$) resulting from a spring-type medium or material to be proportional to the linear displacement ($\vec{x}$) while under the influence of the medium, with proportionally constant that is characteristic of the medium, the spring constant k_{spring}, where the force opposes the displacement as $\vec{F} = -k_{spring}\vec{x}$ (see Figure H.42).

Figure H.42 Expression of Hooke's law for the jumping motion with a "pogo stick."

Hoop stress (σ_h)

[biomedical, mechanics] A TANGENTIAL STRESS in the WALL of a PIPE (i.e., cylindrical vessel) acting in a cross-sectional plane perpendicular to the longitudinal axis of the pipe $\sigma_h = Pr_i/\delta$, where P is the internal pressure on the wall, δ is the wall thickness, and r_i is the inside radius of the pipe. For thin-walled vessels ($r_i \geq 10\delta$), the forces and stress and strains are derived from the LAME'S EQUATIONS (compare to shear stress) (see Figure H.43).

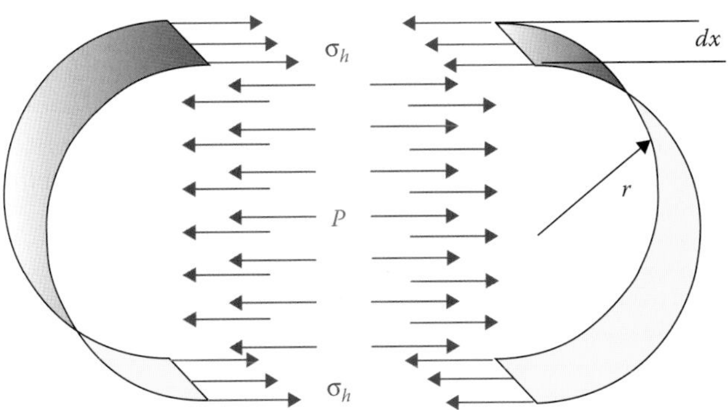

Figure H.43 Diagram illustrating the concept of Hoop stress.

Hormonal signaling

[biomedical, chemical, energy] A glandular secretion of signaling molecules (i.e., hormones) into the BLOOD stream that affects the biological functioning and biological development.

Horsepower (hp)

[general] A measure of power equivalent to watt in the conversion 1 hp = 745.699872 W = 746 W. The unit horsepower was introduced in 1783 by JAMES WATT (1736–1819) in reference to quantifying the performance of steam engines. The unit was based on the efforts by a draft horse, lifting a 150 pound (~68 kg) object attached to a PULLEY while moving at 2.5 miles/h = 4 km/h, however generously overstated not to discredit the performance of the noble horse as the primary mechanism of work in the day (see Figure H.44).

Figure H.44 Clydesdale ploughing field.

H-theorem

[energy, nuclear] *See* **BOLTZMANN'S H-THEOREM.**

Hubble, Edwin Powell (1889–1953)

[astronomy] An astronomer from the United States. Edwin Powell is best known for his contributions to the definition of the existence of multiple galaxies in the UNIVERSE. His observation of our neighboring GALAXY, the Andromeda Nebula, led his discoveries to show that the universe is expanding (see Figure H.45).

Figure H.45 Edwin Powell Hubble (1889–1953).

Hubble space telescope

[general] A SATELLITE equipped with large optical reflective telescope launched in 1990, orbiting the EARTH in GEOSYNCHRONOUS ORBIT. The orbit height is approximately 559 km, providing an unobstructed view of the GALAXY, unhindered by atmospheric disturbances. The Hubble space telescope was notorious for the manufacturing defect and associated failure to check for the quality before sending the TELESCOPE with faulty 2.4 m diameter hyperboloid mirror into space. The MIRROR was not properly polished, generating SPHERICAL ABERRATIONS, distorting the collected data and had to be repaired while in space. The telescope was named in honor of the physicist and astronomer EDWIN POWELL HUBBLE (1889–1953) from the United States. The Hubble space telescope program was initiated in 1977. The telescope is still operational (see Figure H.46).

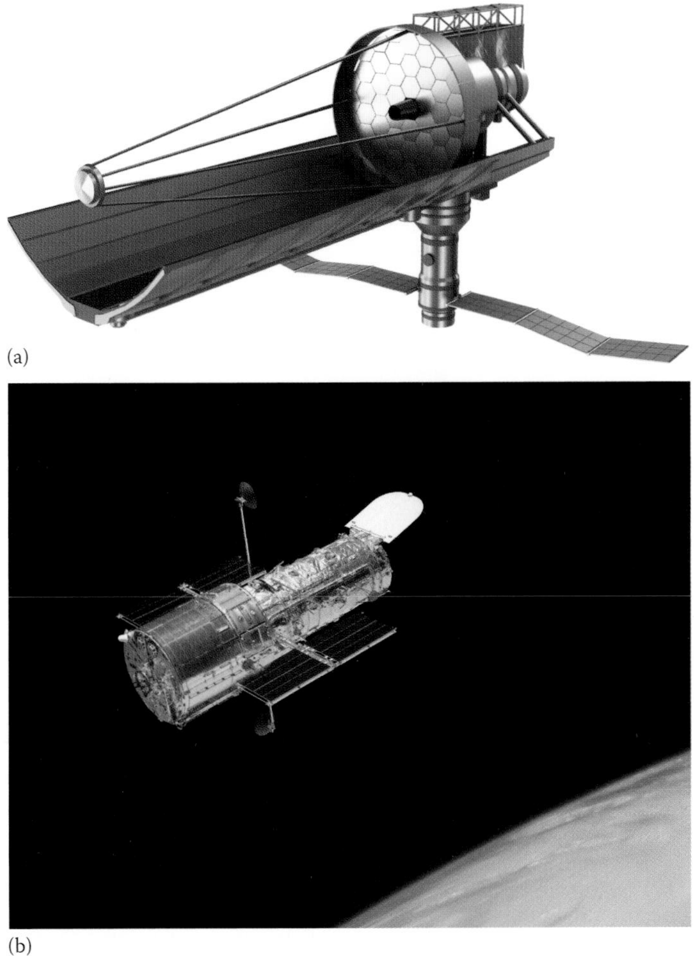

(a)

(b)

Figure H.46 (a,b) Hubble Space Telescope.

Hubble's law

[astrophysics, general] A theoretical description of the rate of EXPANSION of the UNIVERSE, defined as $\vec{v} = H_H \vec{r}$, $H_H = 100 h^{gal}$ km/sMpc, where $\vec{v}$ is the mean recession velocity of the uniformly expanding GALAXY at separation $\vec{r}$, H_H is the Hubble constant, which is undefined at this point due to the inability of placing an absolute value on galactic distances, $0.5 < h^{gal} < 1$ is a dimensionless constant and length expressed in mega parsecs $1\ \mathrm{Mpc} = 3.08610^{22}$ m. There is some evidence indicating that the works of both GEORGES HENRI JOSEPH ÉDOUARD LEMAÎTRE (1894–1966) and ALEXANDER ALEXANDROVICH FRIEDMANN (1888–1925) predate the work of EDWIN POWELL HUBBLE (1889–1953).

Hüfner, Carl Gustav von (1840–1908)

[biomedical, chemical] A physiologist, chemist, and scientist from the Prussian Empire (now Germany). Gustav von Hüfner is best known for his description of the chemical ACTIVITY of hemoglobin with respect to oxygen transport in BLOOD in 1866 (see Figure H.47).

Figure H.47 Gustav von Hüfner. (Courtesy of *Hoppe-Seyler's Zeitschrift für physiologische Chemie*, Vol. 58, November 12, 1908.)

Hüfner's number (*Hü*)

[biomedical] The volume of oxygen that can bind to hemoglobin per gram unit, approximately has a value of 1.34 (technically 1.339), but depends on the boundary conditions. It was determined that 1 g of hemoglobin could maximally bind 0.0598 mmol of oxygen gas, using the molar volume of an IDEAL GAS (22.4 ml/mmol); this provides the scaling parameter 1.339 ml/g, where the MOLECULAR WEIGHT of hemoglobin is 64,458.5. This number is used to determine the oxygen concentration $[O_2]$ in BLOOD from $[O_2] = \mathrm{Hü}[\mathrm{Hb}](\mathrm{SaO_2}/100)$, where $[\mathrm{Hb}]$ is the hemoglobin concentration also called hematocrit and SaO_2 is the oxygen saturation, which can be determined by PULSE-OXIMETER measurement among other ways including analytical blood–gas analysis. The blood–oxygen binding analysis was performed by CARL GUSTAV VON HÜFNER (1840–1908).

Hull, Albert Wallace (1880–1966)

[atomic, nuclear] A physicist from the United States. Albert Hull developed the magnetron (as used in MICROWAVE OVEN) in 1921, while working at General Electric. Hull also developed X-RAY crystallography diffraction technique for the structural analysis of powdered crystalline structures. The diffraction pattern satisfies the BRAGG'S EQUATION. Hull developed his experimental design independently from his contemporaries PETRUS (PETER) JOSEPHUS WILHELMUS DEBYE (1884–1966) and PAUL SCHERRER (1890–1969) in 1917. Additional efforts of Hull were in the development of VACUUM tubes (e.g., dynatron and THYRATRON) (see Figure H.48).

Figure H.48 Albert Wallace Hull (1880–1966). (Courtesy of IEEE, New York.)

Human body

[biomedical, chemical, electronics, engineering, materials sciences, mechanics] A biological entity with a broad range of chemical, physical, and mechanical properties. The human body has an internal semi-flexible rigid structure, composed of a skeleton, providing support, equilibrium, and means to apply force, torque, and HOMEOSTASIS. The motions of the body are supported through a system of muscles: smooth muscle, skeletal muscle, and cardiac muscle. The majority of activities, data processing, and data storage are supported by a central nervous system, consisting of the brain and spinal cord and conjunctively a peripheral nervous system. The brain is organized into compartments with specific functions, such as senses (PERCEPTION), MUSCLE control, emotion, next to memory and computation as well as personal behavioral characteristics ("character"). The senses use a variety of PHYSICS and chemistry phenomena as well as mechanical integration. The senses are VISION, HEARING, smell, touch, taste, and pain. The senses are supported through specialized anatomic organs: vision (ophthalmoception) provided by the eyes, hearing (audioception) mediated by the ears, smell (olfacoception or olfacception) a chemical feature of the nose, taste (gustaoception) a chemical interaction with the tongue in the mouth, and touch (tactioception) has a broad range of specialized sensors (including pressure, temperature, and mechanical shear and strain), whereas pain is a stimulus to the brain primarily provided by open-ended nerve endings, but with other sensory extensions as well. The body uses double and triple redundancy for most of its controls and senses and additionally has separated systems that communicate at critical locations for confirmation and amplification as well as response. The physical activities of the human body are regulated by two separate integral systems: central nervous system and peripheral nervous system. The peripheral nervous system contains the autonomic nervous system and the somatic nervous system. The autonomic nervous system is divided into parasympathetic nervous system, sympathetic nervous system, and enteric nervous system, which can operate independently from each other but can also interact with each other. Muscles provide several functions: stability and equilibrium, RESPIRATION next to BLOOD CIRCULATION as the primary source for survival. Smooth muscles are integral to the vascular blood circulation, food and waste transportation, and reproduction. The cardiac muscle is the main pumping mechanism for blood FLOW. The SKELETAL MUSCLE offers a mechanism of force and torque. Movements of the body are carefully regulated by subconscious (autonomic) mechanisms that provide minimization of effort by means of, for instance, controlling the location of the center of mass during pole jump or increasing the respiratory volume during ACTIVITY. Signal propagation is mediated by nerve cells that use an ACTION POTENTIAL based on a reversible and active (requiring ENERGY to operate) exchange of chemical components. The process of decision making, computing cause and effect and interpretation of data, sensation and relevance to the environmental boundary conditions, and prior history are integrated chemical processes that are still not totally understood. The human body is one of the most in-depth researched topics due to the broad range of resources, but also due to its diversity in parameters. The human body also offers one of the more intriguing challenges for research, continuously seeking novel investigational techniques next to the conundrum of genetic evolution. Examples of investigational topic of interest are the action potential for cellular communications and mechanism of functional activation, next to electrical volume conduction, specifically with respect to the DEPOLARIZATION of the HEART, as well as the FLUID DYNAMICS of the lungs and the blood circulation. Additional fields of ENGINEERING research are in the MECHANICS and control of prosthetic devices, as well as biocompatibility and material durability, including a broad range of quality control aspects. Both diagnostic and therapeutic modalities, including medical device design and development, as well as protection of human subjects (both from the device/mechanism as from the implications of participating in the procedure) are regulated by government institutions such as the Food and Drug Administration (FDA) in the United States, the Medical Device Commission/Council on Medical Devices for the European Union, and the Pharmaceuticals Medical Devices Agency (PMDA) in Japan (see Figure H.49).

Figure H.49 The human body as a multifaceted, multidisciplinary integration of biology, engineering, physics, electronics, and fluid dynamics.

Human eye

[biomedical, optics] *See* **EYE**.

Humidity

[thermodynamics] Water vapor contents in ATMOSPHERE (*also see* **ABSOLUTE HUMIDITY** *and* **RELATIVE HUMIDITY**).

Humidity, absolute

[thermodynamics] The physical quantity of water vapor measured in mass as a portion of a unit volume, units (kg/m^3). Absolute HUMIDITY is most often used in METEOROLOGY.

Humidity, relative

[thermodynamics] For water, the ratio of the partial pressure of the VAPOR in a volume of a mixtures of gasses and water vapor with respect to the pressure of the water vapor as a constituent of the mixture (i.e., partial pressure) that will result in condensation due to SATURATION (related term "DEW POINT") (see Figure H.50).

Figure H.50 Relative humidity meter: hygrometer.

Hund, Friedrich Hermanns (1896–1997)

[atomic, energy, solid-state, thermodynamics] A German scientist and mathematician dedicating his work to SOLID-STATE PHYSICS. Hund started out as the assistant to MAX BORN (1882–1970) and served with other notable scientists such as ERWIN RUDOLF JOSEF ALEXANDER SCHRÖDINGER (1887–1961), PAUL ADRIEN MAURICE DIRAC (1902–1984), WERNER KARL HEISENBERG (1901–1976), and WALTER WILHELM GEORG BOTHE (1891–1957).

Hund's law

[atomic, energy, solid-state, thermodynamics] *See* **HUND'S RULE.**

Hund's rule

[atomic, energy, solid-state, thermodynamics] Every orbit in the Bohr's atomic model of electron distribution has single occupation prior to filling the additional paired electron in each respective orbit. These single occupied electron orbits are containing electrons with the electron spins aligned. This formulation was published by FRIEDRICH HERMANNS HUND (1896–1997) in 1927. This statement is also referred to as HUND'S LAW.

Huxley, Andrew Fielding, Sir (1917–2012)

[biophysics, chemical, electromagnetism, energy] A physiologist and physicist from Great Britain. Sir Andrew Huxley is best known for his contributions to the description of the formation and propagation of the biological ACTION POTENTIAL as related to the giant squid axon in the early 1940s. The action potential is an electrochemical mechanism that provides a binary communication system. The work was performed in collaboration with SIR ALAN LLOYD HODGKIN (1914–1998) which provided them both with the Nobel Prize in Medicine in 1963. Additionally, their joint efforts provided major insight into the processes involved in muscular contraction, published in 1954 (*also see* **HODGKIN–HUXLEY MODEL**) (see Figure H.51).

Figure H.51 Andrew Fielding Huxley (1917–2012) in 2005. (Courtesy of Vmadeira.)

Huygens, Christiaan (1629–1695)

[atomic, general, nuclear, optics] An astronomer, engineer, mathematician, and physicist from the Netherlands. In addition to his work in optics, Huygens contributed to ASTROPHYSICS, MECHANICS (e.g., PENDULUM of a clock), and geometrical mathematics (e.g., definition of the circumference of a circle, revisited for the first time since ARCHIMEDES [287–212 BC] introduced the constant relating radius and circumference as smaller than 3[1/7] and greater than 3[10/71]). He is most famous for his pioneering theoretical analysis of the wave phenomenon of ELECTROMAGNETIC RADIATION: the HUYGENS PRINCIPLE, in this context he (re-)introduced the concept of ETHER as a medium through which light propagates (previously conceptually postulated by ARISTOTLE [384–322 BC]. In OPTICS, Huygens introduced the formal description of REFRACTION and double refraction. His work includes a comprehensive outline of LENS characteristics (FOCAL POINT based on curvature: the lens equation) as well as IMAGE formation in 1652. In 1653, Huygens recognized the principle of chromatic and SPHERICAL ABERRATION and gave an elaborate mathematical description of how to account and compensate for these phenomena. He contradicted Newton's principia (1687), which states that all MOTION is absolute by reiterating his postulate that all motion is relative. There is documented proof of the friendship between Christiaan Huygens's father, Constantijn Huygens (1596–1687), with the Dutch painter Rembrandt Harmenszoon van Rijn (1606–1669). Constantijn Huygens is represented in one of Rembrandt's paintings as well (see Figure H.52).

(a) (b)

Figure H.52 (a) Christiaan Huygens, (1629–1695) painted by Caspar Netscher (1639–1684). (Courtesy of Collection Museum Boerhaave, Leiden, the Netherlands). Long-term use from the "Haags Historisch Museum," Den Haag, the Netherlands, (b) Constantijn Huygens (1596–1687), painted by Rembrandt van Rijn, in 1627.

Huygens principle

[optics] The concept of WAVE properties for light was introduced by CHRISTIAAN HUYGENS (1629–1695) in 1680 and in his 1690 publication *Traité de la Lumière*. The principle defines that every location in the path of a light beam acts as a spherical source. The superposition principle will result in a PLANE WAVE traveling in the direction of the beam of light, away from the LIGHT SOURCE. This principle becomes of critical importance

when a narrow APERTURE is blocking the path of the light ray, or a solid obstruction, both resulting in diffraction (see Figure H.53).

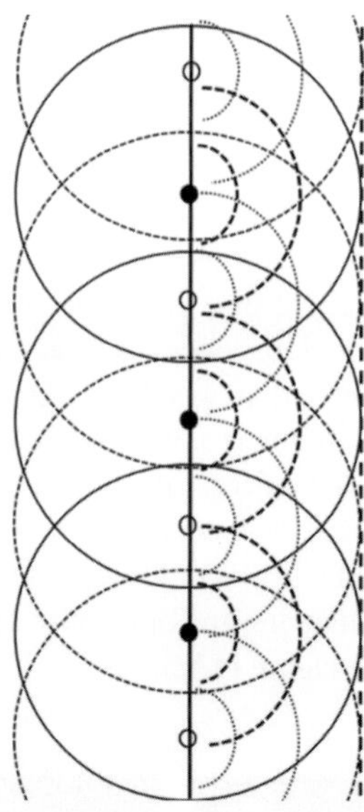

Figure H.53 Illustration of Huygens principle introduced by Christiaan Huygens (1629–1695) for the concept of wave propagation. The same concept is applied in the single slit description under the experimental design of Joseph von Fraunhofer (1787–1826).

Hydraulic impedance

[fluid dynamics] Resistance to FLOW in a tube with cross-sectional area A is expressed as $Z_h = \sqrt{\rho B_{\text{eff}}}/A$, with B_{eff} the FLUID COMPRESSIBILITY MODULUS and ρ the DENSITY of the FLUID.

Hydraulics

[fluid dynamics] Having to do with fluids (liquids and gasses) in MOTION or under steady-state conditions interacting with environmental conditions such as confinement in a container. The word comes from the Greek words for water: ύδρο (hydro) and PIPE: διοχέτευση (diochétefsi: "channeling") (see Figure H.54).

Figure H.54 Hydraulic levelers for scooping up soil and rocks.

Hydrogen atom

[atomic, nuclear] The ATOM of lightest mass and simplest atomic and nuclear structure, consisting of 1 proton with 1 orbital electron. Its mass is 1.008123 mu.

Hydrogen bomb

[atomic, nuclear] *See* **H-BOMB** (see Figure H.55).

Figure H.55 Volumetric expansion under the influence of the heat generated during the explosion of a hydrogen bomb, providing both emission of radiation (heat: infrared, visible, and X-ray as well as beta and gamma radiation), in addition to a pressure wave. Due to the compression of the air outside the volume of atmosphere directly surrounding the explosion, the flow of air will be toward the location of the extinguished explosion directly following the expansion, generating a damped cavitation wave with high Q value ("critically damped").

Hydrogen bond

[atomic, chemical, energy, nuclear] An electrostatic bond between a HYDROGEN ATOM and an electronegative MOLECULE. The most well-known hydrogen bond is with the diatomic molecule oxygen which becomes electronegative as atomic structure in WATER: (H_2O), other examples are hydrogen bonds to nitrogen and fluorine. Water has a strong attraction between the water molecules due to the induced polarity and DIPOLE formation with both hydrogen atoms as positive POLES and oxygen as the negative pole. In water the hydrogen bond of the induced dipole attracts neighboring dipole oxygen atoms in the H_2O structure. Other examples of hydrogen bonding are in the DNA double-helix structure (see Figure H.56).

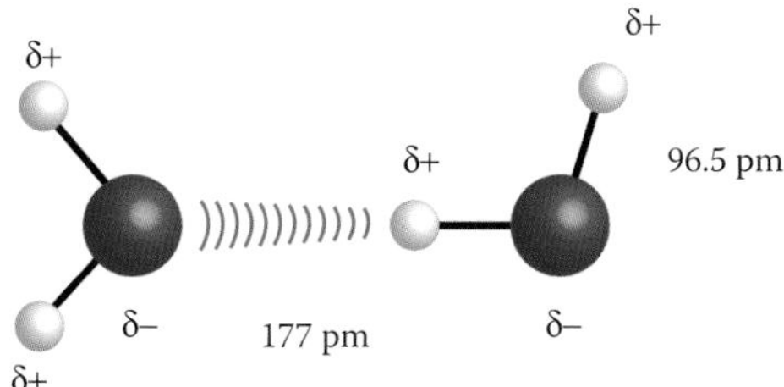

Figure H.56 The effects of the hydrogen bond in water.

Hydrogen spectra

[biomedical, general, imaging, optics] A technique used to map detailed spectral emission profiles as a function of wavelength, based on two-dimensional location. FLUORESCENT and PHOSPHORESCENT LUMINESCENT intensity as a function of wavelength is collected over relatively narrow bands of the ELECTROMAGNETIC SPECTRUM (primarily spanning the visible and infrared), segmented in often hundreds of wavelength ranges. Each segment holds particular information, often overlooked when using standard broadband SPECTROSCOPY. The spectral emission peak are specifically connected to unique ATOMIC structural forces, hence providing MOLECULAR composition details. The critical backdrop to this form of analysis is the existence of a thorough, extensive and detailed look-up table for spectral phenomena (peaks, slope, "groupings," etc.) to reference against for recognition and identification. For instance in minerals the graphical representation of the SPECTRAL absorption and emission is a direct function of the chemical composition and the crystalline structure, in addition to temperature effects and ambient conditions (dissolved/dry). Specifically the VALENCE of an ELEMENT in a structure can dramatically change the spectral performance on a subnanometer level. The technique was used initially in geographic surface mapping pertaining to oilspills, weather conditions, and agricultural information (e.g., use of herbicides/spectracides/disease localization and optimal growth conditions determination) as examples of REMOTE SENSING. A commercial example is the airborne visible/INFRARED imaging spectrometer (AVIRIS) operated by the NASA Jet propulsion Laboratory. Additionally galactic spectroscopy is used to identify ELEMENTS in the surface construction of remote planes as well as the composition of elements in the incineration flames produced during the NUCLEAR FUSION and FISSION processes on stars. In medical diagnostic endoscopic devices based on FIBER-OPTIC construction (i.e., catheter) are used to graphically localize the configuration of atherosclerotic plaque in arteries, in addition to cervical dysplasia diagnostics to name but a few examples. For the use and history of the units in spectroscopy (*see* **SPECTROSCOPY**) (see Figure H.57).

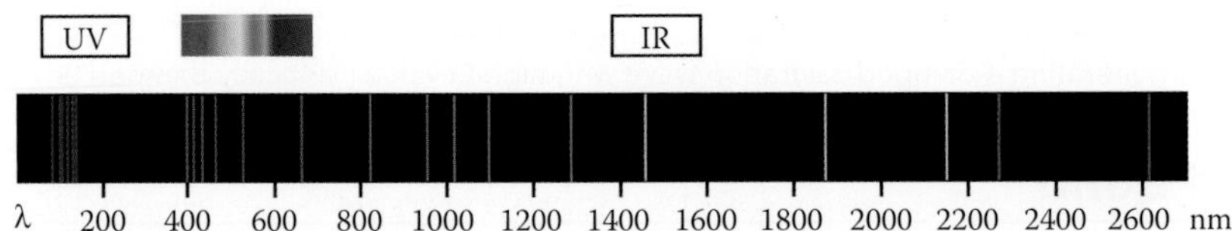

Figure H.57 Hydrogen emission spectrum.

Hydrology

[energy, fluid dynamics, general, geophysics] The field of PHYSICS dealing with physical phenomena in the liquid part of Earth's ATMOSPHERE directly related to the FLOW and PHASE transitions of the oceans and large and small bodies of water.

Hydrostatic paradox

[general] The pressure on the bottom of a closed reservoir filled with LIQUID is independent of the weight of the liquid.

Hygrometer

[energy, fluid dynamics, general, geophysics] A device that measures HUMIDITY. Examples are found in materials that change shape on length in response to the relative number of water vapor molecules in a volume of AIR. One of the oldest and most reliable techniques uses a horses tail hair, which expands and contracts under the influence of water vapor (see Figure H.58).

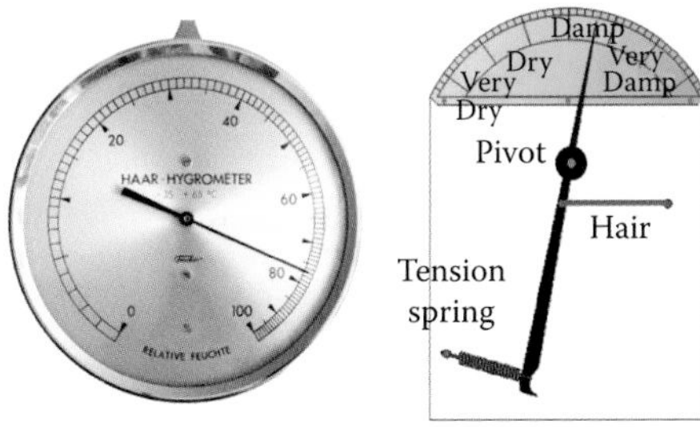

Figure H.58 Hygrometer. (Courtesy of Daniel FR.)

Hyperfine constant

[atomic, energy, nuclear, optics] The constant that describes the split in spectral lines for a specific ELEMENT based on the intrinsic NUCLEAR MAGNETIC MOMENT ($\mu_{I_n} = g_n\left(m_e/M_n\right)\left(e/2mc\right)I$), with g_n the nuclear g-factor, $\left(m/M\right)$ the ratio of the electron mass (m_e) over the nuclear mass (M_n), and $\vec{I}$ the nuclear SPIN.

Hyperfine structure

[atomic, energy, nuclear, optics] The emission lines from EXCITED STATES of atomic electron orbits are influenced by both external MAGNETIC FIELD (B) (*see* **FINE STRUCTURE**) and NUCLEAR MAGNETIC MOMENT ($\vec{\mu_n} = \left(Zeg_n/2M_nc\right)\vec{I}$, with $\vec{I}$ the nuclear spin vector, Z the total number of charges, $e = 1.60217657\times10^{-19}\,\mathrm{C}$ the electron charge, M_n the nuclear mass, $c = 2.99792458\times10^{8}\ \mathrm{m/s}$ the speed of light, and g_n = the nuclear g-factor). The orbital electron produces an inherent magnetic field (B_e) which interacts with the nuclear magnetic moment creating a hyperfine structure: $\mathcal{H}_{hf} = a_{hf}\vec{I}\cdot\vec{J}$, where a_{hf} is the HYPERFINE CONSTANT, $\vec{I}$ the nuclear spin, $\vec{J} = \vec{L}+\vec{S}$ the TOTAL ANGULAR MOMENTUM (with total angular momentum quantum number j), combining the ORBITAL ANGULAR MOMENTUM ($\vec{L}$, with orbital angular momentum quantum number ℓ) and the SPIN angular momentum ($\vec{S}$, with spin QUANTUM number s). The fundamentals of the spectral split came from the work of WILLIS EUGENE LAMB (1913–2008). The hyperfine ENERGY split can be described based on the first-order PERTURBATION THEORY of the interaction of the electron MAGNETIC MOMENT ($\mu_e = (e/mc)\vec{S}$) with the MAGNETIC FIELD $\Delta E = -\vec{\mu_e} \cdot \vec{B}$, yielding

$$\Delta E = (2/3)\left(Z\alpha_{hf}\right)^4 \left(m/M_n\right)\left(mc^2\right) g_n \left(1/n^3\right)\left(\left(2/\hbar^2\right)\left(\vec{S}\cdot\vec{I}\right)\right) = (2/3)\left(Z\alpha_{hf}\right)^4 \left(m/M_n\right)\left(mc^2\right) g_n \left(1/n^3\right)\left(j\left(j+1\right)-(3/2)\right)$$

(*also see* **ZEEMAN EFFECT**) (SEE FIGURE H.59).

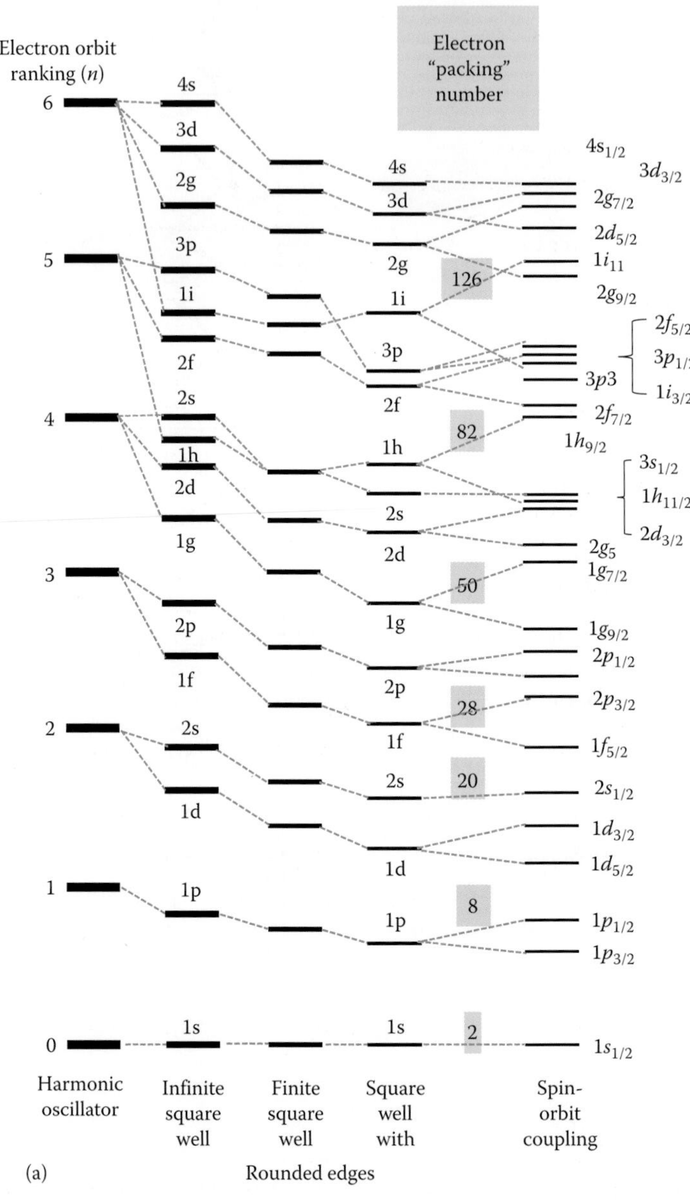

Figure H.59 (a,b) Illustration of the energy split leading to a hyper fine structure, with minute wavelength differences in the emission spectrum. *(Continued)*

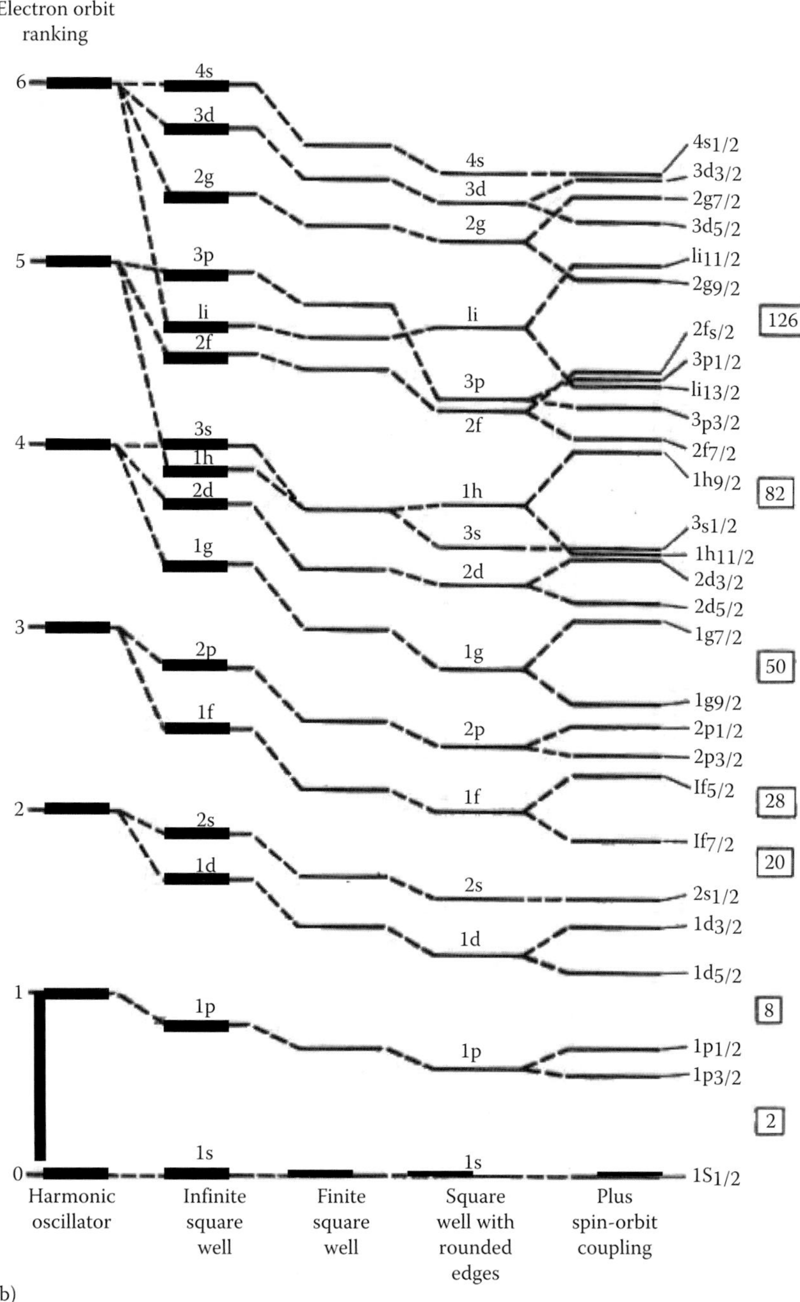

Figure H.59 (Continued) (a,b) Illustration of the energy split leading to a hyper fine structure, with minute wavelength differences in the emission spectrum.

Hypernuclear physics

[atomic, general, solid-state] Physical phenomena associated with BARYONS called hyperons, heavier than protons or neutrons. Strangeness is not conserved in hyperon DECAY with lifetimes in the order of 10^{-10} s, in contrast to preservation in strong nuclear interactions.

Hyperspectral

[general, optics] Fine RESOLUTION spectral analysis of a physical process involving the emission or attenuation of ELECTROMAGNETIC RADIATION. Hyperspectral sensing usually references to the combination of the acquisition of an IMAGE or a pattern in electromagnetic detection composed of multiple bandwidth of information, that is, multiple sources or multiple scanning ranges providing a high resolution wavelength decomposition (*also see* **SPECTROSCOPY**). The spectral decomposition provides the means of discrimination between spectra from sources (e.g., emission/reemission and fluorescence) or components (e.g., attenuation) that are remarkably similar in spectral performance. The process usually involves advanced mathematical processing, primarily using second-order derivative analysis. The multiple spectral scans can be considered to configure an n-dimensional space in the data domain.

Hysteresis

[computational, electronics, electromagnetism, fluid dynamics, mechanics] A phenomenological feature often associated with some form of capacitive effect, which includes a spring. The hysteresis phenomenon applies to mechanical procedures, electrical activities as well as MAGNETIC processes. Under the external influence, a change in mechanical (including fluidic), electrical, or magnetic ENERGY configuration is facilitated with a nonlinear response, often a delay effect; for example, the process appears to try to catch up. The phenomenon describes the condition where the change of state of a system is not accurately reversible under external influences. The change of state in one direction follows a different energy path as the reverse from the final point. The area enclosed by the graph outlining the transition process describes the energy loss per cycle. The most appropriate representation of the hysteresis phenomenon is by means of graphs. In electrical GENERATOR design and the alternating current that is directly associated with the generation of ELECTRICITY, the concept of hysteresis was most important due to the inherent losses associated with it and was recognized as a phenomenon that deserved greater attention by Charles Proteus Steinmetz (1865–1923), a mathematician and electrical engineer from the Prussian Empire (now Poland). The hysteresis provides a major concern for loss when linked multiple generators together, such as found in a wind power "farm" where all the wind generators are out of PHASE and do not turn with the same revolutions (no identical frequencies across the entire field of generators) since the wind velocity and TURBULENCE conditions are different as a function of location in three-dimensional atmospheric volume of flowing AIR (see Figure H.60).

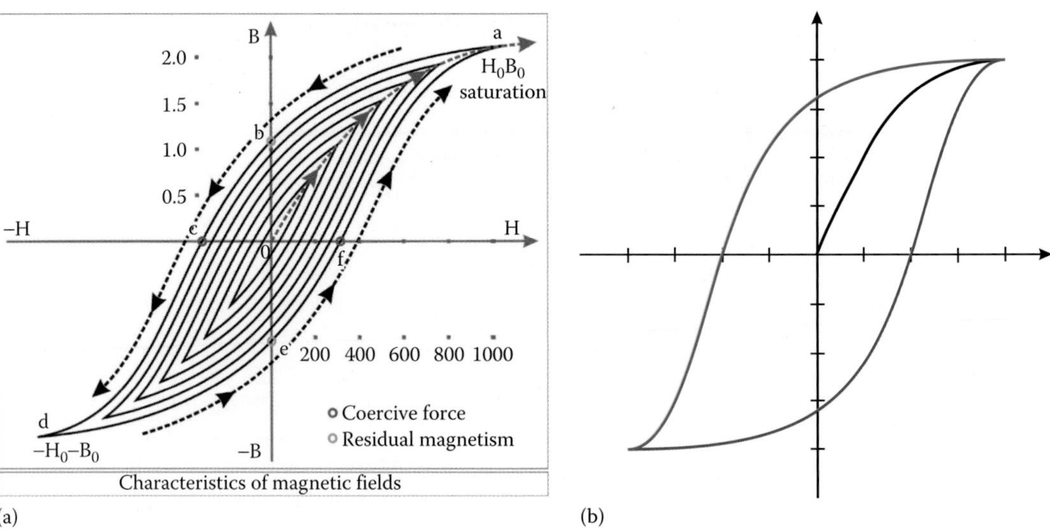

Figure H.60 (a,b) Hysteresis, represented by a delay in expression of force resulting from a change in applied magnetic field.

IC (integrated circuit)

[electronics, general] A microprocessor chip, semiconductor-layered structure with a specific arrangement of *PN*-junctions to accommodate the creation of an electronic circuit resembling resistors, capacitors, operational amplifiers, and switches as well as digital memory (see Figure I.1).

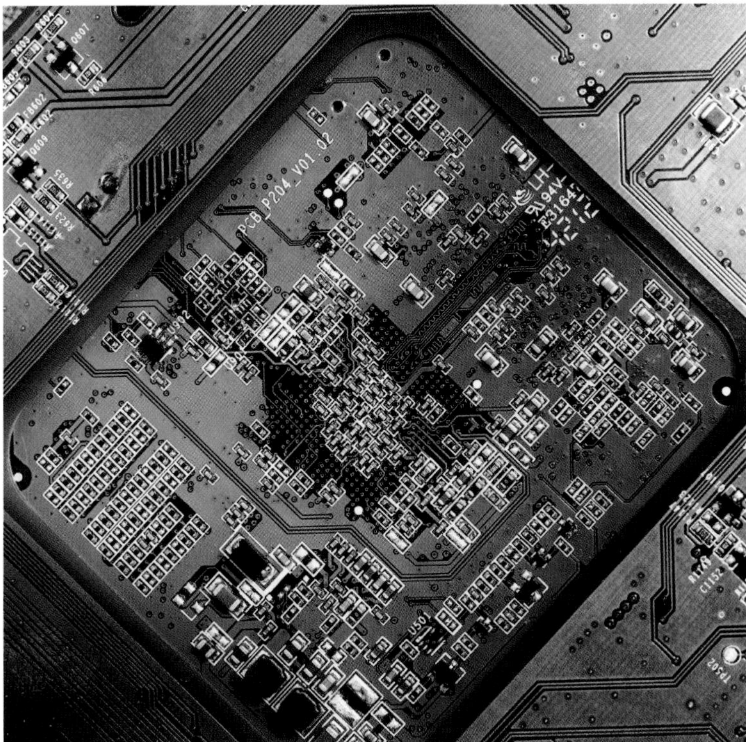

Figure I.1 Microscopic view of printed circuit board of an integrated circuit chip.

Ideal behavior of a mixture

[thermodynamics] An ideal gas mixture is referred to as a Gibbs–Dalton mixture, based on the contributions from Josiah Willard Gibbs (1839–1903) and John Dalton (1766–1844). The gas is ideal when the pressure (P) is sufficiently low and the temperature (T) is high enough to support a vapor state of the substances confined in a closed volume. Under these conditions, the intermolecular forces will be sufficiently weak so that the presence of the molecules of other constituents is relatively unnoticeable on a force scale. Under these conditions, the individual constituents (total r constituents), with respective amounts: $n_1, n_2, \ldots, n_r$ all at equilibrium volume and respective pressure (p_{ii}) with the respective internal energy (u_{ii}) and entropy (s_{ii}), yield for the energy (U) and ENTROPY (S) of the system: $U(T,P,n)=\sum_{i=1}^{r} n_i u_{ii}(T,p_{ii})$, respectively, $S(T,P,n)=\sum_{i=1}^{r} n_i s_{ii}(T,p_{ii})$, that is, the sum of the conditions for the components in the volume. Inherent to these conditions is the fact that the total pressure is the sum of the partial pressures for the constituents, defined by the DALTON LAW OF PARTIAL PRESSURES: $P=\sum_{i=1}^{r} p_{ii}(T,p_{ii},y)$, where $y=n_i/n=(x_i/M_i)/\sum_{j=1}^{r}(x_j/M_j)$: $y_1, y_2, \ldots, y_r$, represent the MOLE fractions of the constituents, with $M = m/n$ the MOLECULAR WEIGHT of the mixture with mass m and x_i the respective mass fractions.

Ideal behavior of a substance

[thermodynamics] Apart from ideal gases, there are solids and liquids to consider as well, each with the respective conditions define an ideal substance. For solids and liquids, the equilibrium enthalpy between the constituents, under conditions of PRESSURE (P, respectively, the specific pressure: p) and TEMPERATURE (T) and VOLUME (V) constraints, is one of the factors that delineates the IDEAL INCOMPRESSIBLE BEHAVIOR. Ideal incompressible behavior is defined by the SPECIFIC HEAT ($c_v = du/dT$) and internal energy (U, respectively, the specific internal energy: u) as well as the entropy (S, respectively, the specific entropy: s), using the coefficient of isobaric EXPANSION: $\alpha_p=(1/v_m)(dv_m/dT)_p$, with $v_m = m/V$ the mass-specific volume, m the mass of the constituent: $du = c_v dT + [(\alpha_p T/\kappa_T) - p] \cong c_v dT$, with $\kappa_T = -(1/v_m)(dv_m/dP)_T$ the coefficient of isothermal compressibility; $ds = (c_v/T)dT + (\alpha_p/\kappa_T)dv_m \cong (c_v/T)dT$; and respectively the ideal approximation for the enthalpy (H, respectively, the specific enthalpy: h): $dh = Tds + v_m dp \cong c_v dT + v_m dp$. Additionally, the chemical potential will be consistent for all constituents; *see* **CHEMICAL POTENTIAL** *and* **FUGACITY**. This defines the ideal substance in general, LIQUID, solid, or GAS.

Ideal fluids

[fluid dynamics, general] *See* **IDEAL BEHAVIOR OF A SUBSTANCE**.

Ideal gas

[fluid dynamics, thermodynamics] A FLUID mixture with constituents that are far enough apart that the internal ENERGY is not affected by the proximity of other molecules. Generally, a diluted gas, with conditions that are far from SATURATION conditions.

Ideal gas law

[general] The PRESSURE (P) and VOLUME (V) of a GAS are inherently connected through the number of molecules of the gas (moles of substance: n) and the temperature, expressed as $PV = nRT = Nk_BT$, where $R = 8.3144621(75)\,\mathrm{J/Kmol}$ is the universal gas constant, which is linked to the AVOGADRO'S NUMBER ($N_A = 6.022137 \times 10^{-23}\,\mathrm{J/K}$) through the BOLTZMANN CONSTANT ($k_b = 1.3806488 \times 10^{-23}\,\mathrm{m^2kg/s^2K}$) as $k_b = R/N_A$, and N represents the number of molecules of gas. The ideal gas law is derived from the experimental observations performed by ROBERT BOYLE (1627–1691) and JACQUES ALEXANDRE CÉSAR CHARLES (1746–1823). In 1662, Robert Boyle recognized that a fixed quantity of gas at constant temperature hold a fixed relation between pressure and volume $P_1V_1 = P_2V_2$, while Jacques Charles in 1787

discovered the relationship between volume and temperature (in KELVIN) under constant pressure as $V = \text{Const} \times T$. Further contributions by JOSEPH LOUIS GAY-LUSSAC (1778–1850) in 1802 showed that the pressure of a gas is directly proportional to its temperature $P/T = \text{Const}$. The ideal gas law is a property under the EQUATIONS OF STATE for a medium. The ideal gas law is often referred to as the BOYLE–GAY-LUSSAC LAW (see Figure I.2).

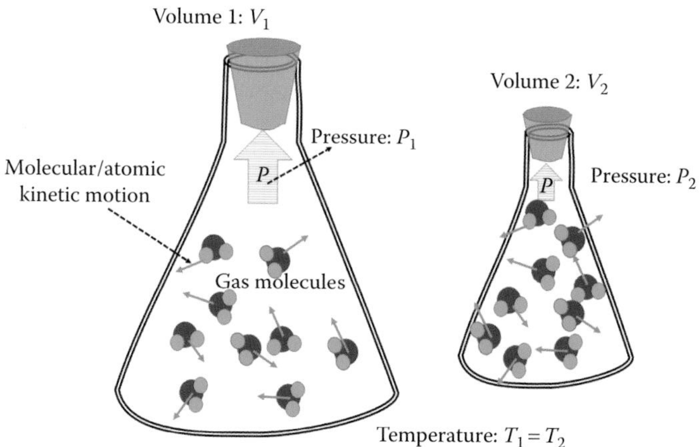

Figure I.2 Ideal gas law conditions.

Ideal gas mixture

[thermodynamics] *See* **IDEAL BEHAVIOR OF A SUBSTANCE** *and* **IDEAL SOLUTION.**

Ideal incompressible behavior

[thermodynamics] *See* **IDEAL BEHAVIOR OF A SUBSTANCE.**

Ideal solution

[thermodynamics] A SOLUTION is defined as a mixture of two components, for which one constituent has a greater quantity than the other and the prevailing component of the AGGREGATION is the SOLVENT and the minority constituent the SOLUTE. The solvent will be in LIQUID form where the solution is considered dilute when the molar fraction of any of the respective solutes is significantly smaller than the MOLE fraction of the solvent. Under conditions of dilution, a weak solution provides the conditions that the nearest neighbors to any respective solute MOLECULE are primarily solvent molecules. The CHEMICAL POTENTIAL ($\mu_i = \left(\partial G/\partial N_i\right)_{T,P,N_{j\neq i}}$, also known as the partial molar ENERGY, where G represents the Gibbs free energy, and N_i represents the particulates for the respective constituents, under the operational conditions (concentration [ION], pressure [P], and temperature [T] for a dilute solution provided as $\mu_i = \mu_{ii}\left(T,P\right) + \mathrm{RT}\ln y_i$, where $\mathrm{R} = 8.3144621(75)\,\mathrm{J/Kmol}$ is the universal GAS constant, and $y = n_i/n = (x_i/M_i)/\sum_{j=1}^{r}(x_j/M_j)$ represent the mole fraction for the respective constituents. In the composition, the following notation is introduced: $\square_{ii} = y_i$ Parameter, for the ith constituent.

This yields for the enthalpy $h_i = h_{ii}(T,P_i)$, $H(T,P_i,n_1,n_2,\ldots,n_r) = \sum_{i=1}^{r} n_i h_{ii}(T,P_i)$; respectively, for the entropy for a system for r constituents: $S(T,P_i,n_1,n_2,\ldots,n_r) = \sum_{i=1}^{r} n_i s_{ii}(T,P_i) - R\sum_{i=1}^{r} n_i \ln y_i$; for the internal energy: $u_i = u_{ii}(T,P_i)$, $U(T,P_i,n_1,n_2,\ldots,n_r) = \sum_{i=1}^{r} n_i u_{ii}(T,P_i)$; the respective partial volume: $V(T,P_i,n_1,n_2,\ldots,n_r) = \sum_{i=1}^{r} n_i v_{ii}(T,P_i)$, with $v_m = m/V$ the mass-specific volume.

Ideal voltage source

[electronics] Voltage source with zero internal RESISTANCE (*also see* **ELECTROMOTIVE FORCE**).

Identical particles

[atomic] Atomic, nuclear, and SUBATOMIC PARTICLES are considered to be identical under conditions of identical mass, identical half-integral intrinsic SPIN (for fermions), identical integral intrinsic spin (for bosons), and identical charge.

Identical states

[thermodynamics] A system with multiple constituents with respective values of the parameters for constituents that are all identical as well as the respective magnitudes of all the properties for each respective state are identical between all states of the components for the system. In case any of the values and properties are different from each other, the states are considered to be different.

Identical systems

[thermodynamics] Two or more systems are considered to be identical if they are experiencing the same forces, are composed of the exact same constituents in the same quantities, and have the same parameters for entropy and pressure, volume, and so on and operate under the same constraints.

Image

[acoustics, biomedical, fluid dynamics, imaging, quantum] The definition of an IMAGE is a two- or three-dimensional array of datapoints, in contrast to a one-dimensional single observation. Images are acquired by various technological means, ranging from optical techniques using OPTICAL COHERENCE TOMOGRAPHY to regular microscopy, next to the following examples of a wide array of imaging technology and imaging ENGINEERING features: POSITRON EMISSION TOMOGRAPHY, X-RAY, MAGNETIC RESONANCE IMAGING (MRI), ELECTRON MICROSCOPY, helium-ion microscopy, ULTRASOUND, and general PHOTOGRAPHY. Images can be analyzed for content and feature extraction, such as functional aspects based on TRACERS in fMRI or based on time- and frequency-dependent encoding in pulse oximetry. A wide range of spectral imaging techniques are available to reveal signature-based features of components and events, such as "RED-SHIFT" or "BLUE-SHIFT" with respect to DOPPLER modified acquired SIGNAL due to relative MOTION. The graphical representation of data in a diagram or plot may also be considered an image under certain circumstances. In particular, diagrams containing detailed information about a process or a phenomenon are an image formation of the feature, for instance, the Raman spectral profile represents the chemical, energetic, and structural information on a molecular scale, which cannot be imaged directly (see Figure I.3).

(a)

(b)

Figure I.3 (a) Image of a sail boat on a river, providing two-dimensional information about the location of the shore with respect to the boat, in addition to virtual three-dimensional information about the extent of the channel, next to information about the weather conditions, direction of the wind based on the orientation of the flag and relative humidity of the air (no fog), as well as additional information about the materials may be derived and (b) image presenting the spectral profile of a soap bubble. In pollution control, the disposal of waste oil on open waters by ships can be tracked by spectral analysis of the oil-slick floating on top of the water in the ocean. The oils sold in many harbors for lubrication purposes is generally mixed with agents that can be traced based on the spectral signature, acquired by patrolling monitoring planes. Hence, the polluters may potentially be identified.

Imhotep (approx. 2725 BC)

[biomedical, general] The first recorded analytical physician as well as priest from Egypt. Documented as routinely using analytical processes for diagnostic and derivation of cause of an ailment and the most logical cause of action for the most effective treatment based on the available information and the available treatment options in the day (see Figure I.4).

Figure I.4 Engraved teachings of the Egyptian "high-priest" of medicine, Imhotep (approx. 2725 BC), and illustrations of a selection of medical instruments.

Immiscible substances

[thermodynamics] Two substances are considered to be miscible under the condition that they are mixed in any proportion and they will always form a single liquid PHASE, for instance, ALCOHOL and water (limited boundary conditions). In contrast, two substances are considered to be immiscible under the condition that when mixed in any proportion they will always form two separate phases, for instance, under LIQUID form water and mercury.

Immunoglobulin superfamily

[biomedical, chemical] In biology, there is cell-to-cell binding and communication interaction that can be divided into four types of receptors: CADHERINS, selectins, INTEGRINS, and immunoglobulin superfamily. The immunoglobulin superfamily has a molecular structure that is similar to immunoglobulins. Examples of the immunoglobulin superfamily are found in intracellular connective molecular chains and for neural CELL molecular binding.

Impedance (Z)

[acoustics, electronics, general] An expression of the complex relationship between two phenomena based on the combined effects of RESISTANCE, inductance, "recoil," and capacitance (i.e., partial energetic storage). Both for acoustic WAVE propagation and electronic wave propagation, there are a set of independent material properties that combine to form the impedance for the system. In ACOUSTICS, the mechanical impedance is the primary factor that determines the conditions in IMAGE formation for ULTRASONIC IMAGING as in the determination of flaws (gradients) or failure (discontinuity) based on the definition $Z = \vec{F}(\lambda)/\vec{v}(\lambda)$, where $\vec{F}$ represents the local force, $\vec{v}$ the velocity vector, and λ the wavelength of the phenomenon (ultrasound FREQUENCY ($\nu = v_s(r)/\lambda$, where $v_s(r)$ the location-specific speed of SOUND), which can be linked to the ELASTIC MODULUS (E_Y) for a MASS (m) distribution over a volume of medium (V) as $Z = \sqrt{E_Y(m/V)}$. Alternatively, in ELECTRONICS the impedance is the combined effect provided by the series in parallel configuration of electronic components with base features resistance (R, SCALAR); inductance ($X_L = \omega L$, referred to as the inductive reactance, with $\omega = 2\pi\nu$ the ANGULAR FREQUENCY of the alternating phenomenon; complex vector value) and capacitance ($X_C = 1/\omega C$, referred to as the capacitive reactance; complex vector value). The total impedance is the combined effect of the residual components expressed as $Z = \sqrt{\{R^2 + (X_L - X_C)^2\}}$ (see Figure I.5).

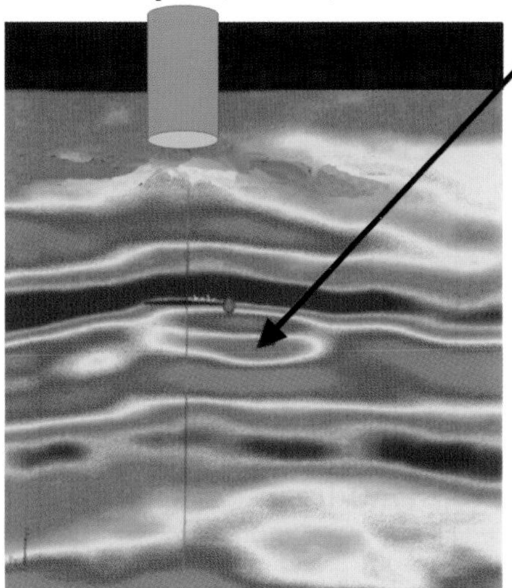

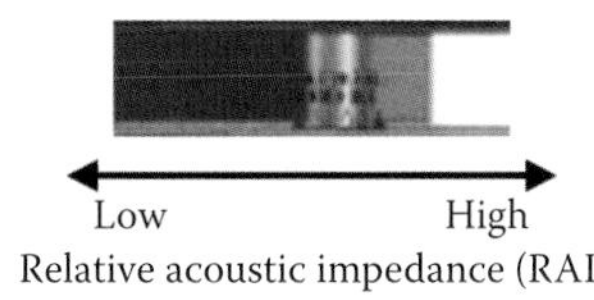

Figure I.5 False-color illustration of the acoustical impedance as a function of depth for the earth's crust in a single location with respect to the identification of risk assessment in seismic features and seismic potentials. (Courtesy AAPG datapage. Online journal for E&P Geoscientists. http://www.searchanddiscovery.com/documents/2005/strecker/images/03.html.)

Impedance spectroscopy

[biomedical, electronics, imaging] An imaging technique that collects the FREQUENCY SPECTRUM as a function of location, derived from line-intersect value reconstruction. The fact that the impedance is a function of frequency of electronic perturbation provides a mechanism of action for discrimination of media or conditions of media based on location. The frequency DISPERSION as well as PHASE delays introduced by gradual transitions or respectively boundaries creates discontinuities that result in partial or full reflection as well as DOPPLER shifts and phase modulations that can be retraced and used to form a virtual IMAGE of the electronic properties. The electronic properties are inherently linked to the material phase, the biological ACTIVITY, or the local temperature and can be retraced to the physical composition and functional analysis based on look-up tables and theoretical analysis. The theoretical analysis uses the parallels between ELECTRONICS and SOLID-STATE values, respectively, as biological activity and the measured frequency response. Electrochemical impedance spectroscopy provides the tools for characterization of electrochemical systems. The applications of impedance spectroscopy are of particular importance in the characterization of materials. Impedance spectroscopy applications range from characterization of coatings, quality control on batteries and fuel cells, as well as in nondestructive testing applied, for instance, to corrosion phenomena. It also provides investigational mechanism for the quality, composition, and density distribution of constituents in electrodeposition, electrodissolution, passivity, and corrosion studies, next to the investigation of biosensors and semiconductor interfaces (see Figure I.6).

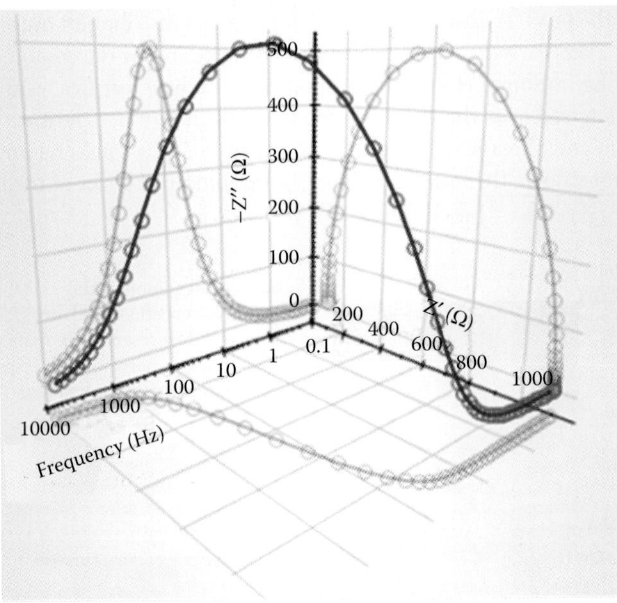

Figure I.6 Impedance spectroscopic recording.

Implicit approximate factorization method

[fluid dynamics] A mathematical algorithm used to analytically solve steady-state FLOW under transonic conditions. The implicit need for the development of an appropriate approximation is the fact that this type of problem generally requires a finite ELEMENT approach. The computational FLUID DYNAMICS approach is required due to the fact that the conditions involve mixed elliptic–hyperbolic functions. The implementation of the implicit approximate factorization method involves the introduction of a small perturbation to the potential (ϕ) equations, for instance, as $\left[k-\left(d\phi/dx\right)\right]\left(d^2\phi/dx^2\right)+\left(d^2\phi/dy^2\right)=0$, which in turn suggest the introduction of a recursive series for substitution in the analog solution process, for instance, defined as $\left(d^2\phi/dx^2\right)^{n+1}+\left(d^2\phi/dy^2\right)^{n+1}=\left[\ell+\left(d\phi/dx\right)^{n}-k\right]\left(d^2\phi/dx^2\right)^{n}$, where k and ℓ are functional constant derived from the discrete Laplacian used to solve matrix equations.

Impulse ($\vec{J}$)

[general, mechanics] The rate of change in MOMENTUM ($\vec{p}$) accumulated over a period of TIME (t) equals the accumulated net applied force ($\vec{F}$) during that same interval, expressed as $\vec{J}=\int_{t0}^{t_1}\left(d\vec{p}/dt\right)dt=\overrightarrow{p_1}-\overrightarrow{p_0}=\int_{t0}^{t_1}\vec{F}dt$. The impulse is primarily of importance when a force is applied over a short period of time, and during this brief moment, the force can be relatively large, such as a hammer hitting a nail. However, in most short-duration events, the momentum is a more useful concept. Alternatively, the applied force is the rate of change in impulse (see Figure I.7).

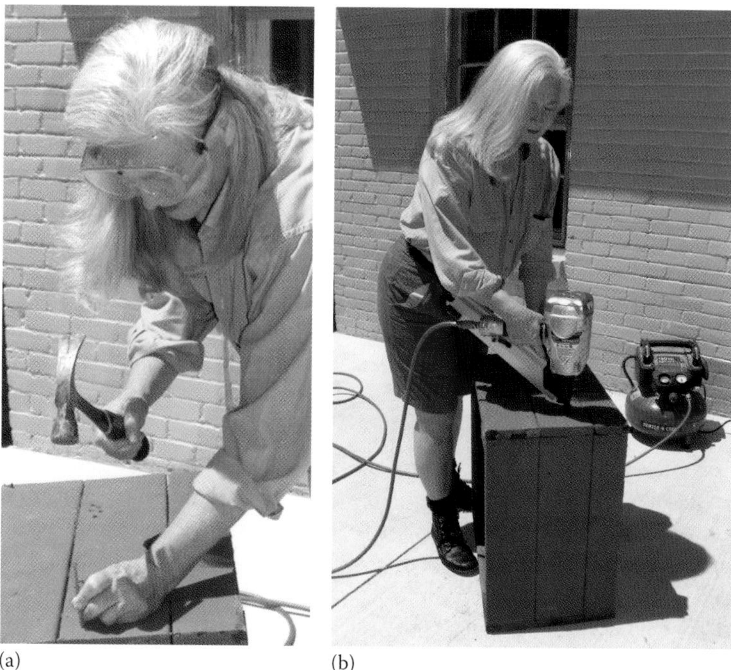

(a) (b)

Figure I.7 Impulse used in practical applications: (a) impulse from a hammer and (b) impulse from a pneumatic nail-gun.

Impulse noise

[biomedical, electronics, thermodynamics] Noise in SIGNAL detection due to faulty ELECTRONICS. This stands in contrast to GAUSSIAN NOISE, which is more indicative of thermal NOISE in the operations of the electronics.

Impulse response

[acoustics, electromagnetism, general, optics, theoretical] The spatial and frequency response of a system with respect to a delta function excitation process. Generally, the spatial response will widen the field due to DISPERSION and diffraction properties; additionally, the FREQUENCY SPECTRUM can be altered in wavelength-SPECIFIC WEIGHT as well as providing specific RESONANCE frequencies where the response is more intense. The output is coupled to the input for the impulse response through the transfer function. The impulse can be a delta function with respect to location or with respect to time; otherwise, the impulse may be a line or a cross, for a two-dimensional line source. The response is generally referred to as the point-spread function. The impulse response can be originating in the excited medium or can be a property of the sensor device and instrumentation acquiring the responses in the medium that is probed by the impulse. In the frequency domain, the response is referred to as the modulation transfer function, denoting the FOURIER TRANSFORM of the point-spread function when considering the spatial information as a discrete distribution of secondary sources separated by intervals, defining a spatial frequency. The "IMAGE" ($i(x', y')$) formed is defined by the convolution (⊗) of the source or "object" ($o(x, y)$) and the respective point-spread function ($h(x, y)$) as $i(x', y') = o(x, y) \otimes h(x, y)$, which is applied directly to lens use in OPTICS. In optics, the focal DISTANCE of the LENS forms the foundation for the point-spread function, with additional details provided by the RAYLEIGH CRITERION. In the Fourier domain, the impulse response is defined as the cross product of the Fourier transform of the input signal ($O(\xi,\eta)$) and the modulation transfer function ($H(\xi,\eta)$), which yields the "image" ($I(\xi',\eta')$) defined as $I(\xi',\eta') = H(\xi,\eta) \times O(\xi,\eta)$ (see Figure I.8).

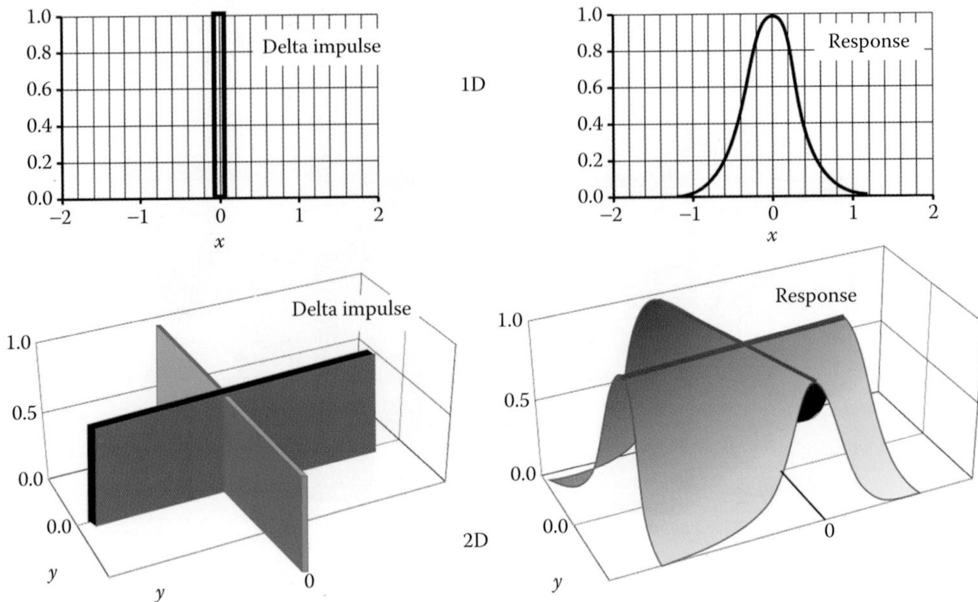

Figure I.8 Graphical illustration of an impulse response for a system.

Incompressible fluid

[fluid dynamics, thermodynamics] Fluid (liquid of GAS) that will not change density under applied external pressure.

Increasing criticality

[nuclear] The term "criticality" refers to the NEUTRON balance in a nuclear reaction for a nuclear power plant. A system is subcritical when the loss of neutrons, generated by the FISSION process, resulting from the implementation of a MODERATOR is larger than the generation of new neutrons. Gradual removal of the moderator will result in an increasing criticality, generally targeting a perfect balance between neutron production and neutron quenching. The rate of increase should adhere to specific safety boundaries.

Indeterminacy principle

[atomic, nuclear] *Also see* **UNCERTAINTY PRINCIPLE.**

Index of refraction (*n*)

[general] Optical density of a medium expressed as the ratio of the speed of light in VACUUM ($c = \sqrt{\mu_0\varepsilon_0}^{-1} = (\mu_0\varepsilon_0)^{-1/2} = 2.99792458 \times 10^8$ m/s) divided by the local speed of light in the medium (v): $n = c/v$ (see Figure I.9).

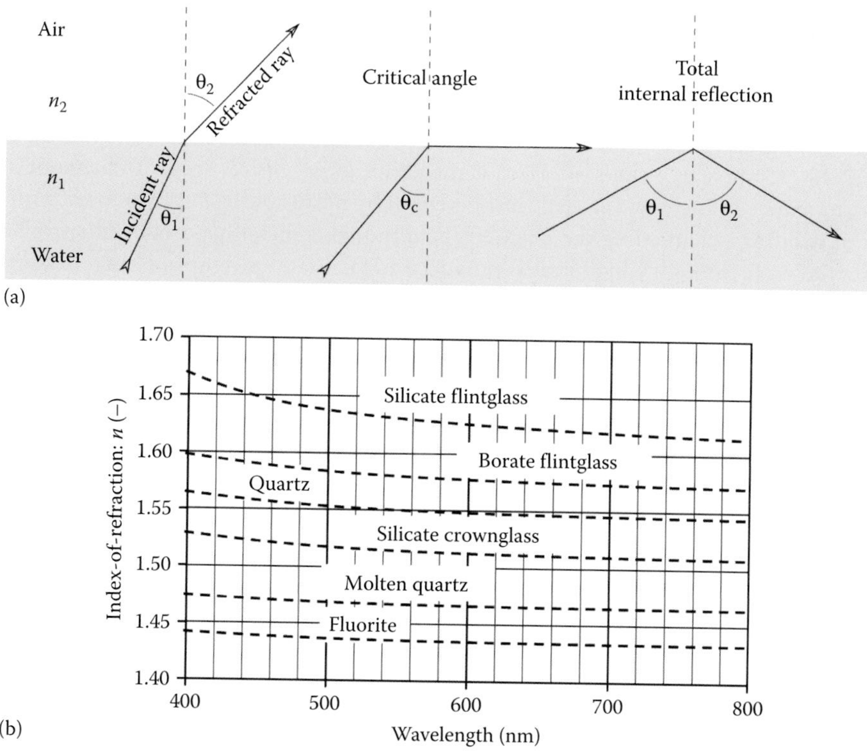

Figure I.9 (a) Illustration of the redirection of the path of a ray under a discontinuity of the index of refraction at the interface between two media. The velocity of propagation in medium 2 is less than medium 1, causing the Poynting vector to redirect, resulting in diffraction and (b) the index of refraction of certain media as a function of wavelength.

Induced emf (electromotive force)

[general] Electrical potential created as a result of changes in the electric and or magnetic fields with respect to a wire loop. For an INDUCTOR, this is described as $\varepsilon_{emf} = -L(dI/dt)$, with L representing the inductance for the wire loop and I the current generating the MAGNETIC FIELD. This translates for a wire loop with N-windings into $\varepsilon_{emf} = -N\left(d\phi_B/dt\right)$, where $\phi_B = \mathrm{BA}\cos\theta$ indicates the magnetic flux of the perpendicular component of a magnetic field (B) through a loop with area A. In case the ANGLE changes over time, the magnetic field piercing the area will inherently change in MAGNITUDE, as found for the rotating wire loop of a GENERATOR (*also see* **FARADAY'S INDUCTION LAW**) (see Figure I.10).

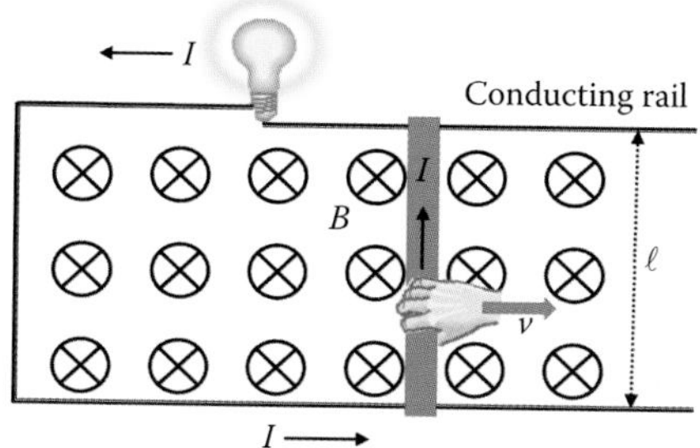

Figure I.10 Induced EMF generation process.

Inductance (*L*)

[electronics, general] The property of a coil of wire with a CURRENT (I) passing through to generate an electromotive force in its own circuit based on the produced MAGNETIC FIELD (B) with magnetic flux $\Phi_B = BA$ through the area of the coil (A) with N winding expressed as $N\Phi_B = LI$, which provides $L = \mu_0 N^2 A/I$, where $\mu_0 = 4\pi \times 10^{-7}$ H/m is the permeability of free space. Inductance is used in transformers to reduce or increase the electrical potential by means of linking two loops with a different number of windings, channeling the magnetic field though a metallic portal. Inductive heating is one of the several ways through which heat is produced to facilitate stovetop cooking, resulting from ENERGY conversion based on the fact that the induction process by choice is not ideal. Inductive heating requires special equipment, whereas conduction or convection heating primarily requires a material that conducts heat.

Induction motor

[electromagnetism, general, mechanics] A rotational device that relies on the interaction of a changing magnetic field with respect to a current loop, either the MAGNETIC FIELD changes due to a changing current in a wire loop, with a steady-state current loop (DC) placed within the magnetic field gradient, or alternatively the current changes as a function of time while placed in a steady-state magnetic field. The force that results from this interaction produces a torque that provides the means for rotation when one of the loop systems is mounted on an axle that is centered in the outside mechanism. The torque is defined as a function of the magnetic field vector ($\vec{B}$) in relation to the current $\tau = \overrightarrow{\mu_m} \times \vec{B}$, where $\mu_m = NIA$ is the magnetic moment for a CURRENT (I) loop with N winding with a cross-sectional area A. This is derived from the fact that the force on a wire with length ℓ conducting a current I exposed to a magnetic field under ANGLE θ is $F_B = \ell\vec{I} \times \vec{B} = \ell|\vec{I}||\vec{B}|\sin\theta$. The induction concept was researched extensively by NIKOLA TESLA (1856–1943) (see Figure I.11).

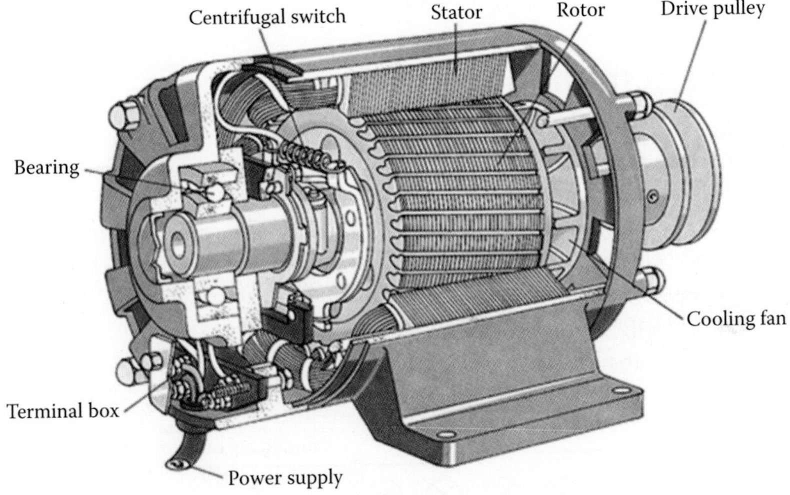

Figure I.11 Outline of an induction motor.

Inductive reactance (X_L)

[general] The complex definition with respect to the temporal response of a coil with inductance L is $X_L = \omega L$, where $\omega = 2\pi\nu$ is the ANGULAR FREQUENCY of the temporally changing phenomenon, operating at a frequency ν.

Inductor

[general] A wire loop that produces a MAGNETIC FIELD that attempts to counteract the magnetic field produced by the current flowing through the wire in the multiple loops, referred to as SELF-INDUCTANCE. Alternatively, the inductor is a wire loop that generates an electromotive force (electrical potential) that is the result of the changing magnetic field through the wire loop (see Figure I.12).

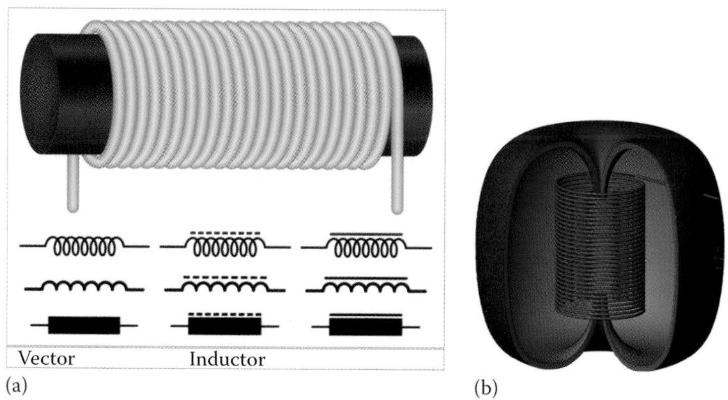

Figure I.12 (a,b) Diagram of a wire-loop inductor.

Inelastic collisions

[biomedical, general, mechanics] Collision where some ENERGY is converted from kinetic to other forms of energy, sometime deformation, sometimes heat, or may result in conversion from a portion of translational energy into rotational energy (see Figure I.13).

Figure I.13 Example of a totally inelastic collision. All kinetic energy has been converted in deformation energy.

Inelastic scattering

[nuclear] *See* **CROSS SECTION** *and* **NUCLEAR REACTION.**

I

Inertia

[general] General unwillingness to change motion; an object in MOTION will remain in motion when there are no external forces acting (which includes the absence of FRICTION and/or AIR DRAG), recognized as such by SIR ISAAC NEWTON (1642–1727) (see Figure I.14).

Figure I.14 Example of almost frictionless motion for a bobsled (bobsleigh). The initial kinetic energy supplied while running for take-off can sustain a constant velocity for a considerable time on a level surface. The conversion of potential energy to kinetic energy during down-hill slide is not impulse, but is converted into impulse.

Inertia, moment of (*I*)

[general] *See* MOMENT OF INERTIA.

Inertial reference frame

[general, mechanics] A reference frame in which NEWTON'S FIRST LAW is validated. For example, a reference frame relative to the first fixed STAR is inertial, specifically the velocity of the Sun in our SOLAR SYSTEM does not vary more than 10^{-10} with respect to other stars. The earth's movement with respect to the sun's inertial frame is technically not inertial since, due to the rotation and revolution trajectory around the Sun, there is acceleration involved; however in most cases, the deviation can be neglected ($< 3.4\times10^{-2}\,\mathrm{m/s^2}$) and reference frames attached to the earth's surface are considered inertial (by approximation) (see Figure I.15).

(a)

Figure I.15 Inertial reference frame on the moving sailboat (a) with the reference frame with respect to a plane in motion.

(Continued)

(b)

Figure I.15 (Continued) (b) Inertial reference frame on the moving sailboat in the land-based frame of reference.

Infinite square well

[atomic] *See* **POTENTIAL WELL.**

Infrared

[general, optics] A spectrum of ELECTROMAGNETIC RADIATION beyond the visible red, starting approximately at a wavelength of 660 nm, extending to the MICROWAVE range of 1 mm, discovered in 1800. Infrared pictures reveal thermal vibrations of ELECTRIC CHARGES, yielding the temperature profile of an object with respect to background (see Figure I.16).

Figure I.16 Image showing the infrared radiation emitted from a heated house, with special attention to surface areas that have a lower insulation value with respect to other areas, such as the windows.

Infrared electromagnetic radiation

[general, optics] *See* **Infrared.**

Infrared spectroscopy

[imaging, optics] *See* **Spectroscopy.**

Infrasound

[acoustics, general] Acoustic waves with frequencies below the audible range, below the cut-off frequency of 20 Hz, and wavelength in air exceeding 17.2 m in air, respectively.

Ingenhousz, Jan (Ingen-Housz or Ingen Housz) (1730–1779)

[biomedical, geophysics, thermodynamics] A medical doctor, physiologist, chemist, and scientist from the Netherlands attributed with describing the concept of photosynthesis. As a physician, he was an avid supporter of inoculation and disease prevention (see Figure I.17).

Figure I.17 Jan IngenHousz (1730–1779).

Inner ear

[biomedical, general] The cochlea of the ear that contains the transfer mechanism from wave mechanics to binary electric signal by the organ of Corti for transmission to the brain with subsequent processing. The inner ear is connected to the middle ear by means of the oval window, sealing off the liquid-filled cochlea from the middle ear that is connected to the outside air via the Eustachian tube. The inner ear is liquid filled with two distinct types of liquids that conduct the acoustic waves, referred to as the perilymph and the endolymph. The cochlea is shaped in the form of a snail-shell labyrinth with two canals. The sensory cells are located in the basilar membrane of the labyrinth located in the vestibular system, which have a frequency response that is location (r, primarily a linear function of the distance into the cochlear loops only) specific. The location-specific frequency response is as follows, with the sensor cells at the beginning, close to the oval window sensitive to high frequencies (~20 kHz down) while the lowest audible frequencies in the 20 Hz range are toward the opposite and far end. The frequency response is anatomically configured to be optimal based on the local resonance conditions (ω_0), hence providing a high degree of acuity and narrow frequency bandwidth as a function of location. The FREQUENCY ($\omega = 2\pi\nu$, where ω is the ANGULAR FREQUENCY and ν the actual temporal frequency) response of the basilar membrane in the cochlea can be modeled as a frequency-dependent ACOUSTIC IMPEDANCE (Z) defined by the stiffness of the local segment of the partition ($K_{\text{basilar membrane}}(r)$), a location specific dampening factor ($D(r)$) has been found to obey a function defined as $Z(r,\omega) = 1/A^2(r)\sqrt{\{M(r)\omega_0 - [K_{\text{basilar membrane}}(r)/\omega_0]\}^2 + D^2(r)}$, where $A(r)$ is the local cross-sectional area at a specific location in the cochlea and $M(r)$ the mass at a specific location of the cochlear partition. The acoustic impedance is a parameter linking the local pressure ($P_d(r,\omega)$), during pressure perturbation) to the displacement velocity of the local media ($v_d(r,\omega)$) as $v_d(r,\omega) = Z(r,\omega)P_d(r,\omega)$, respectively expressed in terms of ACOUSTIC INTENSITY (I_a) as $I_a(r,\omega) = P_d^2(r,\omega)/Z(r,\omega)$, hence creating the ideal RESONANCE in a specific location for the appropriate frequency (i.e., an acoustic filter), exciting only those sensors designed to record a specific frequency, which is subsequently conveyed to the brain for signal processing, convolution, and interpretation. The acoustic impedance also results in phase delays and DISPERSION effects that are compensated for in the integral structure of the inner ear. The WAVE traverses the vestibule, once inward via the utricle half of the vestibule and on return through the saccule, where the SOUND traverses the path of the looped bony labyrinth outlining the cochlea, which consists of 2(2/3) turns. The conversion (and associated transfer function) for the displacement of the endolymph FLUID in mechanical MOTION takes place by special cells in the ORGAN OF CORTI that are stretched by the LIQUID displacement. The stretch of these "hair-cells" appears, where the hairs wave as the underwater kelp of the beach shore on the ocean front. The mechanical distortion of the hairs in the organ of Corti changes the ION migration through pores in the CELL MEMBRANE generating a transmembrane potential that will eventually exceed the DEPOLARIZATION threshold, at which point causing the cell to send off an ACTION POTENTIAL that contains the binary indication of a received frequency that is specific for the location of the cell that stretched (i.e., location-specific frequency encoding) (see Figure I.18).

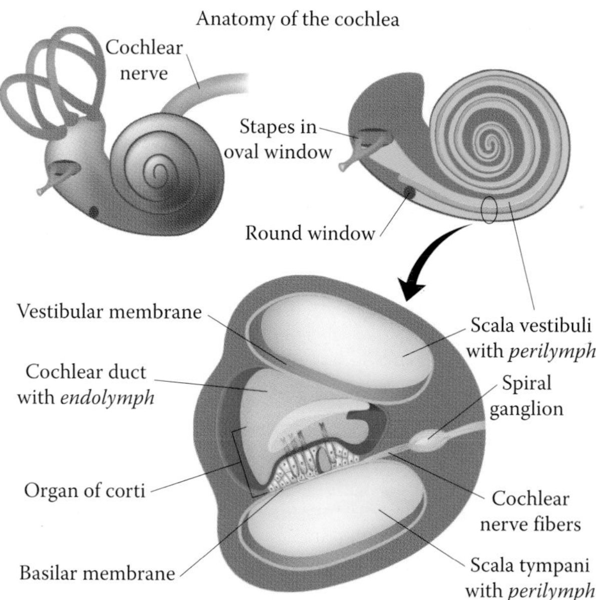

Figure I.18 The inner ear with operational aspects and components.

Inspiratory capacity

[biomedical, fluid dynamics] During TIDAL BREATHING, the maximum volume of GAS that can be inhaled after a normal exhalation. The average inspiratory capacity is 3500 ml (see Figure I.19).

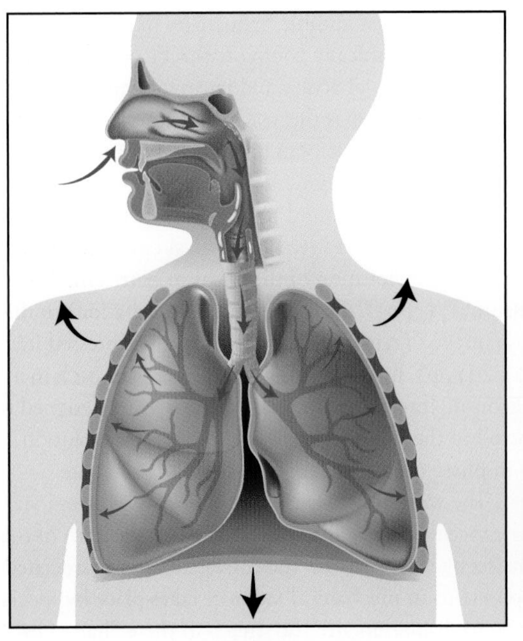

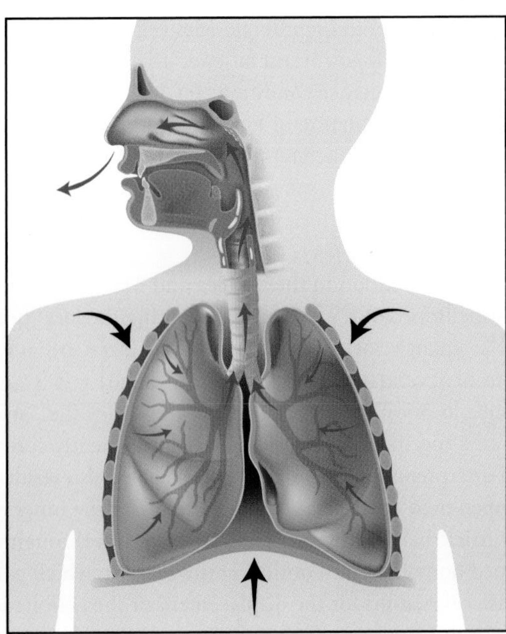

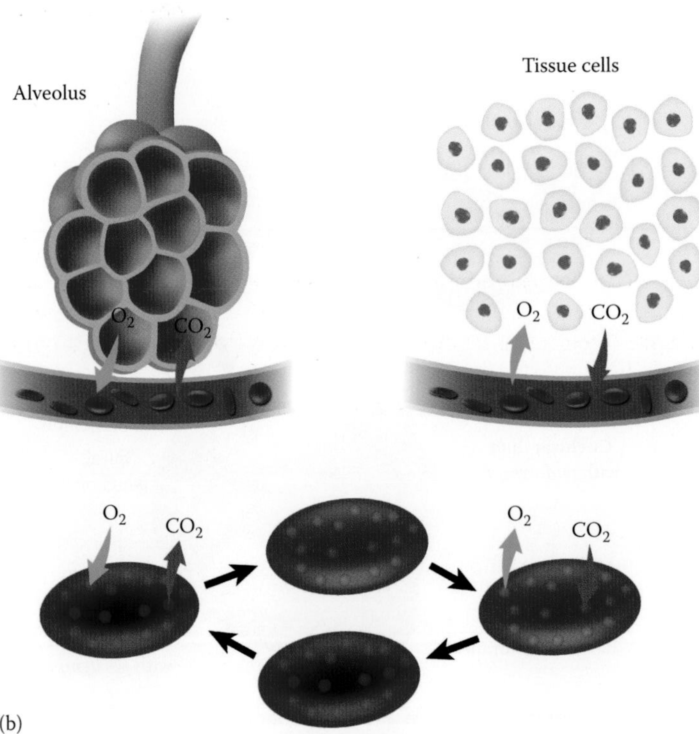

Figure I.19 (a,b) Respiration, gas exchange. The volume respiration diagram uses the following abbreviations: FRC, functional reserve capacity, the volume remaining in lungs at resting expiratory levels: the combined volume of the alveoli: (60%–70%) as well as the respiratory bronchioles and alveolar ducts (30%–40%): also referred to as the alveolar volume A.

Inspiratory reserve volume

[biomedical, fluid dynamics] Excess quantity of AIR that can be inhaled after normal inhalation during gentle TIDAL BREATHING. Inspiratory reserve volume and other tidal breathing parameters can be measured with a spirometer (see Figure I.20).

Figure I.20 Man breathing in spirometer in order to establish the lung function.

Insulator

[atomic, electronics, general] A material made of ELEMENTS with specific ELECTRON configuration. An ATOM has the electrons arranged according to the BOHR ATOMIC MODEL with electrons in specific allowed ENERGY LEVELS or ORBIT SHELLS. In comparison with either INSULATOR or CONDUCTOR, the electron configuration falls between these two. In an insulator, the CONDUCTION BAND containing free electrons is unpopulated and separated by a forbidden gap from the VALENCE BAND, whereas in conductor configuration the valence band is overlapping the conduction band, hence populating the conduction mechanism of action with free electrons (see Figure I.21).

Figure I.21 Insulation for above-ground residential high-voltage power cord separation from metal support mast.

Integrated circuits

[electronics, general] *See* **IC**.

Integrins

[biomedical, chemical] A type of transmembrane-binding receptor in biology that provides cell-to-cell interaction. The full interaction mechanism can be divided into four types of receptors: CADHERINS, selectins, INTEGRINS, and IMMUNOGLOBULIN SUPERFAMILY. Integrins are molecular groups that bind to specific ligands across the extracellular space toward the target CELL. Some integrins may rely on ACTIN filaments. Integrins are, for instance, found on white BLOOD cells.

Intensity (*I*)

[biomedical, electromagnetism, energy, thermodynamics] The AMPLITUDE of a phenomenon squared, measure of the magnitude of ENERGY. The amplitude of an acoustic WAVE is one of the most common examples. Acoustic LOUDNESS is generally presented in DECIBEL units. The decibel is a unit that was introduced in 1923 and is a logarithmic scale (10-log), in $dB = 20\log I$, but also found as $dB = 10\log I$ and is generally measured against a baseline value as a relative MAGNITUDE. The decibel was originally designed to quantify the SIGNAL strength and respective loss in telephone communications by the Bell laboratories. The original "bell" unit was ten times the power loss over 1 mile of cable at 795.8 Hz, expressed as the ratio of the signal strength at the distal end with respect to the input power. Alternatively, intensity can measure the number of particles collected with respective energy content (incorporating both PARTICLE velocity and quantity). For ELECTROMAGNETIC RADIATION, the concept of intensity is inappropriate due to the combination of two energy sources: electric and MAGNETIC FIELD. For electromagnetic radiation, the use of radiance or fluence is the standard.

Interference

[acoustics, optics, theoretical] The superposition of multiple WAVES, primarily from a single source that is split and recombined. The troughs of the WAVE pattern will cancel out against the crests in overlapping locations, which is a propagation path length and WAVELENGTH ($\lambda = v/\nu$, where v is the propagation velocity and ν the OSCILLATION frequency) related phenomenon. Positive interference (RESONANCE) will take place when the path difference is a whole number times the wavelength ($n\lambda$), while negative interference (cancelation) will occur at odd number intervals times the half-wavelength ($(2n+1)(\lambda/2)$). The INTERFERENCE term of two waves (with the same frequency) expressed as $A_1 = A_{01}\sin(\omega t + kx + \varphi)$ (where $\vec{x}$ the DISTANCE traveled from the source in a selected frame of reference, $\omega = 2\pi\nu$ the ANGULAR FREQUENCY, ν the frequency, $k = 2\pi/\lambda$ the wave number, and φ the PHASE locally of the wave) yields the superposition interference ($I = A^2$) for intensity with the term $2\sqrt{I_1 I_2}\cos\left[k(x_1 - x_2) + \varphi_2 - \varphi_1\right]$; this yields for the total wave pattern $I = I_1 + I_2 + 2\sqrt{I_1 I_2}\cos\left[k(x_1 - x_2) + \varphi_2 - \varphi_1\right]$. For consistent interference, the source will need to be coherent; otherwise, the interference will be randomized by the shifts in phase for each component. For optical interference, *see* **OPTICAL COHERENCE TOMOGRAPHY** (see Figure I.22).

Figure I.22 Illustration of the concept of interference of surface wave on liquid.

Interferometer

[atomic, nuclear, optics] A device used in ELECTROMAGNETIC RADIATION and quantum-mechanical PARTICLE waves (de Broglie principle) INTERFERENCE to provide details about the WAVE process and the media the waves are traveling in. Interferometers specifically use a single source which is split into two separate paths, one reference and one measurement path. Optical interferometers have been designed over the past century, for instance, the MICHELSON INTERFEROMETER, Rayleigh interferometer, and the FABRY–PÉROT INTERFEROMETER. The Fabry–Perot interferometer is specifically used as a selection tool, isolating a single operating condition as a viable option, such as used in the Q-switched laser (*also see* **INTERFERENCE** *and* **OPTICAL COHERENCE TOMOGRAPHY**). The Michelson interferometer is one of the most used and relatively elementary in construction, also the first known optical interferometer constructed in 1887 by Albert Abraham Michelson (1852–1931). The Michelson interferometer provided one of the experimental means to verify aspects of the special theory of relativity (see Figure I.23).

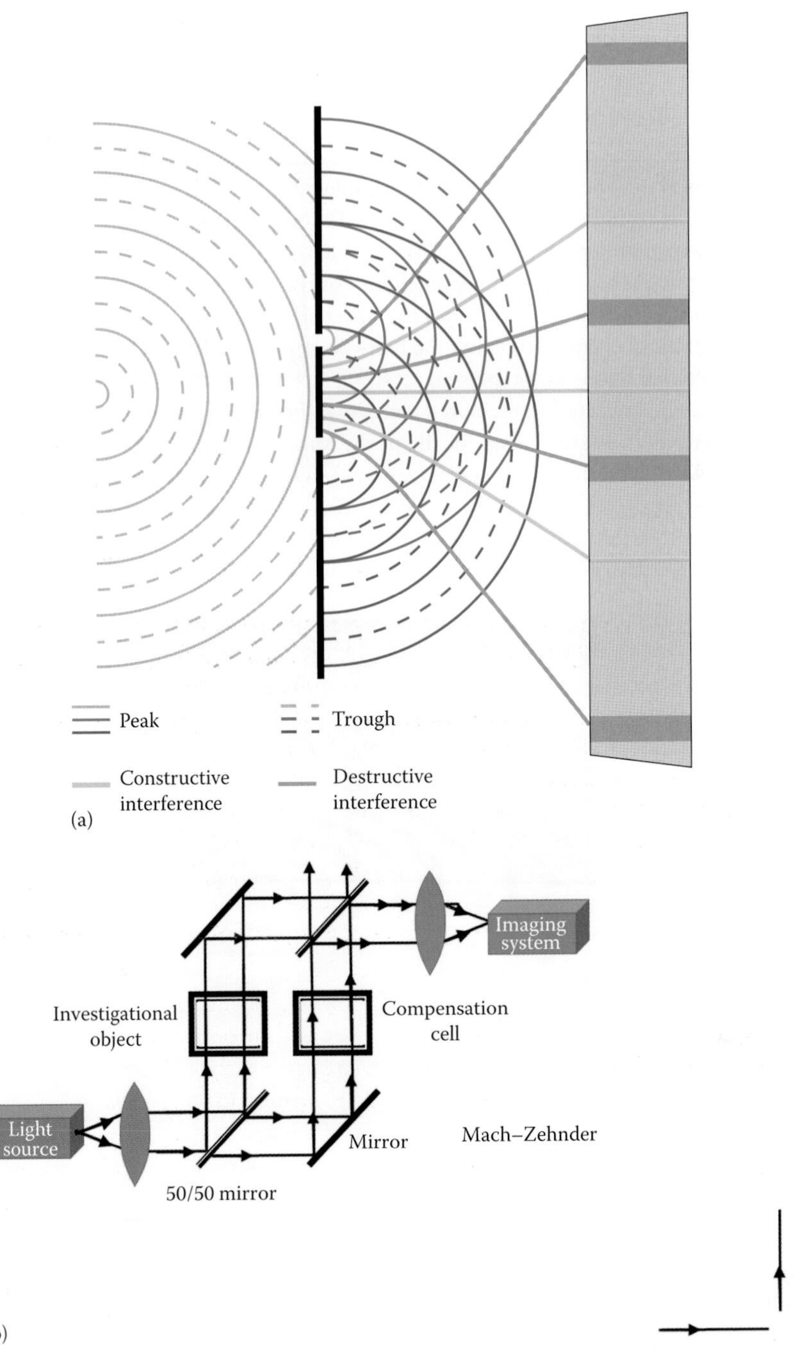

Figure I.23 Representation of one of the choices in interferometer design. (a) Rudimentary optical device with interferometric capacity: double slit and (b) optical interferometer: Mach–Zehnder interferometer. *(Continued)*

(c)

Figure I.23 (Continued) Representation of one of the choices in interferometer design. (c) Radio interferometer, submillimeter array in Mauna-Kea, Hawaii.

Intermolecular forces

[atomic, chemistry, quantum, solid-state] On a nuclear level, the anticipated forces are primarily repulsive due to the composition of protons and neutrons, and on the whole the electronic forces are only forming a portion of the attractive and repulsive system in the atomic and molecular structure. The classification of forces operating on the atomic and molecular level is as follows: gravitational forces; weak force; electromagnetic force, and strong force. The gravitational force and electromagnetic force generally have unlimited range, whereas the WEAK FORCE has a range in the order of 10^{-17} m, respectively, the strong force range is in the order of 10^{-15} m. On an atomic level, this translates into DIPOLE forces that rely on charge distribution as well as covalent forces that involve "sharing" electrons between atoms. The covalent force is a very strong force. Hydrogen bonds are very strong (one of the strongest intermolecular bonds), since they resemble "proton sharing," mimicking nuclear interaction.

Internal combustion engine

[thermodynamics] A ENGINE that burns fossil fuels and may operate on a four-stroke or two-stroke mechanism of compression and EXPANSION next to certain rotary engine designs. Diesel engines use compression to generate enough heat for autocombustion, whereas propane (natural gas) or gasoline engines require a spark plug that is linked to a timing mechanism that initiates a spark to provide the ignition of the hydrocarbon–oxygen mixture resulting in OXIDATION and is an EXOTHERMIC REACTION. The combustion provides the ENERGY to perform work, displacing a cylinder that is transferred to an axle, primarily through a gear system, that will make the device perform a mechanical action of movement or to rotate a magnet/coil in an electrical GENERATOR system (see Figure I.24).

(a) (b)

Figure I.24 (a,b) Internal combustion engine.

Internal conversion

[atomic, energy, nuclear] In the process of ELECTRON CAPTURE, the convergence of a PROTON and the captured electron are transformed into a NEUTRON and a NEUTRINO $p_{\text{proton}} + e^- = n_{\text{neutron}} + \bar{\nu}$. The electron capture process may result in gamma RADIATION, which can in turn be captured by an orbital electron. The transfer of ENERGY to the electron will result in ejection of the electron. AUGER ELECTRONS are the direct result of INTERNAL CONVERSION associated with CHARACTERISTIC X-RAY radiation (see Figure I.25). A nuclear mechanism that involves the interaction of the WAVE function of a lower shell electron with the NUCLEUS, converting nuclear "RESONANCE" energy into kinetic energy, resulting in the emission of the lower shell electron (not emission of the VALENCE electron) at relatively high energy. The internal conversion can be regarded as the exchange of energy through a virtual PHOTON, "emitted" (virtual gamma radiation, with energy equivalent to the transition energy within the nucleus minus the electronbinding energy for the ATOM) by the nucleus.

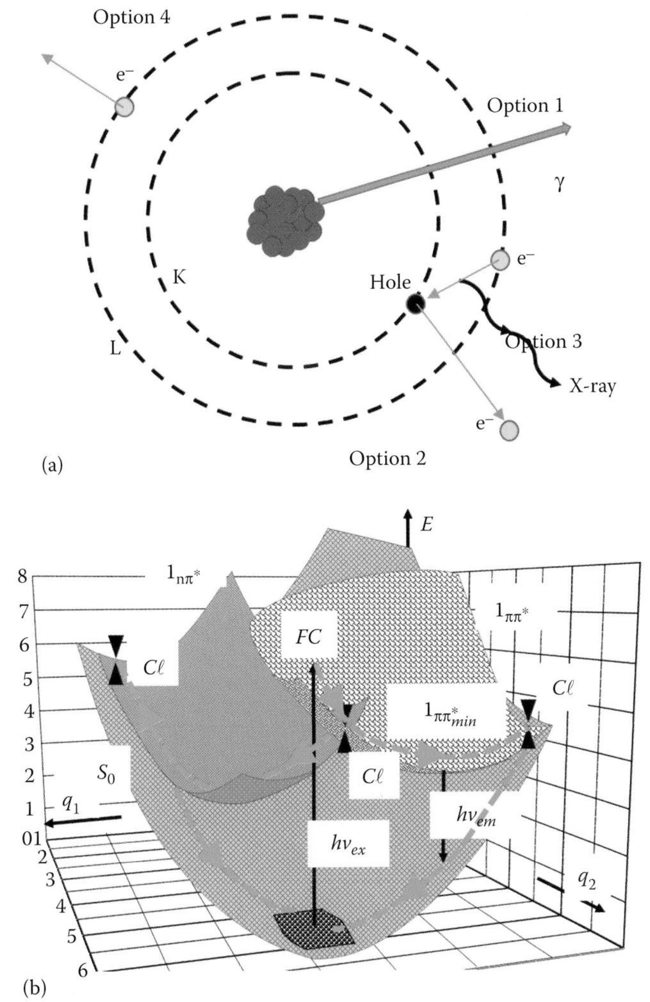

Figure I.25 Diagram of the energy and constituent restructuring process under internal conversion. (a) A schematic of de-excitation mechanism an atomic nucleus. The nucleus can be de-excited by emission of X-ray (option 1) and emission of a closely bound electron from the atom, most prevalent is the emission of a K-electron, however an electron in the L-shell or a higher shell can also be emitted, that is, conversion electron (option 2). The electron hole left behind is subsequently filled by another electron, with the potential for X-ray emission photon (option 3), or initiates the emission of an Auger electron (option 4). (b) Internal conversion in molecular form. Schematic of a potential nonradiative decay mechanism for the pyrimidines represented in two arbitrary coordinate axes, as a function of energy. After the molecule has been excited to the $1_{\pi\pi^*}$ state (black/white pattern), the energy population migrates toward the minimum within this state ($1_{\pi\pi^*_{min}}$), passing through a $C\ell$ condition with the 1 state, highlighted in blue. Upon leaving the condition of $C\ell$, the energy balance can migrate either toward $1_{\pi\pi^*_{min}}$ with the potential for the emission of fluorescence (with total energy: $h\nu_{em}$; with h the Plank's constant, and ν_{em} the emission frequency), alternatively the decay will branch to the $(1_{\pi\pi^*}/S_0)C\ell$ (path outlined to the right of center), or goes toward the minimum of the $1_{\pi\pi^*}$ state (path on the left). After the molecule has spent time in the $(1_{\pi\pi^*}/S_0)C\ell$ state it will relax to the black checkered patch in S_0 (outlined by the yellow energy "shell"). The latter may only be achieved by means of tunneling.

Internal energy (U)

[biomedical, fluid dynamics, general, thermodynamics] The amount of heat produced by a system minus the work performed. An ISOLATED SYSTEM does not exchange heat nor does it perform work, hence has constant internal ENERGY. The sum of the chemical, kinetic, potential, nuclear, and all other known and yet unknown energies of the particles that make up a system. Internal energy is a fundamental state variable for a system and signifies the MOLECULAR MOTION (*also see* **FIRST LAW OF THERMODYNAMICS**).

Internal pair production

[nuclear] Energetic interaction of the lowest electron orbit with the nuclides that releases an electron–positron pair instead of emission of gamma RADIATION. The ENERGY content is the NUCLEON energy minus the BINDING ENERGY of the electron in the lowest orbit.

International Bureau of Weights and Measures

[general] An organization responsible for standards and calibration of accepted quantities for the description and definition of specific phenomena and objects.

Invariable plane

[astronomy/astrophysics, computational] The gravitational action of the Sun results in a PRECESSION of satellites about the normal to the invariable plane. The invariable plane is inclined by an ANGLE θ_i with respect to the planetary equator, expressed as $2J_2\sin(2\theta_i) = (\omega_{\odot}/\omega_s)^2\left(\sqrt{(1-e^2)}\right)^{-1}\sin\{2(\theta_\varepsilon - \theta_i)\}$, where J_2 is the second-order BESSEL FUNCTION, $\omega_{\odot}$ the earth's angular velocity, ω_s the angular velocity of the SATELLITE in orbit, $\sqrt{(1-e^2)}$ the ratio of the major axis of the elliptic orbit with respect to the minor axis (subject to Kepler's rule), and θ_ε the obliqueness of the satellite axis with respect to the planetary orbit; which defines the interaction to the lowest order. The invariable plane normal vector lies between the planetary SPIN vector and planetary orbit normal. These three respective normals are coplanar. The INVARIABLE PLANE is also known as the Laplacian plane (see Figure I.26).

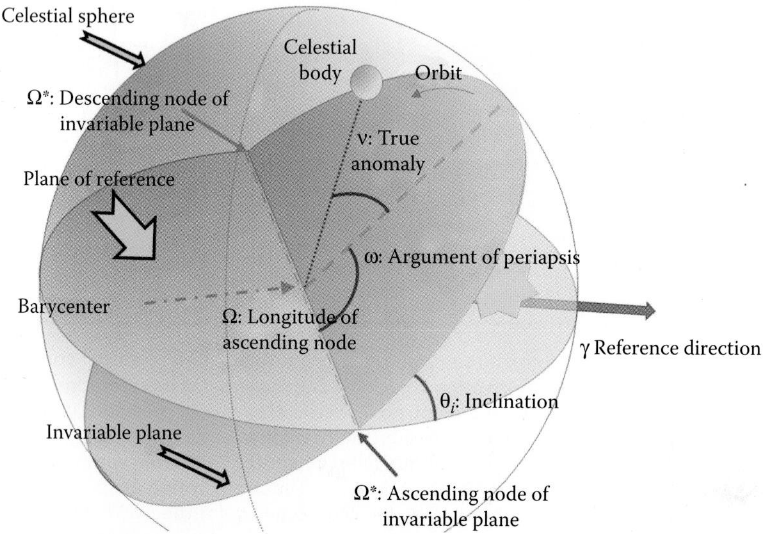

Figure I.26 Geometric representation of the invariable plane.

Inversion

[acoustics, biomedical, geophysics, imaging, molecular, solid-state, theoretical, thermodynamics] An inversion generally refers to a process that changes sign or direction or has a discontinuity when the boundary conditions change. Inversion applies specifically to the areas of ACOUSTICS, METEOROLOGY, and molecular QUANTUM MECHANICS, each in its own specific manner. The field of acoustical inversion ranges from seismologic imaging to biological imaging. In acoustics, inversions refer to the process where SEISMIC phenomena (e.g., acoustic probing) provide reflections of the pressure WAVE based on geologic discontinuities. Seismic inversion can provide an indication of natural GAS or OIL reservoirs imbedded in rock formations. The lower density LIQUID or GAS bordering a solid rock will provide a PHASE shift in the acoustic waveform. In acoustic imaging for medical applications and in nondestructive testing, the same inversion can yield mechanical information about abrupt changes in structural density, highlighting soft tissues. Inversion mode imaging for biological applications specifically provides insight in fetal FLUID structures. In METEOROLOGY, inversion indicates a layered ATMOSPHERE with a temperature profile that instead of decreasing with altitude has an INVERSION POINT where the temperature is higher than at lower altitude. Inversion layers can support violet thunderstorms due to the rapid condensation. In MOLECULAR DYNAMICS, specifically molecular vibration, an ENERGY hierarchy can be recognized from spectroscopic analysis. The VIBRATION process can be separated into vibrational and rotational processes. The vibrational spectral lines are in the INFRARED (1000 cm^{-1} region), while the rotational transitions are in the microwave (1 cm^{-1} region). The vibrational transitions are separated into an energy POTENTIAL WELL diagram by a POTENTIAL BARRIER around the parabolic minimum, yielding two respective minima. The MICROWAVE transitions for certain molecules can switch minima, this is referred to as inversion. The spectral profile will illustrate the switches in a representative inversion spectrum for the molecular group in question. In the molecular inversion process, the formation of "instantons" provides dominant TUNNELING paths derived based on the QUANTUM dynamical Feynman path-integral. Instantons are the energy "surfaces" of unstable orbits with respect to inverted potential energy surfaces (see Figure I.27).

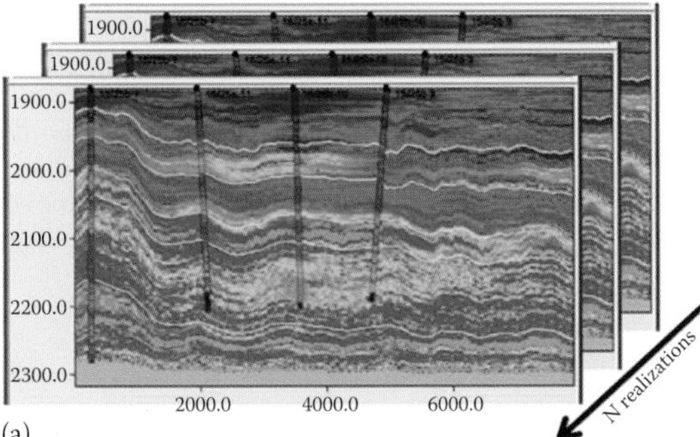

(a)

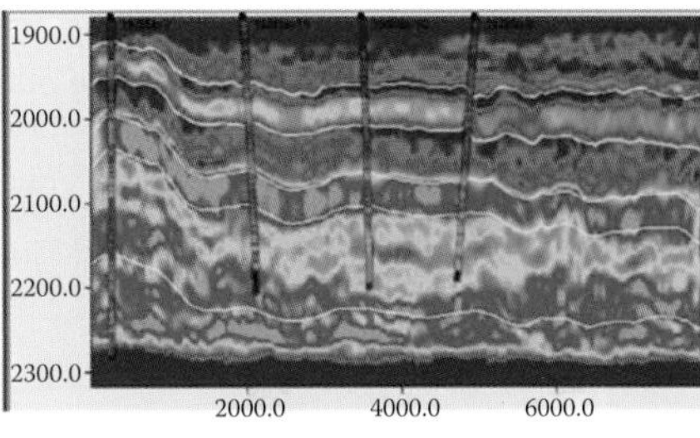

(b)

Figure I.27 (a) Example of one of the forms of atmospheric (meteorological) inversion and (b) acoustical impedance image of seismic inversion. (Courtesy of Ikon-Rokdoc, Ikon Science; The Causeway, Teddington, London, United Kingdom.) The acoustic impedance graphs indicate three geostatistical inversion realizations (a, left) as well as the deterministic acoustic impedance representation (a, right) over the same arbitrary line. As part of the geostatistical inversion, the match at the wells is verified, next to the fact that the frequency content is quantifiably higher. *(Continued)*

(c)

Figure I.27 (Continued) (c) Illustration of the potential energy surface inversion with respect to molecular inversion producing a tunneling effect with respect to the water-trimer (in a water cluster, the water molecules are capable of forming hydrogen bond networks with one potential configuration the trimer: D_2O_3), what is known as an "instanton." (Courtesy of Jeremy Richardson, Stuart C. Althorpe, and D. J. Wales, The Althorpe Group; University of Cambridge, Cambridge: United Kingdom.)

Inversion curve

[thermodynamics] The locus of the INVERSION points associated with the VAPOR phase of the respective constant enthalpy ($h_e = U + PV$ for the individual constituents of the system H, where U is the internal ENERGY, P the pressure, and V the volume) processes in the temperature versus pressure diagram. Under constant enthalpy, the process is defined by the JOULE–THOMPSON COEFFICIENT $\mu_{JT} = (\partial T/\partial P)_{h_e}$, with T the temperature (in KELVIN), in which case the inversion curve separates the positive from the negative values (*also see* **JOULE–KELVIN EFFECT** *and* **INVERSION POINT**) (see Figure I.28).

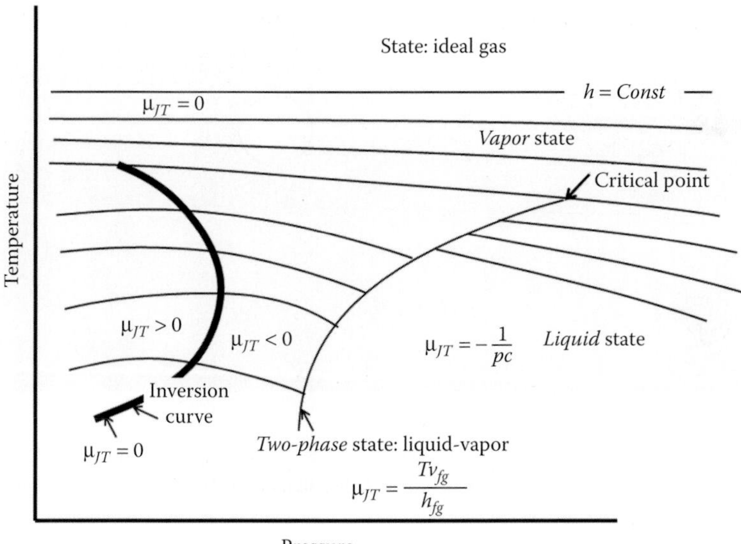

Figure I.28 Inversion curve for the vapor phase of.

Inversion point

[thermodynamics] In a system of throttles and valves, the temperature versus pressure diagram for the enthalpy, the vapor PHASE associated with the constant–enthalpy curve will provide a maximum value when the temperature is sufficiently low; these locus are the inversion points for the processes (*also see* INVERSION CURVE).

Inviscid flow

[fluid dynamics] Fluid flow for a FLUID with no APPARENT VISCOSITY, ideal fluid. FLOW pattern generally attributed to conditions with high REYNOLDS NUMBER, Re >> 1.

Ion

[atomic, nuclear, solid-state] An ATOM, atomic particle, or chemical radical (i.e., group of chemically combined atoms) having a net electrical charge, either negative or positive, respectively, resulting from an excess or deficiency of electrons.

Ion channel

[biomedical, chemical, thermodynamics] In the MEMBRANE of biological cells, there are ION passages. The channels are voltage-mediated gates that regulate transmission of certain ions or molecules by activating changes in the transmembrane electrical potential or by activating extracellular or intracellular transport molecules, called LIGANDS, that attach to the select ions and molecules. The membrane potential directly depends on the respective ion concentrations on opposite sides of the CELL MEMBRANE, for example, POTASSIUM (K^+), sodium (Na^+), and chlorine (Cl^-). The transmembrane-resting potential is based on the NERNST EQUATION, further expanded into the GOLDMAN VOLTAGE EQUATION (see Figure I.29).

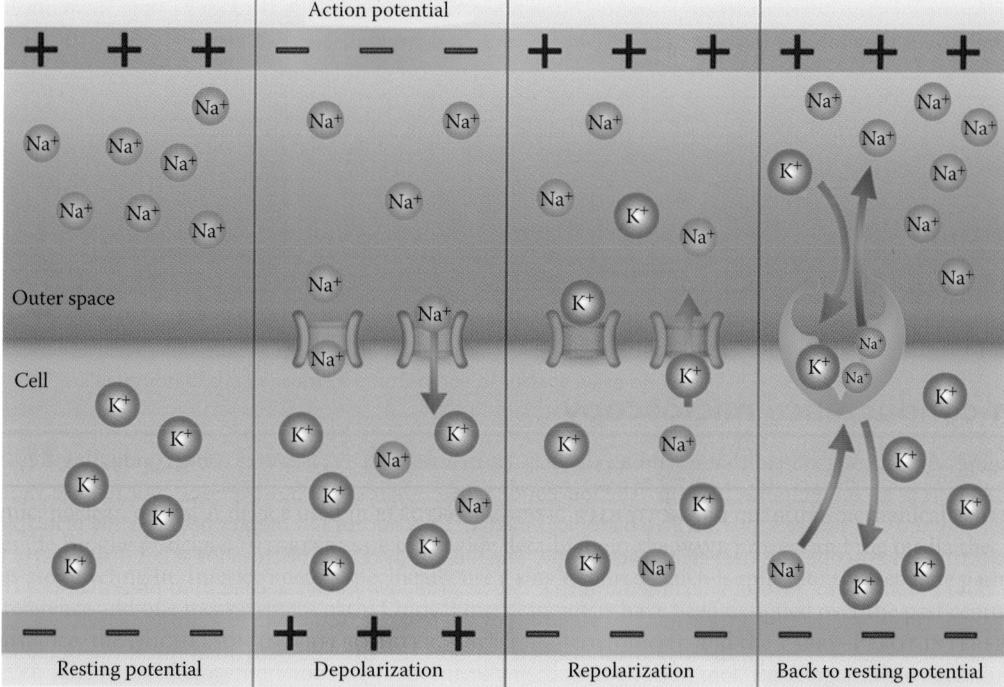

Figure I.29 Representation of the cellular ion channel for biological media: (a) simulation of transmembrane ion transport. *(Continued)*

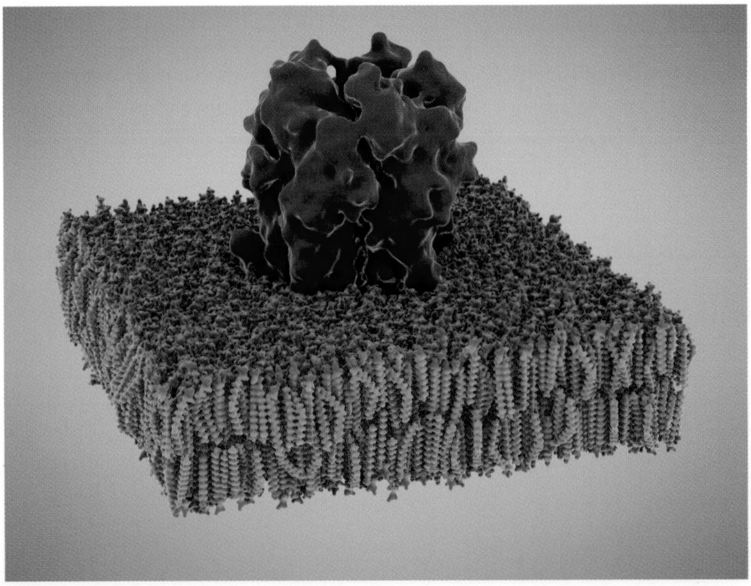

(b)

Figure I.29 (Continued) Representation of the cellular ion channel for biological media: (b) impression of the ion channel in detail.

Ion mobility

[atomic, molecular, solid-state] The velocity achieved by an ION moving through a gaseous medium when an external unit electric field is applied μ_{ion}. For a mixture, this translates into $\mu_{ion} = \left(\sum_{i=1}^{n} f_i/\mu_{ion,i}\right)^{-1}$, where f_i is the fractional value for constituent i, and $\mu_{ion,i}$ the respective ION MOBILITY (BLANC'S LAW). The reduced ion mobility is the mobility in the parent gas, which is often defined for a density ($\rho_{mol} = 2.69 \times 10^{25}\ m^{-3}$) of and is in the order of $10^{-4}\ m^2/sV$, for instance, for a LITHIUM ion in helium gas $\mu_{Li^+} = 25.6 \times 10^{-4}\ m^2/sV$ at normal (standard) pressure and temperature. The mobility depends on the purity of the GAS and is also a function of the electric field strength (E) and the Loschmidt constant (N_L), describing the moles per volume at standard pressure and temperature): E/N_L.

Ion pair

[chemical, solid-state] Halides and metallic molecules generally consist of an electronegative and electropositive ATOM (-group), consisting of a pair, which can be separated. Salt SOLUTION forms an equal amount of positive and negative ions, for example, NaCl.

Ion-conductance microscopy

[imaging] An imaging system that resembles the ELECTRON MICROSCOPE, however using conducting free-flowing ions as an imaging mechanism. The ion-conductance microscope however does not require VACUUM conditions and can be used to study live biological media. The concept is a merger between the principles of the electron microscope and near-field microscopy. The ion-conductance microscope relies on a pipette that is in close proximity to the biological medium that delivers the low-voltage acceleration potential, less than 1 V range. Image acquisition is provided by scanning of the ION release pipette in a preset pattern to gradually fill a database array. The locally established ion-flow can provide both anatomical (topographical)

and physiological details based on the selection of ions with respect to the cellular activities under investigation (see Figure I.30).

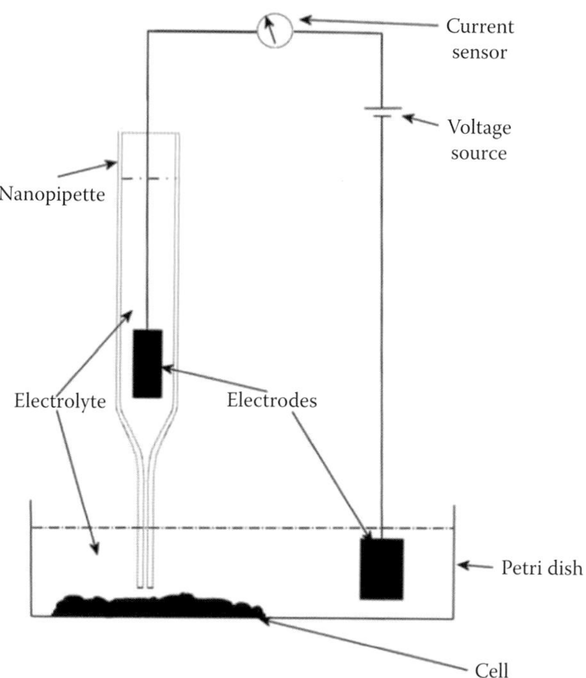

Figure I.30 Schematic diagram of the operation for an ion conductance microscope.

Ionization

[atomic, biomedical, chemical, electromagnetism, energy, nuclear, solid-state] The act or result of any process by which a neutral ATOM or MOLECULE acquires either a positive or a NEGATIVE CHARGE, respectively, emits or acquires an electron. It is the process of removal or addition of an electron to an atomic structure, primarily in the VALENCE BAND of the outer shell of the atom, process of creating an ION (*also see* **SPARK, CORONA,** *and* **LIGHTNING**) (see Figure I.31).

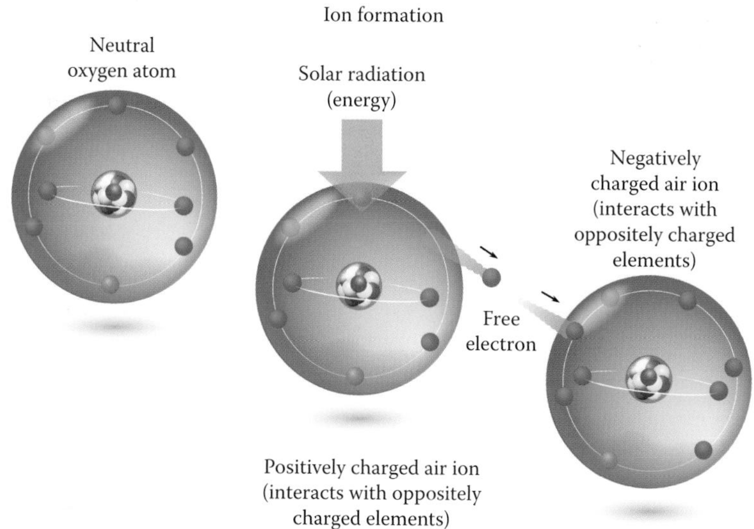

Figure I.31 Schematic representation of the process of ionization.

Ionization energy

[atomic, nuclear, solid-state] The electronic potential (V_i) that can result in the formation of an ION based on the internal ENERGY configuration of an ATOM, with the individual charge energy for the respective PHASE, the atom (ϵ_a), electron (ϵ_e), and the ion (ϵ_i) to yield $V_i = \epsilon_e + \epsilon_i - \epsilon_a$ (*also see* **SAHA EQUATION**).

Ionization potential

[general] The electrical potential necessary to separate one (1) electron from an ATOM with the formation of an ION having 1 elementary charge.

Ionosphere

[atomic, energy, geophysics, thermodynamics] Layer of the Earth's atmosphere. In the ionosphere, a considerable number or atoms and molecules have been ionized as a result of the interaction with solar ENERGY, primarily in the ULTRAVIOLET and shorter wavelength region. The ionosphere additionally contains a large number of free electrons. The ionosphere extends from an altitude of approximately 50 to 1,000 km. In RADIO communications, the ionosphere can provide a transition layer with a high-reflection coefficient. Radio WAVE reflections from the ionosphere are primarily noticeable for long wave radio transmissions, allowing propagation half-way around the world without the need for amplifiers (*Note*: cell-phone communications require support antennas serving as repeaters to be placed at regular intervals to ensure reliable communications) (*also see* **AURORA**) (see Figure I.32).

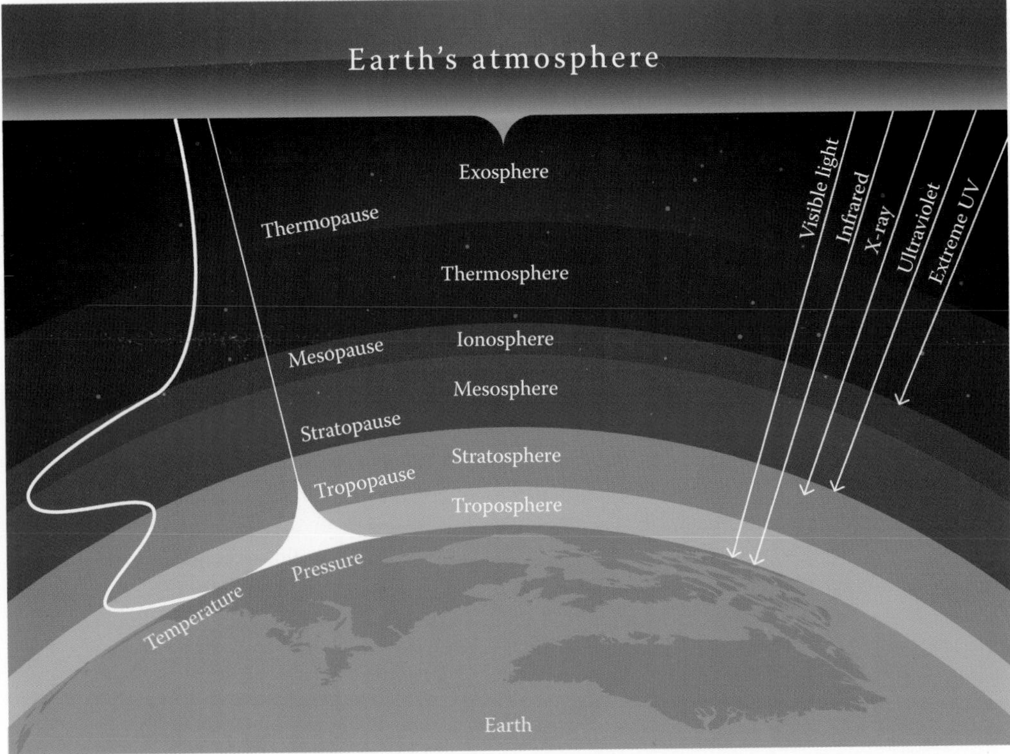

Figure I.32 The Earth ionosphere in reference to the classification of atmospheric layers.

Iron

[biomedical, chemical, solid-state] A metal ELEMENT: $^{26}_{56}\mathrm{Fe}$. Iron is the most common element on the planet EARTH, forming most of the core and shell, by mass. The iron ion (Fe^{2+}) is an elementary component for human life since it forms the foundation for the hemoglobin affinity to oxygen (O_2): $C_{2952}H_{4664}O_{832}N_{812}S_8Fe_4$.

Irradiance (I)

[general] The ENERGY flux (i.e., PHOTON energy) crossing the surface of a volume of medium, which is equal to the RADIANT ENERGY FLUENCE RATE. When the incident FLUX is orthogonal to the surface, this is equivalent to the FLUENCE RATE (*see* **RADIANT ENERGY FLUENCE RATE, RADIANCE,** *and* **POYNTING VECTOR**).

Irrotational flow

[fluid dynamics] Flow in which the individual "fluid particles" will not rotate around their axis (MACROSCOPIC spin equivalent); however, the entire FLOW may still form a rotation, that is, TURBULENCE. This is one of the conditions defining the boundary conditions for Bernoulli flow. Irrotational flow is defined by considering a loop between two separate points "(flow particles") in the flow: A and B, where A and B are connected by means of two separate paths: ACB and ADB, respectively, where ACBDA forms a closed loop. In irrotational flow, the following now hold true for the VELOCITY ($\vec{v}$) as a function of location ($\vec{r}$): $\int_{\mathrm{ACB}}\vec{v}\cdot d\vec{r}+\int_{\mathrm{AdB}}\vec{v}\cdot d\vec{r}=0$. In this case, the velocity potential ϕ_v is a SCALAR function linked to the local velocity vector as $\vec{v}=-\nabla\phi_v$, the gradient in the VELOCITY POTENTIAL, and the irrotational behavior is set as $\omega_{\mathrm{rot}}=\nabla\times\vec{v}=0$. Adding incompressibility will yield the LAPLACE EQUATION, since also $\nabla\cdot\vec{v}=0$, providing $\nabla^2\phi_v=0$.

Irrotational (curl-free) vector field

[computational, fluid dynamics] A fundamental component of HELMHOLTZ DECOMPOSITION in vector calculus. In three-dimensional space, the vector field composed of sufficiently smooth, rapidly decaying vectors can be decomposed into the sum of two "orthogonal" components, one consisting of an IRROTATIONAL (CURL-FREE) VECTOR FIELD and the second segment composed of rotational (divergence-free) or solenoidal vector field (*see* **CURL-FREE VECTOR FIELD**).

Isaac Newton (1642–1727)

[fluid dynamics, general, mechanics, nuclear, solid-state] *See* **NEWTON, ISAAC, SIR (1642–1727)**.

Isentropic

[fluid dynamics, thermodynamics] A system or process with constant entropy (S), thus $dS=0$. Under these conditions, the following applies: $dU=-PdV$, where U represents the internal ENERGY, P the pressure, and V the volume; respectively, $dU=\delta Q^{\leftarrow}-\delta W^{\rightarrow}$, where $Q^{\leftarrow}$ is the FLOW of heat into the system and $W^{\rightarrow}$ the work performed by the system. From this, it follows that only under certain conditions, an ISENTROPIC PROCESS is reversible and adiabatic.

I

Isentropic flow

[fluid dynamics] Flow process that has ISENTROPIC characteristic, primarily confined to a system where the FLOW changes gradually and in relatively small increments. This kind of flow process is reversible and based on the SECOND LAW OF THERMODYNAMICS inherently isentropic. The generation of SOUND waves is an ISENTROPIC PROCESS. One specific example is the NOZZLE flow going from subsonic to supersonic. When there is "shock" involved or oblique flow than the conditions are no longer supporting isentropic flow (see Figure I.33).

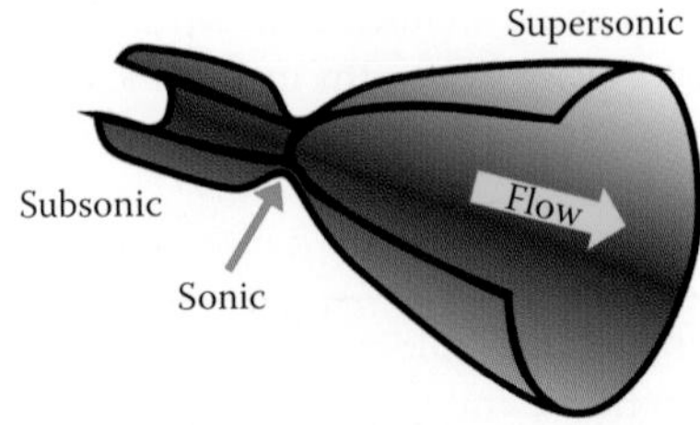

Figure I.33 Representation of Isentropic flow parameters.

Isentropic process

[thermodynamics] *See* ISENTROPIC.

Isentropy

[general] Constant MAGNITUDE of disorder of the molecular states of a thermodynamic or mechanical system. Consider that entropy is the representation of the possible energetic states (N_{mol}) on molecular scale $S = k_B \log N_{mol}$, where $k_B = 1.3806488 \times 10^{-23}\ \mathrm{m^2kg/s^2K}$ is the Boltzmann coefficient.

Ising, Ernst (1900–1998)

[computational] A physicist from Germany. Ising's work revolved around MAGNETIC moments and the special case where they line up in a linear chain. The (atomic) magnetic SPIN moments, in this case, can take two states: "1" or "up" and "0" or "down", while their interactions are coupled to the nearest neighbors in a LATTICE structure (see Figure I.34).

Figure I.34 Ernest Ising (1900–1998).

Ising model

[computational] A mathematical model of FERROMAGNETISM in statistical MECHANICS named after the implementer ERNST ISING (1900–1998) in 1925, following the lead of his professor Wilhelm Lenz (1888–1957) who introduced the concept in 1920. The Ising model provides theoretical support for PHASE transitions. The two-dimensional model is much more complex than the one-dimensional model.

ISO standards

[biomedical, electromagnetism, general, mechanics] Engineering normalization, standardization, qualification, and COMPLIANCE definitions introduced and regularly updated by the International Organization for Standardization (ISO), a multinational association with its headquarter in Switzerland. The ISO body and standardization was introduced in 1947. The most well-known ISO standards for production and quality management and the requirements for the facility are ISO 9000, respectively, ISO 9001. In total, there are close to 400 documented standard specification documents with targeted reference numbering. In order to be accepted and recognized for the manufacturing of certain devices and systems, corporations will be required to obtain certification for the appropriate and pertinent ISO standards.

Isobar

[nuclear, thermodynamics] A graphical representation of a system showing lines for processes that occur under constant pressure in a T–V (temperature vs. volume) diagram. In nuclear PHYSICS, the term isobar refers to nuclides with identical mass number (A): $A = Z + N$, where Z is the atomic number (i.e., the number of protons in the NUCLEUS), and N the NEUTRON number (see Figure I.35).

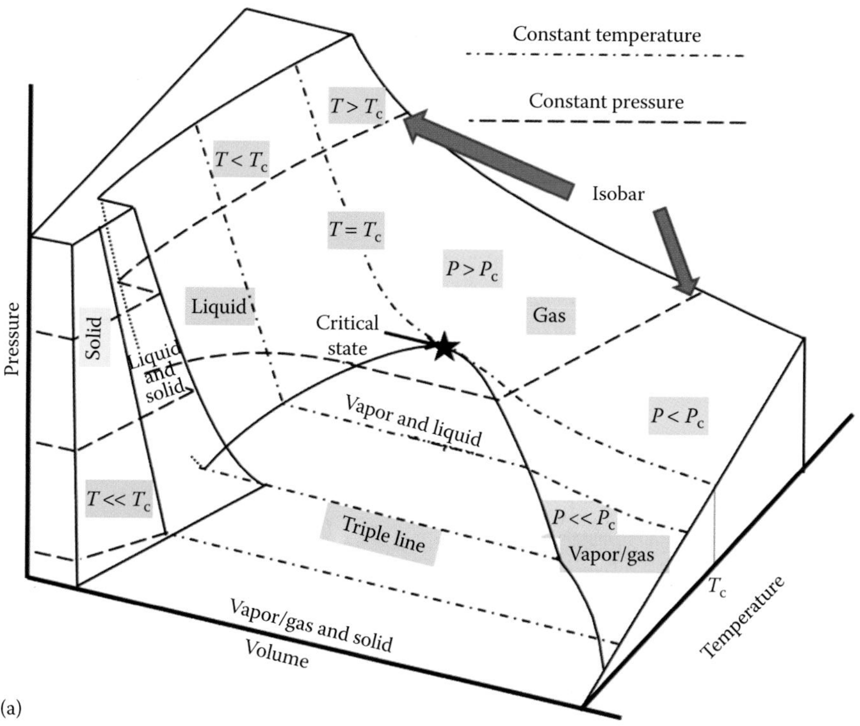

Figure I.35 (a) Graphical illustration of constant pressure in a temperature versus volume diagram with respect to fluid conditions, specifically for water.

(Continued)

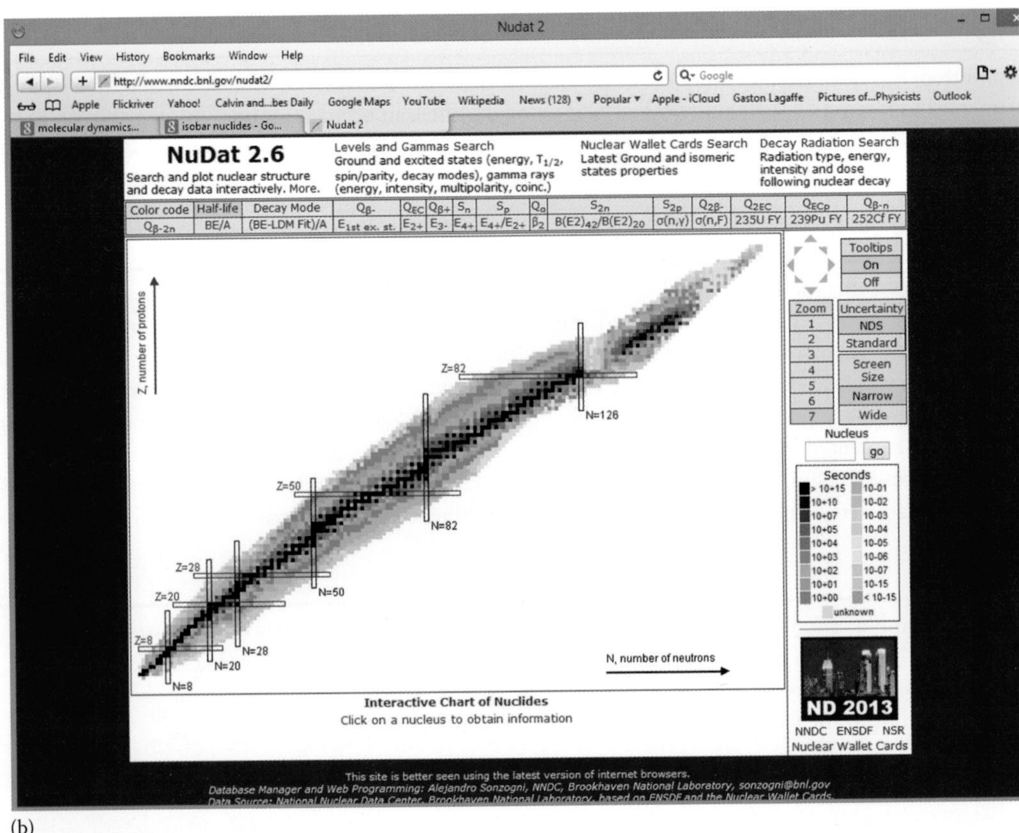

(b)

Figure I.35 (Continued) (b) Nuclide isobar chart. The isobars in this chart are represented by the diagonal lines crossing from the upper left of the diagram to the lower right. Stable nuclides are represented by the line of beta-stability, shown in black. The individual pockets of noncontinuous isotopes are a consequence of the Mattauch isobar rule. (Data Source: National Nuclear Data Center, Brookhaven National Laboratory, based on ENSDF and the Nuclear Wallet Cards.)

Isobaric change

[fluid dynamics] Temperature change with associated change in volume that holds a constant pressure for a FLUID. Isobaric changes are found in two stages of the reversible RANKINE CYCLE, one single stage of the DIESEL CYCLE and two segments of the JOULE–BRAYTON CYCLE.

Isochor

[thermodynamics] A graphical representation of a fluid-solid system showing lines for processes that occur under constant volume in a *P–T* (pressure vs. temperature) diagram (see Figure I.36).

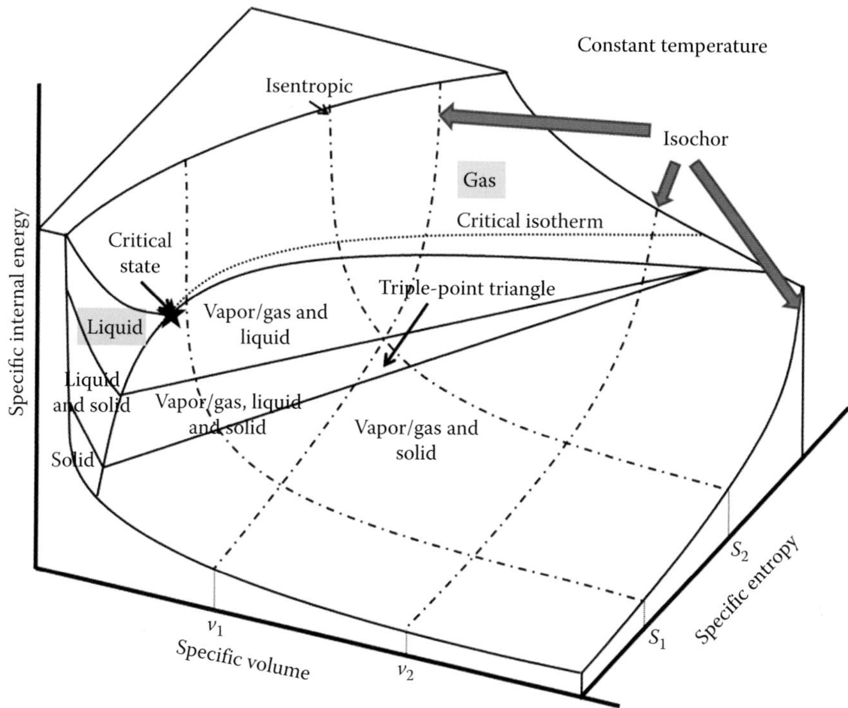

Figure I.36 Representation of the isochor in a fluid/solid system phase-diagram, indicating constant volume, in this case constant specific volume.

Isochoric process

[fluid dynamics, thermodynamics] Under the constraints of constant volume, the change in INTERNAL ENERGY (U) reduces to the temperature (T) multiplied by the change in entropy (S), which is the partial change in HEAT TRANSFER (Q): $dU = TdS = \delta Q^{\leftarrow}$. Alternatively, the change in internal energy for a system with constant constituents (n) is the heat capacity (c_v) multiplied by the change in temperature: $dU = \left(\partial U/\partial T\right)_{V,n} dT = c_v T$. The OTTO CYCLE has two segments that are isochoric, whereas the DIESEL CYCLE only has one out of four processes evolved under isochoric conditions, and the STERLING CYCLE has two stages of change that are isochoric.

Isolated system

[general, thermodynamics] A system that has no external ENERGY supplied or removed, hence the isolated system cannot influence the environment it is part of. An isolated system can only experience spontaneous changes of state.

Isomeric nuclei

[atomic] The isomeric model of the NUCLEUS is based on the BOHR MODEL, assuming a spherical shape. Based on the ENERGY, configuration of the sphere predictions can be made for the isomeric transitions (e.g., K-ISOMERISM) and the associated half-lives (τ_e and τ_m for electric and MAGNETIC transitions, respectively) as a function of the energy (E) released or introduced for the transition based on the mass number A, the MULTIPOLE order (ℓ_{multi}) and the occurrence of PARITY change (α_{parity}). The half-life is a function of the electric ("E") and magnetic ("M") reduced PROBABILITY defined as $B(E\ell_{\text{multi}})$ and $B(M\ell_{\text{multi}})$, yielding $\left[\tau_e(1+\alpha)\right]^{-1} = B(E\ell_{\text{multi}})E^{2\ell_{\text{multi}}+1}A^{2/3}$ and $\left[\tau_m(1+\alpha)\right]^{-1} = B(M\ell_{\text{multi}})E^{2\ell_{\text{multi}}+1}A^{(2\ell_{\text{multi}}-2)/3}$. The same model provides the means for defining the retardation in comparison with shell models through the introduction of the hindrance factor $H_{\text{isometric}}$ as $\log_{10}(H_{\text{isometric}}) = 2(\Delta K_{\text{quant}} - \ell_{\text{multi}})$, where K_{quant} represents the QUANTUM number of nuclear SPIN along the axis of symmetry. The hindrance factor indicates the retardation in transition from a state with high spin (I) to GROUND STATE, which is indicated by the direction coinciding with the axis of symmetry as $K_{\text{quant}} = I$.

Isomers

[atomic, nuclear, solid-state] Two or more aggregates consisting of the same components that are arranged in different formats, with intrinsic different ENERGY, plural. Specifically, two nuclei of the same atomic species that persist in a different energy state, of which at least one energy state is metastable, are referred to as isomers (see Figure I.37).

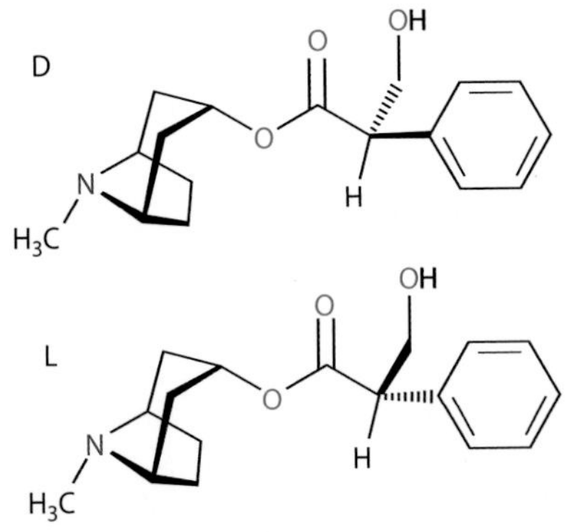

Figure I.37 Graphical representation of atropine L- and D-stereoisomer molecules.

Isometric

[biomedical, mechanics] Force applied by MUSCLE to compensate for external applied force, without a change in length (see Figure I.38).

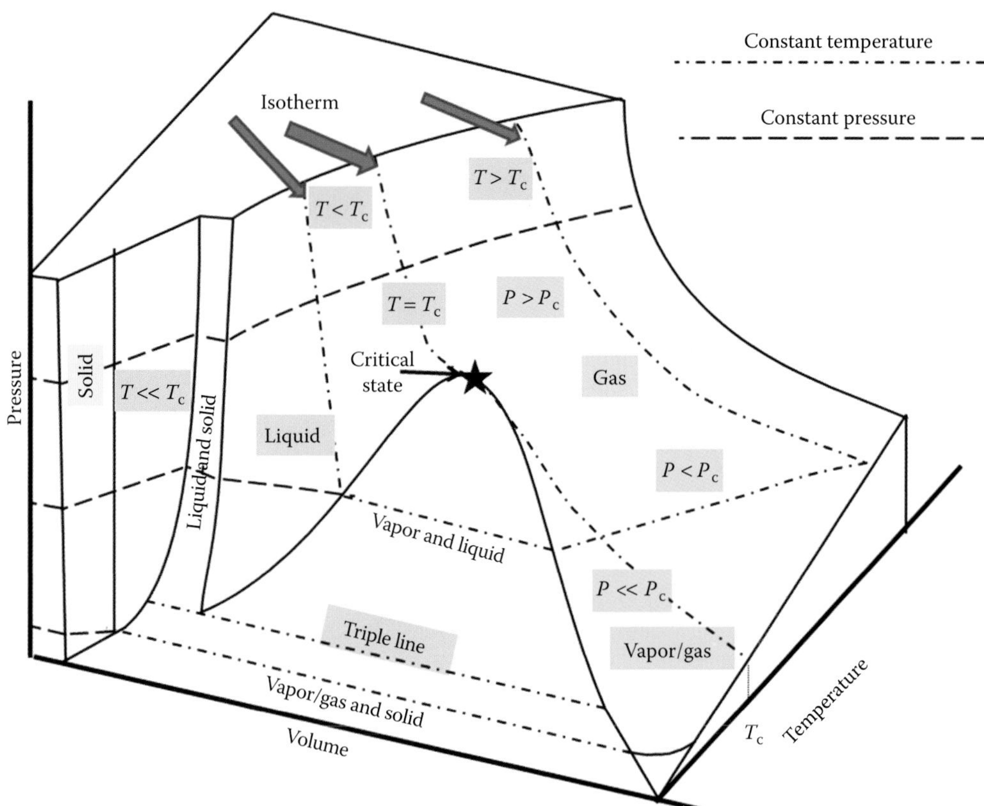

Figure I.38 Isothermal condition in a phase diagram of a system that has a linear relation between volume and temperature. This is in contrast to water, which has its highest density at 4°C.

Isospin (*I*)

[atomic, nuclear] System of particles, in particular hadrons, that interact on a NUCLEAR FORCE level which are in IDENTICAL STATES and have the same ordinary spin (J) and identical PARITY (π); generally, isospin multiplets are labeled J^{π}. The isospin is a dimensionless quantity (not specifically associated with an angular momentum) that describes the quantum number (I), which defines the conditions of the interactions in nuclear force; weak isospin refers to WEAK INTERACTION. Early references to the concepts of isospin date back to the 1932 Werner Karl Heisenberg (1901–1976) considerations of the differences between the proton and neutron in the nucleus as two "identical" particles with different spin (and inherently different charges), which are affected equally by the nuclear force. The isospin also has an associated directional projection, which is the isospin vector squared (I_3). Theoretically, nuclear (strong) interactions of nuclides (e.g., baryons) are not affected by the direction of the isospin vector. It is also referred to as isotopic or isobaric spin. The isospin concept provided tools for the definition of quarks (*also see* **Yang–Mills theory**).

Isotherm

[thermodynamics] A graphical representation of the locus of states in a system showing lines for processes that have the same temperature in a state diagram (pressure versus volume) or in a T–S diagram (temperature vs. entropy). Specifically, the phase changes of vaporization, sublimation, and solidification/fusion (respectively, their inverse processes) take place at constant temperature (see Figure I.39).

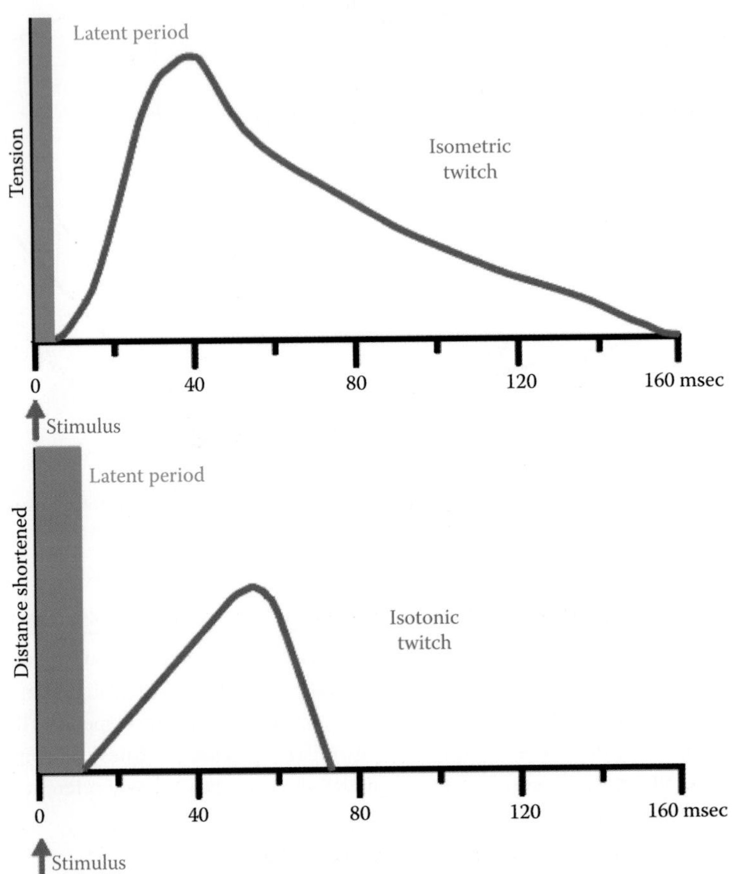

Figure I.39 Force diagram representing isometric muscle contraction.

Isothermal change

[general] A thermodynamic process that develops under constant temperature during at least one of the stages of a sequence of events. The STIRLING CYCLE has two phases that are isothermal, so does the LINDE–HAMPSON LIQUEFACTION CYCLE in refrigeration. The CARNOT CYCLE has two processes that are isothermal with respect to change in entropy.

Isotone

[atomic, nuclear] Two or more nuclides with the same number of neutrons (i.e., identical neutron number: A); however, the number of protons is different (i.e., different atomic number: Z), hence different mass number (A): $A = Z + N$. These isotones may also be isotopes with a limited lifetime. Examples of isotones are 36-sulfur, 37-chlorine, 38-argon, 39-potassium, and 40-calcium, each with 20 neutrons. The term was introduced in 1934 by the scientist Kurt Martin Guggenheimer (1902–1975) from Germany, based on the existing term ISOTOPE for equal number of protons. Guggenheimer realized that there had to be a third set of nuclear species, the NEUTRON, hence substituting the "n" for neutron in the definition of the existing definition for ISOBAR, indicated, respectively, with "p" for PROTON.

Isotonic

[biomedical] A MUSCLE contraction with constant force (see Figure I.40).

Figure I.40 Illustration of isotonic muscle contraction on left, whereas the muscle contraction applied to the weights on the right will most likely be a function of muscle contraction velocity.

Isotonic

[chemical] Two or more fluids with solutes that provide the same OSMOTIC PRESSURE. Generally, this consideration applies to solutions separated by a SEMIPERMEABLE MEMBRANE, such as the CELL wall in biological systems or artificial membranes in chemistry for PARTICLE separation. In biomedical use, the term "TONICITY" refers to the shape of a cell, which can be influenced by the internal pressure with respect to the extracellular FLUID composition (see Figure I.41).

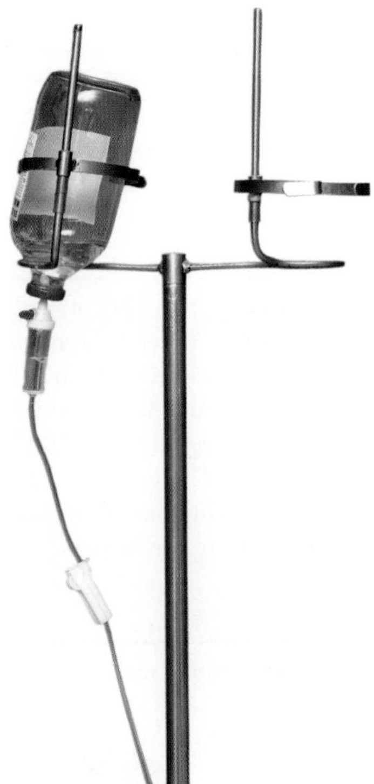

Figure I.41 Infuse for delivery of isotonic fluids during surgery.

Isotope

[atomic, biomedical, imaging, nuclear] One of two or more forms of an ELEMENT having the same ATOMIC NUMBER (Z) (NUCLEAR CHARGE, representing the number of protons in the NUCLEUS) and hence occupying the same position in the periodic table. All isotopes are identical in chemical behavior, but are distinguishable by small differences in ATOMIC WEIGHT. The nuclei of all isotopes of a given element have the same number of protons but have different numbers of neutrons. The concept of isotopes was discovered by FREDERICK SODDY (1877–1956) in 1913 (see Figure I.42).

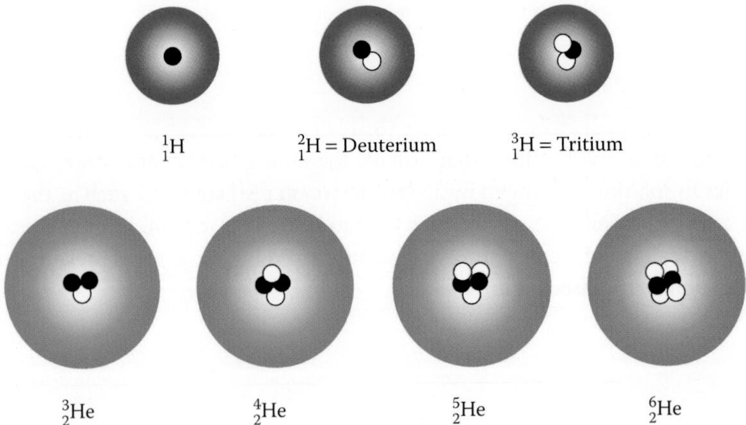

Figure I.42 Hydrogen and helium isotopes.

Jacobi, Carl Gustav Jacob (1804–1851)

[computational] A mathematician from the Prussian Empire, Germany. Jacobi's primary contributions in calculus-based PHYSICS are in the description of ellipsoids. Other work is in special solutions to complex integral equations. JACOBIAN calculus provides a range of SOLUTION mechanisms for various mathematical and practical problems. A specific area of interest is the Jacobi ellipsoids in techniques for solving complex problems (see Figure J.1).

Figure J.1 Carl Gustav Jacob Jacobi (1804–1851).

Jacobi method

[computational] A computational method based on an iteration process for solving a matrix equation with respect to a "reduced" pentadiagonal matrix (no zeros on its main diagonal). This defines the preferred algorithm for determining the solutions of a system of linear equations where the main diagonal in a matrix (M) representation contains the largest absolute values with respect to each row and column. The definition matrix is decomposed into a diagonal matrix (D) and the residue (R), which is a hollow matrix for a square matrix: $\boldsymbol{y} = [M]\boldsymbol{x}$, where

$$[M] = \begin{bmatrix} a_{11} & \cdots & a_{1n} \\ \vdots & \ddots & \vdots \\ a_{m1} & \cdots & a_{mn} \end{bmatrix} = [D] + [R] = \begin{bmatrix} a_{11} & & \cdots & & 0 \\ & a_{22} & & 0 & \\ \vdots & & a_{kl} & & \vdots \\ & 0 & & \ddots & \\ 0 & & \cdots & & a_{mn} \end{bmatrix} + \begin{bmatrix} 0 & & \cdots & & a_{1n} \\ & 0 & & a_{2,n-1} & \\ \vdots & & \ddots & & \vdots \\ & a_{m-1,2} & & 0 & \\ a_{m1} & & \cdots & & 0 \end{bmatrix},$$

$$\boldsymbol{y} = \begin{bmatrix} f_1 \\ \vdots \\ f_n \end{bmatrix}, \text{ and } \boldsymbol{x} = \begin{bmatrix} x_1 \\ \vdots \\ x_n \end{bmatrix}.$$

The solutions for the functions can be found through iteration from $\boldsymbol{x}^{(\ell+1)} = [D]^{-1}\left(\boldsymbol{y} - \boldsymbol{x}^{(\ell)}\right)$.

Jacobi's ellipsoids

[computational, fluid dynamics] The Jacobi polynomials and ellipsoids are documented in great detail in M. Abramowitz (1915–1958) and I. A. Stegun's (1919–2008) *Handbook of Mathematical Functions.*

Jacobian

[computational, thermodynamics] In transformation ALGEBRA the POLAR COORDINATES are given as u, v and can be written as $u = v\cos\theta$ and $v = v\sin\theta$. To execute a coordinate transformation, the Jacobian is used and is given by

$$J = \begin{bmatrix} \dfrac{\partial u}{\partial v} & \dfrac{\partial u}{\partial \theta} \\ \dfrac{\partial v}{\partial v} & \dfrac{\partial v}{\partial \theta} \end{bmatrix} = \begin{bmatrix} \cos\theta & -v\sin\theta \\ \sin\theta & v\cos\theta \end{bmatrix} = v$$

J

Jahn–Teller effect

[general] The general tendency of a molecular system to become distorted under the influence of electronic DEGENERACY. Based on Coulombs' law, the electronic field effects and associated ENERGY are generally a linear function of DISTANCE within the molecular assembly. The elastic energy is proportional to the square of displacement. As a result, the displacement may lead to a reduction in energy of the system. In contrast, linear molecules such as CO_2 are not following the linear dependency to the displacement and hence may not be prone to distortion since the energy will not reduce. Photon resonant-electron absorption will generally be broadband based on the Jahn–Teller effect (i.e., dynamic Jahn–Teller effect), which may be subject to quenching due to spin-orbit coupling. The phenomenon was based on Landau's theoretical predictions in 1934 and postulated by HERMANN ARTHUR JAHN (1907–1979), a scientist from Great Britain, and Ede (Edward) Teller (1908–2003), a scientist from Hungary—also known as "the father of the HYDROGEN BOMB"—in 1936. The static Jahn–Teller effect explains the energy configuration that leads to crystal structures incorporation METAL ions.

Jakob number ($Ja = c_p(T_s - T_{sat})/\Delta H_{vap}$)

[thermodynamics] A dimensionless number expressing the ratio of heat or more generally the enthalpy change during a PHASE change to ENERGY of vaporization, specifically during the LIQUID to VAPOR or solid to liquid change in material phase (and vice versa), with c_p being the SPECIFIC HEAT under constant pressure, T_s the temperature of the liquid, T_{sat} the temperature of the ambient saturated vapor GAS PHASE (the temperature for a solid surface and liquid in contact, which may be best exemplified by dipping an ice-cream cone in a chocolate emulsion), and H_{vap} the LATENT HEAT of vaporization or more generally the heat required to initiate a phase change. Generally, the Jakob number is small, for instance during the transformation from water to ice: $Ja = 0.058$.

Jansen, Hans (early/mid-sixteenth century–early seventeenth century)

[optics] A scientist and optical engineer from the Netherlands. Working under the inspiration of his son ZACHARIAS JANSEN (1580–1640), they started making complex microscopes.

Jansen, Zacharias (1580–1640)

[optics] A scientist and engineer from the Netherlands. Zacharias Jansen was a spectacle maker by profession with an interest in producing complex devices for investigational purposes. He was part of the father-son team, which is the first known manufacturer of a compound microscope between 1590 and 1608. The MICROSCOPE had a power of approximately nine times magnification (9×), and later model up to 30×. The father HANS JANSEN (early/mid sixteenth century–early seventeenth century) contributed equally. The microscope was later refined by HANS LIPPERSHEY (1570–1619) around 1608. He is also found as Zacherias Janssen and Zacharias Janssen (see Figure J.2).

Figure J.2 Zacharias Jansen (1580–1640).

Jefimenko, Oleg Dmitrovich (1922–2009)

[computational] A mathematician and scientist from the Ukraine. Oleg Jefimenko is known for his contributions to ELECTRICITY and MAGNETISM, specifically under special relativity terms. Additional work of Oleg Jefimenko was in designing electromotor (see Figure J.3).

Figure J.3 Oleg Dmitrovich Jefimenko (right) (1922–2009).

Jefimenko's equations

[computational, electromagnetism] Equations describing electric and MAGNETIC FIELD behavior based on charge distribution (charge density: $\rho_e[3-D]$) and/or current density (J_e) distribution with respect to time retardation: $t_r = t - \left[\left(\vec{r} - \vec{r}'\right)/c\right]$, where $c = 2.99792458 \times 10^8$ m/s the speed of light, all with respect to location $\vec{r}$, and $\vec{r}'$ location in the charge distribution. The concept was introduced by OLEG DMITROVICH JEFIMENKO (1922–2009). The electric filed is derived from:

$$\vec{E}(\vec{r},t) = (1/4\pi\varepsilon_0)\int\left\{\left\{\left[\rho_e\left(\vec{r}',t_r\right)/\left|\vec{r}-\vec{r}'\right|^3\right] + \left[\left(1/\left|\vec{r}-\vec{r}'\right|^2 c\right)\left[\partial\rho_e\left(\vec{r}',t_r\right)/\partial t\right]\right]\right\}\left[\vec{r}-\vec{r}'\right]\right.$$
$$\left. -\left[\left(1/\left|\vec{r}-\vec{r}'\right|^2 c\right)\left(\partial\vec{J}\left(\vec{r}',t_r\right)/\partial t\right)\right]\right\} d^3\vec{r}',$$

where $\varepsilon_0 = 8.85419 \times 10^{-12}\,\mathrm{C^2/Nm^2}$ the permittivity of free space. Note the resemblance to the Coulomb expression. The magnetic field follows from

$$\vec{B}(\vec{r},t) = \mu_0/4\pi\int\left\{\left[\left[\vec{J}\left(\vec{r}',t_r\right)/\left|\vec{r}-\vec{r}'\right|^3\right] + \left(1/\left|\vec{r}-\vec{r}'\right|^2 c\right)\left[\partial\vec{J}\left(\vec{r}',t_r\right)/\partial t\right]\right]\left[\left(\vec{r}-\vec{r}'\right)\times\left(\vec{r}-\vec{r}'\right)\right]\right\} d^3\vec{r}',$$

with $\mu_0 = 4\pi \times 10^{-7}\,\mathrm{H/m}$, the permeability of free space.

Jensen, Johannes Hans Daniel (1907–1973)

[general, nuclear] A physicist from Germany who worked on nuclear ENERGY generation and the production of uranium isotopes. Jensen also illustrated that the number of states in the shells of the BOHR ATOMIC MODEL are equivalent to the MAGNETIC quantum numbers. Johannes Jensen received the Nobel Prize in Physics in 1963 for his work on the definition of the atomic nuclear SHELL MODEL defined in 1949, which he shared with MARIA GOEPPERT-MAYER (1906–1972) and EUGENE WIGNER (1902–1995) (see Figure J.4).

Figure J.4 Johannes Hans Daniel Jensen (1907–1973).

Jet

[fluid dynamics] The forceful projection of a LIQUID or GAS PHASE from a narrow ORIFICE: NOZZLE. It is also used to describe an ENGINE used for PROPULSION, known as jet engine. Similarly, it is used to describe the airplane that uses the jet engine as a propellant mechanism. Liquid jets are used in propulsion for water crafts (e.g., water scooter) and also to cut materials (see Figure J.5).

(a)

(b)

Figure J.5 (a) Jet engine and (b) water jet cutting steel.

Jet force

[fluid dynamics] Newton's third law force: "for every action there is an equal and opposite reaction" resulting from the excretion of a MASS (m) of GAS or LIQUID, the forces ($\vec{F}$) are in all directions, with only one WALL that can be displaced under the influence of the release, hence moving this wall in the opposite direction of the ejected FLUID. The MOTION can be approximated using the LAW OF CONSERVATION OF MOMENTUM ($p = mv$) yielding $F = dp/dt = d(mv)/dt$, when neglecting FRICTION and thermal effects, while considering the DENSITY (ρ) and surface area (A) involved for the mass aspect, and the average FLOW velocity is $\vec{v}$, when applied in a single direction: $\sum F_z = \int \rho v_z (\vec{v} \cdot \vec{n}) dA$.

Jet plane

[fluid dynamics] Airplane propelled by TURBINE jet ENGINE, using the combustion as the propellant, in contrast to a PROPELLER plane (see Figure J.6).

Figure J.6 US Air force Thunderbirds fighter jets in air show.

Jet theory for capillary phenomena

[fluid dynamics] The pressure at the NOZZLE of a JET is $P = (T_s/R) + \text{Const}$, where T_s is the SURFACE TENSION of the FLUID and R is the radius of the ORIFICE. The emerging jet from the nozzle will have a WAVE phenomenon, resulting from edge effects and subsequent INTERFERENCE. The VIBRATION modes (n) are a direct function of the surface tension and inversely proportional to the average radius of the orifice cubed as $\nu_{vib} = \sqrt{\{(n+1)(n-1)(n+2)(T_s/\rho' R^3)\}}$, with respect to density ρ' (see Figure J.7).

Figure J.7 Wave effect at a nozzle that is generating a water-jet.

J-fet

[electronics] Junction gate field-effect transistor. This type of field effect transistors uses a voltage controlled gate for regulation of RESISTANCE in an amplifier circuit. This design provides the most simple transistor mechanism. The voltage applied to the base of the TRANSISTOR controls the gate current. The applied voltage modulates the DEPLETION LAYER in the npn or pnp semiconductor configuration.

j-j coupling

[atomic, solid-state] ELECTRON SPIN coupling based on the angular momentum: $\vec{J} = \vec{L} + \vec{S}$, where $\vec{L} = \sum_i \vec{l}_i$ the total ORBITAL ANGULAR MOMENTUM, with on-axis component $L_z = m\hbar$, where m represents the momentum quantum number and $h = 6.62606957 \times 10^{-34}\ \mathrm{m}^2\ \mathrm{kg/s}$ Planck's constant, $\hbar = h/2\pi$ and $\vec{S} = \sum_i \vec{S}_i$ the SPIN momentum. The total kinetic ENERGY with respect to the atomic state is defined by $\vec{J} = \sum_i \vec{L}_i$ with respect to the sum of the kinetic moment of the ith electron in orbit for the ATOM. The j-j coupling (jj-coupling) accounts for the atomic kinetic energy configuration for heavy atoms, whereas Russel–Saunders, or L–S COUPLING, describes the energy configuration primarily pertaining to light atoms. The electron condition is confined by the sum of the kinetic (E_k) and potential energy ($V(r)$), defined through the HAMILTONIAN OPERATOR (H) for the VALENCE electrons as $H = E_k + V(r) + H_{ee} + H_{ss} + H_{s\ell}$, with H_{ee} being the electrostatic interaction for the external electrons, H_{ss} the spin–spin interaction—Hamiltonian, and $H_{s\ell}$ the spin–orbital interaction under the boundary conditions: $H_{s\ell} \ll H_{ee}$ and $H_{s\ell} \ll H_{ss}$ (see Figure J.8).

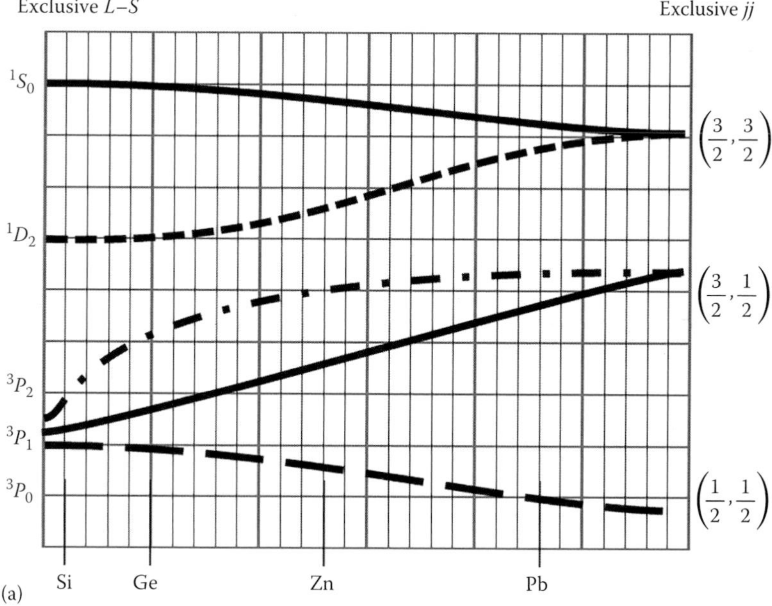

Figure J.8 (a) Correlation between L–S–j-j coupling for elements in the fourth main group of the periodic table: Silicon (Si); Germanium (Ge); Zinc (Zn); and Lead (Pb). *(Continued)*

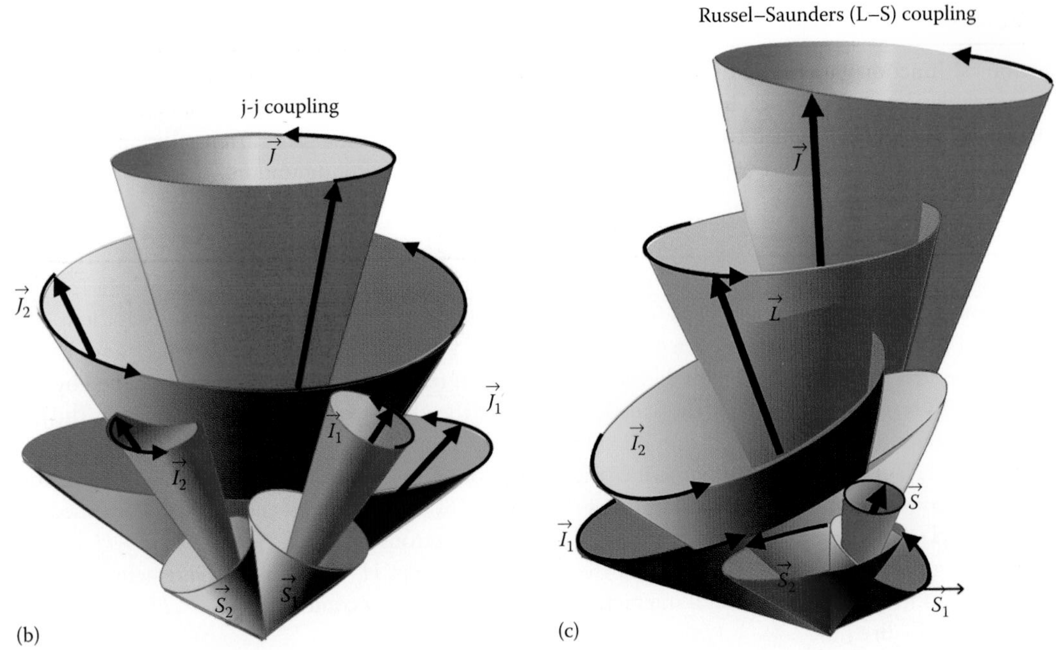

Figure J.8 (Continued) (b) illustration of j-j coupling (c) illustration of L–S Coupling (Russel–Saunders).

Johnson noise

[atomic, electromagnetism, nuclear] Thermal NOISE in signals resulting from random electron movement.

Joint reaction force

[biomedical] Inertial force between two adjacent bones in a flexing joint, such as a knee, wrist, or shoulder.

Joint strength

[acoustics, mechanics] Bond strength between two formations. Quantifiable measure for nondestructive testing using ULTRASOUND, based on the derived local elastic modulus.

Joints

[biomedical] Flexible structure merging two or more bone structures held together by collagen strands (e.g., tendons), often cushioned by a collagen disk placed between the pivoting bone structure (see Figure J.9).

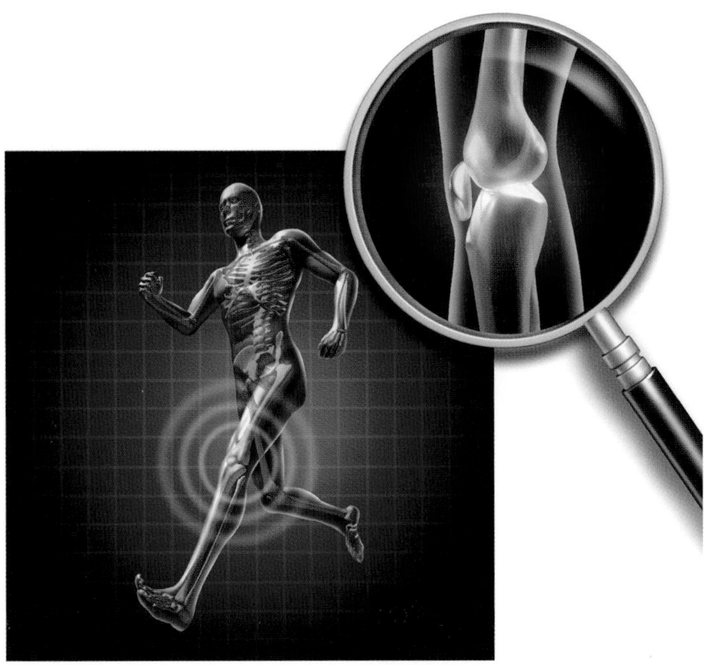

Figure J.9 Person running with several anatomical joints highlighted and a close-up of the joint at the knee of the leg with the meniscus "friction-plate."

Joliot (Joliot-Curie), Jean Frédéric (1900–1958)

[general, nuclear] A scientist from France, and husband of Irène Joliot-Curie (1897–1956). Their work lead to the formation of several long-time stable radioisotopes (long in the range of minutes, not nanoseconds).

Joliot-Curie, Irène (1897–1956)

[general] A scientist from France, daughter of Marie (Manya) Sklodovska Curie (1867–1934) and Pierre Curie (1859–1906), and husband to Jean Frédéric Joliot-Curie (1900–1958). The husband and wife team received the Nobel Prize in Chemistry for their work on the bombardment of light metals with alpha

particles and hence managed to generate phosphor out of aluminum. The phosphor remained artificially radioactive for a considerable time, emitting positrons and reducing to silicon (see Figure J.10).

Figure J.10 Irène Joliot-Curie [Irène Joliot] (1897–1956) at the 1933 Solvay conference seated between Erwin Schrödinger (1887–1961) and Niels Henrik David Bohr (1885–1962) on the front left. Behind her stands her husband Jean Frédéric Joliot (1900–1958).

Josephson, Brian David (1940–)

[condensed matter, solid-state] A physicist from Great Britain. Johnson worked on SUPERCONDUCTIVITY, specifically pertaining to the QUANTUM effects of solids. Johnson received the Nobel Prize in Physics in 1973 for his description of the "TUNNELING" effect resulting in superconductivity, outlined in 1962 (*also see* **JOSEPHSON EFFECT**) (see Figure J.11).

Figure J.11 Brian David Josephson (1940–).

Josephson effects

[condensed matter, electronics, solid-state] Superconductivity resulting from COOPER PAIRS, resulting in a supercurrent crossing an interface between two superconductors made up from a thin conducting or insulating barrier (JOSEPHSON SUPERCONDUCTING JUNCTION), named after the work of BRIAN DAVID JOSEPHSON (1940–) released in 1962. The supercurrent will prevail as long as the current remains below a certain threshold value. As a result of a VOLTAGE (V) across the span an "alternating current" will result, with a frequency $\nu = 2e(V/h)$, and an alternating phase difference ($\Delta\varphi$) that applies to the pair phase between the two respective superconductors as $(\partial/\partial t)\Delta\varphi = 2e(V/\hbar)$, where e is the electron charge and $\hbar = h/2\pi$, with $h = 6.62606957\times10^{-34}\,\mathrm{m^2kg/s}$. Planck's constant, and t is time. In case the POTENTIAL DIFFERENCE is constant, the PHASE difference will gradually increase as $\Delta\varphi(t) = 2e(V_0t/\hbar) + \Delta\varphi(0)$. The Johnson effect support high-speed switches for supercomputers and can form a standard to measure fundamental constants. When an (additional) alternating potential (V_1) is applied the junction CURRENT (I) becomes $I = I_0\sin\left(2e(V_0t/\hbar) + 2e(V_1t/\hbar\omega)\sin(\omega t) + \Delta\varphi(0)\right)$, where ω is the modulation frequency (primarily in the radio-frequency range).

Josephson superconducting junction

[condensed matter, electronics, solid-state] BARRIER between two superconductors that may act as a superconductor, while in fact consisting of a material that has low conductivity or even an INSULATOR, but only a thin film (see Figure J.12).

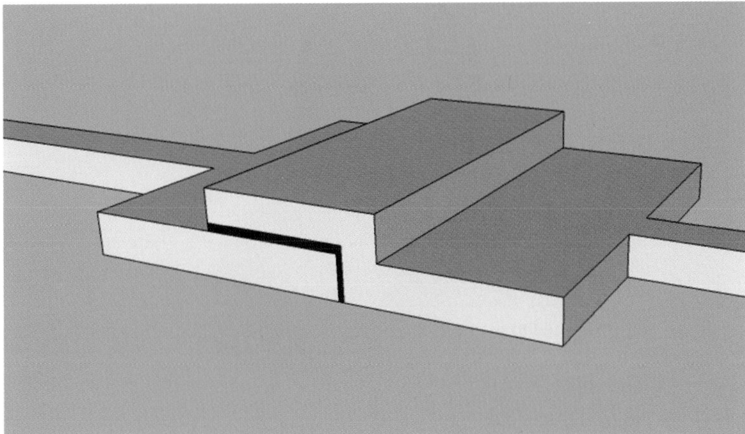

Figure J.12 Illustration of the Josephson superconducting junction.

Jost function

[computational, mechanics, solid-state] Scattering function that defines the collision PROBABILITY and related processes as a tool for solving the SCHRÖDINGER EQUATION in nonrelativistic interaction of acoustic imaging as well as PARTICLE interaction, for example, electron microscopy. The Jost function applies in particular to the time-independent Schrödinger equation. Introduced by Res Jost (1918–1990), theoretical physicist from Switzerland.

Joukowski's hypothesis

[fluid dynamics] In AERODYNAMICS this describes the conditions forming a CIRCULATION in flow, specifically around the WING of a plane. The phenomenon pertains to the LIFT of an AIRFOIL. Generally, the FLOW is prevented from passing the trailing edge of the "rear stagnation point," as identified in cross-sectional view. In case the flow reaching the tip of the wing approaches at an ANGLE with the axis of the airfoil that is not too large, the circulation will adjust itself to compensate for this "break-off" point. This captures the principles of Joukowski's hypothesis. *See* **KUTTA–JOUKOWSKI HYPOTHESIS**, named after **NIKOLAI ZHUKOVSKY JOUKOWSKI** (1847–1921) and (1867–1944). *Also see* **KUTTA CONDITION**.

Joukowsky, Nikolay (1847–1921)

[computational, fluid dynamics] *See* **ZHUKOVSKY, NIKOLAY.**

Joukowsky equation

[fluid dynamics] Describing the pressure change resulting from a sudden change in FLOW velocity of a fluid ELEMENT due to a blockage, narrowing, curve or other restriction based on Newton's laws of MOTION combined with the EQUATION OF CONTINUITY yields the expression: $\delta P/\delta t = \rho a(\delta v/\delta t)$, with P being the PRESSURE (in pascal), v the flow velocity, t the time, and $a = \sqrt{(K/\rho)/[1+(D/b)(K/E)\mathrm{Const}]}$ the free-flow velocity in a flexible tube with the LIQUID flow density ρ. Based on the work of NIKOLAY JOUKOWSKY (NIKOLAY ZHUKOVSKY) (1847–1921).

Joule, James Prescott (1818–1889)

[general, thermodynamics] A scientist from Great Britain, best known for his quest to find the common-denominator linking work to ENERGY and heat. The SI unit for energy is named after him ([J], joule). One specific topic of his work was in the heat generated by the current FLOW through a RESISTOR (i.e., JOULE HEAT) (see Figure J.13).

Figure J.13 James Prescott Joule (1818–1889).

Joule (*J*)

[general, thermodynamics] A unit of work or ENERGY, mechanical equivalent of heat. This concept and unit was named after the pioneering work by JAMES PRESCOTT JOULE (1818–1889). This relates to the other unit in heat (calorie) as $4.186\,\mathrm{J} = 1\,\mathrm{cal}$.

Joule heat

[general, thermodynamics] The power (P_E) generation (alternatively: power dissipation) resulting from a CURRENT (I) through a RESISTOR (R) under an applied VOLTAGE (V) expressed by JAMES PRESCOTT JOULE (1818–1889) as $P_E = I^2R = V^2/R$ in 1841 ("heating power"). The THERMAL ENERGY produced in this manner is referred to as "joule heat."

Joule law

[general, thermodynamics] The HEAT (Q) generated from a CURRENT (I) through a RESISTOR (R) under the influence of an applied voltage (V): $Q = I^2Rt = \left(V^2/R\right)t$, where t is the time duration for the event.

Joule–Brayton cycle

[thermodynamics] Cyclic GAS compression/EXPANSION process consisting of two ISENTROPIC (i.e., constant entropy) and two isobaric components (i.e., constant pressure). This mechanism applies to certain gas-turbine ENERGY conversion processes, specifically for AIR compression. The efficiency of the Joule–Brayton cycle ENGINE is a direct function of the pressure ratio in the upper and lower portion of the cycle in a reversible process. This falls in the same category as the STIRLING CYCLE (see Figure J.14).

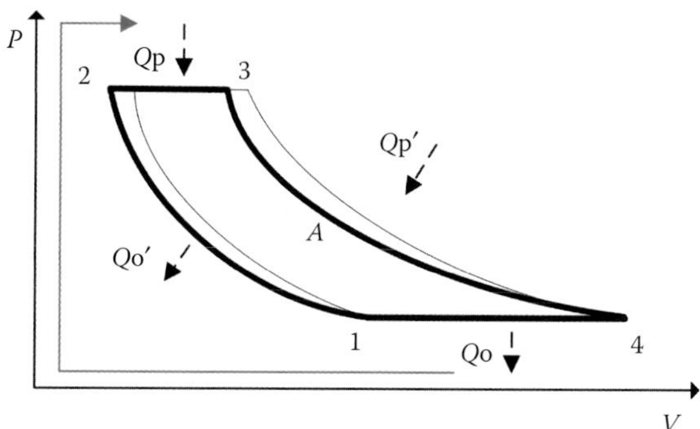

Figure J.14 Diagram of the mechanical processes in the Joule–Brayton cycle.

Joule–Kelvin effect

[thermodynamics] When a GAS expands while exiting from a porous plug or ORIFICE, it may reduce or increase in temperature. The temperature change will depend on the specific isenthalp for the gas. Temperatures will rise on EXPANSION on one side (right side) of the isenthalp, whereas the gas temperature will decrease on the opposite side (*also* **JOULE–THOMPSON EFFECT**) (see Figure J.15).

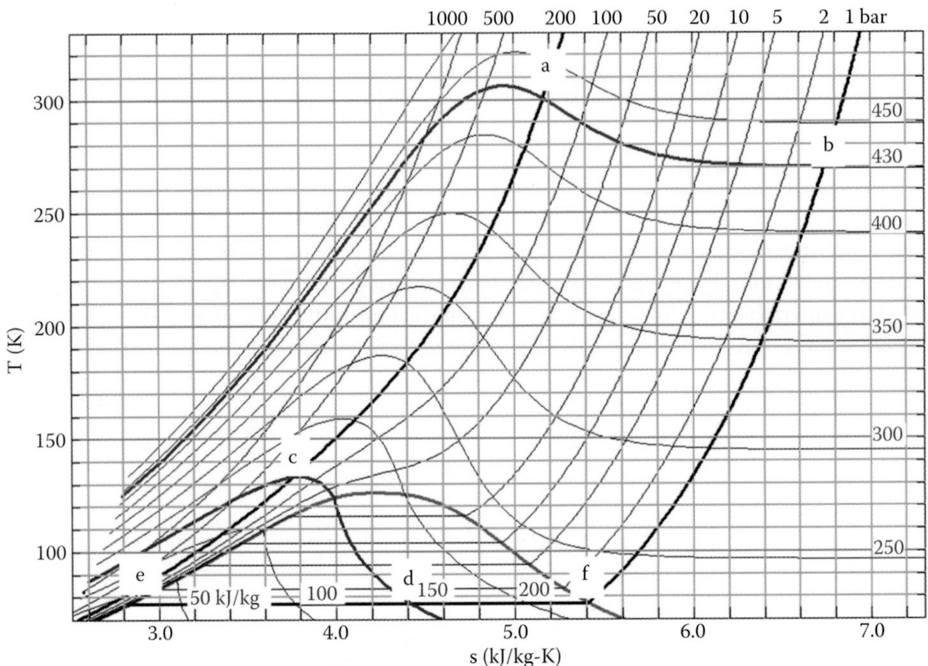

Figure J.15 Joule–Kelvin effect for nitrogen T-s diagram of nitrogen. The red dome represents the two-phase region with the low-entropy side (the saturated liquid) and the high-entropy side (the saturated gas). The black curves give the T-s relation along isobars. The pressures are indicated in bar. The blue curves are isenthalps (curves of constant specific enthalpy). The specific enthalpies are indicated in kJ/kg. The specific points a, b, and so on are treated in the main text. (Data from http://en.wikipedia.org/wiki/Joule–Thomson_effect# Throttling in the Ts diagram of nitrogen. http://en.wikipedia.org/wiki/Joule–Thomson_effect#mediaviewer/File:Throttling_in_Ts_diagram_01.jpg.)

Joule–Thomson coefficient

[thermodynamics] Partial derivative of temperature (T) against PRESSURE (P) in an expansion/compression scheme: $\left(\partial T/\partial P\right)_h = \left(V/c_p\right)\left(T\alpha_p - 1\right)$, where α_p is the coefficient of isobaric expansion, c_p is the SPECIFIC HEAT of the medium under constant pressure (which follows from the EQUATION OF STATE), V is the volume, and h is the LATENT HEAT of the vapor-liquid equilibrium. Note that the EXPANSION is a nonreversible, but frequently it is an ADIABATIC PROCESS. This phenomenon can accompany a rapid expansion followed by crystallization of the emerging gas, for example, carbon dioxide from a fire extinguisher. When the GAS is above the INVERSION temperature before expansion the Joule–Thompson coefficient is negative and the gas will increase in temperature on expansion, while when it is below the inversion temperature it will cool, because the Joule–Thompson coefficient is positive. Note that the change in pressure is always negative on expansion (see Figure J.16).

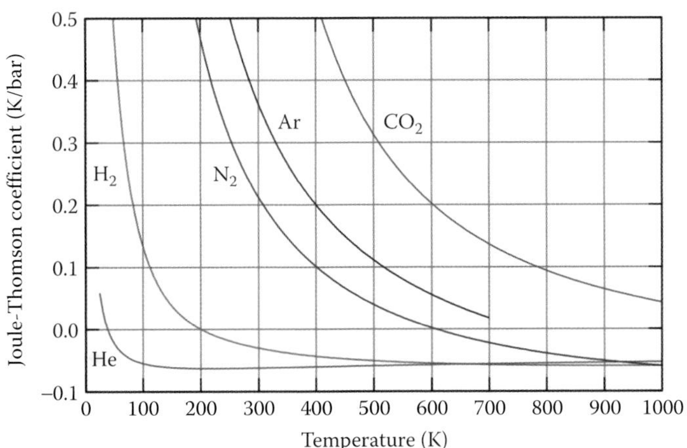

Figure J.16 Joule–Thomson coefficient for several gases as a function of temperature. (Data from http://en.wikipedia.org/wiki/File:Joule-Thomson_curves_2.svg.)

Joule–Thomson effect

[thermodynamics] The nontemperature effects resulting from a rapid EXPANSION of a GAS from a porous stopper or NOZZLE. In most cases, the expansion is adiabatic. In case the expansion is ISENTROPIC, it will be reversible and positive work that is performed. On the other hand, the process may be free expansion and will be irreversible. The (specific) enthalpy in this case remains constant, no change in kinetic ENERGY (i.e., constant temperature). The Joule–Thompson effect will occur for most ideal gases, with the exception of helium, hydrogen, and neon gases on expansion; these three gases cool on expansion. This effect was discovered by JAMES PRESCOTT JOULE (1818–1889) and WILLIAM THOMPSON (1824–1907) (i.e., Lord Kelvin) in 1852 (*also see* **JOULE–KELVIN EFFECT** *and* **JOULE–THOMSON COEFFICIENT**).

Journal bearing

[fluid dynamics] Shaft (also referred to as "journal") that rotates in a METAL sleeve under tight tolerance, for instance, used in supporting the crank-shaft of automobile and motorcycle engines. In comparison, the majority of bearings only have rolling RESISTANCE, relying on balls or tubs rolling in two close-fit opposite grooves. The FRICTION in this close metal-to-metal contact and sliding lubrication is usually provided by forced injection of lubricant ([semi-]lubricated bearing) or by means of a low-friction sleeve insert made out of PTFE, teflon, or NYLON (i.e., "dry-journal bearing"). The theory of lubrication for journal bearings uses an intricate FLUID DYNAMICS approach. The OIL in a lubricated bearing will tend to "accumulate" in the direction of MOTION, causing a pressure gradient in the lubricant that is antiparallel to the direction of motion. Because of the tight tolerances, the gap in the journal bearing spacing is narrow, but finite and the shaft will be able to move radially and place the shaft in an eccentric position. The highest pressure is at the rear side of the point of contact from the direction of motion. A special phenomenon is "oil-whirl." Pressures in journal bearings can exceed 40 MPa. A related example of the "LUBRICATION" process for a journal bearing is experienced during hydroplaning of an automobile tire (see Figure J.17).

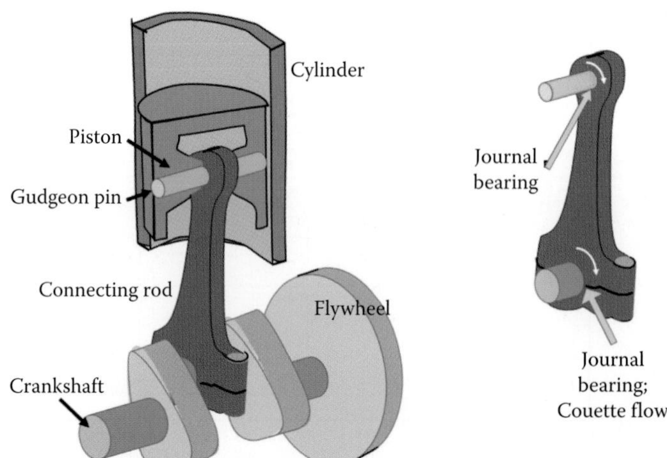

Figure J.17 Journal bearing.

Junction diode

[electronics, general] *pn*-junction with DEPLETION LAYER sandwiched between acting as a current controlled INSULATOR, where the depletion layer is deprived of charges and acts as a CAPACITOR. The *p* material (e.g., single crystalline *p*-type GALLIUM-doped silicon) has an effective POSITIVE CHARGE due to lack of electrons and the *n* semiconductor (e.g., *n*-type Arsenic-doped silicon) is negatively charged due to an excess of electrons (gallium-arsenide DIODE, GaAs) (see Figure J.18).

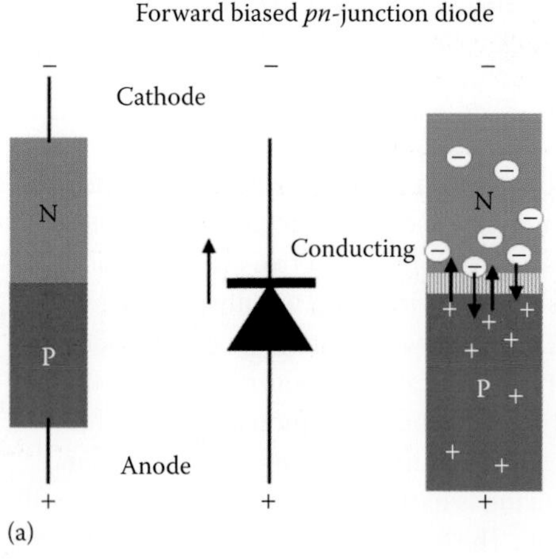

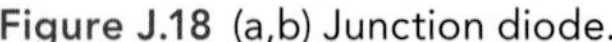

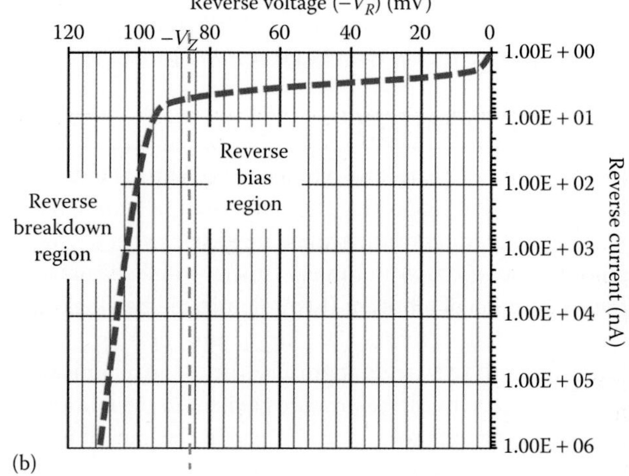

Figure J.18 (a,b) Junction diode.

Junction rule

[electronics] In a circuit at any junction (connection point of two or more "wires"), the sum of all the currents will be zero, where FLOW to the junction is positive and away is represented as negative (*also* **KIRCHHOFF'S FIRST RULE**).

Junction transistor

[electronics, general, solid-state] A TRANSISTOR consisting of two pairs of *pn*-junctions, which are in tight proximity for current control. The respective *pn*-junctions are in close proximity. The one *pn*-JUNCTION will serve as forward-based emitter, whereas the second forms the reverse-biased collector. One junction forms the forward-biased emitter, whereas the other is configured as a reverse-biased collector. The transistor in nonoperational when the transistor is powered in a way where the collector and emitter are both reverse biased. When both the collector and emitter are reverse-biased, the transistor is switched off. The first junction transistor was developed in 1949 by William Shockley (1910–1989) at Bell Laboratories, Murray Hill, New Jersey (see Figure J.19).

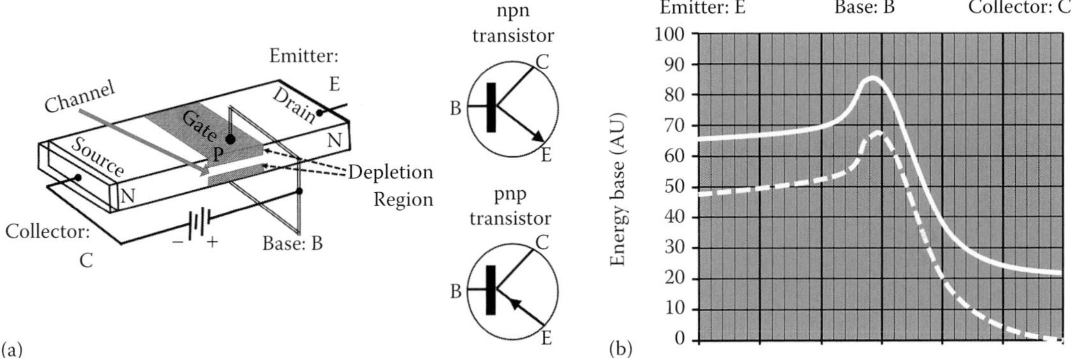

Figure J.19 (a,b) Junction transistor.

Junge power law

[chemistry, energy, fluid-dynamics, molecular, solid-state] An expression for the size distribution function of AEROSOL particles in suspension, defined as $dn/d\log r = c_{\text{const}} r^{-b}$, where r is the PARTICLE radius, dn the segment of particles within a specific logarithmic size range, $b \sim 3$ a parameter which usually can be taken as 3, and c_{const} a constant that depends on the boundary conditions such as source, relative HUMIDITY, and SATURATION. Generally, the particle distribution peaks between 0.1 μm and 20 μm. Frequently, a NORMAL DISTRIBUTION is assumed for the size. Sources may include smoke produced by combustion and dust or pollen. The concept was introduced by Christian Junge (1912–1996) in 1969. He was one of the first researchers who performed a systematic and detailed analysis of the chemical composition of atmospheric aerosols and their respective size/volume distribution between 1953 and 1963 (see Figure J.20).

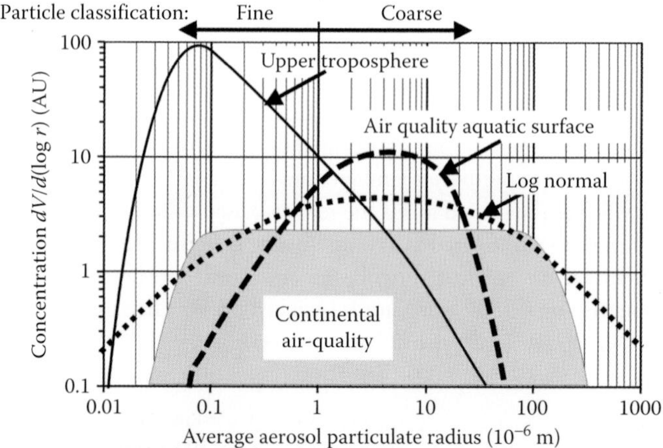

Figure J.20 Outline of the volume distribution for several atmospheric aerosols as described by Christian Junge (1912–1996) in 1969; the Junge power law. (Data from http://www.iara.org/newsfolder/pioneers/6AerosolPioneerEditedAugJunge.pdf.)

Jupiter

[astrophysics/astronomy, general] It is the fifth PLANET away from the Sun. Jupiter has one moon: Io. Jupiter is called a GAS giant, and the flowing GAS has an unstable turbulent VORTEX (anticyclonic storm), known as the "Great Red Spot," which has been reducing in size over the observation time. Jupiter does not have a MESOSPHERE, that is, no solid core. The revolution around the Sun measured in EARTH time is 11.8618 year, whereas in Jupiter days it is 10,475.8 Jupiter days. The radius at the equator is $71,492 \pm 4\,\text{km}$, which is 11.209 times the radius of the Earth at the equator (see Figure J.21).

Figure J.21 Jupiter.

K characteristic X-rays

[atomic, electromagnetism, nuclear] *See* **X-RAY**.

K meson

[atomic, nuclear] Unstable zero-spin mesons that DECAY into ION pairs; also referred to as "K-ons": kaons. The kaons with zero SPIN are K^+, $\underline{K}^-$, K^0, and its respective anti-particle K^0, with respective decay PION components: $K^0 \rightarrow \pi^+ + \pi^-$; $K^0 \rightarrow \pi^0 + \pi^0$; $\underline{K}^+ \rightarrow \pi^+ + \pi^0$ (where the pions decay into leptons or phonons: $\pi^+ \rightarrow \mu^+ + \nu_\mu$, respectively $\pi^- \rightarrow \mu^- + \overline{\nu}_\mu$. The mesons were always produced in pairs: K^0 and the LAMBDA PARTICLE Λ^0, called "strange particles," due to their relatively long decay time in the order of nanoseconds. The KAON K^0 and K^+ has a strangeness +1, whereas the counterpart BARYON Λ^0 has a strangeness −1.

K Series

[nuclear] *See* ***K*-ALPHA LINES**.

K-alpha lines

[atomic, energy, nuclear] Characteristic emissions spectral lines. Emission lines resulting from the excitation of the *k*-shell electrons: 2p orbit. *K*-lines are X-RAY emissions. The DECAY is predominantly between the $2p_{3/2}$ (at 933 eV) and $2p_{1/2}$ (at 952 eV) to the $1s_{1/2}$ ENERGY level at 8979 eV. In contrast to the *K*-beta line which is associated with the transition between $3p$ at 76 eV to 1s. The emission lines are doublets (two closely separated lines that may not always be resolved) with the highest known energy, labeled as $K\alpha_1$ and $K\alpha_2$, where $\Delta E\alpha_1 > \Delta E\alpha_2$. For instance, for copper $K\alpha = 1.54184$ Å (split: $K\alpha_1 = 1.54056$ Å and $\alpha_2 = 1.54439$ Å), and for another popular ANODE material in X-ray sources, molybdenum $K\alpha = 0.71073$ Å (see Figure K.1).

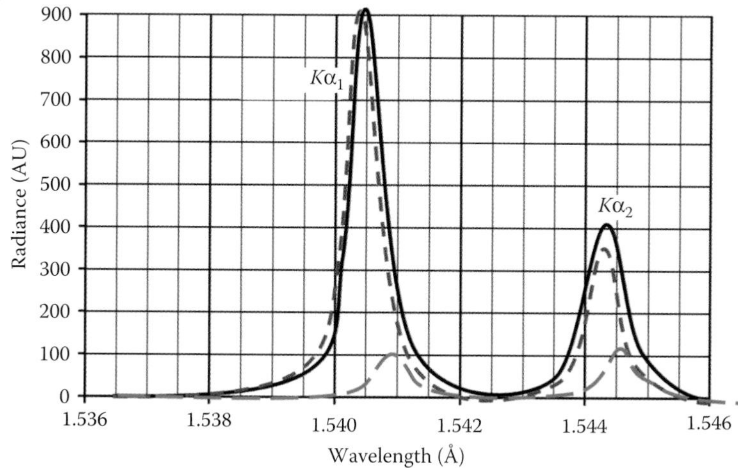

Figure K.1 *K*-alpha line spectrum for copper (Cu).

K-electron capture

[atomic, nuclear] Radioactive decay involving the capture of high ENERGY *K*-shell electrons by the NUCLEUS of the ATOM. During this charge integration, protons convert into NEUTRON and the nuclide decreases in atomic number, while an electron NEUTRINO is emitted. Examples include the conversion of aluminum to magnesium ($^{26}_{13}\text{Al} + e^- \rightarrow ^{26}_{12}\text{Mg} + \nu_e$) and potassium to argon ($^{40}_{19}\text{K} + e^- \rightarrow ^{40}_{18}\text{Ar} + \nu_e$).

k-Epsilon model

[computational, fluid dynamics] Mathematical and computational model for turbulent FLOW calculations using two sets of transport equations. The first set of equation is the transport of kinetic ENERGY within the turbulent flow, and the second set represents the turbulent dissipation, that is, the MAGNITUDE of TURBULENCE. When the pressure gradients become too large the model will result in errors and deviations (*also* **k-e** MODEL).

K-isomerism

[nuclear] Nuclear transitions in reference to the QUANTUM NUMBER "K_{quant}," which denotes the component of the nuclear SPIN along the rotational axis of symmetry. The GROUND STATE of a deformed NUCLEUS with even–even configuration (i.e., Z = even, where Z defines the atomic number designating the number of protons in the nucleus, and N = even represent the number of neutrons; examples are URANIUM (^{238}U) and protactinium (^{234}Pa). (*Note*: $Z + N = A$, with A the mass number of the ATOM.) For specific even–even nuclei the condition applies $K^{\pi}_{\text{quant}} = 0^+$ for the rotational band with respect to *K*-isomerism. *K*-isomeric transitions are mainly between states indicated by multipolarity states: $E1$, $M1$, and $M2$. The multipolarity transition states are associated with the corresponding electric ("E") and MAGNETIC ("M") reduced PROBABILITY defined as $B(E\ell_{\text{multi}})$ and $B(M\ell_{\text{multi}})$, where ℓ_{multi} is the MULTIPOLE order. In *K*-isomerism mainly the $E1$, $M1$, and $M2$ transitions are retarded for the isomeric nucleus with respective values $B(E1) = 1.0 \times 10^{14}$, $B(M1) = 2.9 \times 10^{13}$, and $B(M2) = 8.4 \times 10^{7}$ (see Figure K.2).

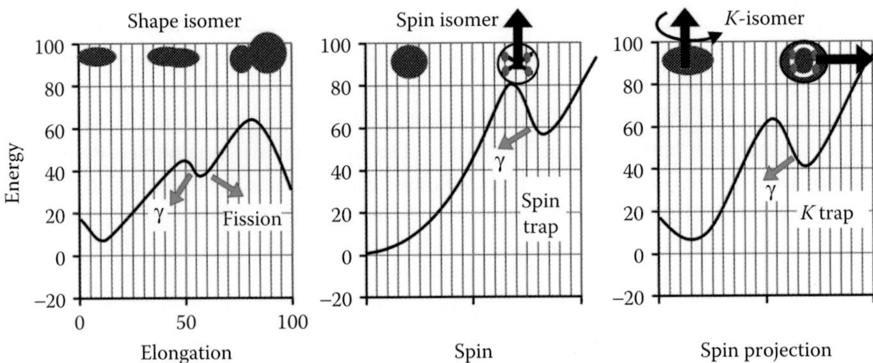

Figure K.2 Graphical representation of the *K*-isomerism phenomenon.

K-space

[condensed matter, computational] Abstract concept that refers to the two- or three-dimensional FOURIER TRANSFORM of the magnetic resonance image (MRI) into a data matrix consisting of the raw MRI. An MRI is a map composed of complex numbers representing the spatial distribution of the transverse magnetization: M_{xy} within the specimen (e.g., biological medium) at a specific time point as the result of an excitation by a radiofrequency perturbed MAGNETIC influence (analog to "spin echo"). The concept of *k*-space was introduced by RICHARD S. LIKES (twentieth century) in 1979 and further refined by S. LJUNGGREN (twentieth century) and independently by D. TWIEG (twentieth century) in 1983. In the convolution from temporal to spatial IMAGE space, the *k*-space in MRI defines the spatial frequency domain by two wave vectors:

$k_{FE} = \gamma_{GM} m G_{FE} \Delta t$ and $k_{PE} = \gamma_{GM} n G_{PE} \Delta t$, G_i the MAGNETIC FLUX (vector, with PHASE [PE] and frequency [FE] encoding), γ_{GM} the GYROMAGNETIC RATIO, m the sample number in the spatial domain in the FE direction, respectively n in the PE direction, where FE (representing frequency encoding) and PE (representing PHASE ENCODING) are perpendicular to each other; $\Delta t = 1/\nu$ the SAMPLING time, and ν the SAMPLING frequency. Specifically, for MRI based on the Larmor frequency $\gamma_{Larmor} = -eg_a/2m_e$, the gyromagnetic ratio with g_L the electron orbital g-factor e = the electron charge, m_e the mass of the precessing electron, and B the applied MAGNETIC FIELD strength. Additionally, the use of k-space in ULTRASONIC IMAGING provides a means of correlating the transmitted and received SIGNAL for deconvolution of the lateral response, assuming the "diffraction" of a monochromatic POINT SOURCE to form an approximation of the real-life conditions. The k-space occupies a spatial frequency domain (see Figure K.3).

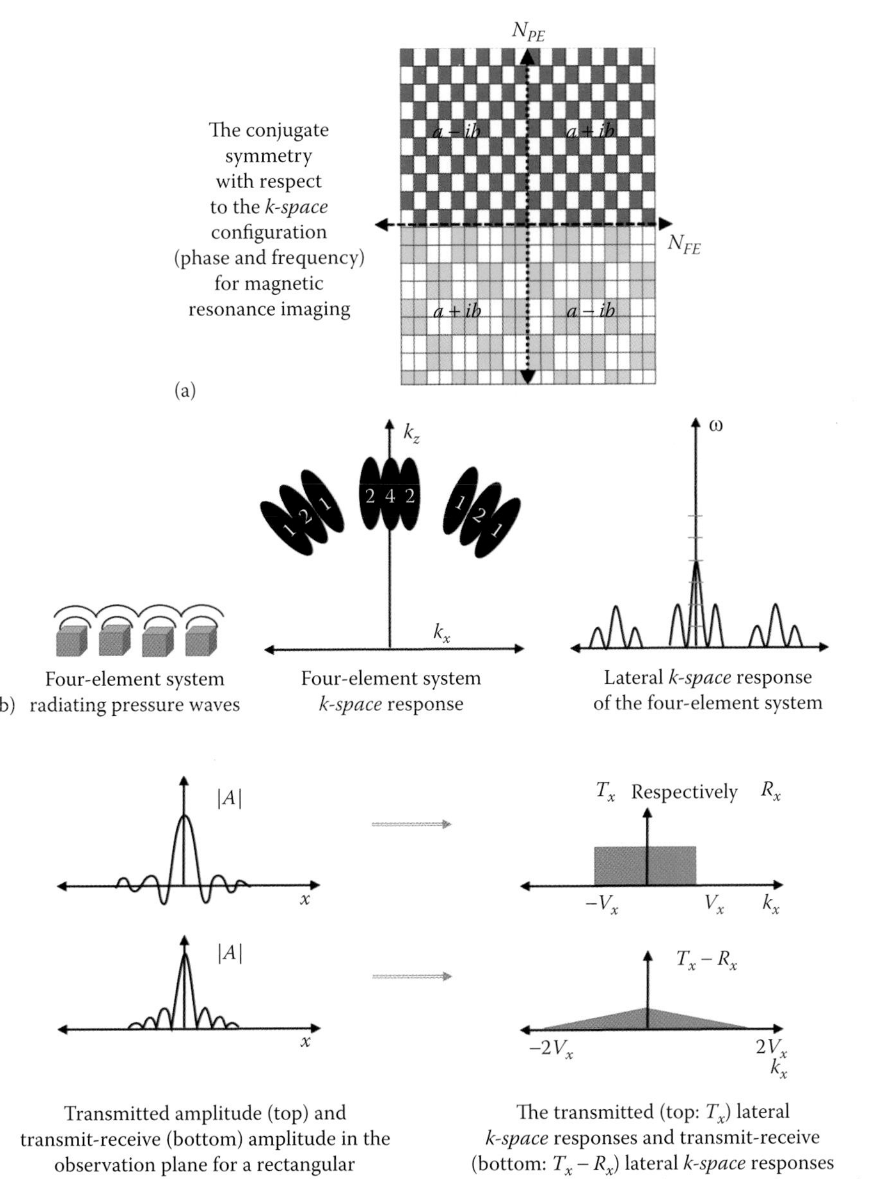

Figure K.3 (a–c) Illustration of the *K*-space concept in imaging, specifically for ultrasonic imaging in this case.

Kadomtsev–Petviashvili equation

[acoustics, computational, fluid dynamics, mechanics] Mathematical function for two-dimensional waves ($f(x, y, t)$) as an extension to the KORTEWEG–DE VRIES EQUATION, allowing for marginal nonlinearities and minor DISPERSION for a wide bandwidth FREQUENCY SPECTRUM as a SOLUTION to the differential equation: $d/dx\{[df(x,y,t)/dt]+2f(x,y,t)[df(x,y,t)/dx]+[d^3f(x,y,t)/dx^3]\}=-3\sigma^2[d^2f(x,y,t)/dy^2]$, where σ is a constant representing the geometry of the situation. This can apply to pressure waves (i.e., ACOUSTICS), water waves, or PLASMA waves and more.

Kamerlingh Onnes, Heike (1853–1926)

[general, thermodynamics] Physicist from the Netherlands and is the discoverer of SUPERCONDUCTIVITY in 1911. A significant amount of work of Kamerlingh Onnes was in CRYOGENICS, resulting in liquefying helium in 1908, reaching the lowest temperature on record at the time of 0.9 Kelvin (0.9 K) (see Figure K.4).

Figure K.4 Heike Kamerlingh Onnes (1853–1926).

Kant, Immanuel (1724–1804)

[biomedical, general] Philosopher from Germany with influences on the modern thinking in esthetics, epistemology, ethics, and metaphysics, as well as political philosophy. The works of Kant influence the modern evolution of critical thinking, based on his statement that all observations are subjective and require analysis and independent verification. His philosophy formed the basis of modern ethics in clinical trials and human as well as animal participation in any form of research (avoiding coercion and fraud) (see Figure K.5).

Figure K.5 Immanuel Kant (1724–1804).

Kaon

[general] *See* ***K*** MESON.

Kapitza, Pyotr Leonidovich (1894–1984)

[solid-state, thermodynamics] Scientist from Russia, later USSR. Kapitza discovered the superfluidic properties of helium during his low temperature work, for which he received the Nobel Prize in Physics in 1987 (see Figure K.6).

Figure K.6 Pyotr Leonidovich Kapitza (1894–1984). (Courtesy of Piotr Barącz.)

Kaplan, Irving (1913–1997)

[nuclear] Chemist and scientist from the United States, collaborator on the MANHATTAN PROJECT, the development team of the NUCLEAR BOMB. Additionally, Irving Kaplan introduced the Department of Nuclear Engineering at the Massachusetts Institute of Technology (see Figure K.7).

Figure K.7 From left to right in the picture: Dr. Irving Kaplan, Dr. Francis Bonner, Dr. E.O. Lawrence, and Dr. Harrison Scott Brown. (http://www.gilderlehrman.org/history-by-era/postwar-politics-and-origins-cold-war/interactives/manhattan-project; http://www.gilderlehrman.org/sites/default/files/imagecache/inline-3col-full/content-images/slide3_2.jpg.)

Kármán, Theodore von (1881–1963)

[fluid dynamics] Physicist from Hungary, with primary interests in fluid-dynamic topics related to aeronautics and astronautics (see Figure K.8).

Figure K.8 Theodore von Kármán (1881–1963). (Courtesy of NASA, Washington, DC.)

Kármán eddy current vortex street

[fluid dynamics] Also referred to as Kármán vortex or Kármán street (*also see* WAKE). A VORTEX pattern in the wake of an obstruction in a FLUID flow, resulting from flow detachment from a bluff body with virtually symmetric curved pattern surface, introduced by THEODORE VON KÁRMÁN (1881–1963). The detachment or shedding will take place at different angular locations on either side of the obstruction with respect to the direction of the FLOW. For instance, in oceanic flow the obstructions can be islands, in addition to the airflow around the AIR column mounted on an island (higher temperature than the surrounding water, resulting in a microclimate) creating a vortex street of clouds based on the CORIOLIS EFFECT between the stagnant air column and the airflow. The vortex effect requires assumption of interaction with essentially cylindrical objects under conditions of a REYNOLDS NUMBER of $50 < Re < 300$. When the Reynolds number exceeds 300, the shedding progressively starts generating more TURBULENCE while developing full fluid-dynamic chaos or full turbulent flow characteristics. The shedding will occur at a rate known as the VORTEX-SHEDDING FREQUENCY (ν_V), which is a function of the flow conditions and SURFACE ROUGHNESS of the bluff object. At smaller Reynolds number the flow will be laminar with little noticeable flow pattern generation. Under certain conditions, the vortex shedding frequency may match the NATURAL FREQUENCY of the obstruction/object which may result in RESONANCE, eventually leading to wide-scale impact (e.g., destructive forces, Reference: aeolian sounds, as illustrated by the TACOMA NARROWS BRIDGE). The formation of a KÁRMÁN VORTEX street on a line or wire held tightly in airflow may generate sounds known as AEOLIAN TONES (see Figure K.9).

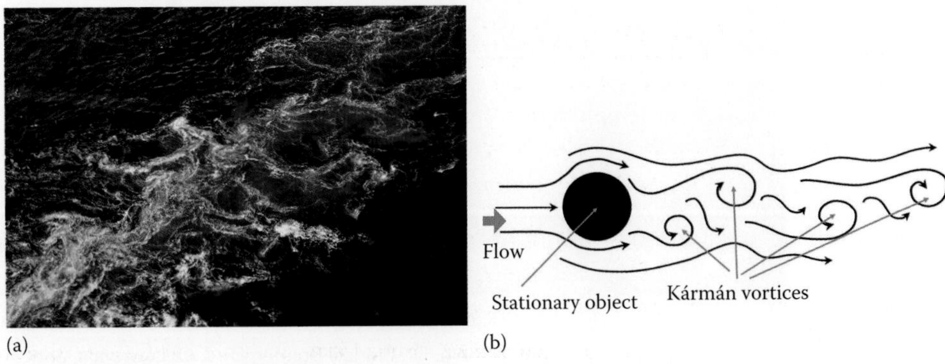

Figure K.9 (a,b) Examples of Kármán vortices.

Katz, Bernard, Sir (1911–2003)

[biomedical, chemical, electromagnetism] Scientist from Germany who made ground-breaking discoveries in the biological cellular transmembrane ION transport and the generation of the MEMBRANE potential. Katz worked closely with SIR ALAN LLOYD HODGKIN (1914–1998), and DAVID E. GOLDMAN (1910–1998) next to SIR ANDREW FIELDING HUXLEY (1917–2012) on the transmembrane potential (*also see* **GOLDMAN EQUATION**) (see Figure K.10).

Figure K.10 Bernard Katz (1911–2003). (Courtesy of Society for Neuroscience, Washington, DC.)

Kaufmann, William Weed (1918–2008)

[atomic, nuclear] Nuclear scientist from the United States.

Kaufmann and Bucherer experiments

[atomic, nuclear] The determination of the momentum ($p = mv$, where v is the velocity) of elementary building blocks (electrons, etc., in the early twentieth century) with respect to its mass (m), performed independently by Walter Kaufmann (1871–1947), Alfred Heinrich Bucherer (1863–1927), and Günther Neumann (late nineteenth century–early twentieth century). These experiments were performed between 1901 and 1915 and provided verification of the special relativity concepts (*also* Kaufmann–Bucherer–Neumann experiments).

Kedem–Katchalsky formalism

[biomedical, thermodynamics] Theoretical model describing the permeability of biological membranes. The MEMBRANE is defined by hydraulic conductivity (ρ_p), reflection coefficient (σ_r), and solute permeability ($\mathbb{P}_s$). The REFLECTION coefficient is used for the transportion of water and solute, but can often be neglected. The change in volume of the cellular water and solute volume (V_{W+S}) is described as a function of the molar OSMOLALITY with respect to the inner cellular concentration $\left([M]^{\text{in}}\right)$ and extracellular concentrations $\left([M]^{\text{ex}}\right)$ for both the permeating ($\square_{\text{per}}$), and nonpermeating solutes ($\square_{\text{np}}$), expressed as $dV_{W+S}/dt = -\rho_p\left(AR_yT\right)\left\{\left([M]^{\text{ex}}{}_{\text{np}} - [M]^{\text{in}}{}_{\text{np}}\right) + \sigma_r\left([M]^{\text{ex}}{}_{\text{per}} - [M]^{\text{in}}{}_{\text{per}}\right)\right\}$, where A represents the surface area of the CELL, the GAS constant $R = 8.3144621(75)\,\text{J/Kmol}$, and T the temperature, and the permeability of the solute can be defined as $\mathbb{P}_s = \omega_{\text{solute}}RT$ with ω_{solute} the mobility of the SOLUTE. Based on this the rate of change of solute (N_{sol}, in OSMOLE units) as a result of transmembrane transport (permeating the membrane) is given as $dN_{\text{sol}}/dt = \left[(1-\sigma_r)/2\right]\left([M]^{\text{ex}}{}_{\text{per}} + [M]^{\text{in}}{}_{\text{per}}\right)\left[dV_{W+S}/dt\right] + \mathbb{P}_sA\left([M]^{\text{ex}}{}_{\text{per}} - [M]^{\text{in}}{}_{\text{per}}\right)$.

Keenan, Joseph Henry (1900–1977)

[thermodynamics] Physicist from the United States. Keenan established steam tables that were beneficial in the calculations for steam power generators next to his work on JET propulsion (see Figure K.11).

Figure K.11 Joseph Henry Keenan (1900–1977). (Courtesy of Massachusetts Institute of Technology, Cambridge, MA.)

Keesom, Willem Hendrik (Wilhelmus Hendrikus) (1876–1956)

[atomic, nuclear, solid-state, thermodynamics] Material scientist and theoretical and experimental physicist from the Netherlands. Willem Keesom discovered the cryogenic mechanism that allowed for LIQUID helium to be solidified. The theoretical work of Dr. Keesom involves the description of the attractive and repulsive forces between two DIPOLE formations: DIPOLE–DIPOLE INTERACTION. One specific example of the dipole–dipole attraction, or rather induced dipole (i.e., POLARIZATION, induced shifts in charge on one ATOM or MOLECULE or group of molecules by a dominant charge distribution on one of the constituents of the mixture) is in the hydrogen–chloride bond (HCl), which is not a standard example of hydrogen bonding. (*Note*: Atoms rarely form a permanent dipole, rather than molecules which will indeed form permanent dipoles.) Willem Keesom also defined the LAMBDA POINT in SPECIFIC HEAT transition for helium, a variation of the TRIPLE POINT in "high-temperature" PHYSICS (see Figure K.12).

Figure K.12 Wilhelmus Hendrikus Keesom (1876–1956). (Courtesy of Huygens ING, The Hague, the Netherlands.)

Keesom force

[atomic, nuclear, solid-state, thermodynamics] *Also* **Keesom interaction.** Intermolecular force based on polarized DIPOLE–DIPOLE INTERACTION. The Keesom ENERGY associated with the inter-dipole force degrades with the inter-dipolar DISTANCE to the 6th power $E_{\text{attraction}}^{\text{Keesom}} = -u_1^{\,2} u_2^{\,2} / (4\pi\varepsilon_0)^2\, k_b T r^6$, which bares some resemblance to the Coulomb force ($F_{\text{attraction}}^{\text{Coulomb}} = -q_1 q_2 / 4\pi\varepsilon_0 r^2$, with q_i the respective charges), with u_1 and u_2 the respective DIPOLE moments, $\varepsilon_0 \cong 8.85418717620 \times 10^{-12}\,\text{F/m}$ the DIELECTRIC permittivity in VACUUM, r the separation between the dipoles, $k_b = 1.3806503 \times 10^{-23}\,\text{m}^2\text{kgs}^{-2}\text{K}^{-1}$ the Boltzmann constant, and T the relative temperature (in Kelvin). In contrast, the atomic force between fixed dipoles decays with the separation DISTANCE to the third power. A different attraction is between an ION and an induced dipole, which fall under electric attraction/repulsion.

Keesom interaction

See KEESOM FORCE.

Kelvin, 1st Baron (Lord William Thomson) (1824–1907)

[general, thermodynamics] British scientist and engineer and is the creator of the Kelvin scale. William Thomson proposed this scale in 1848, for which he was knighted as Lord Kelvin (see Figure K.13).

Figure K.13 Lord William Thomson; 1st Baron, Lord Kelvin (1824–1907).

Kelvin (K)

[thermodynamics] Kelvin scale, based on the constant volume THERMOMETER concept. In theory at $0\,\text{K}$ the GAS reduces to a nonexisting volume in the limit approaching $T \downarrow 0$. The scale uses the same increments as the CELSIUS SCALE, also using the boiling point and MELTING POINT of water (373.15 K and 273.15 K, respectively) as references for calibration in a decimal configuration.

Kelvin effect

[geophysics, thermodynamics] The influence of SURFACE TENSION on the equilibrium diameter of a droplet or hygroscopic aqueous AEROSOL particle. The VAPOR PRESSURE of a droplet in suspended circumstances in equilibrium with an aqueous solution will depend on the concentration and constituents of the SOLUTE as well as the diameter of the droplet. This condition plays a role in the determination of atmospheric conditions. The droplet radius (r_σ) as a function of surface tension ($\sigma_{surface}$), partial molar water volume for the SOLUTION ($\overline{V}_{MolH_2O}$), and the ambient temperature (T) as $r_\sigma = 2\overline{V}_{MolH_2O}\,\sigma_{surface}/RT$, where R is the universal GAS constant.

Kelvin's circulation theorem

[fluid dynamics, thermodynamics] Fluid DYNAMICS model for a flow that has negligible viscous strain and the medium is incompressible. This may apply for boundary layers that are extremely small with respect to the FLOW phenomena, such as the AERODYNAMICS of wings of an airplane or propellers of a helicopter. Since there are no viscous forces there is no vorticity. In this model the use of a parameter called "CIRCULATION" indicates the. The circulation is the average flow velocity (i.e., wind velocity) on a path looping around the perturbation (i.e., WING), and can be represented as the closed loop integral of the vorticity within the enclosed path. Where the vorticity is the degree of "rotation" experienced in flow VELOCITY ($\vec{v}$) as a function of location ($\vec{r}$) and time (t), which is the "curl" of the velocity at a given place. This yields for the circulation $\oint_c \vec{\varpi}(\vec{r},t)d\vec{s} = \oint_c \nabla \times \vec{v}(\vec{r},t)d\vec{s}$. The circulation at the boundary of the phenomena will be finite, the outer (i.e., horizontal) edges of the wings create a VORTEX that is at the edge of the WAKE.

Kelvin's theorem of minimum energy

[fluid dynamics] An inviscid, irrotational fluid FLOW of an incompressible medium has ENERGY enclosed in an arbitrary enclosure surface (S) that describes the kinetic energy (KE_{rot}) of the VELOCITY POTENTIAL of the ideal FLUID in rotational motion. The MINIMUM ENERGY statement relates to the integral over a volume with irrotational motion compared to any other region of fluid motion with the same kinematic boundary conditions. This is expressed by integration of the all-around velocity potential ($\Phi_{velocity}$), the rotational velocity $\overrightarrow{u_{flow}}$ defined as $KE_{rot} = \iint_{S_0} \Phi_{velocity}\left(\widetilde{\overrightarrow{u_{flow}}} \cdot \vec{n}\right)d\vec{S} \geq 0$, where $\widetilde{\overrightarrow{u_{flow}}} = \overrightarrow{u_{flow}} - \langle \overrightarrow{u_{flow}} \rangle$ is the vortical component of MOTION, with the irrotational velocity field: $\langle \overrightarrow{u_{flow}} \rangle = \nabla\Phi_{velocity}$, $\overrightarrow{u_{flow}}$ the velocity field, and $\vec{n}$ an outward normal vector to the surface $\vec{S}$. Kelvin's theorem is applied to calculate the VORTEX SHEDDING $d\Gamma/dt = 0 = [\partial\Gamma(t)/\partial t] + (\partial\Gamma_\omega/\partial t)$, where "omega" is the rotation "perpendicular" to the plane of the page (see Figure K.14).

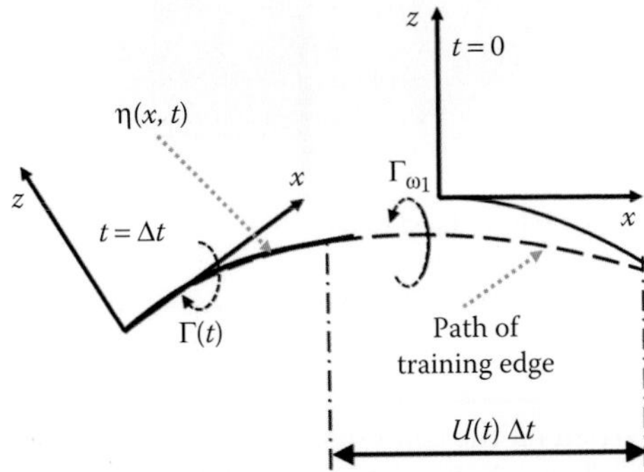

Figure K.14 Illustration of the principle of Kelvin's theorem applied to vortex shedding.

Kelvin–Helmholtz instability

[astrophysics/astronomy, computational, energy, fluid dynamics] During the FLOW of incompressible inviscid fluids with respect to each other, an external perturbation at the interface of the VORTEX sheet may create an oscillatory effect and the layers roll over, creating a MIXING layer. The shear layer between the two flow creates vorticities. The two fluids are immiscible. The layers may be AIR masses sliding over each other with respective moisture content and different temperatures and hence different densities. The shear velocity will need to be high enough to support this effect. In solar FLUID DYNAMICS, as part of thermonuclear instabilities within a solar flame, the flare propagation becomes instable, *see* **LANDAU–DARRIEUS INSTABILITY** (see Figure K.15).

(a) (b)

(c)

Figure K.15 (a, b) Examples of Kelvin–Helmholtz instability waves. (c) Examples of Kelvin–Helmholtz instability waves. (Courtesy of Alison Bee.)

Kelvin–Helmholtz relation

[astrophysics/astronomy, computational, energy, fluid dynamics] The equilibrium between a LIQUID drop at specific TEMPERATURE (T) and the surrounding vapor with VAPOR PRESSURE (P_{vapor}) is linked to the SATURATION PRESSURE (P_{sat}) as $P_{vapor} = P_{sat}(T)\exp\left[2\left(F_s V_f'/r\mathrm{RT}\right)\right]$, where V_f' the partial volume per unit mass of the FLUID constituent, r the bubble radius, $\mathrm{R} = 8.3144621(75)\,\mathrm{J/Kmol}$ the GAS constant, and F_s the SURFACE TENSION.

Kelvin–Planck statement

[thermodynamics] *See also* **SECOND LAW OF THERMODYNAMICS.** It is not possible to convert heat into work with 100% efficacy, without experiencing losses; that is, heating of devices and ambient environment.

Kepler, Johannes (1571–1630)

[geophysics, mechanics] (syn.) {use: planetary objects orbits, planet, comet} German astronomer and mathematician. Kepler observed that PLANETARY MOTION is not necessarily circular and the velocity of the orbiting planets around the Sun is not uniform. His observations were captured by three laws (see Figure K.16.

Figure K.16 Johannes Kepler (1571–1630).

K

Kepler's first law

[geophysics, mechanics] (syn.) {use: planetary objects orbits, planet, comet} In our SOLAR SYSTEM the planets revolve around the Sun in an elliptical orbit with the Sun in one of the focal points (C_1; C_2). EARTH rotates around the Sun in 365.26 days, whereas HALLEY'S COMET has a period (T) of 75.32 years.

Kepler's laws

[astronomy/astrophysics, computational, general] Laws describing the MOTION of planets around the Sun known in the seventeenth century: Mercury, VENUS, EARTH, MARS, JUPITER, and SATURN. The laws describe the gravitationally defined PLANETARY MOTION based on the documented observations made by his mentor TYCHO BRAHE (1546–1601). The discovery of the planets Uranus, Neptune, and Pluto provided additional verification and validation. The laws are Kepler's first, second, and third law.

Kepler's second law (Kepler's law of planetary motion)

[geophysics, mechanics] (syn.) {use: planetary objects orbits, planet, comet} An object revolving around a PLANET or STAR marks out a path that delineates equal areas over equal time intervals, whether the orbit is a circle or an ellipse, the path trajectory is confined by the gravitational pull. In fact the orbit of the EARTH around the Sun is close to circular, but the elliptic orbit makes a significant difference. This difference is even more pronounced for HALLEY'S COMET.

Kepler's third law

[geophysics, mechanics] (syn.) {use: planetary objects orbits, planet, comet} As part of the orbital MOTION of the various planets in our SOLAR SYSTEM the trajectories of all the planets can be linked as follows: the ratio of the average DISTANCE to the Sun of each planet ($\bar{r}$) to the third power over the square of the period of rotation (T) is constant; $\bar{r}^3/T^2 = \text{Constant}$, the "Keplerian constant." The PLANET closest to the Sun, Mercury revolves in 85.5 days or 0.24 EARTH years, whereas SATURN (the outermost planet) moves with a period of 29.5 years. Satellites generally move in a circular orbit with orbital speed v_0, confined by the CENTRIPETAL FORCE as defined by Newton's LAW OF UNIVERSAL GRAVITATION between two bodies with the SATELLITE mass m

and the planet mass M, respectively, yielding the centripetal force $F_C = G\left(mM/r^2\right)$, where the universal gravitational constant $G = 6.67259\,\mathrm{Nm}^2/\mathrm{kg}^2$, yielding $G\left(mM/r^2\right) = m\left(v_0{}^2/r\right)$, which provides one of the boundary conditions for a GEOSTATIONARY ORBIT as the velocity $v_0 = \sqrt{GM/r}$.

Kerma (K_c)

[biomedical, energy] (also "collision Kerma") Acronym for "kinetic ENERGY released in the medium," in RADIATION THERAPY this indicates the hypothetical potential for the biological effect caused by radiation delivered at locations $\vec{r}$ in direction $\vec{s}$ with respect to the surface of an absorbing volume. The Kerma dose (K_c) is a direct function of the fluence $\vec{L}\left(\vec{r},\vec{s}\right)$ of photons with energy E that can be transferred to kinetic energy of charged particles in the medium ($E_{\text{transfered}}$) that can have ionizing effects (e.g., electrons and protons), with respect to the energy delivered per unit mass (m): $D_c = \Delta E_{\text{transfered}}/m$. The Kerma is different from the absorbed in the fact that the Kerma describes the energy transferred between the RADIATION applied and the medium the radiation is migrating through, no absorption of radiation is assumed. Kerma is expressed in gray: $\left[Gy\right] = 1\,\mathrm{J/kg} = 100\,\mathrm{rad}$. Kerma is different from "radiation exposure."

Kerr effect

[energy, general, optics, thermodynamics] Change in the optical axis of a medium under the influence of an externally applied electric field and applied MAGNETIC FIELD, respectively. Also considered to be part of the BIREFRINGENCE phenomenon. The local INDEX OF REFRACTION (n) can be described in a Taylor series to depend on the local MAGNITUDE of the ELECTRIC FIELD (E) as a function of time expressed as $n\left(E,\vec{r},t\right) = n\left(\vec{r},t\right) + \left[dn\left(\vec{r},t\right)/dE\right]E\left(\vec{r},t\right) + (1/2)\left[d^2n\left(\vec{r},t\right)/dE^2\right]E\left(\vec{r},t\right) + \cdots$. Assuming that the higher order effects are negligible this becomes the POCKELS EFFECT. In case the medium is symmetric (i.e., $\left(E,\vec{r},t\right) = n\left(-E,\vec{r},t\right)$), the first term is zero and the birefringence is described as dominated by the second term $n\left(E,\vec{r},t\right) = n\left(\vec{r},t\right) + \left[d^2n\left(\vec{r},t\right)/dE^2\right]E\left(\vec{r},t\right)$. Under closer examination, the index of refraction will need to consider a complex number with a real and imaginary part that respond individually to the external electric field. The Kerr effect can reach time frames in the picosecond range (see Figure K.17).

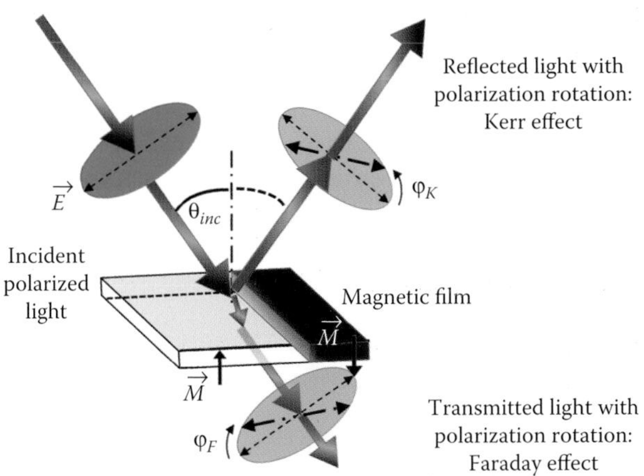

Figure K.17 Graphical representation of the Kerr effect. The Kerr effect is expressed in the reflected mode, whereas the transmitted light is subject to the Faraday effect with respect to the rotation of the electric filed under the influence of an external magnetic field.

Kerst, Donald William (1911–1993)

[atomic, nuclear] Physicist and engineer from the United States. Kerst constructed a PARTICLE ACCELERATOR used for the investigation of the atomic and nuclear structure, namely, the BETATRON. The betatron uses BETA PARTICLES (i.e., electrons) to investigate the nuclear composition and the involvement of SUBATOMIC PARTICLES (see Figure K.18).

Figure K.18 Donald William Kerst (1911–1993). (Courtesy of the personal collection from the late Donald W. Kerst.)

Ketoacidosis

[biomedical, chemical] Accumulation of ketones and organic acids in the BLOOD and urine as a result of insufficient METABOLIC ACTIVITY due to lack of the hormone insulin in the blood, which affects the chemical conversion of carbohydrates. The blood GLUCOSE level in this case is often more than twice the upper limit for a healthy person over an extended period of time, usually for weeks or months. Alternatively, excessive consumption of ALCOHOL over a long period of time may also lead to ketoacidosis. Ketoacidosis may result in a blood serum pH associated with the condition that in severe cases may drop below 7 (compared to a tightly controlled pH = 7.35 to 7.45 for a healthy adult) (see Figure K.19).

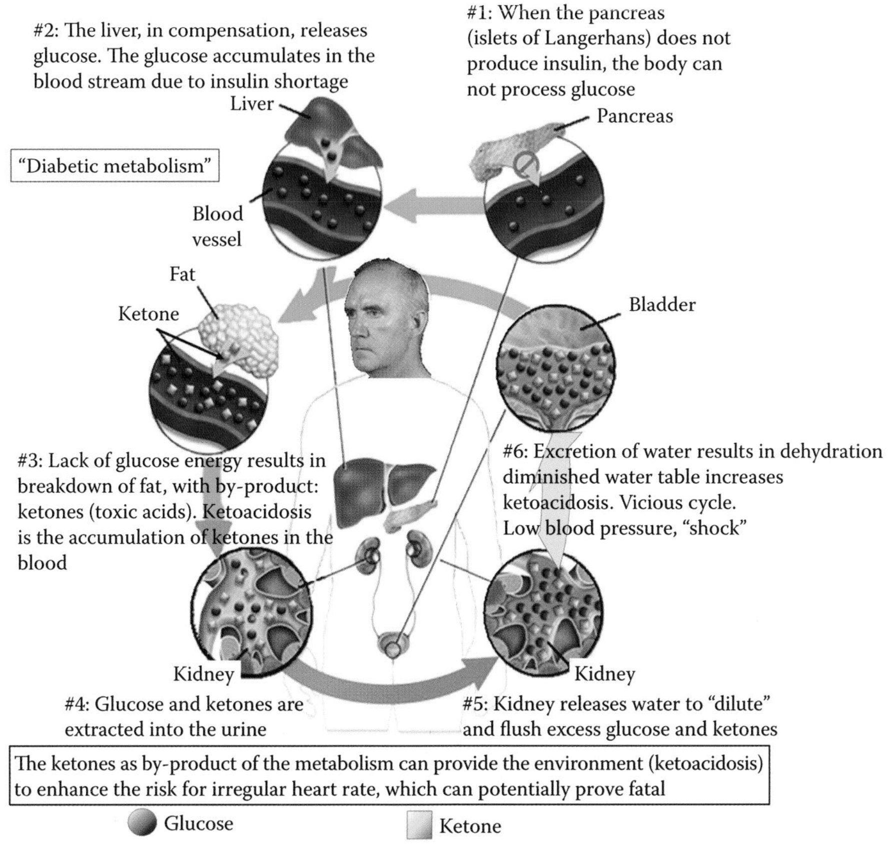

Figure K.19 Diagram explaining the process and biological implications involved in ketoacidosis.

Keulegan–Carpenter number (K_c)

[computational, fluid dynamics, mechanics, thermodynamics] Indication of fluid flow TURBULENCE. $Kc = 2\pi(a/D)$, where a is the turbulent AMPLITUDE of the FLOW behind the bluff object (i.e., cylinder) with diameter D. The value a is a flow characteristic indicating the FLUID particle motion in back-and-forth MOTION at the down flow end of the cylindrical object placed in the fluid flow. (*Note*: The position of the cylinder will be vertical for planar or surface WAVE interaction; e.g., tidal flow, thin cloud banks flowing over an island with an AIR column raised above.)

Kevlar®

[chemical, general, mechanics] Synthetic fiber, registered trademark of DuPont™, developed in 1965. Kevlar® is used in many medical device fabrics. It has high tensile strength per unit CROSS SECTION (greater than 3.620 MPa) and is also used in body armor as well as bicycle tires and brake linings. The woven fabric is stronger than METAL cable when submerged under water. The para-aramid holds its strength down to –196°C, and up to 260°C, with a reduction of 50% yield after exposure at or beyond this elevated temperature of 70 h or less (higher temperatures). Kevlar® is however subject to ULTRAVIOLET degradation. An aramid is a polyamide with a minimum of 85% of the amino bonds linked to aromatic rings (see Figure K.20).

Figure K.20 (a) Special Forces persons wearing Kevlar® protective clothing. (b) Kevlar® canoe.

Kidney

[biomedical, chemical, fluid dynamics, general] Biological organ used for LIQUID purification and filtration based on OSMOTIC PRESSURE gradients. The kidney also plays a major role in maintaining the BLOOD acidity/base balance (pH level) at a very strict level, between pH = 7.35 and 7.45. The removal of unwanted chemicals from the blood is excreted from the kidney with urine (see Figure K.21).

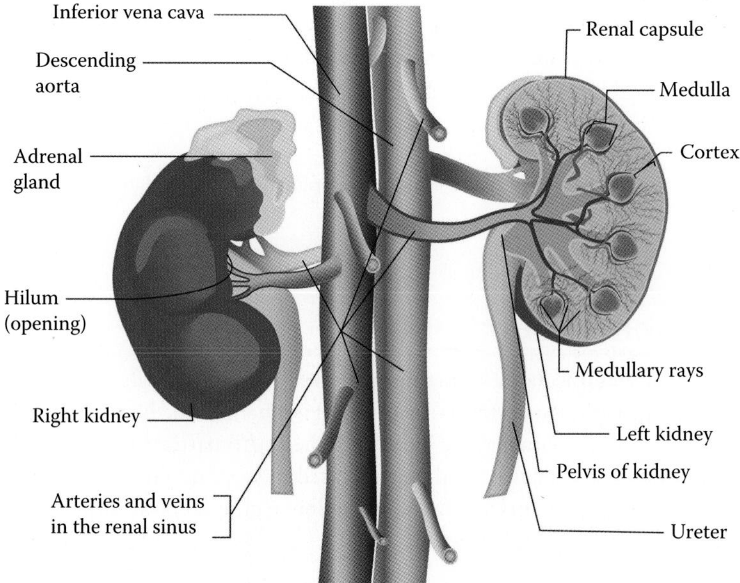

Figure K.21 Diagram of the kidney with several functions highlighted.

Kienböck, Robert (1871–1953)

[biomedical, nuclear] Physician from Austria/Germany. Inventor of a mechanism to implement dosimetry and exposure to X-RAY radiation using silver bromide paper (photographic paper). The paper becomes oxidized as a function of the exposure and after developing the paper turns a grade of gray, which can be measured optically for QUANTIFICATION of exposure. Kienböck also identified a skeletal bone disease in which the lunate bone, specifically in the wrist, breaks down (see Figure K.22).

Figure K.22 Robert Kienböck (1871–1953). (Courtesy Collection of the Medizinischen Universität Wien—Josephinum, Bildarchiv; Vienna, Austria.)

Kill, Fredrick (1921–)

[biomedical] Scientist from Norway who invented an advanced parallel-plate KIDNEY dialysis machine in 1960, which was used through the late 1990s (see Figure K.23).

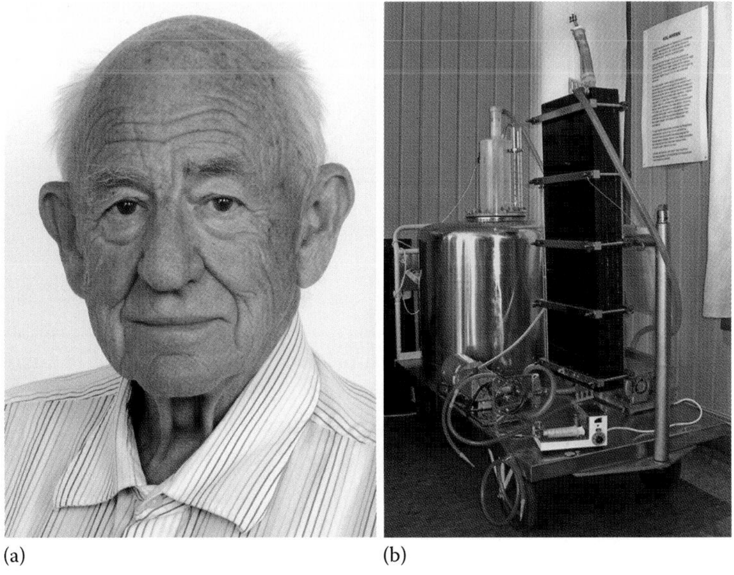

(a) (b)

Figure K.23 (a) Fredrick Kill (1921–) and (b) kidney dialysis machine designed by Fredrick Kill.

Kilocalorie (kcal)

[general] Thermodynamic quantity used to describe the ENERGY requirement to raise 1 kg of water by 1°C. The SI equivalent is 1 kcal = 1 Cal = 4184 J.

Kilogram (kg)

[general] System International (SI) unit for mass, note that the gram is not the SI unit and is defined in 1795 as the mass of 1 l of water at 4°C. The dimensional value for 1000 g. At this moment there is a movement to use Planck's constant as the scaling factor for calibration of mass. Historically, the basis is a block of cast IRON held at the Paris Le Système International d'Unités and weighs 1.000025 l of pure H_2O.

Kinematic coefficient of viscosity (μ_K)

[fluid dynamics] The coefficient that links the FRICTION force (f_K) observed during MOTION of a mass while sliding over a surface that expresses a normal force (N) toward the object expressed as $f_K = \mu_K N$. The normal force is a function of the contact area, whereas the weight of an object is irrespective of contact to any surface. The KINETIC FRICTION is generally less than or equal to the static friction, observed when attempting to bring an object to motion. Also found as kinetic coefficient of friction or COEFFICIENT OF KINETIC FRICTION (see Figure K.24).

Figure K.24 Illustration of the kinematic viscosity of honey sliding over a spoon.

Kinematic parameters

[general, mechanics] Definitions used in either liner approximation of MOTION or in angular motion for DISTANCE, velocity, and acceleration. Linear to angular coupling is as follows: for distance, $\ell = r\theta = r\cos\theta$, with length ℓ, radius of curvature r, and ANGLE of span of segment θ; for velocity, $v = r\omega$, with ω the ANGULAR VELOCITY; and for acceleration, $a = r\alpha$, with α the angular acceleration and the linear acceleration (a) will be in the tangential direction.

Kinematic viscosity

[biomedical, fluid dynamics, general] *See* **VISCOSITY, KINEMATIC.**

Kinematics

[general, mechanics, thermodynamics] Motion (i.e., [relative-] position and displacement) without considering the cause of relative displacement of the object or a point on an object (in contrast to DYNAMICS).

Specific topics in kinematics are velocity, acceleration, and trajectory of MOTION. Objects may be considered in relative motion with respect to each other, moving in curved motion (rotation) or in linear motion. The velocity (v) is the rate of change in location ($v = \partial x/\partial t$, note that this applies to all directions), and acceleration (a) is the rate of change in velocity ($a = \partial v/\partial t$, all with respect to direction) (see Figure K.25).

Figure K.25 Kinematics of hitting the bell on the post, "high striker." An attraction created at the end of the nineteenth century. At that time the news was highly influenced by Hendrik Jacobus Jut (1851–1878), a waiter from The Hague, who had committed a double murder in December 1872. The game in the Netherlands hence references the hitting of the head of "Jut" (Dutch: "kop van Jut"). The patented design dates to 1908 for the United States.

Kinetic diagram

[biomedical, mechanics] Diagram of vector representation of forces, MOTION, and masses of objects in a system, as well as the definition of the physical association between the objects. In the HUMAN BODY, skeletal bones move somewhat independent of each other but are tied together by ligaments and MUSCLE mass as well as SKIN. Fixed flexing locations will have all forces balanced within the compound body. All forces can be assumed to act in the center of mass of the segment under consideration (see Figure K.26).

Figure K.26 Representation of the kinetics during a rowing motion.

Kinetic energy (*KE*)

[general, mechanics] ENERGY associated with movement, in contrast to potential energy which is only converted into kinetic energy when the appropriate conditions apply: $KE = (1/2)mv^2$, m the mass of the object in MOTION with velocity v (*also see* ENERGY) (see Figure K.27). For a rolling body, the kinetic energy also comes from the MOMENT OF INERTIA expressed as $KE = (1/2)Mv_{CM}^{2} + (1/2)I_{MCM}\omega^2$, where the contributions of all the constituents (total mass: M) need to be accounted for in their respective influences and hence the unit of objects can be described by the center-of mass properties (subscript CM) of velocity and moment of inertia (I_M), and the object is rotating with ANGULAR VELOCITY ω (see Figure K.28).

Figure K.27 Kinetic energy on a roller coaster ride, back-and-forth conversion from kinetic to potential energy, in addition to mechanical assistance by machinery to replenish the kinetic energy based on electrical power resulting from the kinetic energy released by splitting atoms, chemical exothermic reactions, or the kinetic energy provided by wind flow.

Figure K.28 Kinetic energy of wind-powered water pumps used to drain the water from land below the water level in Kinderdijk, the Netherlands; converting wind flow energy into mechanical energy into water flow.

Kinetic energy, relativistic

[mechanics, thermodynamics] Kinetic ENERGY in relativistic terms uses the fact that velocity (v) is defined differently when particles with mass m traveling at speed close to the speed of light (c). Applying Lorentz transforms to the velocity and this rolls over into the energy as $KE_{rel} = \left\{ mc^2 / \sqrt{[1-(v^2/c^2)]} \right\} - mc^2$. Note that the relativistic kinetic energy approaches infinity as the velocity of the object approaches the speed of light. The inherent requirement now also becomes that the work that needs to be performed to increase the velocity to increase to the speed of light also becomes infinitesimally large. Note that the classical kinetic energy is $KE = (1/2)mv^2$ (see Figure K.29).

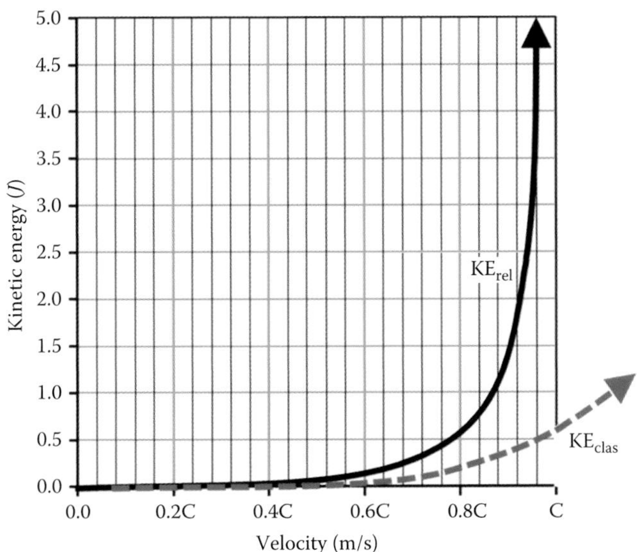

Figure K.29 Graphical representation of the relativistic approach to kinetic energy.

Kinetic energy of a bulk-flow state

[mechanics, thermodynamics] For a FLOW of mixed medium with total mass m_{TOT}, in equilibrium with or without rotation the average kinetic ENERGY can be described using the velocity of the center of mass of the total liquid (φ_{cm}), expressed as $KE = m_{TOT}\varphi_{cm}{}^2/2$.

Kinetic energy of a solid moving through a liquid

[fluid dynamics] A single solid body with mass m and MOMENT OF INERTIA I, in MOTION in a LIQUID will contain both translational and rotational ENERGY and the equation becomes $KE_{rot+trans} = (1/2)[\Phi]\cdot(\vec{v}+\vec{\omega})^2$, where $\vec{v} = (v_1, v_2, v_3)$ is the translational velocity vector and $\vec{\omega} = (\omega_I, \omega_{II}, \omega_{III})$ the rotational angular velocity vector, $\vec{r}$ the location of the portion in motion, and $[\Phi]$ the VELOCITY POTENTIAL matrix coefficients, which accounts for the components of translational energy: $KE_{trans} = (1/2)mv^2$, and rotational energy: $KE_{rot} = (1/2)I\omega^2$, with the moment of inertia of the object I. The velocity potential matrix coefficients follow from the Kirchhoff theorem. The velocity potential (ϕ) is defined for the translation motion, with $(dv_1/dx_1) = [(\partial\phi/\partial x_2)+(\partial\phi/\partial x_3)] + i[(\partial\psi/\partial x_2)+(\partial\psi/\partial x_3)]$, and so on. For instance, the coefficient $\phi'_{11} = -\rho\iint \phi_1(\partial\phi_1/\partial n)dS$, where ρ the density of the liquid, ϕ_1 is the first ELEMENT in the velocity potential, n the normal to a small but finite portion of the surface (S) of the solid. Whereas the coefficients for the angular velocity components (rotational aspects) follow from $\phi'_{jj} = -\rho\iint \Omega_j(\partial\psi_j/\partial n)dS$, where ψ is the angular velocity potential for rotational or angular motion, with ω_1 correlated to $\partial\psi/\partial\alpha$, split out in a multidimensional complex number derivative composite formulation resembling the translational velocity potential. The factor $\rho\phi$ describes the impulse pressure on the surface of the solid, while $r\rho\psi$ can be regarded as an indication of the shear stress on the surface. The choice of an appropriate reference frame is essential in limiting the complexity for solving this equation.

Kinetic energy of recoil

[nuclear] In atomic scattering the introduction of high-energy photons can result in (partial-) absorption resulting in ENERGY conversion of electron "collision," the COMPTON EFFECT. The Compton effect transfers some of its momentum (p) to the BALLISTIC MOTION of the electron: $p = h\nu/c$, where $h = 6.62606957 \times 10^{-34}\ \mathrm{m^2kg/s}$ is Planck's constant, ν the electromagnetic frequency, and c the speed of light. The kinetic energy of the electron with REST MASS m_0 resulting from PHOTON recoil is $KE_e = mc^2 - m_0c^2 = m_0c^2\{[1/\sqrt{1-(v^2/c^2)}]-1\}$, where v is the recoil velocity of the electron (see Figure K.30).

Figure K.30 The recoil of a ball thrown at the target of a dunk tank will trip a level that makes the person seated fall into the water basin.

Kinetic friction

[general] Force experienced by an object in MOTION while in contact with another system. The FRICTION force is opposite to the direction of motion, or opposite the applied external force that initiates the motion. Kinetic friction is frequently greater than static friction, meaning that it is harder to bring an object into motion than maintaining motion (see Figure K.31).

(a) (b)

Figure K.31 (a) Kinetic friction exerted by disk brakes to achieve a reduction in velocity of a moving vehicle. (b) A similar principle applies to the clutch of a gear transmission to the drive axle, only to match the angular velocity of two axles.

Kinetic stability

[fluid dynamics] In a tidal WAVE, or wave-like MOTION of AIR mass (e.g., KELVIN–HELMHOLTZ INSTABILITY), the conditions for stability are defined by the relationship between the kinetic ENERGY in the relative motion of the rolling wave ($KE_{rol\_rel} = (1/2)\sum m(\dot{x}^2 + \dot{y}^2 + \dot{z}^2)$, where $\dot{x} = \partial x/\partial t$), the potential energy of the crest and trough of the wave phenomenon (U_{wave}) and the rotational kinetic energy ($KE_{rot} = (1/2)\omega^2\sum m(x^2 + y^2)$ without relative motion within the system, assuming forward motion in the z-direction and the wave performs a circular motion with ANGULAR VELOCITY ω, with volume of average mass m). The stability is defined by $KE_{rol\_rel} + (U_{wave} - KE_{rot}) = \text{Constant}$. In case of the absence of external forces the following conditions also applies: $\Delta\int_{t_0}^{t_1}(KE_{Trot} - U)\,dt = 0$, where $KE_{Trot} = KE_{rol\_rel} + KE_{rot} + \omega I'$, with $I' = \sum m(x\dot{y} - y\dot{x})$. In this scenario, the relative coordinates (x, y, z) can be replaced for small disturbances by the displacements (d_i) in linear transformation for a three-dimensional format, resulting in a vector formulation: $KE_{rol\_rel} = (1/2)(c_1\dot{d}_1^2 + c_2\dot{d}_1^2 + \cdots + c_n\dot{d}_n^2)$ and $(U_{wave} - KE_{rot}) = (1/2)(e_1d_1^2 + e_2d_2^2 + \cdots + e_nd_n^2)$, where the coefficients c_i are the principal coefficients of INERTIA and e_i are the principal coefficients of stability.

Kinetic theory

[general] Concept of MOLECULAR MOTION transferring ENERGY as first introduced by PLATO (427–347 BC) and reaffirmed by GALILEO GALILEI (1564–1642) and described theoretically by SIR FRANCIS BACON (1561–1626). The principles of kinetic theory were further refined by JAMES CLERK MAXWELL (1831–1879) around 1860 and later by LUDWIG EDUARD BOLTZMANN (1844–1906). Also found as "kinetic theory of gases." The kinetic theory provides the basis for the definition of temperature (T) as the average kinetic energy: $T = (2/3k_b)\sum m_i v_i^2$, where m_i is the respective mass of the constituents, v_i the velocity of the individual mass units, and $k_b = 1.3806488 \times 10^{-23}\ \text{m}^2\text{kg/s}^2\text{K}$ Boltzmann coefficient. Using kinetic theory the PRESSURE (P) of a GAS can be expressed in terms on KINETIC ENERGY (KE) as $P = (2/3)(NKE/V)$, where N is the number of gas particles and V the gas volume.

Kinetic theory versus caloric theory

[general] CALORIC THEORY, introduced in the 1760s defined THERMAL ENERGY as a fluid; CALORIC. Caloric was supposedly indestructible and could not be created. This medium of energy was a radical change from concepts of internal MOTION hypothesized as far back as PLATO (427–347 BC). The work of BENJAMIN THOMPSON (COUNT RUMFORD) (1753–1814) repealed the caloric concept in 1798 to the base concepts of Plato and further theoretical evolution of the KINETIC THEORY, reiterating that work performed can generate heat.

Kinetics, chemical

[chemical, nuclear] The chemical kinetics consider the rate processes of chemical reactions and the ENERGY exchange between the initial and final components. For a chemical reaction with components with respective concentrations $[A]$, $[B]$, and end products $[C]$, $[D]$, and respective fractional quantities in the reactions *a*, *b*, *c*, *d*, the reaction can be described as $a[A] + b[B] \rightleftharpoons c[C] + d[D]$. This yields a chemical reaction rate $\nu_{chem} = -(1/a)(d[A]/dt) = -(1/b)(d[B]/dt) = -(1/c)(d[C]/dt) = \cdots$. This chemical reaction rate can also be written with respect to the reaction rate constant (k_{chem}), which also relies on the presence of chemical species ($[K]$) that are not directly involved in the chemical reaction, but that do influence the energy state (can be a catalyst), or more generally provides a charge exchange mechanism: $\nu_{chem} = k_{chem}[A]^{\alpha}[B]^{\beta}[C]^{\gamma}[D]^{\delta}[K]^{K}$, the reaction factors α, β, γ, δ, and K are real numbers. The reaction is generally a function of temperature (T) and well as the respective concentrations and their ratio. The chemical rate constant is linked to the reaction activation energy (E_{chem}) as $k_{chem} = A\exp\left(-E_{chem}/RT\right)$, where $R = 8.3144621(75)\,J/Kmol$ is the universal GAS constant, and $A = (N/V)\left(m/2\pi k_b T\right)^{3/2}$ an Arrhenius constant derived from the total number of particles: $N = \iint f d^3x d^3v$, the Maxwell distribution of particles (also referred to as the MAXWELL–BOLTZMANN DISTRIBUTION), integrated over space: $d^3x = dxdydz$ as a function of location and as a function of velocity $d^3v = dv_x dv_y dv_z$, and the BOLTZMANN COEFFICIENT $k_b = 1.3806488 \times 10^{-23}\,m^2kg/s^2K$.

Kinetics, nuclear

[nuclear] Generally, the ENERGY content of nucleotides and electrons needs to be handled in relativistic terms or approaches this. The equivalence of mass and energy forms the foundation of all nuclear energy projects. The mass–energy concept can be converted into heat and can be used to generate steam to drive a TURBINE that generates ELECTRICITY. The kinetic energy of nucleotides and potentially electron as well, each with respective REST MASS m_0 is $KE_{nuclear} = mc^2 - m_0c^2 = mc^2\left\{\left[1/\sqrt{1-(v^2/c^2)}\right]-1\right\}$, where v is the velocity of the PARTICLE, c the speed of light, and $E = mc^2$ is the rest mass energy.

Kinetostatics

K

[fluid dynamics] Fluid-dynamic system in cyclic motion. Since the time average translates to a quasistatic event this term was introduced to solve the equilibrium conditions of flow. The ENERGY is in this case represented by a static component (KE_{stat}) and a dynamic component (KE_{dyn}), which can be differentiated with respect to locations in system (χ_i) to obey $\left(\partial KE_{stat}/\partial\chi_i\right)+\left(\partial KE_{dyn,0}/\partial\chi_i\right) = 0$. Under these conditions, the forces ($F_{Q,i}$) influencing the FLOW aspects that neutralize the pressure of the solids on the liquids to neutralize the cyclic influences expressed as the components of the extraneous forces: $F_{Q,i} = \partial KE_{stat}/\partial\chi_i$; note that the flowing LIQUID expresses forces in the form $F_{Q,i}' = \partial KE_{dyn}/\partial\chi_i$, due to the equilibrium condition. The solids can be walls and blades or particles (see Figure K.32).

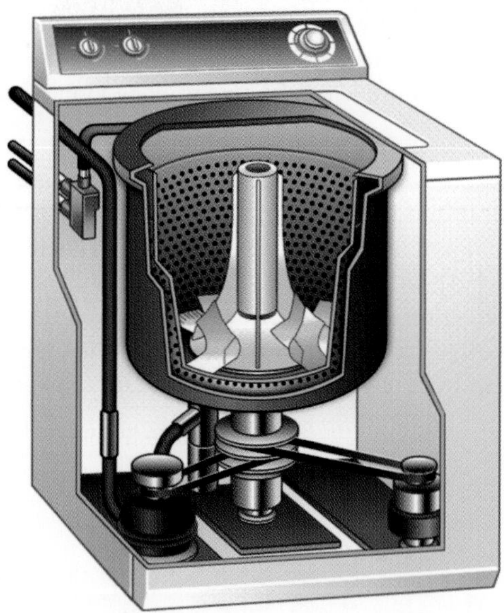

Figure K.32 Kinetostatics in a rotating central agitating top loader washing machine.

Kink

[computational, quantum, thermodynamics] Mathematical artifice, specifically used in field theory. The "kink" can define the POTENTIAL WELL pertaining to a free electron in a doped CONDUCTOR, specifically with respect to the theoretical formulation of the KONDO EFFECT and the electrical conductivity "around" an atomic LATTICE impurity.

Kirchhoff, Gustav Robert (1824–1887)

[electromagnetism, general, optics] Physicist from Germany. Kirchhoff postulated and verified several rules for electrical circuits; the Kirchhoff rules: "loop" and "node" rules. Additional work of Kirchhoff provided the radiation law. During a collaborative effort with ROBERT WILHELM EBERHARD BUNSEN (1811–1899) they performed optical experiments, identifying spectral profiles of molecules in the ATMOSPHERE. This work was instrumental in explaining the theoretical and experimental work by JOSEPH VON FRAUNHOFER (1787–1826) on the "FRAUNHOFER LINES" (see Figure K.33).

Figure K.33 Gustav Robert Kirchhoff (1824–1887).

Kirchhoff radiation integral

[acoustics, fluid dynamics] In the detection scheme for acoustic and in general pressure WAVE signals, the velocity potential function (ϕ) as a function of location can be found by integration of the direct beam using the Fourier double integral theorem. The FLUX of ACOUSTIC WAVES is found for irrotational MOTION as $\Phi = -\iint(\partial\phi/\partial n)dS = -\iint f(t)dS$, where n is the normal vector to the surface (S) of integration. The simple HARMONIC OSCILLATION is solved using GREEN'S THEOREM, providing the VELOCITY POTENTIAL at any point (P). The Kirchhoff integral providing the "FLOW" in any point as a function of time (t), at location $\vec{r} = (x, y, z)$ with respect to the reference frame with P as the origin, is given as $\phi_P(t) = -(1/4\pi)\iint f\left(t-(r/v_{\text{sound}})\right)/r\,dS + (1/4\pi)\iint(\partial/\partial n)\left[\phi\left(t-(r/v_{\text{sound}})\right)/r\right]dS$, where v_{sound} is the local speed of SOUND. Also referred to as Kirchhoff's integral of the general equation of sound.

Kirchhoff's laws

[biomedical, electromagnetism, solid-state] There are three laws or rules postulated by Kirchhoff: LOOP RULE; node rule, and the radiation law. KIRCHHOFF'S LOOP RULE defines the CONSERVATION OF ENERGY by calculating the sum of all the electrical potentials in an electrical circuit for any loop and this should add up to zero. KIRCHHOFF'S NODE RULE defines the CONSERVATION OF CHARGE for any node in an electrical circuit requiring the sum of the currents to equal zero, hence no charge accumulation. A node, or junction, is a connection of two or more wires. The KIRCHHOFF'S RADIATION LAW describes the equilibrium between absorbed RADIATION and black-body radiation from the walls of a system. The Kirchhoff laws can be used to reduce the complexity of a system by step-wise replacing inner loops by single component circuit loops, hence gradually reducing the total number of loops in a circuit (e.g., replacing parallel paths with a single equivalent path). Frequently the use of the Kirchhoff rules is combined with OHM'S LAW. The Kirchhoff laws can be applied to fluid-dynamic principles using the equivalence of pressure with voltage and FLOW with current.

Kirchhoff's loop rule

[electromagnetism, general] In an electrical circuit the sum of all the electrical potentials in any loop adds up to zero. A loop constitutes a continuous electrical path, including electronic components such as capacitors, resistors, and inductors (*also* **KIRCHHOFF'S VOLTAGE LAW**) (see Figure K.34).

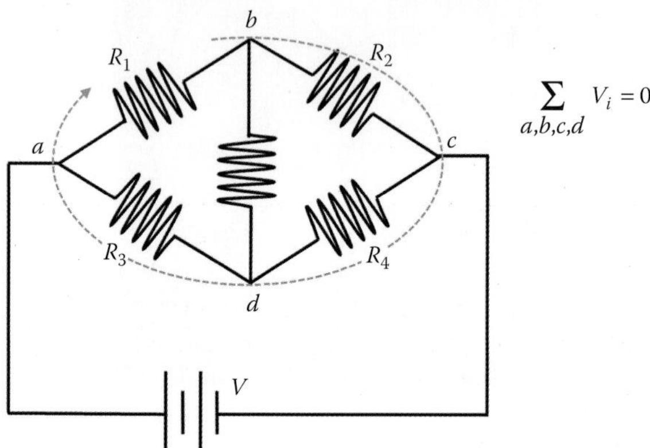

Figure K.34 Diagram of Kirchhoff loop rule.

Kirchhoff's node rule

[electromagnetism, general] In an electrical circuit at any node the sum of the currents equals zero, that is, no charge accumulation. A node, or junction, is a connection of two or more wires (*also* **Kirchhoff's current law**) (see Figure K.35).

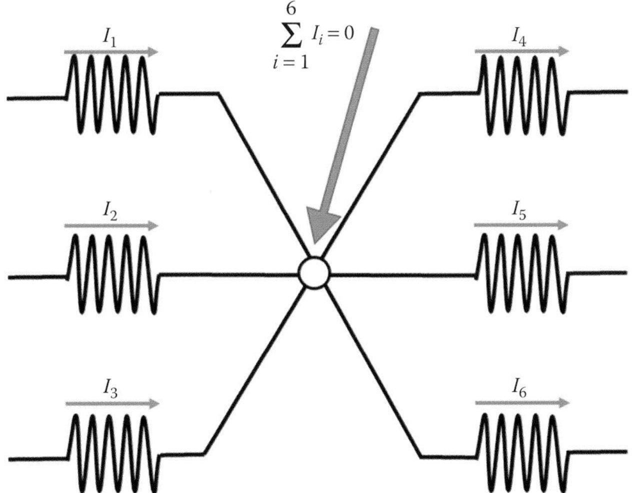

Figure K.35 Diagram of Kirchhoff node rule.

Kirchhoff's radiation law

[general, optics] The total amount of ENERGY absorbed by the walls of a system in THERMAL EQUILIBRIUM will emit an equal amount of RADIATION on thermal emission. The absorbed photon energy will be a fraction of the total thermal (i.e., infrared and visible) radiation energy MAGNITUDE with a wavelength-dependent distribution function: I_λ. The PHOTON energy absorbed within a certain bandwidth ($\Delta\lambda$, the radiation band) will experience a particular absorption coefficient: α_λ. The energy emission (ε_λ) may be in a respectively different wavelength region (i.e., lower or equal energy band), expressed as $\varepsilon_\lambda/\alpha_\lambda = I_\lambda$ (*also see* **black-body radiation**) (see Figure K.36).

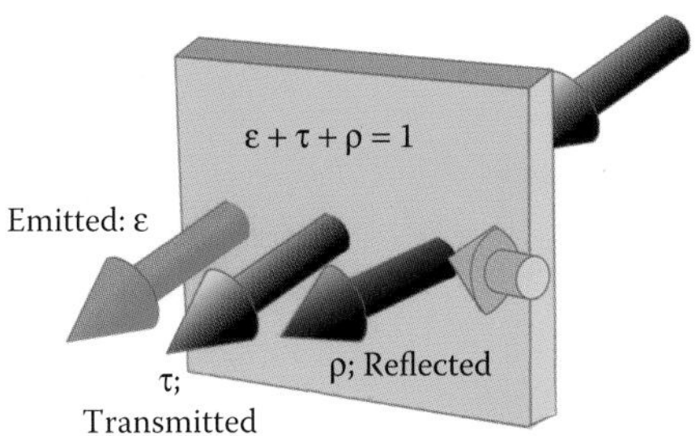

Figure K.36 Kirchhoff's radiation law.

Kirkwood gap

[astrophysics/astronomy, computational] Gaps or dips in the semimajor axis distribution of main-belt ASTEROIDS within the asteroid belt (i.e., the rings of JUPITER, a set of three concentric dense PARTICLE and dust torus belts) as a result of gravitational interactions with the PLANET Jupiter, equivalently the gaps can be localized by orbital period. The gaps were recorded and explained by Daniel Kirkwood (1814–1895) in 1886 (see Figure K.37).

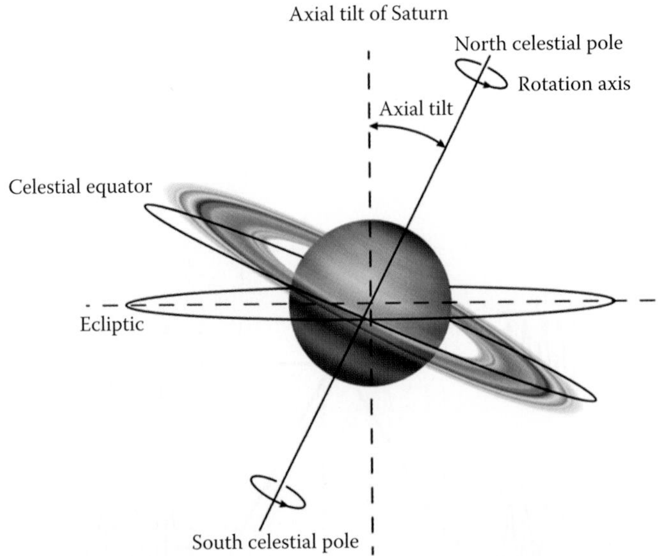

Figure K.37 Kirkwood gap for Saturn's rings.

Kissing number (*K(d)*)

[computational, geometry] In space defined by d-dimensions, the maximum number of individual unit spheres of equal size that can touch a given sphere (centered) with same dimensions. In two dimensions ($d = 2$); $K(2) = 6$ and in three dimensions $K(3) = 12$ (see Figure K.38).

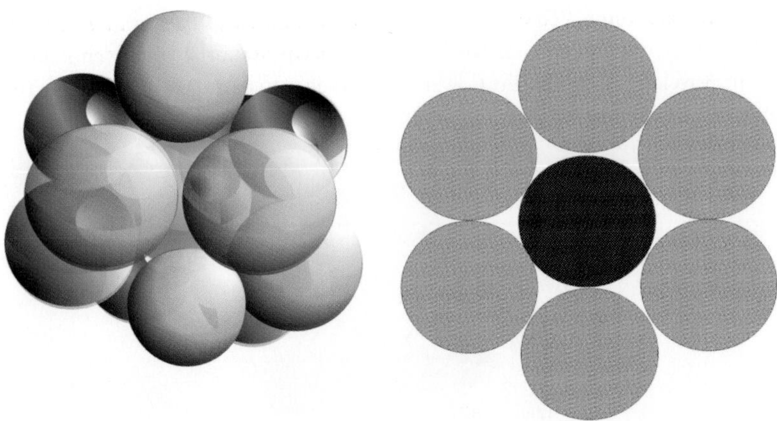

Figure K.38 Graphical representation of the Kissing number phenomenon.

Kittel, Charles (1916–)

[computational, nuclear, quantum, solid-state] Physicist from the United States. Kittel is well known for his contributions to SOLID-STATE and theoretical PHYSICS. Author of several established and recognized reference books (see Figure K.39).

Figure K.39 Charles Kittel (1916–).

Kleist, Ewald Jurgens von (1700–1748)

See **VON KLEIST, EWALD JURGENS (1700–1748)**.

Kline bursting phenomenon

[fluid dynamics] Periodicity in turbulent events: "bursts" as discovered by Stephen Jay Kline (1922–) in 1967, using hydrogen BUBBLES (i.e., "trace technique") in turbulent BOUNDARY LAYER in AIR. The REYNOLDS

NUMBER where this phenomenon has been observed range from Re = 1505 to Re = 2492. This phenomenon also defines the under-water periodicity of ridges found near the shore of a sandy beach (see Figure K.40).

(a) (b)

Figure K.40 (a) Kline bursting phenomenon as experienced at the beach under the tidal water flow, running parallel to the shoreline and (b) in the desert due to wind blowing over the surface, respectively.

Klystron

[electronics, mechanics, radiation, solid-state] Vacuum tube that has a CATHODE ray (i.e., electron beam) which is modulated in applied voltage, hence modulating the electron beam velocity profile. The electron beam thus creates density fluctuations and gradients. The klystron can act as a MICROWAVE amplifier or as an OSCILLATOR. During modulation the electron FLOW forms a WAVE pattern where fast electrons gain on slow electrons and overtake (DISPERSION), causing the electron density to fluctuate (see Figure K.41).

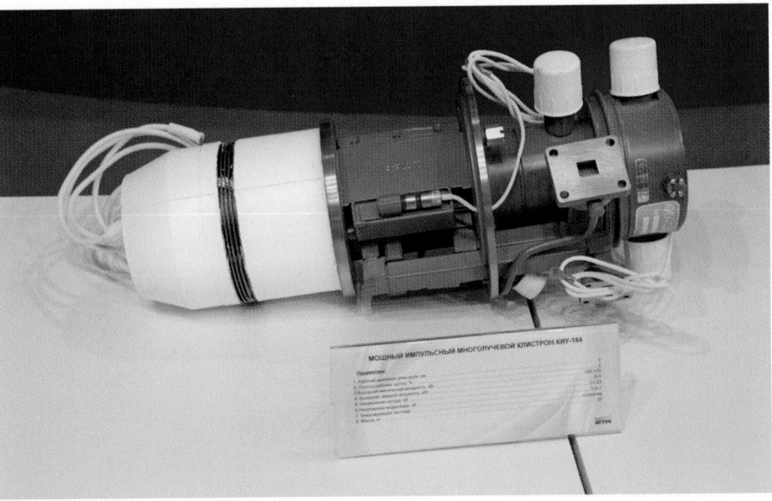

Figure K.41 Klystron.

Knee extensor

[biomedical] Muscle connected to the tibia to extend the lower part of the LEG, for instance, to kick a ball or ride a bicycle. The knee-extensor mechanism is formed by a complex integration of muscles, ligaments, and tendons. The knee extensor interaction is designed to stabilize the patellofemoral joint. The patellofemoral joint consists of the knee cap (patella) and the end of the thigh bone (femur) (see Figure K.42).

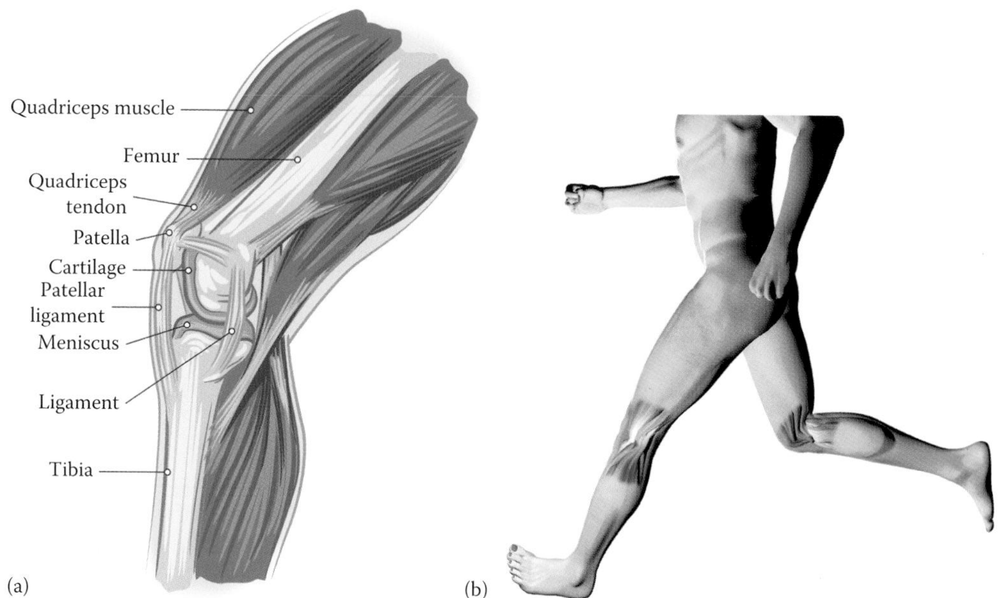

Figure K.42 (a) Knee extensor detail and (b) functional diagram of knee extensor during running.

Knife-edge detector

[acoustics, optics] A detector that is demarcated by an edge that is thin with respect to the phenomenological wavelength, in order to minimize edge effects resulting from diffraction.

Knight, Walter David (1919–2000)

[nuclear, solid-state] Physicist from the United States. Knight is best known for his discovery of frequency shifts of the nuclear magnetic resonance frequency spectrum (NMR) observed in (paramagnetic-) METAL exposure, named after him: Knight shift. The shifts appear to be linked to electric quadrupole resonance and MAGNETIC RESONANCE in metal LATTICE and crystalline structures (see Figure K.43).

Figure K.43 Walter David Knight (1919–2000). (Courtesy of the Physics Department, UC Berkeley, Berkeley, CA.)

Knipping, Paul (1883–1935)

[atomic, nuclear] Physicist from Germany. Experimental physicist whose work on excitation/IONIZATION ENERGY for hydrogen and helium formed the basis of the helium LYMAN SERIES. Additional work by Knipping involved the X-RAY diffraction analysis of the atomic structure of crystals, deriving the LATTICE matrix and general regularities (see Figure K.44).

Figure K.44 Paul Knipping (1883–1935).

Knudsen, Martin Hans Christian (1871–1949)

[computational, fluid dynamics, mechanics, thermodynamics] Danish physicist specialized in FLUID DYNAMICS and more specifically RHEOLOGY. Knudsen introduced the kinetic molecular theory, primarily in relation to low-pressure GAS phenomena. He was instrumental in the development of what is now known as the Knudsen CELL, one of the primary components in MOLECULAR BEAM EPITAXY systems (see Figure K.45).

Figure K.45 Martin Hans Christian Knudsen (1871–1949) in 1934, photographed by Friedrich Hund.

Knudsen number (Kn=λ/L)

[computational, fluid dynamics, mechanics, thermodynamics] Dimensionless number in GAS mechanics used to determine the computational regime for staging the mathematical approach. Ratio of the free path for MOLECULAR MOTION ($\lambda_{molecule}$) and a characteristic length of the system (L): $Kn = \lambda_{molecule}/L_{char} = kT/\sqrt{2}\pi\sigma^2 PL$, where k is the BOLTZMANN CONSTANT ($1.3806504(24) \times 10^{-23}$ J/m, T the temperature of the system, σ the PARTICLE hard shell diameter, and P the pressure. Primarily originating from the computational needs in FLUID DYNAMICS for RHEOLOGY and rarified gases, specifically related to momentum transport theory. For instance, a Knudsen number of $Kn \leq 0.1$ sets the boundary conditions where the FLUID can be treated as a continuous medium, with the MACROSCOPIC parameters such as pressure, temperature, volume, velocity, and density. More confined is the regime: $0 < Kn \leq 0.1$, describing slip flow. No slip flow is characterized by $Kn = 0$. Under the condition of $Kn \geq 1$, the theoretical approach for the fluid requires a MICROSCOPIC or molecular approach. Specifically under the conditions of $Kn \geq 1$, the trajectories of individual molecules need to be mechanically analyzed as macroscopic variables. Additionally, for $Kn \geq 10$ there are no statistically significant molecular interactions and the fluid is considered to be free molecular or collisionless. The segment $0.1 < Kn < 1$ is the transition slip flow regime, treating the fluid as a continuous medium allowing for discontinuities at the boundaries in characteristics such as temperature and velocity while the FLOW transitions from diffusive (CONTINUUM) to ballistic or free molecular flow. The Knudsen number expresses the ratio of the mean free path length of molecular MOTION (e.g., BROWNIAN MOTION) with respect to a characteristic length. The MEAN FREE PATH is inversely proportional to the fluid density. The characteristic length will be a direct function of the situation that needs to be computed, such as the dimensions and shape of an object submerged in a LIQUID or the diameter of a fluid flow in a PIPE. An archetypal example of a small characteristic length is the flow of an AEROSOL through small diameter APERTURES and small size tubing. The Knudsen conditions will require Monte Carlo simulations in order to solve the fluid dynamics issues under the complex boundary conditions. The Knudsen number indicates the validity of either line of sight ($Kn > 1$) or continuum ($Kn < 0.01$) for gas models.

Koch curve

[computational] Fractal line, defined by a mathematical function, derived by the Swedish mathematician HELGE VON KOCH (1870–1924) in 1904. One of the first fractal images described, also known as the Koch snowflake. The Koch curve can be constructed by an iteration process starting out from an equilateral triangle. The edges of the triangle are subdivided into three equal length segments, and a new triangle is drawn outward from the central segment, and the base segment is removed. This process is repeated for as many times as possible, starting each time with the outward facing two edges of the equilateral triangle. Over time, the shapes have been modified with artistic flare.

Köhler curve

[fluid dynamics, geophysics, thermodynamics] Plot of the KÖHLER EQUATION illustrating the point of supersaturation where the cloud droplet is in equilibrium with the environmental conditions over a range of droplet radii. The shape and value of the Köhler curve will depend on the constituents of the droplet as well as relative and absolute concentrations, respectively (see Figure K.46).

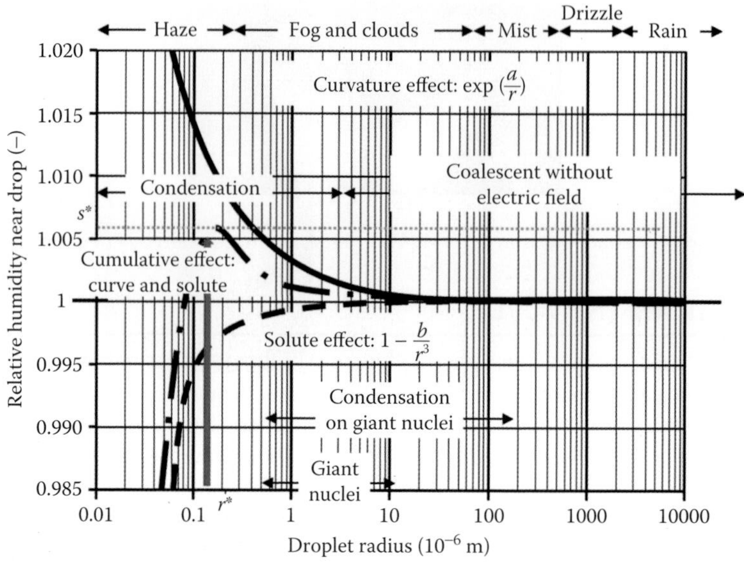

Figure K.46 Köhler curve.

Köhler equation

[fluid dynamics, geophysics, thermodynamics] Theoretical equilibrium saturation (S_{eq}) with respect to the KÖHLER THEORY, in which the formation of clouds from water vapor condensation is described as $S_{eq} = \exp\left[\left(2M_w\sigma_s/RT\rho_w r\right) - \left[n_{ion}\Phi_{osm}M_w\left(m_s/M_s\right)/\left((4/3)\pi\rho_{particle}r^3 - \left(m_s - m_{insol}\right)\right)\right]\right] = \mathrm{RH}/100\%$, with M_w the MOLECULAR WEIGHT of water, Φ_{osm} the osmotic coefficient, n_{ion} the number of ions giving the VAN'T HOFF FACTOR: $n_{ion} \times \Phi_{osm}$, σ_s the SURFACE TENSION of the LIQUID medium with SOLVENT, R the IDEAL GAS constant, T temperature, ρ_w density of the water, $\rho_{particle}$ the colloid particulate density in the haze (fog) with SATURATION s, m_s the mass of the SOLUTE, M_s the molecular weight of the solute, $m_s = \left(1-\varepsilon_{insol}\right)m_{insol}$ the soluble PARTICLE mass, ε_{insol} the insoluble mass fraction, $m_{total} = m_s + m_{insol}$ the total mass of the AEROSOL, m_{insol} the insoluble mass of the aerosol particulate, and r the aerosol particle radius (i.e., radius of droplet in cloud). In this equation the second term represents the molar ratio of solute to water at a given relative HUMIDITY.

Köhler theory

[fluid dynamics, geophysics, thermodynamics] Theory describing the formation of clouds from water vapor condensation. The Köhler theory combines the SATURATION PRESSURE of a medium described by RAOULT'S LAW with the changes in VAPOR PRESSURE resulting from a curved surface formulated in the KELVIN EFFECT.

Kohlhörster, Werner Heinrich Gustav (1887–1946)

[atomic, nuclear] Physicist from Germany. Scientist involved with the description of terrestrial ELECTRICITY, predominantly the IONIZATION in the ATMOSPHERE, not limited to the IONOSPHERE. He also studied the circadian variations in RADIATION reaching the earth's surface under the influence of the reshaping of the electronic composition and gradients in Earth's ATMOSPHERE. Contemporary and contributor in global efforts with PIERRE VICTOR AUGER (1899–1993). Kohlhörster used balloons to collect his data, traveling to heights of 9,300 m (see Figure K.47).

Figure K.47 Werner Heinrich Gustav Kohlhörster (1887–1946).

Kohlrausch, Friedrich Wilhelm Georg (1840–1910)

[general] Scientist from Germany. Kohlrausch researched the conductive properties of conductive media, more specifically electrolytes. Together with WILHELM EDUARD WEBER (1804–1891) they derived the DIELECTRIC permittivity ($\varepsilon_0 = 8.85419 \times 10^{-12}\, \mathrm{C^2/Nm^2}$) and permeability ($\mu_0 = 4\pi \times 10^{-7}\, \mathrm{H/m}$) in 1856, which was later combined with the speed of light measured in 1849 by ARMAND HIPPOLYTE LOUIS FIZEAU (1819–1896) and by JAMES CLERK MAXWELL (1831–1879) in 1865 as: $c = \left(\varepsilon_0 \mu_0\right)^{-1/2}$ (see Figure K.48).

Figure K.48 Friedrich Wilhelm Georg Kohlrausch (1840–1910). (Courtesy of Otto Patzig.)

Kohn anomaly

[atomic, solid-state, thermodynamics] Phonon spectrum associated with electron–phonon interaction in CHARGE DENSITY WAVES, introduced by Walter Kohn (1923–). Under the influence of dopings in, for instance, metals or SEMICONDUCTORS, the Raman spectrum is changing due to DISPERSION. The Kohn anomaly predominantly lowers the density wave (phonon) ENERGY with respect to charge density waves in LATTICE structures. Discontinuities in the FREQUENCY SPECTRUM derivative indicates lattice distortions (see Figures K.49 and K.50).

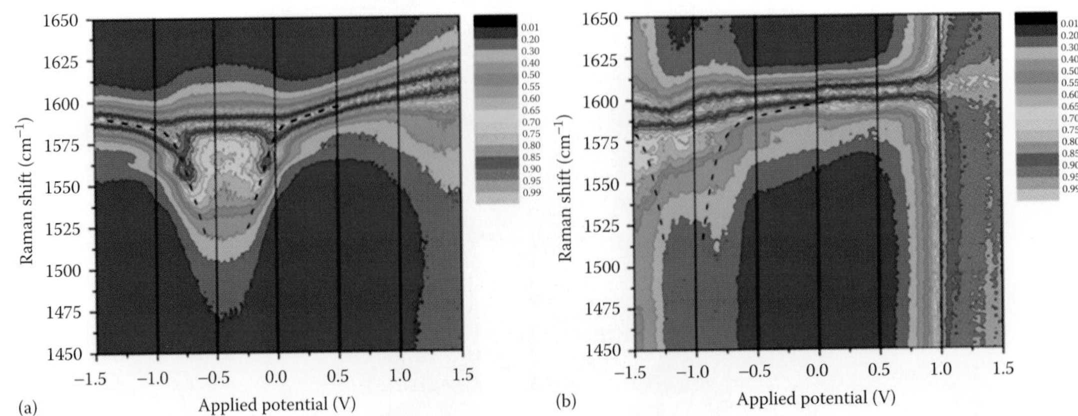

Figure K.49 Kohn anomaly shift illustrated by the Raman scattering map of the charge density waves (phonon wave) for charged virgin single-walled carbon nanotubes (a) and CuCl-doped single-walled carbon nanotubes (b). (Courtesy of 2011 Andrei Eliseev, Lada Yashina, Marianna Kharlamova, and Nikolay Kiselev. Originally published in [short citation] under CC BY-NC-SA 3.0 license. Available from: http://dx.doi.org/10.5772/19060.)

Figure K.50 Walter Kohn (1923–). (Courtesy of Markus Pössel.)

Kolff, Willem Johan (1911–2009)

[biomedical, chemistry, fluid dynamics] Physicist, engineer, and scientist from the Netherlands who perfected the dialysis machine used by GEORGE HAAS (1886–1971) in 1943; pioneer in hemodialysis. Another artificial organ invented by Kolff is the artificial heart. The design is different from the artificial kidney invented by Jack Rack Leonards (1919–1978) and Leonard T. Skeggs, Jr. (1918–2002) (see Figure K.51).

Figure K.51 Willem Johan Kolff (1911–2009).

Kolff kidney

[biomedical] Rotating wooden drum wrapped in a cellophane membrane, new material at the time of introduction in 1947. The constructed centrifuge had tubing coiled around the drum, which was submerged in a solution of electrolytes (carefully selected chemicals configuring a solution called "dialysate") that applied osmotic pressure to circulating arterial blood for diffusion of uremic toxins. The arterial blood was returned to a vein. Modern dialysis techniques apply a surgical shunt between the artery and the vein in the wrist for repeated access to apply "artificial kidney" mechanism (see Figure K.52).

Figure K.52 Kolff kidney.

Kondo, Jun (1930–)

[computational, electronics, quantum, solid-state] Theoretical physicist from Japan. Researcher in the anomalous behavior of electron clouds with respect to CONDUCTOR lattice impurities, specifically providing a detailed understanding of the thermal effects on conduction, leading to highly accurate THERMOCOUPLE design (see Figure K.53).

Figure K.53 Jun Kondo (1930–). (Courtesy of National Institute of AIST [Advanced Industrial Science and Technology], Tsukuba, Ibaraki, Japan.)

Kondo effect

[electronics, quantum, solid-state] Temperature effects pertaining to material properties such as thermal parameters, electrical properties, and MAGNETIC conditions in nonmagnetic metals that have imbedded minute magnetic impurities. This phenomenon was established by JUN KONDO (1930–) in 1964. Alloys of certain materials used as thermocouples are examples of this phenomenon, chromium and manganese DOPING of copper or silver provide a mechanism for measuring temperature based on RESISTANCE. The thermal response to resistance becomes more pronounced at specific temperature that is linked to the Fermi ENERGY of the alloy structure in question, the KONDO TEMPERATURE. Alloys can use the following nonmagnetic base metals such as gold, silver, copper, magnesium, aluminum, and zinc, respectively, with a doping of the following metals, but not limited to IRON, cobalt, manganese, vanadium, TITANIUM, chromium, or nickel. Each doping interface has a specific temperature range and sensitivity (i.e., RESOLUTION), such as the Chromel–Alumel juncture, one of the premier examples of thermocouples. In the 1930s, the Kondo effect was observed primarily at temperatures approaching ABSOLUTE ZERO, while in the 1960s the same principles appeared to apply for temperatures well exceeding the room temperature conditions for the right alloy structures. The Kondo effect exhibits a logarithmic decrease in conductivity with decreasing temperature. Other material properties also display anomalous behavior for these material structures when approaching the Kondo temperature, such as heat capacity (c_v; c_p) and MAGNETIC SUSCEPTIBILITY (χ_{mag}) (see Figure K.54).

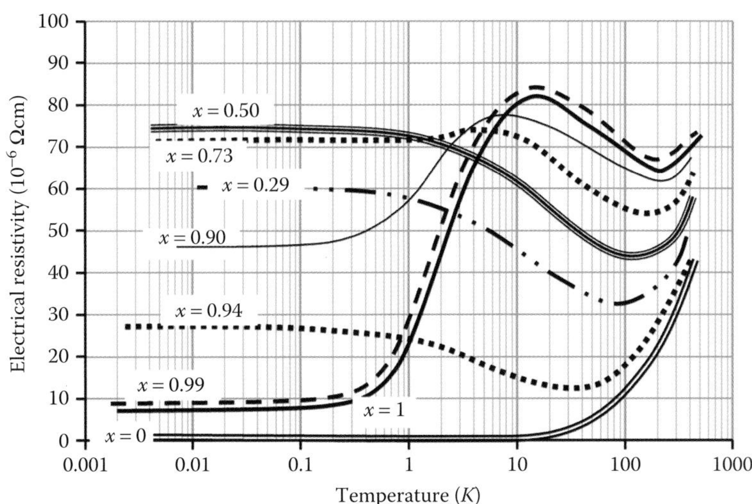

Figure K.54 Illustration of the resistivity as a function of temperature under the Kondo effect for the rare earth cerium (Ce) alloy compound $La_{1-x}Ce_xCu_6$, as a function of composition "x".

Kondo temperature

[electronics, quantum, solid-state] $T_K \approx \epsilon_F J_{exch}{}^{1/2} \exp\left(-1/nJ_{exch}\right)$, where ϵ_F is the Fermi ENERGY of the metal LATTICE structure (pertaining to the kinetic ENERGY of the free electrons), J_{exch} is the EXCHANGE INTERACTION between the DOPING ATOM and the free electrons in a CONDUCTOR metal base, and n the number of QUANTUM states.

Koopman's theorem

[chemistry, computational, solid-state] In a one-dimensional, one-electron atomic model the eigenvalues for the ENERGY for the free electron exchange energy are given as the one-electron IONIZATION ENERGY, making this a limited binary system. Koopmans' theorem in particular describes the removal of an electron from any of the available molecular electron orbits, hence forming a positive ION and can define the ionization energy for the process. In most other approximations the energy is defined by transition states, pertaining to the electron SHELL MODEL. Named after TJALLING CHARLES KOOPMANS (1910–1985) from the Netherlands, who introduced the concept in 1934 and received the Nobel Prize in Physics in 1975.

Köppen climate classification

[geophysics, general] Systematic classification process with categories of major climate and subcategories describing seasonal variations. This system was devised by a Prussian (German) climatologist WLADIMIR KÖPPEN (1846–1940) in 1884. The five main categories are (1) tropical, (2) dry, (3) mid-latitude with mild winters, (4) mid-latitude with severe winters, and (5) polar. The subcategories are divided in severity and period of rainfall (summer/fall/winter/spring), as well as general state of HUMIDITY next to coldest and warmest episodes, primarily pertaining to the polar climate. A third tier class in this system scale the peak and average temperature distribution (mean annual temperature; warm/cold summer, and combinations of warm/cold seasons) in the respective region outlined under the first and connected consecutive second class. One full-scale classification would, for instance, be mid-latitude with severe winters, severe dry winters, and hot summer season (see Figure K.55).

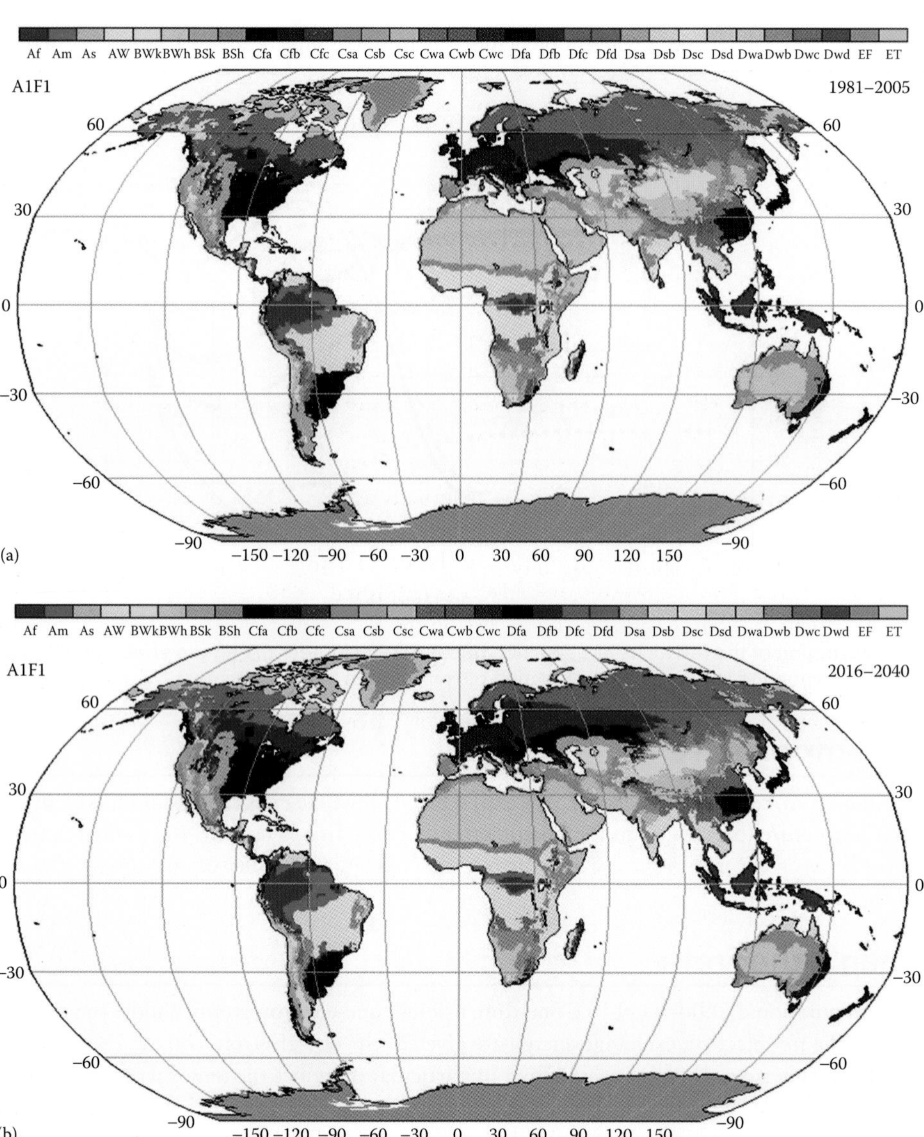

Figure K.55 Example of the Köppen Climate Classification for the years 1981 (a) and 2016 (b) in comparison, illustration of the "global warming." Group A: tropical/megathermal climates; Group B: dry (arid and semiarid) climates; Group C: temperate/mesothermal climates; Group D: continental/microthermal climates; and Group E: polar and alpine climates. The subclassification is rather convoluted and changes with the main category. Subclassifications; second letter: "W": desert or "w": dry winter, "S": steppe or "s": dry summer, and additionally "f" signifies abundant precipitation in all seasons. The third letter (sometimes the second letter) denoting temperature. Originally, the indicator "h" represented low-latitude climate (climate with an average annual temperature exceeding 18°C), and the indicator "k" was used to describe a middle-latitude climate (climate average annual temperature never exceeding 18°C). Alternatively, "h" is to use to describe the coldest month average temperature exceeding 0°C, whereas "k" indicates at least one month has a temperature average below 0°C. Additionally, "a" defines the warmest month with an average temperature above 22°C and at least four months above 10°C average, "b" describes the warmest month with an average below 22°C, and in addition at least four months with an average temperature exceeding 10°C, and finally "c" defines a climate condition where three or fewer months out of the year are above an average temperatures of 10°C. (Courtesy of Dr. Markus Kottek, Carinthian Government, Carinthian Institute for Climate Protection [KIKS], A-Klagenfurt am Wörthersee, Austria, and Dr. Franz Rubel, University of Veterinary Medicine Vienna, Institute for Veterinary Public Health, Vienna, Austria; After Rubel, F. and M. Kottek, 2010: Observed and projected climate shifts 1901–2100 depicted by world maps of Koppen-Geiger climate classification. *Meteorol. Z.*, 19, 135–141.)

Korotkoff, Nikolai Sergeyevich

See **Nikolai Sergeyevich Korotkov.**

Korotkoff sounds

[acoustics, biomedical, fluid dynamics] Sounds produced as a result of a restriction in lumen of a FLOW passage under the influence of a periodic pressure profile. Specifically, the cuff of a SPHYGMOMANOMETER wrapped around the upper arm is pressurized to close-off the BLOOD flow through the brachial artery that is accessible in the antecubital space of the elbow (the crease of the elbow). The flow through the artery can be observed with the assistance of a statoscopes or MICROPHONE. First, the applied pressure from the cuff closes off the blood flow, after which the pressure is gradually released to the point where the pressure in the vessel during systole matches the applied external pressure, from this point on with reducing cuff pressure the blood will intermittently flow through a narrow spacing, acting as a reed in a flute. The short squirts of blood generate an OSCILLATION and inherent TURBULENCE at the compressed oval opening when the intervascular pressure briefly exceeds the externally applied pressure. The mechanical VIBRATION resulting from the forced passage generates an audible acoustic sounds, referred to as the Korotkoff sound, named after the person that recognized its usefulness, NIKOLAI SERGEYEVICH KOROTKOV (1874–1920). Under diagnostic conditions the pressure applied to the cuff is reduced at a rate that allows for a certain level of RESOLUTION in pressure detection depending on the operator or electronic device. The sounds initiate at the point when the applied pressure reaches the SYSTOLIC PRESSURE and when the pressure drops further it will pass the point of diastole, from where the blood will flow freely and the sounds at the pinched lumen cease (sometimes also found as: "Korotkov") (see Figure K.56).

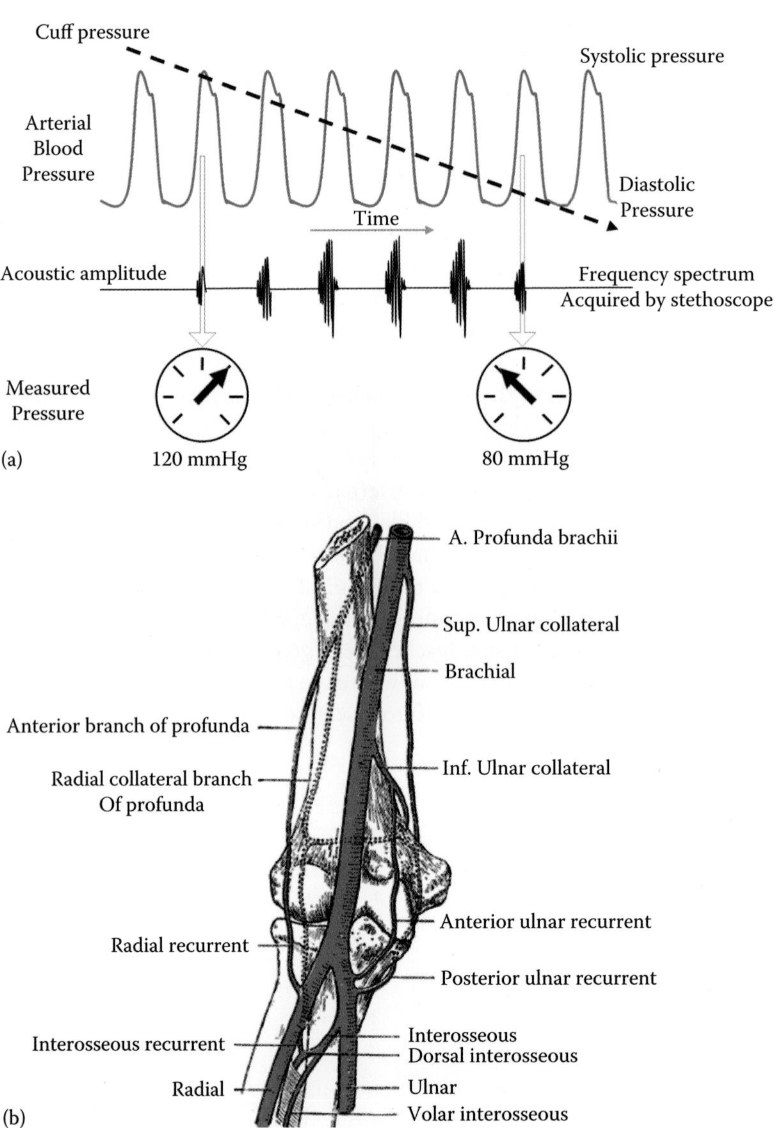

Figure K.56 (a) Illustration of the onset and disappearance of the Korotkoff sounds as a function of the diminishing pressure applied on the brachial artery in the elbow by means of a pressure cuff and (b) outline of the arteries in the arm near the elbow.

Korotkov, Nikolai Sergeyevich (Николай Сергеевич Коротков) (1874–1920)

[acoustics, biomedical, fluid dynamics] Physician and surgeon in what was at the time known as Russia, later named the Union of Soviet Socialist Republics (USSR) and at present known again as Russia. Korotkov is known for his invention of the auscultatory method for the determination of arterial BLOOD PRESSURE by listening for SOUND from the blood being squeezed through a narrow ORIFICE obtained from local compression of the vessel as introduced in 1905 and later in detail in Korotkov's thesis in 1910 (see Figure K.57).

Figure K.57 Nikolai Sergeyevich Korotkov (1874–1920) in 1900.

K

Korteweg–de Vries equation

[acoustics, computational, fluid dynamics, mechanics] Mathematical function for one-dimensional waves ($f(x,t)$; which can describe pressure or displacement, or other wave-dependent parameters) that allows for minor nonlinearities and trivial DISPERSION for a wide bandwidth FREQUENCY SPECTRUM as a SOLUTION to the differential equation: $[df(x,t)/dt]+6f(x,t)[df(x,t)/dx]+[d^3f(x,t)/dx^3]=0$. For a solitary wave the solution is $f(x,t)=2c_1^2\text{sech}^2\{c_1(x-4c_1^2t-x_0)\}$, where c_1 and x_0 are constants. Further implications are in the superposition principle, where two wave interfere elastically, however where the dispersion makes the PHASE VELOCITY of both waves match up after traveling a characteristic asymptotical DISTANCE. The solitary wave solution is also called a SOLITON, representing a WAVE that acts as if it is a PARTICLE. (*Note*: A PHOTON is sometimes referred to as a "wavicle" to describe the particle-like behavior during reflection and certain SCATTERING conditions.) The equation was defined by Diederik Johannes Korteweg (1848–1941) and GUSTAV DE VRIES (1866–1934) in 1895. The Korteweg–de Vries equation can under certain conditions be considered a special case of the Wentzel–Kramers–Brillouin solution method. Also found as KdV equation.

Korteweg–de Vries–Burgers wave equation

[computational, fluid dynamics, mechanics] The Korteweg–de Vries–Burgers equation describes a mathematical model for a nonperiodic SHOCK WAVE. This is based on the work by JOHANNES MARTINUS (JAN) BURGERS (1895–1981) in 1948 which describes weak acoustic burst waves (solitary wave) as a SOLUTION to his expression: $[df(x,t)/dt]+c_1'f(x,t)[df(x,t)/dx]=c_2'[d^2f(x,t)/dx^2]$, which is combined with the Koreteweg–de Vries equation. The Korteweg–de Vries–Burgers equation is defined as: $[df(x,t)/dt]+c_1f(x,t)[df(x,t)/dx]-c_2[d^2f(x,t)/dx^2]+c_3[d^3f(x,t)/dx^3]=0$, where the term $c_2[d^2f(x,t)/dx^2]$ represents viscous dissipation, and c_i are constants. When the term $c_3=0$ this represents Burgers' equation.

Kossel, Walther Ludwig Julius (1888–1956)

[general] Physicist from Germany. Kossel worked on X-RAY diffraction and atomic spectra as well as crystal analysis. His contributions are in theory of the chemical bond, next to the atomic spectra described in the

Sommerfeld–Kossel displacement law, the Kossel effect, and the Kossel–Stranski model for crystal growth (see Figure K.58).

Figure K.58 Walther Ludwig Julius Kossel (1888–1956), 1928.

Kossel effect

[atomic, optics] Crystalline structure analysis with specific applications to semiconductor design and controls based on X-ray diffraction analysis. The Kossel effect describes the reflection pattern based on the Bragg law for crystalline plane spacing resulting in an isotropic emission pattern. In the reflection/backscatter profile one can recognize the grouping of diffracted radiation in cones. The geometrical pattern of conic sections captured as lines on a flat film can be defined based on the Kossel cone with half aperture angle derived as $\sin(\theta_B) = n(\lambda/2)d_{\text{crystal}}$, where θ_B is the Bragg angle, λ the wavelength of the probing X-ray radiation, n the order of the reflection, captured at intervals, $n = 0$ representing the zeroth-order reflection diffraction (directly above the point of incidence), and d_{crystal} the crystal plane spacing constant. This phenomenon was described by Walther Ludwig Julius Kossel (1888–1956) (see Figure K.59).

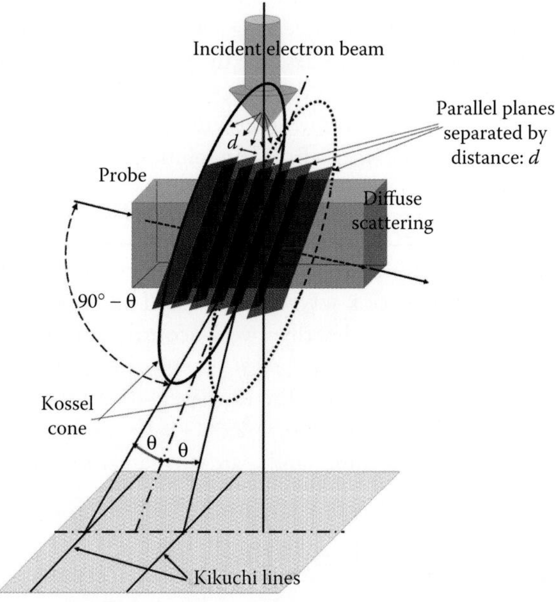

Figure K.59 Graphical representation of the Kossel effect.

Kottler, Friedrich (1886–1965)

[astrophysics, computational, optics] Austrian physicist, primarily focused on theoretical PHYSICS with an interest in ASTROPHYSICS. The work of Kottler in refraction OPTICS by means of relativistic approach was unique in its efforts. Other computational work of Kottler was in theory of relativity applied to GRAVITATION. He is most known for his SOLUTION to the Schwarzschild EQUATION OF RADIATIVE TRANSFER (introduced by KARL SCHWARZSCHILD [1873–1916], for the theoretical description of electromagnetic WAVE propagation through galactic dust) published in 1918. The solution does not account for the light transportation in black holes, thus avoiding accounting for the VACUUM FIELD EQUATIONS as defined by ALBERT EINSTEIN (1879–1955) (see Figure K.60).

Figure K.60 Friedrich Kottler (1886–1965).

Kramers, Hendrik Anthony (Hans) (1894–1952)

[computational, general, optics] Physicist and mathematician from the Netherlands. Hans Kramers is most known for his contributions to function analysis and in particular the KRAMERS–KRONIG RELATIONS (see Figure K.61).

Figure K.61 Hendrik Anthony (Hans) Kramers (1894–1952) at the 1933 Solvay Conference ([Structure et propriétés des noyaux atomiques → Structure & properties of the atomic nucleus; Chair: Paul Langevin], standing, fifth from the left.)

Kramers–Kronig relations

[computational, general, optics] Mathematical relations connecting the real and imaginary parts of any complex function specifically in the imaginary part of the reference frame that has a positive value. The function can be represented by a converging power series. The relations use a complex definition ($f(\varpi) = f'(\varpi) + if''(\varpi)$, where $f'(\varpi)$ and $f''(\varpi)$ are both real), which is as follows: $f'(\varpi) = \mathbb{P}^*/\pi\int_{-\infty}^{\infty} f''(\varpi')/(\varpi' - \varpi)\,d\varpi'$ and $f''(\varpi) = -\mathbb{P}^*/\pi\int_{-\infty}^{\infty} f'(\varpi')/(\varpi' - \varpi)\,d\varpi'$, where $\mathbb{P}^*$ is the Cauchy principal value and ϖ a complex variable, with ϖ' a SINGULARITY that is circumvented. The relation is named after RALPH KRONIG (1904–1995) and HENDRIK ANTHONY (HANS) KRAMERS (1894–1952). One specific example of a function is the pulse response function to an impulse applied at time (t'); providing the functional response of a phenomenon as $f(t - t')$. Another application can be used to solve for the index of REFRACTION.

Krebs cycle

[biomedical, chemical, thermodynamics] GLUCOSE breakdown reaction mechanism in biological systems. Also known as the citric ACID cycle, or tricarboxylic acid cycle (TCA cycle). All aerobic organisms rely on the Krebs cycle, which consists of a series of chemical reactions to generate CHEMICAL ENERGY in the form of ADENOSINE TRIPHOSPHATE. The OXIDATION process involves the conversion of acetate derived from nutrients such as carbohydrates, lipids as well as proteins. In addition, the Krebs cycle creates the building blocks of certain amino acids. It has central importance to many biochemical pathways suggesting a rudimentary component of cellular METABOLISM (see Figure K.62).

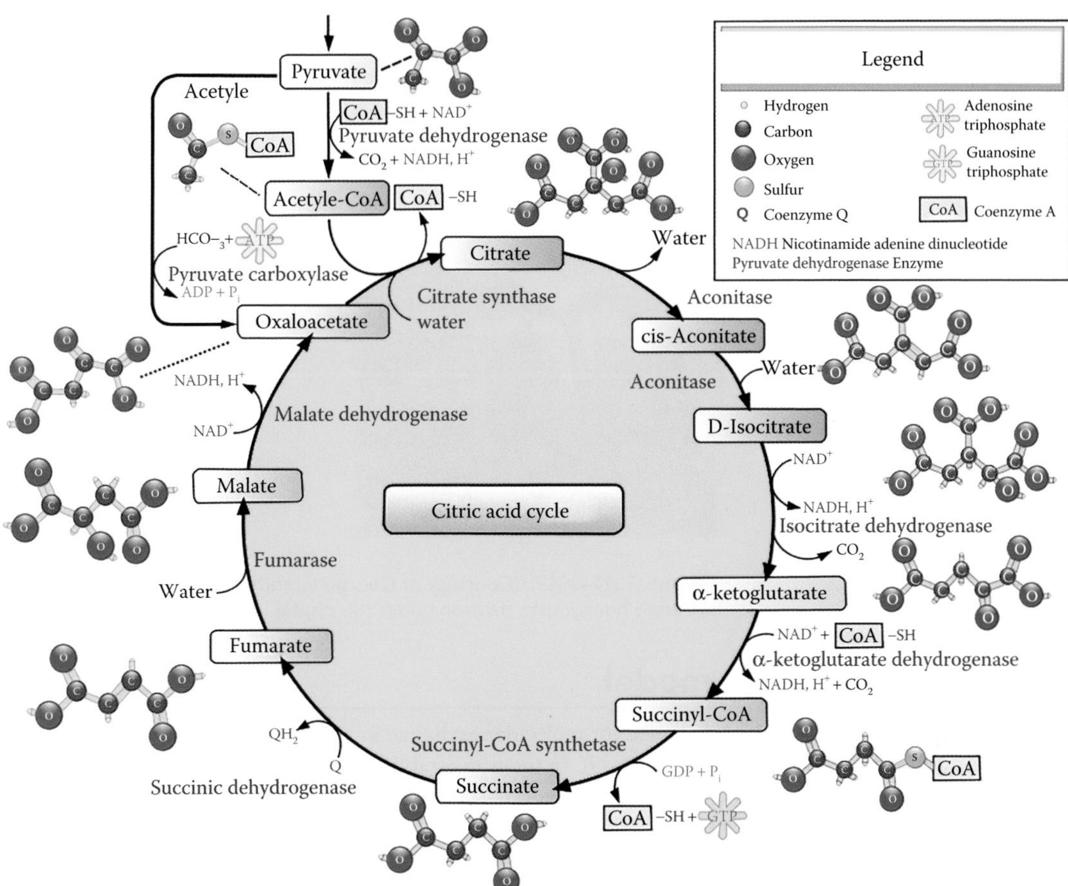

Figure K.62 Diagram of the Krebs cycle process in the renewable energy process for adenosine triphosphate and associated metabolism.

Krimholtz–Leedom–Matthaei (KLM) transducer model

[acoustics, computational, nuclear] Electroacoustic TRANSDUCER finite-element computer modeling tool and piezoarray modeling tool. Computer simulation mechanism to generate the beam shape and intensity pattern as a function of angular position as produced by a piezoelectric array. A pressure (i.e., AMPLITUDE squared) as a function of voltage distribution based on an analog electronic circuit design that mimics the acoustic transducer. The model calculates the force as a result of the applied electrical filed in a piezocrystal and associated velocity of "PARTICLE" displacement.

Krogh, Schack August Steenberg (1874–1949)

[biomedical] Scientist and zoologist from Denmark. Krogh performed research in the respiratory mechanism as well as CAPILLARY function in the PERFUSION of organs. Krogh received the Nobel Prize in Physiology in 1920 for his work on the regulation mechanism of capillary GAS and ionic exchange; the capillary MOTOR. He is one of the founding fathers of exercise science (see Figure K.63).

Figure K.63 Schack August Steenberg Krogh (1874–1949). (Courtesy of George Grantham Bain collection, the United States Library of Congress's Prints and Photographs division under the digital ID ggbain.32006.)

K

Krogh tissue cylinder model

[biomedical, fluid dynamics] Model approach for molecular exchange in vascular flow, developed by SCHACK AUGUST STEENBERG KROGH (1874–1949). In order to establish the DIFFUSION between CAPILLARY FLOW and the surrounding bulk tissue, the tissue is considered over a short length (ℓ) along the vessel only, in cylindrical symmetry. Exploring the tissue diffusion with chemical reaction rate (binding to ligands). (*Note*: Not to be confused with free FLOW diffusion rate.) R_i in radial (r) direction only for a vessel with radius R_0, the individual ($\square_i$) molecular transfer (N_i) of solutes with respective concentrations $\left[C_i\right]$ obeys the following conservation law (CONSERVATION OF MASS): $\left(\partial\left[C_i\right]/\partial t\right)2\pi r\ell\Delta r=\left\{N_{ir}r-N_{ir+\Delta r}\left(r+\Delta r\right)\right\}2\pi\ell+R_i 2\pi r\ell\Delta r$. Combining the conservation of mass with the Fick's diffusion law: $N_{ir}=D_{AB}\left(\partial\left[C_i\right]/\partial t\right)$, where D_{AB} is the DIFFUSIVITY of the SOLUTE that can be solved under certain confined boundary conditions. For oxygen often the diffusion reaction rate is considered to be constant: $R_{O_2}=-c^{m}$, while assuming virtual steady-state conditions during the transfer from BLOOD hemoglobin to tissue hemoglobin, or free tissue oxygen. The Krogh tissue cylinder now holds the oxygen exchange from artery ($\square_a$) to tissue ($\square_t$): $\left[C_{O_2}\right]_a=\left[C_{O_2}\right]_t+\left(c^m/D_{AB}\right)\left[\left(r^2-R_t^{\,2}\right)/4\right]+\left(c^m/D_{AB}\right)\left(R_t^{\,2}/4\right)\ln\left(R_t/r\right)$, with R_t the radius of the Krogh cylinder.

Krogh's diffusion coefficient (K_{Diff})

[biomedical, chemical] The DIFFUSION coefficient in LIQUID phase: $K_{Diff}=\alpha_{sol}D_{diff}$, where α_{sol} is the solubility (Henry's law coefficient), and D_{diff} the diffusion coefficient is GAS PHASE.

Kronecker, Leopold (1823–1891)

[computational] Mathematician from the Prussian Empire (now Poland). Kronecker introduced several basic formulations, including the "delta function," also known as the KRONECKER DELTA FUNCTION (δ) (see Figure K.64).

Figure K.64 Leopold Kronecker (1823–1891), 1865.

Kronecker delta function (δ)

[biomedical, computational, engineering] Function used to selectively isolate certain aspects of a phenomenon as a function of unique locations in time or position. The delta function is defined by two parameters: i and j for which if these equal the function 1, otherwise zero; $\delta_{i,j}$, with $\delta_{i,j} = 1$ for $i = j$ and $\delta_{i,j} = 0$ for $i \neq j$. The existence follows from the summation: $a_n = \sum_i \delta_{i,n} a_i$. In comparison the DIRAC DELTA FUNCTION uses integration: $f(x_0) = \int f(x)\delta(x - x_0)\,dx$. Another use for the Kronecker delta is in vector and TENSOR analysis for determination of matrix coefficients for a transformation between the merates of a contravariant vector χ^i in a coordinate system referred to as unprimed $(\overrightarrow{x^i})$ with respect to the contravariant vector $(\overrightarrow{\chi^{i'}})$ in the primed coordinate system $(\overrightarrow{x^{i'}})$. The transformation is defined by equations that are partial derivatives of the base point coordinates $(\partial x^{i'}/\partial x^i)$, while forming a linear homogeneous relationship, giving $\overrightarrow{\chi^{i'}} = \left(\partial \overrightarrow{x^{i'}}/\partial \overrightarrow{x^{i'}}\right)\chi^i$, respectively the transform for the covariant vector: $\overrightarrow{\zeta_{i'}} = \left(\partial \overrightarrow{x^i} / \partial \overrightarrow{x^{i'}}\right)\overrightarrow{\zeta_i}$, where the coefficients are linked by the Kronecker delta as: $\left(\partial \overrightarrow{x^{i'}}/\partial \overrightarrow{x^i}\right)\left(\partial \overrightarrow{x^i}/\partial \overrightarrow{x^{j'}}\right) = \delta^{i'}_{j'}$ (*also* Kronecker symbol) (see Figure K.65).

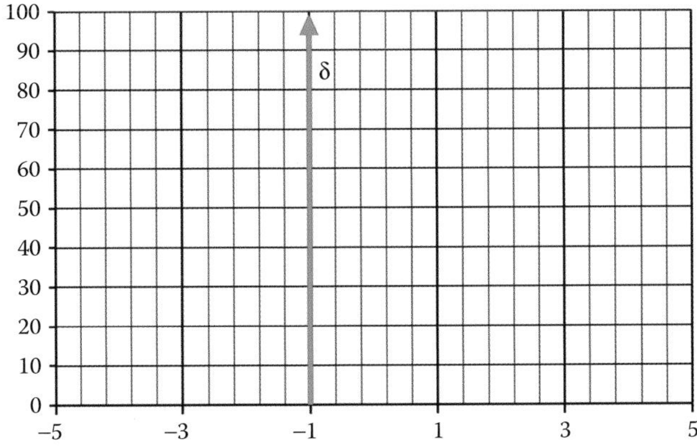

Figure K.65 Graphical representation of the Kronecker delta function.

Kronig, Ralph (1904–1995)

[computational, general, optics, quantum] Physicist from Germany. In 1925 Kronig introduced the idea that an electron spins around its axis, creating a MAGNETIC moment. The electron-spin idea was suggested in 1921 by ARTHUR HOLLY COMPTON (1892–1962), in the format of a perceived GYROSCOPE, but he did not implement this model (see Figure K.66).

Figure K.66 Ralph Kronig (1904–1995).

Kronig–Penney model

[quantum, solid-state] Idealized crystal structure reduced to a one-dimensional model encompassing all the features of any specific real crystal. The electron potential in this model is a one-dimensional function only ($V(x)$), with well-defined potential wells; wells with width w, spacing d, and depth $-V_0$. The electron ENERGY and WAVE function for an electron with mass m_e in this situation can be solved using the SCHRÖDINGER EQUATION. The energy bands in this approximation configuration can thus be defined as: $\sqrt{(2m_e w^2 V_0/d^2)} = 12.0$ where $d/w = 0.1$, the choice of parameters depends on the original crystalline structure with associated energy configuration.

K-shell internal conversion coefficient (α_{icc})

[nuclear] The rate of INTERNAL CONVERSION (ICC) of electron excitation by means of electron to X-ray RADIATION, expressed as: $\alpha_{conv} = (1/\omega_K)\{[(N_{K,\alpha}/\varepsilon_{K,\alpha}) + (N_{K,\beta}/\varepsilon_{K,\beta})]/(N_\gamma/\varepsilon_\gamma)\}$ = number of electron-electron K-shell de-excitaions/number of gamma radiation-electron K-shell de-excitaions, where ω_K is the *K*-shell FLUORESCENCE yield, $N_{K,\alpha}$ is the number of K_α X-ray emissions (i.e., height of peak in spectral profile), N_γ the GAMMA RAY emissions from the RADIOACTIVE ISOTOPE itself, $\varepsilon_{K,\alpha}$ the "efficiency" of the detection of the K_α X-ray emissions, $N_{K,\beta}$ is the number of K_β X-ray emissions, and $\varepsilon_{K,\beta}$ the "efficiency" of the detection of the K_β X-ray emissions. Conversion in this case means the match of electron WAVE function

(in relativistic approach) and associated MAGNETIC and electric transition ENERGY, with respect to the gamma energy. Electric and magnetic fields are generated due to the brief period on NUCLEON rearrangement under external forces. During this electromagnetic interaction the NUCLEUS emits gamma rays, and the energy can be transferred to atomic electrons, which can excite the electros in the high-energy *K*-shell. The conversion is mainly the result of the time-varying Coulomb field of the nucleus. For large atomic number (Z), the relativistic approach becomes more important, with large deviations from the classical approach. In most cases a look-up table is used or computer programs for estimation to determine the specific threshold values for the gamma energy to reach conversion. For verification of the methodology measurements with a SOLENOID beta-ray spectrometer combined with X-RAY spectral analysis can provide QUANTIFICATION (*also see* **INTERNAL CONVERSION** *and* ***K*-SHELL**).

Kurie plot

[nuclear] In nuclear RADIOACTIVITY the plot of the beta RADIATION spectra by means of plotting the FERMI FUNCTION ($F_f(Z_D, p_e)$) against the kinetic ENERGY of the electron ($\mathrm{KE}_e = (1/2)m_e v^2$). Considering that electron emission requires a relativistic approach based on the PARTICLE velocities. The full function for the spectral DECAY is $\Lambda(p_e)p_e - F_f(Z_D, p_e)p_e^2\{\mathrm{KE}_e^{\max} - KE_e\}^2 \delta p_e\left(|\mathcal{M}_{fi}'|^2/2\pi^3c^2\hbar^7\right)$, where $\hbar = h/2\pi$, $h = 6.62606957 \times 10^{-34}\ \mathrm{m^2kg/s}$ the Planck constant, $p_e = m_e v$ the electron momentum for charge with mass m_e, and velocity v for ELEMENT with atomic number Z (number of protons), $c = 2.99792458 \times 10^8$ m/s the speed of light, and $\mathcal{M}_{fi}' = V_{fi}/g_f = \int \Psi_D^*\left(\vec{r}_1, \vec{r}_2, \ldots, \vec{r}_A\right)\Psi_{e^-}^*\left(\vec{r}_{e^-}; Z\right)\Psi_{\bar{\nu}}^*\left(\vec{r}_{\bar{\nu}}\right) \times V_{\mathrm{int}}\Psi_p\left(\vec{r}_1, \vec{r}_2, \ldots, \vec{r}_A\right)d\vec{r}_1 d\vec{r}_2 \ldots d\vec{r}_A d\vec{r}_{e^-} d\vec{r}_{\bar{\nu}}$ the interaction matrix element, with "strength" $g_f = 8.8 \times 10^{-5}\ \mathrm{MeVfm^3}$ of the beta decay process, V_{fi} is the expectation value, represented by the matrix element of the transition operator V, which is tied to the wave function (Ψ) of the PARENT NUCLEUS (see Figure K.67).

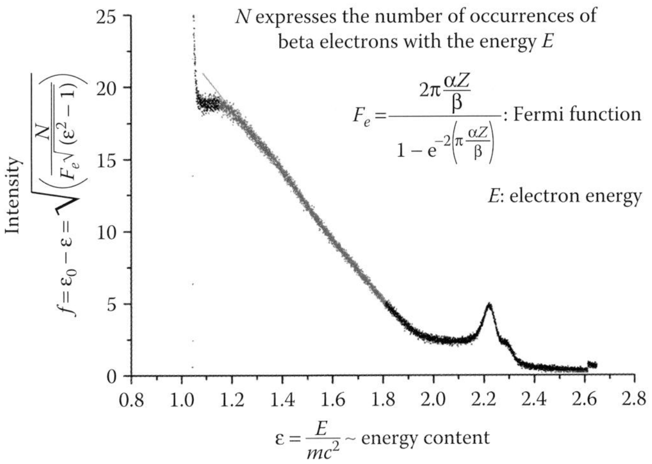

Figure K.67 Kuri plot for the electroweak interactions beta decay process. For instance, in the decay process one of the down quark neutrons is converted to an up quark, which will be converted from a neutron into a proton. During this process a W^- boson is also emitted, which subsequently decays into an electron and an electron–antineutrino pair. Generally, this process can best be described using Feynman diagrams.

K

Kutta, Martin Wilhelm (1867–1944)

[fluid dynamics] Scientist and mathematician from Prussia (Poland). Kutta provided NUMERICAL analysis mechanisms for solving complex differential equations. His work aided in the expedited development of AERODYNAMICS, specifically in collaboration with NIKOLAY ZHUKOVSKY (1847–1921) (see Figure K.68).

Figure K.68 Martin Wilhelm Kutta (1867–1944).

Kutta condition

[fluid dynamics] The fact that under fluid flow viscosity is required, providing a condition that makes FLOW execute a smooth finish when detaching from a training edge of a body that is subjected to LIFT conditions, such as a wing. This outlines the lifting flow conditions. Based on the FLUID DYNAMICS work of MARTIN WILHELM KUTTA (1867–1944) (see Figure K.69).

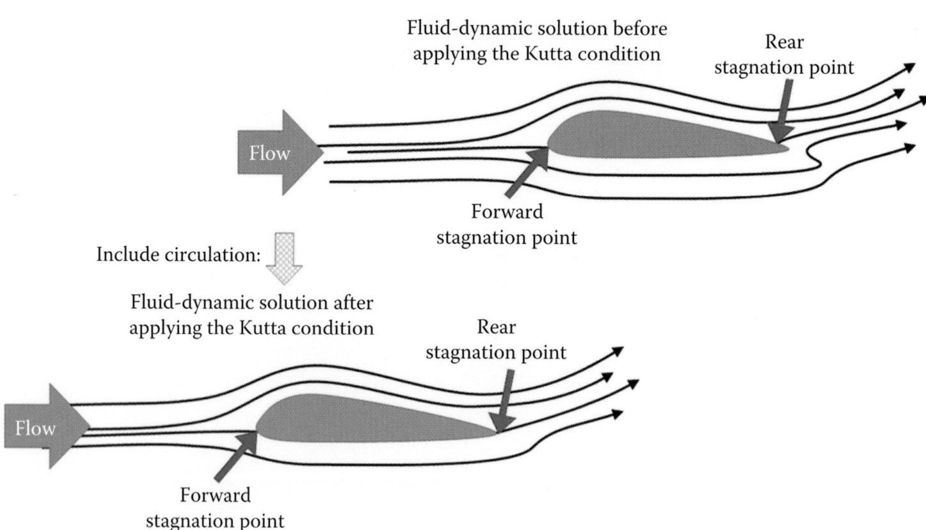

Figure K.69 Graphical representation of the Kurie condition that eliminates the computational conundrum for the calculation providing the conditions for lift by means of incorporating circulation in the flow.

Kutta lift

[fluid dynamics] *See* **Magnus lift**.

Kutta–Joukowski equation

[fluid dynamics] Aerodynamic principle introduced by Martin Wilhelm Kutta (1867–1944) and Nikolay Joukowsky (also: Zhukovsky) (1847–1921) in the early 1990s. The theory described the lift generated by the movement of a cylinder, in horizontal alignment, through a fluid. The lift was found to be a function of the following parameters: relative velocity between the fluid and the cylinder (v), the density of the fluid (ρ), and the circulation (Γ_{circ}). The lift (L_{lift}) is also related to the Bernoulli principle (with pressure P) and yields $L_{lift} = c_{chord}\Delta P = -\rho v \Gamma_{circ}$, where c_{chord} is the length of the chord of the object in flight, in this case the half circumference of the cylinder. Circulation is, in approximation, the closed loop integral of the tangential fluid velocity (*also* **Kutta–Zhukovsky equation**).

K

L

L (angular momentum)

[mechanics, nuclear] For a rigid body with respective mass constituents (m_i) with momentum $\vec{p}$, at respective radii with the axis of rotation ($\vec{r_i}$) and local velocities ($\vec{v_i}$) yields $L = \vec{r} \times \vec{p} = \sum_i \vec{r_i}' \times m_i \vec{v_i} = I\omega$, where I is the MOMENT OF INERTIA and ω the ANGULAR VELOCITY. In nuclear PHYSICS the NUCLEAR ANGULAR MOMENTUM is defined by the angular momentum quantum number, combining the electronic angular momentum and the nuclear angular momentum to provide the TOTAL ANGULAR MOMENTUM for the atomic configuration. The nuclear ORBITAL ANGULAR MOMENTUM $L = \sqrt{\ell(\ell+1)}\hbar$, where $\ell = 0,1,2,\ldots n-1$ (n the PRINCIPAL QUANTUM NUMBER) is the angular quantum number, defining the configuration of the spherical harmonic functions as solutions to the SCHRÖDINGER EQUATION. In reference, the nuclear angular momentum is $I = \sqrt{i(i+1)}\hbar$ (i.e., the PROTON spin; $\hbar = h/2\pi$, with $h = 6.62606957 \times 10^{-34}\ \mathrm{m^2kg/s}$ the Planck's constant) with nuclear angular quantum number i; the electronic angular momentum is $J = \sqrt{j(j+1)}\hbar$, with $j = \ell \mp (1/2)$ the total angular momentum quantum number. The nuclear angular momentum combines with the electronic angular momentum to provide the total angular momentum $\vec{F} = \vec{I} + \vec{J}$. Note that in this case F does not refer force, the convoluted use of parameters is due to the specificity of the fields. The same selection rules and coupling rules apply to electronic and nuclear angular momentum as to the coupling between the total angular momentum S and the orbital angular momentum L (see Figure L.1).

Figure L.1 The use of angular momentum to preserve balance during for instance skating and break-dancing and hence reducing the requirements of muscular force.

$L(\vec{r},\vec{s},t)$

[astrophysics/astronomy, nuclear, optics] Radiance is the MAGNITUDE of ELECTROMAGNETIC RADIATION within a cone of specific SOLID ANGLE of radiated ENERGY emerging from a source, in direction $\vec{s}$ observed at location $\vec{r}$ as a function of time t, that is incident on a surface area; unit $\left[\mathrm{W/m^2sr}\right]$. The Radiance is derived from the Poynting vector: $\vec{S}$, $\vec{S} = \left(\vec{E} \times \vec{B}\right)/\mu$, where $\vec{E}(\vec{r},\vec{s},t)$ represents the electric field strength as a function of time, location and direction, $\vec{B}(\vec{r},\vec{s},t)$ is the coupled MAGNETIC FIELD vector, and μ the DIELECTRIC permeability for the medium (dielectric permeability of free space multiplied by the RELATIVE PERMEABILITY of the medium). The RADIANCE ($L(\vec{r},\vec{s},t)$) is defined as the time average of the length of the Poynting vector, averaged over one or more cycle lengths: $L(\vec{r},\vec{s},t)=(\vec{E}\times\vec{B})/\mu$. When no external forces act on the system, the energy in the system is conserved. The conservation principle is captured by a general balance equation. The balance equation resembles those used to model chemical reactions. For example, the general energy balance follows the Schwarzschild equation of radiative transfer, expressed as a function of time: $(1/c)\left[\partial L(\vec{r},\vec{s},t)/\partial t\right]=-\vec{s}\cdot\nabla L(\vec{r},\vec{s},t)-(\mu_a(\vec{r})+\mu_s(\vec{r}))L(\vec{r},\vec{s},t)+\mu_s(\vec{r})\int_{4\pi}P(\vec{s},\vec{s}')L(\vec{r},\vec{s},t)d\varpi'+S(\vec{r},\vec{s},t)$. The EQUATION OF RADIATIVE TRANSFER was introduced by KARL SCHWARZSCHILD (1873–1916) in 1906 to describe the propagation of RADIATION from galactic sources through cosmic dust, with additional initial work by SIR ARTHUR SCHUSTER (1851–1934) in 1905 (describing light propagation through a foggy ATMOSPHERE) and FRIEDRICH KOTTLER (1886–1965) in 1918, followed in 1947 by the work of SUBRAHMANYAN CHANDRASEKHAR (1910–1995). The RADIATIVE TRANSFER equation also applied to propagation of light through a smaller turbid medium, such as tissue, to define the laser interaction for biological application. The balance equation describes the accumulation of electromagnetic radiation within a system equals the inflow through the system boundaries minus the outflow through the system boundaries plus the generation of radiation within the system and subtracting the consumption (annihilation) within the system. The system is defined by three MICROSCOPIC terms, representing the attenuation (absorption) $\mu_a(\vec{r})$, SCATTERING $\mu_s(\vec{r})$, and redirection of propagation $P(\vec{s},\vec{s}')$. A derived parameter is the total attenuation $\mu_t(\vec{r})=\mu_a(\vec{r})+\mu_s(\vec{r})$. A second derived parameter is the scattering anisotropy factor (g), which follows for the angular PROBABILITY distribution for scatter as $g=\int_{4\pi}P(\vec{s},\vec{s}')\cdot(\vec{s},\vec{s}')d\varpi'=\int_{4\pi}P(\theta)\cos\theta d\varpi'$, θ the ANGLE with the original direction of propagation. The latter is also referred to as the SCATTERING PHASE FUNCTION and is also used in the reduced scattering coefficient, representing the scattering back into the original direction of propagation $\mu_s'(\vec{r})=(1-g)\mu_s(\vec{r})$, which can be carried forward to the reduced total attenuation: $\mu_t'(\vec{r})=(1-g)\mu_t(\vec{r})$. The equation of radiative transfer defining the radiance is constructed from the "loss" and "gain" components, all considered for a finite small unit of volume. The term $(1/c)\left[\partial L(\vec{r},\vec{s},t)/\partial t\right]$ represents the rate of change in radiance per unit volume, with c the speed of light. The term $\vec{s}\cdot\nabla L(\vec{r},\vec{s},t)$ signifies the loss (minus sign) through the boundaries. The term $(\mu_a(\vec{r})+\mu_s(\vec{r}))L(\vec{r},\vec{s},t)$ indicates the loss (minus sign) of ELECTROMAGNETIC ENERGY in radiance due to attenuation resulting from both absorption and redirected scattering out of the original path of the incident beam. The term $\mu_s(\vec{r})\int_{4\pi}P(\vec{s},\vec{s}')L(\vec{r},\vec{s},t)d\varpi'$ represents the recovery (gain) of radiance from scattering back into the original direction: $\vec{s}'$ into direction $\vec{s}$ with angular probability distribution $P(\vec{s},\vec{s}')$. The final term $S(\vec{r},\vec{s}',t)$ is a source term, either FLUORESCENCE or other means of generating electromagnetic radiation such as a FIBER-OPTIC placed inside a tumor volume (see Figure L.2).

Figure L.2 Representation of $L(\vec{r},\vec{s},t)$ radiance.

L characteristic X-rays

[atomic, electromagnetism, nuclear] Class of X-RAY spectral lines as defined by CHARLES GLOVER BARKLA (1877–1944) in 1908. Characteristic lines are a function of the medium used for emission. The characteristic L lines are the second group following the K lines, and followed by M, N, and so on. The L-spectrum belongs to orbital electron transitions from the 2*s* ENERGY configuration. The emission lines follow the Moseley law (*also see* **K-CHARACTERISTIC X-RAY**) (see Figure L.3).

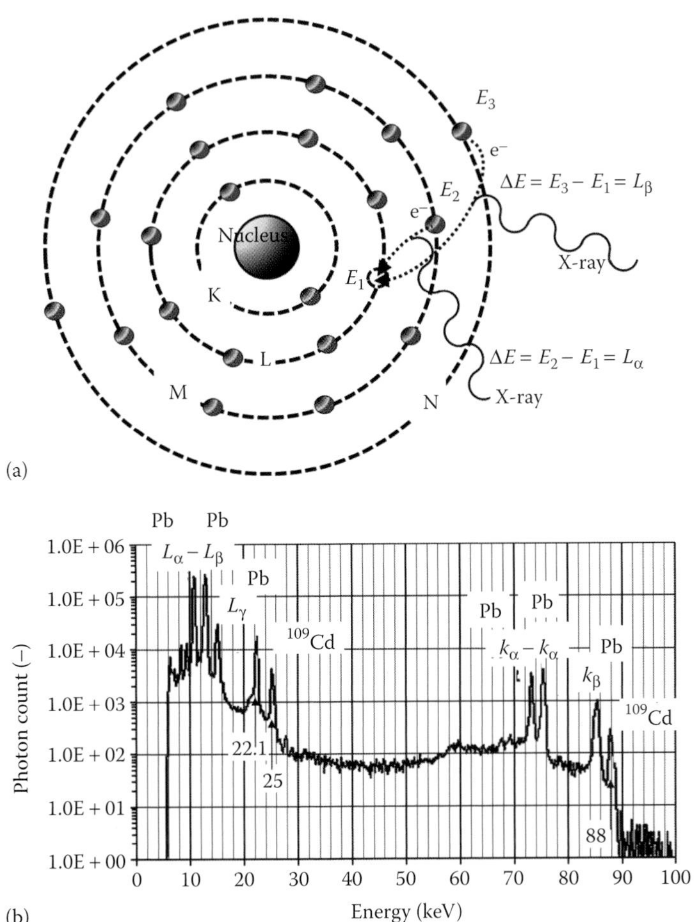

Figure L.3 (a) L line transition. When a vacant spot is generated by primary excitation X-ray or, alternatively, by the previous transition in the L shell, an electron originating from the M shell or the N shell will migrate to occupy the formed vacancy. In this process the transition generates a characteristic X-ray unique to the particular element. As a result a vacancy in the M or N shell is produced, (b) L-characteristic X-ray lines observed in X-ray spectroscopy for the fluorescence of lead (Pb) from cadmium (^{109}Cd).

L series

[nuclear] CHARACTERISTIC X-RAY—L transition (L CHARACTERISTIC X-RAYS), *see* **L-CHARACTERISTIC X-RAYS** (*also see* **LYMAN SERIES**).

L

La Systeme International d'Unites

[astrophysics, computational, fluid dynamics, general, mechanics, nuclear] *See* **SI** UNITS.

Lagrange, (Joseph-Louis) Giuseppe Luigi comte de (1737–1813)

[astronomy, computational, electromagnetism, general, quantum, thermodynamics] French/Italian astronomer, scientist, and mathematician, partially during the time of Napoleon Bonaparte (1769–1821). Lagrange was a contemporary of LEONHARD EULER (1707–1783) and JEAN-BAPTISTE LE ROND D'ALEMBERT (1717–1783). Lagrange formulated several definitions of equilibrium for THERMODYNAMICS, FLUID DYNAMICS, and MECHANICS. The work of Lagrange followed on the work of JULES HENRI POINCARÉ (1854–1912) and ALEKSANDR MIKHAILOVICH LYAPUNOV (1857–1918) (see Figure L.4).

Figure L.4 Giuseppe Luigi comte de Lagrange (Joseph Louis Lagrange) (1737–1813). (Courtesy of R. Hart.)

Lagrangian equations in generalized co-ordinates

[atomic, fluid dynamics, mechanics] Description of points with mass (e.g., particles) under influence of external and/or mutually interactive forces. Generally when HAMILTONIAN MECHANICS is insufficient to describe complex systems, a Lagrangian approach may account for the multitude of DEGREES OF FREEDOM in the ENERGY of the system.

Lagrangian finite strain tensor

[computational, fluid dynamics, mechanics] A measure of the difference between the deformation TENSOR ($C = F^T F$, where F represents the deformation gradient) and ($I = (I_1, I_2, I_3)$) the undeformed configuration location vector; expressed as $E_{\mathrm{LK}} = (1/2)\left(C - I\right) \sim \nabla\vec{v} + \left(\nabla\vec{v}\right)^T$ where $\vec{v}$ is the deformation rate or FLOW velocity (solid or FLUID, respectively).

Lagrangian for classical gravitational field

[computational, electromagnetism, general, quantum] $\mathcal{L}_g\left|\vec{x},t\right| = -\mu\left|\vec{x},t\right| Z\left|\vec{x},t\right| - (1/G8\pi)\left(\nabla Z\left|\vec{x},t\right|\right)^2$, where $Z\left|\vec{x},t\right|$ is the potential of the GRAVITATIONAL FIELD, tying in with the equation of MOTION as $m\ddot{\vec{x}}\left(t\right) = -m\nabla Z\left|\vec{x}\left(t\right),t\right|$ and $\mu\left|\vec{x},t\right|$ is the mass density as a function of the vector location $\vec{x}$ in TIME (t)

Lagrangian form of the hydrodynamical equations

[computational, fluid dynamics] The EQUATIONS OF MOTION of a mass of FLUID applied to flow with respect to local DENSITY (ρ) and PRESSURE (P). The system assumes a "PARTICLE" in the FLOW to be at location (x_1, y_1, z_1) at a point in TIME (t) with respective velocities $(\partial x/\partial t, \partial y/\partial t, \partial z/\partial t)$ and acceleration $(\partial^2 x/\partial t^2, \partial^2 y/\partial t^2, \partial^2 z/\partial t^2)$ under externally applied force with components (F_x; F_y; F_z) provides $\partial^2 x/\partial t^2 = F_x - [(1/\rho)(\partial P/\partial x)]$; $\partial^2 y/\partial t^2 = F_y - [(1/\rho)(\partial P/\partial y)]$; $\partial^2 z/\partial t^2 = F_z - [(1/\rho)(\partial P/\partial z)]$, respectively. Using transformation this provides the Lagrangian hydrodynamic equations: $((\partial^2 x/\partial t^2) - F_x)(\partial x/\partial x_1) + ((\partial^2 y/\partial t^2) - F_y)(\partial y/\partial x_1) + ((\partial^2 z/\partial t^2) - F_z)(\partial z/\partial x_1) + [(1/\rho)(\partial P/\partial x_1)] = 0$; respectively $((\partial^2 x/\partial t^2) - F_x)(\partial x/\partial x_2) + ((\partial^2 y/\partial t^2) - F_y)(\partial y/\partial x_2) + ((\partial^2 z/\partial t^2) - F_z)(\partial z/\partial x_2) + [(1/\rho)(\partial P/\partial x_2)] = 0$; and $((\partial^2 x/\partial t^2) - F_x)(\partial x/\partial x_3) + ((\partial^2 y/\partial t^2) - F_y)(\partial y/\partial x_3) + ((\partial^2 z/\partial t^2) - F_z)(\partial z/\partial x_3) + [(1/\rho)(\partial P/\partial x_3)] = 0$. This applies the Lagrangian method to the principles of flow.

Lagrangian libration point

[computational, geophysics] Location in free space as the "FOCAL POINT" of a space orbit configuration ensuring a position with respect to both the MOON and EARTH simultaneously. The existence of such points in gravitational and orbital mathematics were derived in 1772 by "comte de Lagrange" (GIUSEPPE LUIGI COMTE DE LAGRANGE [1737–1813]), five locations in total: L_1, L_2, L_3, L_4, and L_5. These would be orbital locations where a space station can be placed for stable observation. These free space revolving positions are however unstable, especially since the ORBITS of the Moon is oval (see Figure L.5).

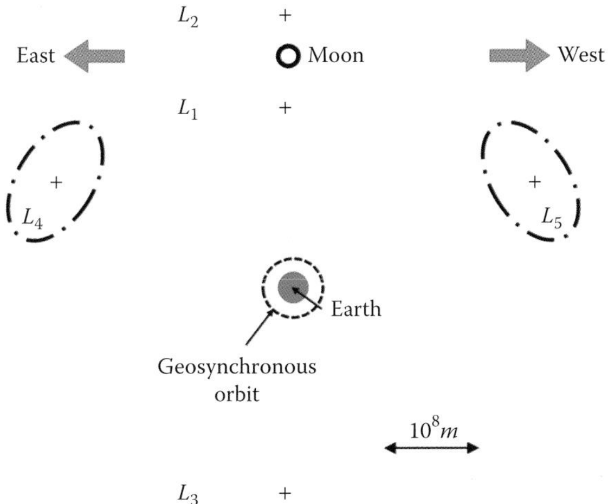

Figure L.5 Lagrange liberation points for Moon orbit.

Lagrangian theory

[computational, mechanics, thermodynamics] Mathematical representation of full-featured equation of MOTION dynamics in a system with less than $3k$ DEGREES OF FREEDOM in a set of n independent EQUATIONS OF MOTION for k particles, independent of the number of particles representing the system. This is in contrast to the convoluted Newtonian formulation, where all particles interact with each other and the system needs to be solved. The generalized format is expressed in the following manner: $(d/dt)(\partial T/\partial\dot{\xi}_i)-(\partial T/\partial\xi_i)=\sum_{j=1}^{k}\overrightarrow{F_j}\cdot(\partial r/\partial\xi_i)$, $i=1,\ldots,n$, where $\xi_i=\xi_i(\vec{r}_1,\vec{r}_2,\vec{r}_3,\ldots\vec{r}_k,t)$ is a transformation of the location ($\overrightarrow{r_x}$), F_j the independently acting forces on the individual particles culminating in a set of generalized forces.

Lamarr, Hedy (1914–2000)

[computational, general, signal] Born: Hedwig Eva Maria Kiesler; female actor and nature philosopher born in Austria, who, together with composer George Antheil [1900–1959], conceived the idea of frequency hopping. The "frequency hopping" concept is a frequency modulation technique that applies to spread FREQUENCY SPECTRUM transmission (frequency hopping spread spectrum: FHSS; based on the conversion of multiple frequencies carrying parts of the total signal/data), preventing any unauthorized receiver to "tune in" to the communication band (i.e., telecommunications jamming). By repeated switching the radio-frequency CARRIER wavelength in a RADIO or telecommunication (e.g., mobile phone) transmission, only a dedicated receiver will be able to continuously acquire the transmitted data. Hedy Lamarr and George Antheil introduced this concept in 1942, during World War II (1940–1945; WW-2). The early mechanism as introduced by Hedy Lamarr was based on musical instruments, specifically the mechanical organ, or player PIANO (pianola), electronic carillon or other various types of orchestrion. The encoding was meant to provide uninterrupted guidance during the launch and trajectory of a torpedo, ensuring, maintaining, and correcting course and guarantee a delivery to the target location. The torpedo should employ a "tuning" role rotating with the same patterns as in the transmitter on the submarine, thus ensuring uninterrupted communications and flawless exchange of information without risk of enemy sabotage prior to striking the target. In comparison to the musical background, the orchestrion (Carillion; barrel organ hurdy-gurdy) uses a role of paper with holes punched in a certain pattern that engage the keys on the instrument for a specific note when the hole passes the trigger switch. The same concept is still applicable to modern spread spectrum frequency communication, such as those applied in cordless telephones, Bluetooth, and WiFi (802.11 wireless internet access). During World War II, the concept encountered much opposition, undoubtable fueled by the musical references ("player piano") in the description of the mechanism of action, leading to the (misguided) rejection of the importance of the principles. The earliest known implementation of the spread frequency concept was not until 1962, during the Cuban Missile Crisis using the work of the engineers at Sylvania Electronics initiated in 1957. The Sylvania Electronics engineers used TRANSISTOR to implement the concept at this point. At this time the patent has expired and Lamarr and Antheil did not receive credit for their contribution. Hedy Lamarr was honored by the Institute of Electrical and Electronics Engineers: IEEE, for her contributions to modern telecommunications in 2002 (*see* **FREQUENCY HOPPING SPREAD SPECTRUM: FHSS**) (see Figure L.6).

(a)

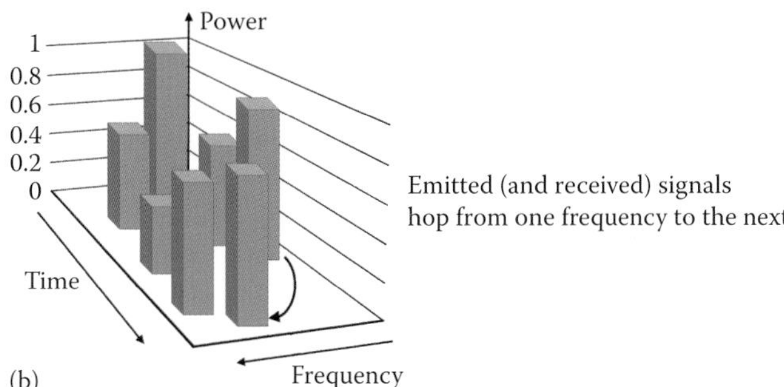

(b)

Figure L.6 (a) Hedy Lamarr (1914–2000), born: Hedwig Eva Maria Kiesler. (Courtesy of Laszlo Willinger [1909–1989]; taken in 1943. Hedy Lamarr's name and likeness, used with permission from Denise Loder-DeLuca.) (b) Frequency-hopping, conceptual spectral outline.

Lamb, Horace, Sir (1849–1934)

[acoustics, geophysics, fluid dynamics, mechanics] Physicists and mathematician from Great Britain. Lamb's work influenced developments in ELASTICITY, SEISMOLOGY, TIDAL MOTION as well as ELECTRICITY AND MAGNETISM. The LAMB WAVE phenomenon is of primary interest to nondestructive testing (see Figure L.7).

Figure L.7 Sir Horace Lamb (1849–1934).

Lamb, Willis Eugene (1913–2008)

L

[acoustics, atomic, computational, general, mechanics, nuclear, solid-state] Physicist from the United States. Lamb was known for his work on quantum-field theory. Lamb received the Nobel Prize in Physics in 1955 for the discovery of the quantum–mechanical shift in ENERGY levels associated with the HYDROGEN ATOM, the Lamb shift. Lamb received the Nobel Prize for his discovery of how the FINE STRUCTURE of hydrogen is revealing a discrepancy in the QUANTUM THEORY with respect to the electron and his concept of "virtual particles" that provide an energy shift named after him as the "LAMB SHIFT." The concept of virtual particles can be interpreted as energy shift through the mass–energy equivalence concept. Lamb studied under JULIUS ROBERT OPPENHEIMER (1904–1967) and was a contemporary of ENRICO FERMI (1901–1954), ISIDOR ISAAC RABI (1898–1988), Edward Teller (1908–2003), and John Hasbrouck Van Vleck (1899–1980), with whom he interacted. While examining the fine-structure of transitions between ${}^2S_{1/2} \rightarrow {}^2P_{1/2}$ and ${}^2S_{1/2} \rightarrow {}^2P_{3/2}$ the high RESOLUTION of 10^{-4} GHz confirmed the Dirac predicted ${}^2P$ fine structure (see Figure L.8).

Figure L.8 Willis Eugene Lamb (1913–2008). (Courtesy of Arizona Daily Star, Tucson, Arizona.)

Lamb shift

[atomic, general, nuclear, solid-state] Shift in hydrogen spectrum resulting from atomic interaction, specifically changes in ENERGY configuration resulting from positron–electron "pair" formation. This interaction can be induced by X-RAY irradiation of the MACROSCOPIC matter. This electromagnetic interaction generates an electric field that influences the photon–photon interaction, acting as a PHOTON scattering catalyst. The resulting shift in the excitation EMISSION SPECTRUM is referred to as Lamb shift. Spectral shift named after the discovery by Willis Lamb (1913–2008) during the LAMB–RETHERFORD EXPERIMENT as published in 1947. While examining the FINE STRUCTURE of transitions between ${}^2S_{1/2} \rightarrow {}^2P_{1/2}$ and ${}^2S_{1/2} \rightarrow {}^2P_{3/2}$ the high RESOLUTION of 10^{-4} GHz revealed that the ${}^2S_{1/2}$ and ${}^2P_{1/2}$ states with energy level at $n = 2$ are, contrary to prediction, not degenerate. It was however shown that the ${}^2S_{1/2}$ energy state was as a MATTER of fact shifted to a higher level by 1060 MHz, known as the Lamb shift. This shift can be attributed to radiative coupling between the electrons. This discovery formed a milestone in the development of QUANTUM electrodynamic theory (see Figure L.9).

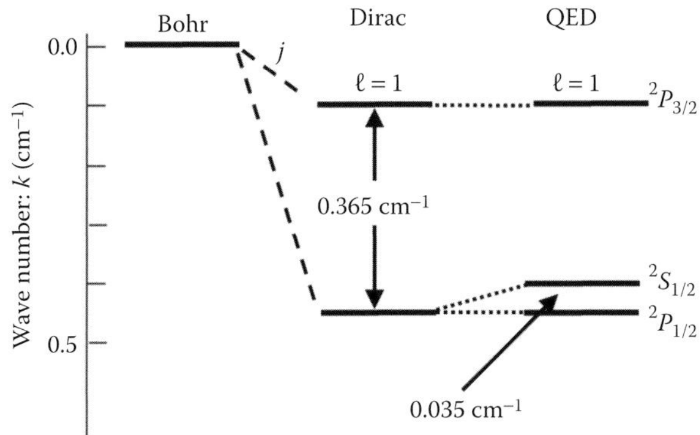

Figure L.9 Representation of Lamb shift. A refinement in the energy structure of the hydrogen $n = 2$ level in accordance with Bohr's theory, Dirac theory, and quantum electrodynamics (QED) theory under the assumption of the Lamb shift. The Lamb shift removes the degeneration resulting from the quantum number j.

Lamb wave

[fluid dynamics, geophysics, mechanics] (Syn.: EVANESCENT WAVE) {use: pressure, imaging, ablation, weather, nondestructive testing}: a LONGITUDINAL WAVE comprised of RAREFACTION and compression traveling in a thin BOUNDARY LAYER or a plate. Described by SIR HORACE LAMB in 1916. Lamb wave require free boundary conditions (equivalent to an infinite wide space), with an infinite number of symmetric and antisymmetric modes. Displacement in the transverse direction within the medium are representative of the antisymmetric modes. Lamb wave can be initiated when the PHASE VELOCITY of a wave that is induced through external influences on a layer matches the phase velocity of a particular mode of Lamb wave. The phase velocity (v_p) of the incident longitudinal wave is derived from the group velocity (v_g) and the ANGLE of incidence (ϕ) with the layer as $v_p = v_g/\sin\phi$. The modes are described as a function of frequency and layer thickness and the derived DISPERSION curves. The modes are defined based on symmetric (S) or antisymmetric (A) format as $S0; A0; S1; A1; \ldots$, respectively. Lamb waves are used in nondestructive testing, identifying cracks in plates, such as the body of an airplane, and pipes. The illustration below shows the condensation pattern (strips of clouds) with an extremely regular interval parallel in one direction. The AIR above Hot Springs, Arizona, prior to this phenomenon showed a sharp horizontal demarcation several hundred meters up in the air, suggesting two air masses with different density parked on top of one another, with a front moving in from the East (sunset in the background). The moving front is squeezed in between two stagnant air masses, causing an elastic deformation RIPPLE to be generated; similar to pursing one's lips and blowing:

whistle (see Figure L.10). (Note that whistling generates a perfect sine wave in most cases, if not a superposition of only several sine waves; depending on any local variability in elastic nature of the SKIN.)

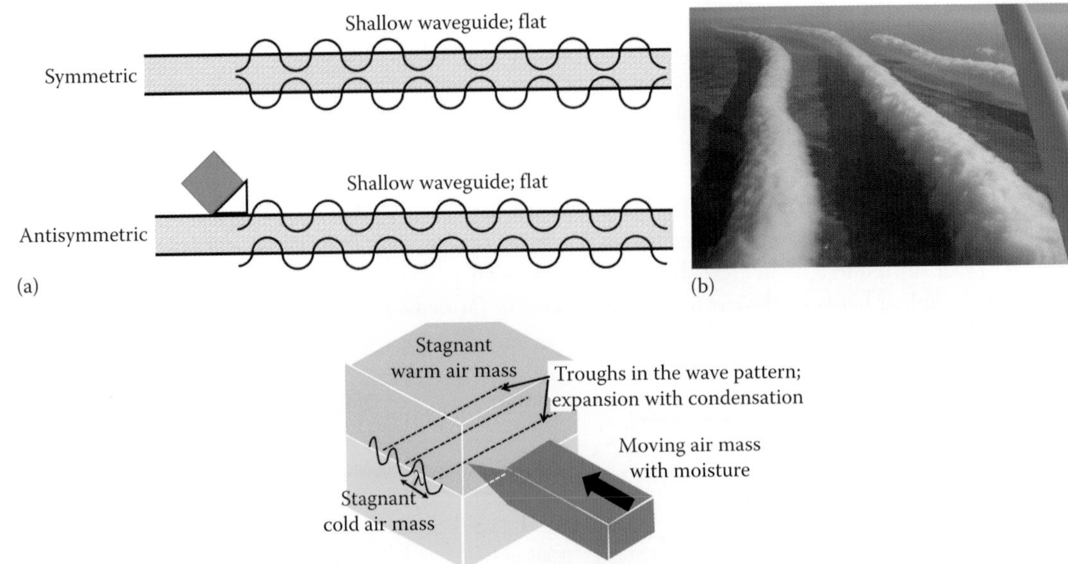

Figure L.10 (a) Lamb wave principle, (b) example of a Lamb wave in the atmosphere (Courtesy of Mick Petroff.), and (c) illustration of the process of the formation of a Lamb wave in the atmosphere.

Lamb–Retherford experiment

[atomic] Experimental configuration that lead to the verification of QUANTUM electrodynamic principles in 1947, as performed by WILLIS EUGENE LAMB (1913–2008) and his student Robert Retherford (1912–1981).

Lambda particle

[atomic, nuclear] BARYON particle as a subclassification of hadrons. Lambda particles have CHARM (c; charm: $_c$) of +1 (quark, spin: $(1/2)\hbar$, where $\hbar = h/2\pi$, with $h = 6.62606957 \times 10^{-34}\ \mathrm{m^2kg/s}$ Planck's constant; not ranking in "antiquark") or strangeness (s; strangeness: $_s$) of −1 (quark), associated flavors are "bottom" ($_b$) and "top" ($_t$). Furthermore, they are either neutral or have elementary charge +1. The nomenclature for the lambda baryons is as follows: Λ^0; quarks : uds, Λ_c^+; quarks : udc, Λ_b^0; quarks : udb, and Λ_t^+; quarks : udt. (*Note*: QUARK flavor—Up : u, Down : d, strange: s, Charmed: c, Bottom : b, and Top : t. The REST MASS of the lambda particle is 1115.60 MeV and has an average lifetime of 2.6×10^{-10} s.)

Lambda point

[atomic, thermodynamics] Transition in SPECIFIC HEAT for helium, specifically the morphing between the states of helium-1 and helium-2. The plot of the specific heat of helium as a function of temperature resembles the shape of the Greek letter lambda: λ (see Figure L.11).

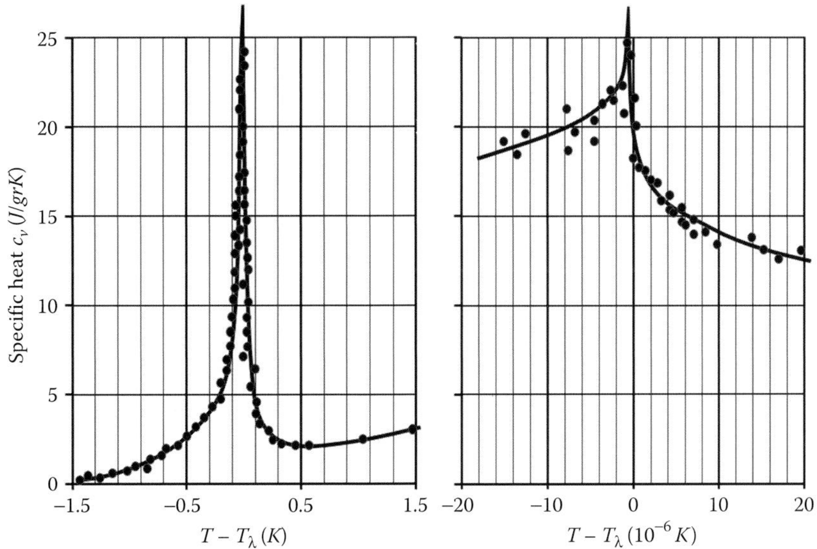

Figure L.11 Lambda point for helium.

Lambert, Johann Heinrich (1728–1777)

[general, thermodynamics] Physicist and mathematician from Switzerland. Lambert's experimental observations using the gas-based thermometer (THERMOSCOPE) as designed by GALILEO GALILEI (1564–1642), indicated the theoretical prediction of an ABSOLUTE ZERO temperature limit in 1770s. Lambert introduced hyperbolic function in trigonometry. Additional work by Johann Lambert is in the formulation of the diffuse emission from a surface (e.g., PHOSPHORESCENCE), known as LAMBERTIAN EMISSION PROFILE. Lambert also formulated the area calculations for hyperbolic triangles (with curved side), which do not have the ANGLES add to π. Additional work on attenuation of light with respect to penetration depth (z) in an attenuation, both SCATTERING and absorbing, medium decays exponentially with DISTANCE: $\Psi(z) = \Psi_0 e^{-i\mu z}$, with Ψ the radiance magnitude of ELECTROMAGNETIC RADIATION (Ψ_0 incident on the surface), and μ_{att} the attenuation coefficient, the combined effect of loss of light from the original path resulting from absorption (extinction) and scattering. The attenuation equation is also known as the Beer–Lambert law. This attenuation is essential in X-RAY diagnostics. The influence of scattering on the attenuation as captured by his introduction of the concept of albedo (α_a), the ratio of the SCATTERING to the combined effect of scattering and absorption. Generally, the albedo is used as an indication of reflectiveness (i.e., BACKSCATTER), where an albedo close to 1 represent total (diffuse) reflectivity (e.g., snow has an albedo of $\alpha_a = 0.9$) (see Figure L.12).

Figure L.12 Johann Heinrich Lambert (1728–1777).

Lambertian emission profile

[general, optics] Surface emission of light is proportional in MAGNITUDE to the cosine of the ANGLE with the normal to the surface: $\Psi \sim \Psi_0 \cos\theta$, in two-dimensional space (see Figure L.13).

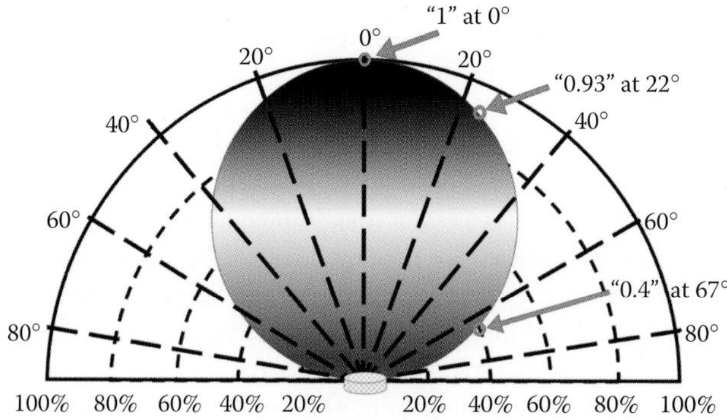

Figure L.13 Graphical representation of the Lambertian emission profile.

Lamé, Gabriel Léon (1795–1870)

[computational, mechanics] French mathematician and physicist who published his approach on stress and strain in cylinders in 1833 (see Figure L.14).

Figure L.14 Gabriel Léon Lamé (1795–1870).

Lamé coefficient

[acoustics, mechanics] In deformation the ELASTICITY of a medium can be defined with the Young's modulus (E_Y) and the POISSON'S RATIO (ν_P). These elastic properties are directly related to the stress $\sigma_{ij} = \lim_{\Delta A_j \to 0}(F_i/A_j)$ for a FORCE (F) in the i direction on a surface with normal in the j direction and strain ($\epsilon_{ii} = \partial v_i/\partial x_i$) in three dimensions as follows: E_Y = tensile stress/lengthwise strain $= \left[\mu_L\left(2\mu_L + 3\lambda_L\right)/\left(\mu_L + \lambda_L\right)\right]$ and ν_P = strain/lengthwise strain = lateral contraction/lengthwise strain $= \lambda_L/2\left(\mu_L + \lambda_L\right)$, where μ_L and λ_L are the Lamé coefficients, introduced by GABRIEL LÉON LAMÉ (1795–1870). The Lamé coefficients follow from the matrix description of three-dimensional deformation which in turn provides the coefficients (TENSOR) C_{mn} which relate stress and strain through $\sigma_{ij} = \sum C_{ijkl}\epsilon_{kl}$, where C_{ijkl} are the elastic moduli, which translates into 6 one-dimensional stress–strain relations as $\sigma_i = \sum C_{ij}\epsilon_j$. The Lamé coefficients are now defined by $C_{11} = C_{22} = C_{33} = 2\mu_L + \lambda_L$, $C_{12} = C_{23} = C_{13} = \lambda_L$, and $C_{44} = C_{55} = C_{66} = \mu_L$ (see Figure L.15).

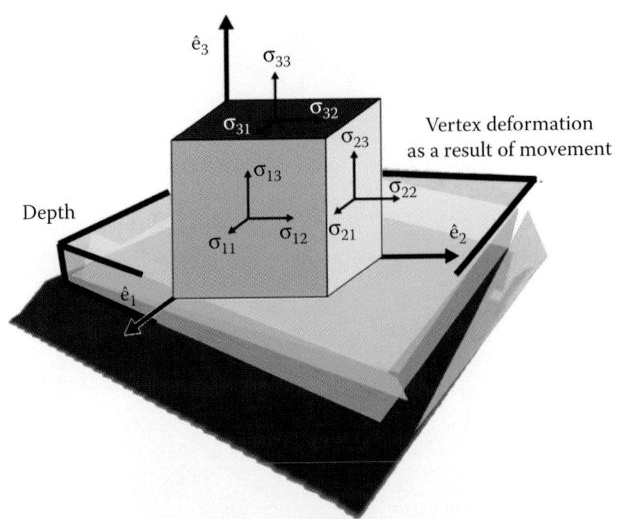

Figure L.15 Graphical illustration of elastic deformation, where ê indicates the normal vector with respect to the three respective surface planes.

Lamé equations

[computational] When changing the coordinate system in Laplace equations to an ellipsoidal coordinate system, the Laplace equations convert to Lamé equations. The Lamé equations were developed by Gabriel Léon Lamé (1795–1870) in 1837 to solve for cylindrical stress. The ordinary differential equation is as follows: $d^2y/dx^2 = \left(C_1 + C_2\mathcal{P}(x)\right)y$, where C_1 and C_2 are constants, and $\mathcal{P}(x)$ is an elliptic function called the Weierstrass elliptic function. The most intriguing case is when $C_1 \sim n(n+1)$, $n =$ integer. In the latter case the solutions include meromorphic functions, which extend into the complex plane. Generally, the solutions are ellipsoidal harmonic functions.

Lamina

[biomedical, fluid dynamics] Infinite wide plate, closed surface with density. In biology, this refers to a the structure and tissue composition of a layer in the wall of a blood vessel (see Figure L.16).

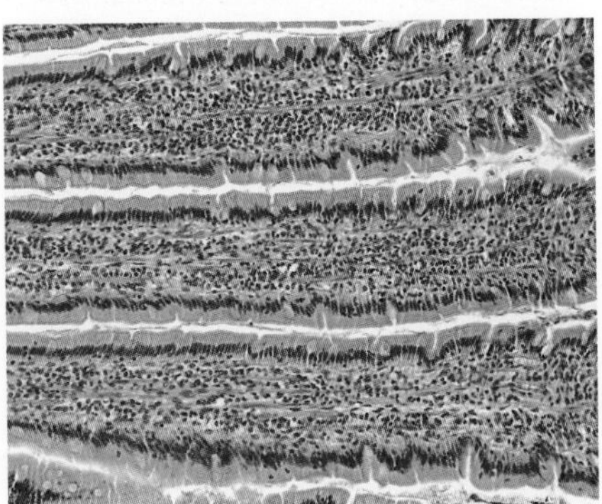

Figure L.16 Light microscope micrograph of the intestinal villi of the ileum portion of small intestine. Each villus contains a central axis of lamina propria covered with single columnar intestinal epithelium.

Laminar boundary layer, flat plate

[fluid dynamics] Flat surface that provides the idealized boundary conditions to maintain laminar flow.

Laminar flow

[biomedical, fluid dynamics, general] Parallel flow pattern devoid of TURBULENCE, very well organized with shear rate ($\dot{\gamma}$) that is linear with SHEAR STRESS (σ_s), as $\sigma_s = \eta(dv/dy) = \eta\dot{\gamma}$, with velocity v perpendicular to the shear direction, throughout the flowing medium (not accounting for BOUNDARY LAYER effects). Laminar flow is considered to occur for REYNOLDS NUMBER: Re < 2040 (see Figure L.17).

Figure L.17 (a) Example of engineering design for high-speed train to ensure laminar flow, (b) 1935 Rolls Royce PII Jonckheere Aerodynamic Coupe which presumably supports laminar flow, (c) aerodynamic bicycle helmet to ensure laminar flow around the head of the cyclist, reducing friction from an apparent vacuum that can appear behind the "irregular" shape of the human head resulting from turbulent flow, and (d) laminar stream lines around the Volkswagen XL1 hybrid automobile. (Courtesy Volkswagen Aktiengesellschaft.)

Laminar flow, pipes

[fluid dynamics] Linear flow in a round tube is symmetric around the central axis, creating a parabolic FLOW pattern with maximum velocity on the central axis. The velocity (v) is defined by the DISTANCE to the

WALL (r), the VISCOSITY of the LIQUID (η), the pressure gradient over the stretch of PIPE (P) with length L as well as the radius of the pipe (R): $v(r) = (P_2 - P_1)(R^2 - r^2)/4\eta L$ (see Figure L.18).

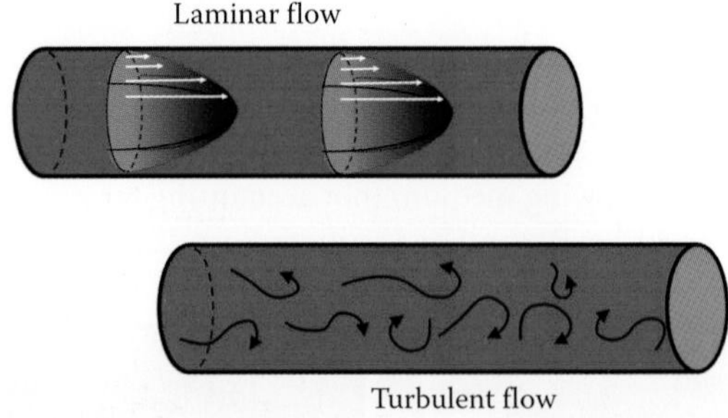

Figure L.18 Laminar pipe flow with velocity distribution. Turbulent flow transports fluids with a slower average velocity than under laminar flow conditions.

Laminar frictional resistance

[fluid dynamics] The effects of the restraining force between adjacent sliding layers (with effective area A), separated over a DISTANCE y, moving with velocity v defined as the VISCOSITY (η): $F = \eta A(v/y)$, also found in differential format (SIR ISAAC NEWTON [1642–1727]) in the format of shear: $\sigma = F/A$, expressed as $\sigma = \eta(dv/dy)$.

L

Laminar sublayer

[biomedical, fluid dynamics] Layer in mixed flow system where turbulent flow is separated from a different medium (e.g., WALL), with no-slip conditions, where the FLOW conditions are laminar. This is also referred to as the viscous sublayer. The REYNOLDS NUMBER decreases on approach to the boundary until laminar conditions are met (see Figure L.19).

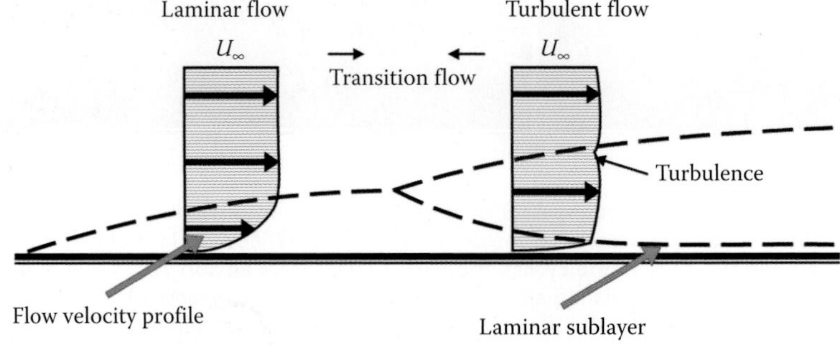

Figure L.19 Laminar sublayer, separating the turbulent layer from a surface over which the flow is guided.

Laminin

[biomedical, chemical] Protein chain in biological media, sometimes used to form peptides. Laminin is an essential component in certain CELL ADHESION processes, the chemical and electric gradient in the anchoring substrate will draw in cells for structural organization (see Figure L.20).

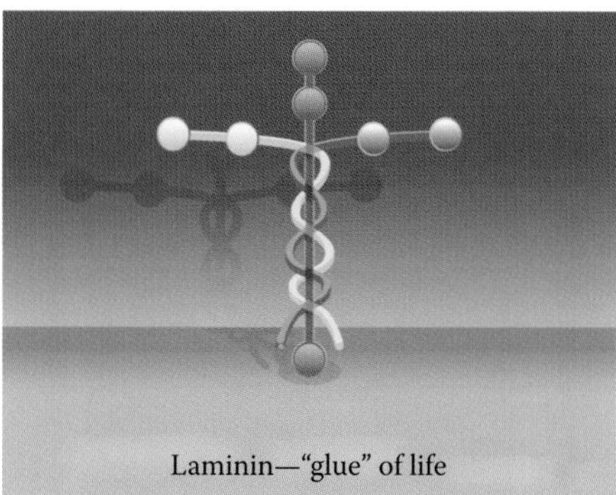

Figure L.20 Laminin protein analogy.

Land, Edwin Herbert (1909–1991)

[chemical, general] Scientist of the United States. Land is best known for his invention of the Polaroid CAMERA and film concept, next to the introduction of a dichroic POLARIZATION selective sheet. The POLYMER film is a NITROCELLULOSE (transparent) with iodoquinine sulfate crystals embedded. The iodoquinine sulfate (herapathite) oxidizes to form an instantaneous fixed IMAGE of the projected representation (see Figure L.21).

Figure L.21 Edwin Herbert Land (1909–1991). (Courtesy of Seymour "Sy" Brody, produced by Art Seiden.)

Landau, Lev Davidovich (1908–1968)

[astrophysics/astronomy, computational, energy, fluid dynamics, general, thermodynamics] Physicist from Soviet Russia (USSR) who contributed to the development of the general foundation of theoretical physics. His work covered the description of thermodynamic equations as well as the introduction of quantum liquid also referred to as Fermi liquid, specifically of the "Bose"-type. Landau received the Nobel Prize in Physics in 1962 (see Figure L.22).

Figure L.22 Lev Davidovich Landau (1908–1968).

Landau theory

[computational, thermodynamics] Classical mechanics mechanism with respect to condensed matter, and in particular superfluidity. One specific area of interest is liquid helium. The theory of second-order phase transitions was introduced by Lev Davidovich Landau (1908–1968) in 1937. The concept relies on the fact that the minimum Gibbs free energy (G) determines the state of the equilibrium situation for a phase of a medium at a critical temperature T_c. The principle uses the fact that the first-order differential for the free energy is not zero: $\partial G/\partial T\big|_{T=T_c} \neq 0$, delivering a situation where the enthalpy (S) and entropy (H) are also not zero; under the condition $G = G_0 + \Delta H - T\Delta S$, note ΔH is the latent heat. Additionally, the following conditions also follow: $\partial^2 G/\partial T^2\big|_{T=T_c} \neq 0$, and $\partial^3 G/\partial T^3\big|_{T=T_c} \neq 0$. Expressed in electron spin field distribution this translates the Gibbs free energy into $G = B\Phi_s + r\Phi_s{}^2 + s\Phi_s{}^4$, where Φ_s represents the spin field, also known as the "total magnetization," $r = r_0\left(T - T_c\right)$, B the external magnetic field and $s = (1/N)\sum_i s_i$ the magnetization. Below the critical temperature the medium may reach superfluidic conditions, resembling the absence of viscosity. In liquid helium this relates to the Bose–Einstein condensate.

Landau–Darrieus instability

[astrophysics/astronomy, computational, energy, fluid dynamics, thermodynamics] A hydrodynamic instability in a solar flare eruption formation. A thermonuclear flame can be described as being affected by gravitational and capillary forces. The deflagration wave of a solar flare (i.e., ejected flame) can experience effects from the ash, which is light compared to the fuel and the vertical (i.e., radially outward) velocity of the ash (v_{ash}) is different from the vertical velocity of the fuel (v_{fuel}). The instability results in "creasing" of the flame. The wave dispersion associated with the wavenumber of the phenomenon (k) in the flare propagation is described by $\tau_{decay}{}^2\left(v_{fuel} + v_{ash}\right) + 2\tau_{decay} k v_{fuel} v_{ash} + k^2\left(v_{fuel} - v_{ash}\right) v_{fuel} v_{ash} - gk\left(v_{fuel} - v_{ash}\right) = 0$, where τ_{decay} represents the

DECAY rate of the combustion and g is the GRAVITATIONAL ACCELERATION on the STAR. The phenomenon is also influenced by Rayleigh–Taylor instabilities as well as Kelvin–Helmholtz instabilities. The dispersion creates TURBULENCE resulting from the convective instabilities next to the deflagration itself (see Figure L.23).

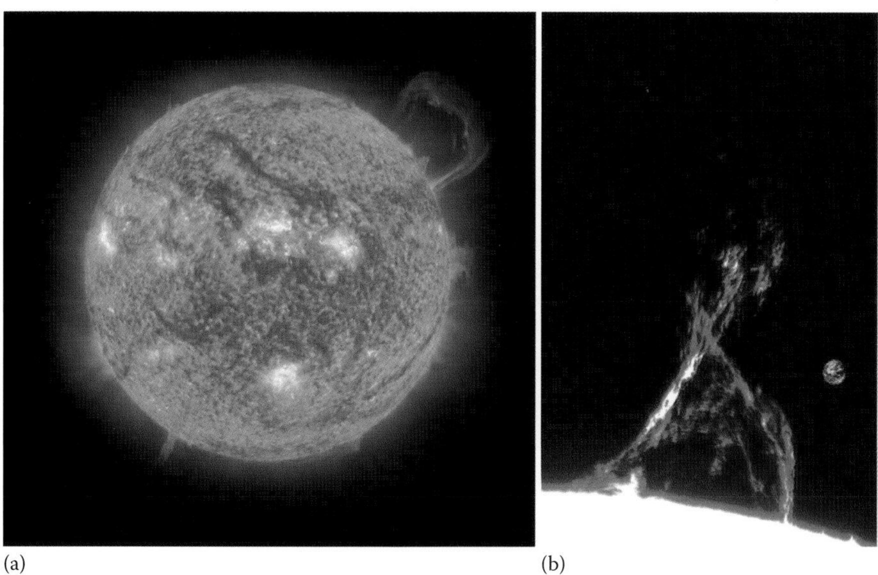

(a) (b)

Figure L.23 (a,b) Landau–Darrieus instability of a solar flare. (Courtesy of National Aeronautics and Space Administration [NASA], Washington, DC.)

Lande's *g*-factor

[atomic] *See* **G-FACTOR, TOTAL ANGULAR MOMENTUM.**

Lane–Emden equation

[astrophysics/astronomy, thermodynamics] Poisson equation expressed in dimensionless format. The Lane–Emden equation defines the gravitational potential in a Newtonian environment pertaining to the hydrostatic equilibrium describing the plasma PRESSURE (P) (as a GAS) of stars: $P = \kappa\rho^{\gamma_\ell}$, where κ and $\gamma_\ell = \left(n_p + 1\right)/n_p$, with n_p the polytropic index, are process constants and ρ the density.

Langevin, Paul (1872–1946)

[acoustics, computational, electromagnetism, imaging, solid-state] Scientist and engineer from France. Langevin worked on PARAMAGNETISM and also introduced the first underwater sonographic probing system. The first operation mechanism of SONOGRAPHY used a QUARTZ transducer operating under the PIEZOELECTRIC EFFECT. The sonograph was used in submarines for range detection and navigation, PAUL LANGEVIN is sometimes referred to as the father of ULTRASONICS. Other contributions of Paul Langevin are in computational PHYSICS with respect to his description of dynamic properties, specifically under paramagnetic conditions captured by the LANGEVIN FORMULA as well as the LANGEVIN EQUATION for PARTICLE displacement in a viscous liquid (see Figure L.24).

Figure L.24 Paul Langevin (1872–1946).

L

Langevin equation

[acoustics, computational, electromagnetism, imaging, solid-state] The equivalence of BROWNIAN MOTION for a PARTICLE with mass m suspended in a LIQUID can be described by an equation of MOTION defined as $m\left(dv/dt\right)+\gamma_{\mathrm{damp}}v=\sum F\left(t\right)$, where v is the velocity of the particle in random motion as a function of time (t), with a dampening force: $\gamma_{\mathrm{damp}}v$ to equal the sum of the external forces changing with time (F). The external forces may be applied based on compression, as under ULTRASOUND wave propagation. The solutions to this Langevin equation provide the coefficients (a and b) to the Fokker–Planck equation: $\partial P/\partial t=(1/2)\left(\partial^2/\partial x^2\right)\left(bP\right)-\left(\partial/\partial x\right)\left(aP\right)$, where P represents the local pressure and making the following substitutions: $a=\alpha v$, $\alpha=\gamma_{\mathrm{damp}}/m$, and $b=2D$, where $\gamma_{\mathrm{damp}}=\left(1/k_bT\right)\int_0^{\infty}F\left(t\right)F\left(0\right)dt$ is the dampening coefficient derived from STOKES' LAW, where Boltzmann coefficient $k_b=1.3806488\times10^{-23}\,\mathrm{m^2kg/s^2K}$. This transforms into an expression for Brownian motion, known as the Ornstein–Uhlenbeck equation: $\partial P/\partial t=D\left(\partial^2/\partial v^2\right)P+\alpha\left(\partial/\partial v\right)\left(vP\right)$.

Langevin formula

[acoustics, computational, electromagnetism, imaging, solid-state] When the MAGNETIC SUSCEPTIBILITY (χ_{magn}) of a material is positive the material is considered to be paramagnetic. The magnetic susceptibility is the Langevin expression for the balance between thermal disorder (as a function of MOTION due to temperature T) and the preferential alignment of the magnetic dipoles, with magnetic moment μ_{mag}, with respect to an externally applied MAGNETIC FIELD (B) as: $\chi_{\mathrm{mag}}=\mu_0N\mu_{\mathrm{mag}}{}^2/3\,\mathrm{kT}$, where $\mu_0=4\pi\times10^{-7}\,\mathrm{Tm/A}$ is the DIELECTRIC permeability of VACUUM, N the number of magnetic dipoles per unit volume, and $k=1.380658\times10^{-23}$ J/K the Boltzmann constant. Also referred to as the MAGNETIC SUSCEPTIBILITY.

Langmuir, Irving (1881–1957)

[atomic, chemical, solid-state] Scientist and chemist from the United States. Langmuir contributed to the theoretical description of the atomic structure and is attributed with the invention of the incandescent light bulb. Langmuir received the Nobel Prize in Chemistry in 1932 (see Figure L.25).

Figure L.25 Irving Langmuir (1881–1957).

L

Langmuir equation

[biomedical, computational, nuclear] Exposure of a surface to the molecules of a SOLUTE or GAS during random MOTION. The surface will adsorb the molecules depending on concentration or pressure respectively (P) within a fractional of the total MAGNITUDE of the medium (θ_L). In order of magnitude, this is expressed as $\theta_L = \alpha_L P/(1+\alpha_L P)$, where α_L is the Langmuir ADSORPTION coefficient which is a function of temperature and adsorption BINDING ENERGY. Also known as the Langmuir isotherm.

Langmuir probe

[atomic, nuclear] Devise inspired by IRVING LANGMUIR (1881–1957) to determine the electron density, electron temperature, and electric potential of a plasma. The mechanism of action is indirect, relying on the addition of one single or more (quantity known) electrons to a system and determining the changes to the PLASMA configuration, specifically under time-varying conditions. The theoretical description is based the characteristic current–voltage of the Debye sheath. The Debye sheath represents a layer in a plasma with excess POSITIVE CHARGE resulting from a greater density of POSITIVE IONS.

Laplace, Pierre-Simon de, Marquis de Laplace (1749–1827)

[astrophysics/astronomy, computational, general] Mathematician, physicist, and astronomer from France. Laplace is best known for his work in PROBABILITY as well as equation of MOTION. His theoretical work on the PLANETARY MOTION as well as the description of orbits and shapes of planets contributed to the first known attempt to describe the formation and stability of the SOLAR SYSTEM. Other work by Laplace involves the theoretical formulation of various thermodynamic and FLUID dynamic concepts. The LAPLACE EQUATION carries his name (see Figure L.26).

Figure L.26 Pierre-Simon Laplace, Marquis de Laplace (1749–1827). (Courtesy of Grands hommes et grands faits de la Révolution française (1789–1804); Jouvet & Cie, éditeurs; Magasin Pittoresque (E. Best), Paris, France, 1889.)

L

Laplace equation

[atomic, biomedical, computational, fluid dynamics] Second-order homogeneous differential equation: $\nabla^2 X = \text{div grad}\, X = 0$, for a general function X describing, for instance, MOTION of heat and ∇^2 the Laplacian operator; a second-order derivative in the coordinate system of preference (e.g., Cartesian, cylindrical, or spherical), introduced by PIERRE SIMON DE LAPLACE, MARQUIS DE LAPLACE (1749–1827).

Laplace law

[biomedical, fluid dynamics, mechanics] {use: lung, pressure, communicating vessels} A vessel under pressure will generally strive for equal distribution of forces, resulting in a spherical geometry. This assumption is based on constant and equal material properties. One example that does not fit the spherical profile is an inflated rubber balloon. A vessel with radius r has the following relationship between the pressure inside the vessel P and the tension T in the WALL: $P = 2T/r$. The condition described by the Laplace law is a result of the force equation describing equilibrium between the force applied by pressure on to half domes and the tension along the circumference of the sphere. Considering a sphere with radius r and pressure P the force on one hemisphere is $F_{\text{pressure}} = \pi r^2 P$, the force exerted by tension is $F_{\text{tension}} = 2\pi r T$. Equating the two forces yields the Laplace condition. In this situation when two vessel of unequal pressure are connected, the higher pressure will induce FLOW due to the PRESSURE GRADIENT and if the generally smaller bulb were flexible it would disappear, otherwise it would merely empty out to the point of equal pressure. In a biological system such as the lung, the situation of unequal pressure between adjacent alveoli is very likely. The alveoli compensate for this by applying a variable tension through a connective matrix of ELASTIN, collagen fiber and the septa, resulting in an omnidirectional tension that is volume/size dependent. Additional traction influences may be provided by means of a coating on the inner surface with a SURFACTANT that diminishes the SURFACE TENSION as the circumference of the bulb decreases. The alveolar structure thus prevents the lungs from gradually turning into one large bulb which significantly reduces surface area, whereas the surface area provides the opportunity for the exchange of oxygen and carbon dioxide and area MAGNITUDE is crucial to the efficiency of the GAS EXCHANGE. The concept was introduced by PIERRE SIMON DE LAPLACE, MARQUIS DE LAPLACE (1749–1827) (*also see* **HOOKE'S LAW**) (see Figure L.27).

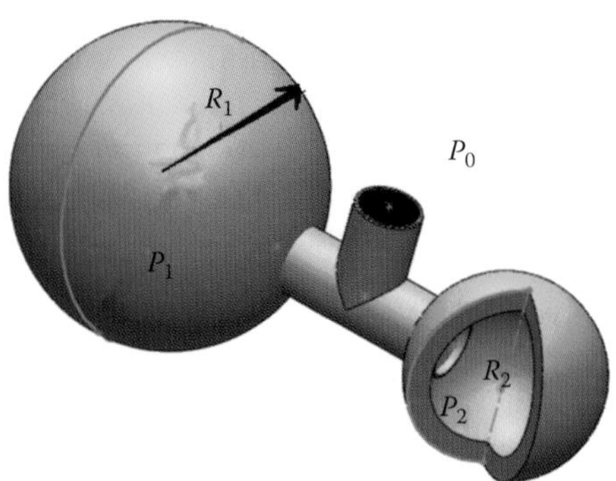

Figure L.27 Illustration of the concept of the Laplace law.

Laplace transform

[computational] The cause–effect description between a perturbation $P_{\text{cause}}(t)$ with response $R_{\text{effect}}(t)$ as a function of time in a linear system can be expressed as $R_{\text{effect}}(t)=\int_{-\infty}^{t}\chi(t-t')P_{\text{cause}}(t')dt'$, where χ describes the response function over time prior to time t, based on the work of PIERRE SIMON DE LAPLACE, MARQUIS DE LAPLACE (1749–1827). The other side of the coin is the fact that this defines the convolution: $R_{\text{effect}}(t)=(\chi * P_{\text{cause}})(t)$. The convolution yields the FOURIER TRANSFORM: $R_{\text{effect}}(\omega)=\int_{-\infty}^{\infty}R_{\text{effect}}(t)e^{-i\omega t}dt=\int_{-\infty}(\chi * P_{\text{cause}})(t)e^{-i\omega t}dt=\chi(\omega)P_{\text{cause}}(\omega)$. The response as a function of time $R_{\text{effect}}(t)$ can be measured to yield the frequency-dependent response function $\chi(\omega)$, where $\omega=\nu 2\pi$, the ANGULAR FREQUENCY and ν the frequency of the event.

Laporte, Otto (1902–1971)

[atomic, computational, nuclear, quantum, solid-state] Physicist from Germany who made significant contributions to the theoretical formulations of quantum PHYSICS concepts, fluid mechanics, WAVE mechanics, and OPTICS (see Figure L.28).

Figure L.28 Otto Laporte (1902–1971).

Laporte rule

[atomic, nuclear, optics, quantum, solid-state] Definition in optical SPECTROSCOPY with respect to atoms, and molecules that are symmetric around an INVERSION center (centrosymmetric), relating the forbidden electron transitions. Named after the work by OTTO LAPORTE (1902–1971). The transitions that only would involve a redistribution of the electrons within a specific SUBSHELL will be forbidden based on ENERGY balance, hence these will not produce emission. In case the symmetry is disrupted, these transitions will now be allowed due to the change in energy. In case these apparently FORBIDDEN TRANSITIONS are observed the local (MOLECULE/ATOM) energy configuration must be disturbed, that is, the structure is no longer centrosymmetric, which may occur in oscillatory form. The periodic disturbance will be experimentally recognized in a periodic spectral emission format.

Large Eddy simulation (LES)

[biomedical, computational, fluid dynamics] Mathematical model used in computational FLUID DYNAMICS, specifically pertaining to TURBULENCE. Fully developed turbulence is achieved under high REYNOLDS NUMBER: $Re \gg 10^3$. The turbulence is captured by a VORTEX stretching term $\vec{\omega} \cdot \nabla \vec{v}$, where $\vec{v}$ is the FLOW velocity vector and $\vec{\omega} = \omega_0 e^{\gamma_v t} e_i$ the "VORTICITY" (equivalent rotational MOTION, with representative angular velocity), where e_i the ith unit vector for dimension in a n-dimensional system $(i < n)$, $\omega_0 = \omega(t)\big|_{t=0}$ and γ_v the EIGENVALUE of the matrix solution $(\mathcal{D})$ to the adjusted Euler/Navier–Stokes approach: $\mathcal{D}\omega/\mathcal{D}t = \mathcal{D}\omega + v\Delta\omega$. This is different than the analytical approach by means of Navier–Stokes equation SOLUTION, even with turbulence incorporated. This is usually solved through finite-element methods. One example of a condition that would illustrate these conditions is the flow from the HEART as the VALVE opens into the AORTA (see Figure L.29).

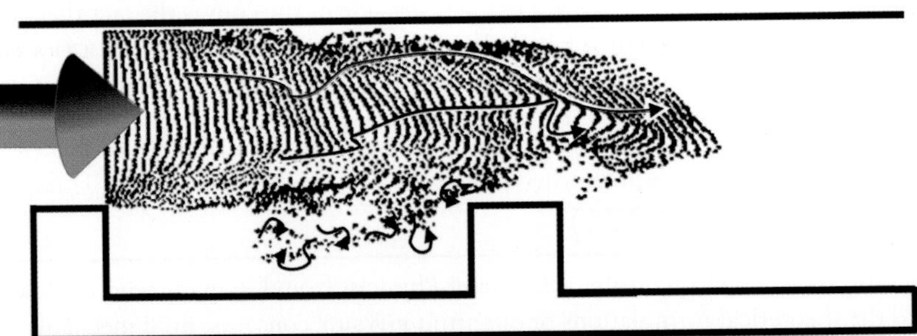

Figure L.29 Graphical representation of a large eddy simulation for turbulent flow over a ridge for Reynolds number Re = 1.10 × 10^4 where the partially dotted lines are isovelocity lines.

Larmor, Joseph, Sir (1857–1942)

[atomic, general, nuclear, thermodynamics] Mathematician and physicist from Great Britain. The work of Sir Larmor dates back to 1901, when he described the particles emitted by CATHODE under high electrical potential as electrons, negatively charged which help a positively charged core. The model does not describe the ATOM with electrons around a NUCLEUS as of yet. Other works of Larmor is in the mathematical description of the axial spinning of the MAGNETIC moment of a charge in which the axis of the magnetic moment has a center point in common with the axis of revolution but where the magnetic moment vector does not line up with the axis of rotation. The vector moves in precession around the axis at a fixed ANGLE under constant ENERGY, that is, LARMOR PRECESSION. The Larmor precession directly relates to magnetic RESONANCE imaging. The PRECESSION occurs with a regularity that is defined by the LARMOR FREQUENCY (see Figure L.30).

Figure L.30 Sir Joseph Larmor (1857–1942).

Larmor frequency (ω)

[atomic, biomedical, nuclear, quantum] Frequency at which the MAGNETIC vector of the ELECTRON SPIN pivots in angular MOTION around the axis of rotation under the influence of an applied external MAGNETIC FIELD (B): $\omega = \gamma B = eH/2mc$, where γ is the GYROMAGNETIC RATIO, e/c the electron charge in electromagnetic units, e electron charge in Coulomb, $c = 2.99792458 \times 10^8$ m/s the speed of light, and $H = B/\mu_0$, where $\mu_0 = 4\pi \times 10^{-7}$ Tm/A $= 4\pi \times 10^{-7}$ H/m $= 4\pi \times 10^{-7}$ N/A^2 is the magnetic permeability for vacuum $\omega_0 = \gamma B_0$. The concept was introduced in 1897 by SIR JOSEPH LARMOR (1857–1942). The Bloch equation describes the magnetization vector behavior as it applies to nuclear magnetic RADIATION found in magnetic RESONANCE imaging as $dM/dt = M \times \gamma B$, where M = magnetization vector and t = time. The operator $\times$ represents vector multiplication.

Larmor precession

[atomic, biomedical, nuclear, quantum] Precession of a (revolving) charged PARTICLE when subjected to an external MAGNETIC FIELD. The PRECESSION will take place with the LARMOR FREQUENCY (see Figure L.31).

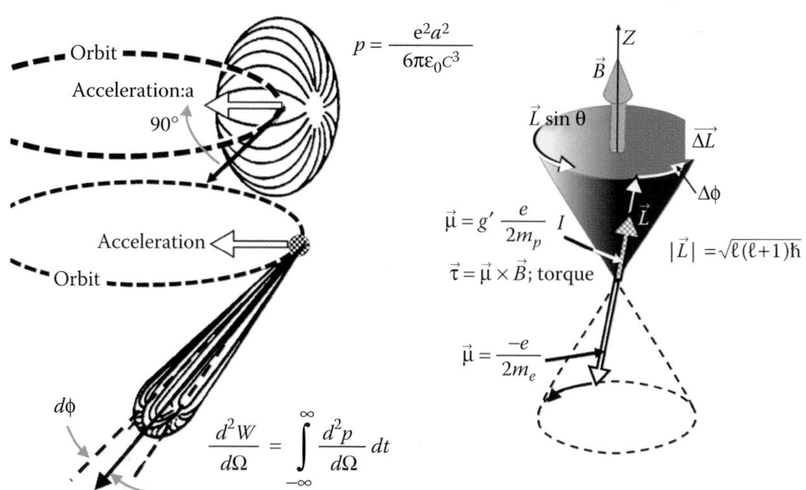

Figure L.31 Graphical representation of the Larmor precession and frequency concept.

LASER

[biomedical, chemical, optics, thermodynamics] Acronym for *L*ight *A*mplification by *S*timulated *E*mission of *R*adiation. Coherent source of directional ELECTROMAGNETIC RADIATION of a single wavelength of a narrow spectral emission bandwidth. The word LASER is documented in the lab notebook of one of the claimed inventors, GORDON GOULD (1920–2005) from the United States, dated November 13, 1957; against the patent claims of constructing the first operational laser by THEODORE HAROLD MAIMAN (1927–2007). Both scientists were inspired by the theoretical work of CHARLES HARD TOWNES (1915–2015) and ARTHUR LEONARD SCHAWLOW (1921–1999) in 1958. The primary concept of "STIMULATED EMISSION" was introduced by ALBERT EINSTEIN (1879–1955) in 1917. The controversial but final decree on the first person to construct a working laser has been granted to Theodore Maiman. Theodore Maiman introduced his ruby laser (Cr_2O_3) in 1960, emitting in the (infra-) red (694.3nm). Stimulated emission is the emission of an identical photon to the PHOTON "passing" the atomic system that has an electron in an excited state with equal or greater ENERGY than the energy of the incident photon. The physical DECAY in energy state produces an accelerated electron, which is the primary requirement for the generation of electromagnetic waves. The electron MOTION by itself produces a current which induces a magnetic field; AMPÈRE'S LAW. An accelerated electron will have a changing electric field (GAUSS'S LAW), resulting inherently in the generation of a changing MAGNETIC FIELD, hence electromagnetic radiation is the ultimate result. All these concepts are captured by the electromagnetic theories of JAMES CLERK MAXWELL (1831–1879). Laser light is coherent, representing the fact that the PHASE of all the photons are aligned, in-phase. Incoherent sources, such as a light bulb, produce light from multiple oscillating charges that are not synchronized, nor do they have any constraints on the emission wavelength. Any LIGHT SOURCE requires a medium, for lasers the restriction on the formulation of the medium are very strict to ensure the generation of either a single wavelength or a narrow EMISSION SPECTRUM that can be confined by optical means to provide laser emission at a single wavelength only. The atoms and molecules in a medium used for stimulated emission interact with electromagnetic radiation in three manners: absorption, spontaneous emission, and stimulated emission. The absorption of photons results in an excited state. EXCITED STATES may also be induced by means of other energy sources, such as electrical current (e.g., gas laser and DIODE LASER) or chemical reactions (chemical laser). The spontaneous emission where the excited electron decays to the GROUND STATE may be the initial photon release, which is subsequently used to excite the decay of an entire population of excited electrons by stimulated emission. The laser mechanism of action relies on the continuous generation of a large quantity of excited electronic states for the atoms and molecules in the medium to provide the "fuel" for the operation of stimulated emission. The release of a single wavelength photon stream constitutes MONOCHROMATIC LIGHT. Furthermore, the optical construction of the excitation mechanism and emission medium results in a parallel beam. The beam is by definition coherent since all photons are traveling in sync and are released though excitation from the initial photon with cascade effect: 1,2,4,8,16,... photons. The optical construction of the laser is called a cavity, confining the photons in a linear path between two mirrors: the total reflection mirror and the output MIRROR with reflectivity slightly less than 100%. In addition to the fact that the excited electron states need to be replenished to maintain the conditions for stimulated emission, the excited states need to have a surplus. The excited states also need to remain stable long enough to allow for stimulated emission to occur, not decay spontaneously. The third requirement is that the photons will need to be confined to the medium in persistent excited states long enough to provide stimulated emission. The excitation mechanism will greatly depend on the type of laser. The long-lived excited state is referred to as a metastable state, with lifetime exceeding 10^{-8} s, to ensure the preferential occurrence of stimulated over spontaneous emission. The metastable excited state condition is the result of the chemical design of the medium; the type of laser. The final requirement is satisfied through a geometric and optical design that confines the photons to a linear path by means of accurate placement of mirrors on opposite sides of the medium with associated optical constraints. One mirror having 100% reflectivity and one mirror with less than 100% reflectivity; reflectivity requirements depend on the application, operation (continuous or pulsed), and the excitation mechanism (chemical constituents of the medium and the excitation energy delivery). The principle of ensuring an excess of stimulated electron energy states for the medium is known as "Einstein population inversion." The Einstein population inversion is based on the work of ALBERT EINSTEIN (1879–1955). The Einstein population inversion will require an amount of energy that is a function of the total number of electron targets for excitation and the excitation efficiency with respect to the interaction between the excitation energy source and the atomic configurations in the "laser medium." The excitation efficiency also will depend on the number and energy configuration of the available excitable states. The excited state may have several bands, which can be split into various modes. Each energy mode will be defined through a characteristic lifetime (τ_c). In the Einstein population inversion scheme, the number of modes ($\square_m$) at a single energy level are defined by the denomination N_m. Assuming for convenience a system with only two modes (N_1 and N_2), the MINIMUM ENERGY requirements for sustained stimulated emission can be derived. In case externally delivered light is used to induce excited states, the excitation photon energy is defined through the Planck relationship: $E = h\nu = h(c/\lambda)$ ($h = 6.62606957 \times 10^{-34}$ m^{2}kg/s the Planck's constant, ν the electromagnetic frequency, λ the associated wavelength, and $c = 2.99792458 \times 10^8$ m/s the speed of light). In order for excitation to be effective, the incident photon energy needs to match the difference in energy level between the ground state (E_1) and the excited state (E_2) in the two-state system: $E_2 - E_1 = h\nu_0$; ν_0 the emission wavelength. The required number of excited states (N_m) to provide a self-sustained operation yield the required pump power: $P = N_m hc/\lambda_0\tau_c$. The POPULATION INVERSION is dominated by the ratio between the characteristic lifetime and the emission lifetime (τ_e). This provides the population difference between the two hypothetical states as the "POPULATION INVERSION": $\Delta N = N_2 - N_1 = N_m\tau_e/\tau_c$. Keeping in mind the initial condition of spontaneous emission, the decay rate for the excited electrons is directly proportional to the number of excited states $dN_2/dt = -A_{21}N_2 = -R_{21}N_2 = -B_{21}U(\nu_0)N_2$, with A_{21} the PROBABILITY coefficient for spontaneous emission, also referred to as Einstein coefficient; B_{21} the stimulation probability; and $U(\nu_0)$ the energy distribution derived from the Planck equation $U(\nu_0)d\nu = \nu^2/c^3 h\nu\left\{\exp(h\nu/k_bT)-1\right\}^{-1} d\nu = E'h\nu n d\nu$ ($k_b = 1.3806488 \times 10^{-23}$ m^{2}kg/s^{2}K the Boltzmann coefficient, T the ABSOLUTE TEMPERATURE, n the average number of resonant energy density states, and E' representing the resonant energy density per photon/excited electron), respectively, under equilibrium boundary conditions: $U(\nu_0) = A_{21}\left\{B_{12}\left[N_1/N_2\right] - B_{21}\right\}$. The factor $R_{21} = \Phi_{phot}\sigma_{21}$ represents the stimulated emission rate, as function of the photon flux (Φ_{phot}) and (σ_{21}) the CROSS SECTION for stimulated emission under influence of an incident photon. The photon absorption providing the stimulated states follows the same principle: $dN_1/dt = R_{12}N_1 = -B_{12}U(\nu_0)N_1$, where B_{12} the absorption coefficient. The coefficients A_{21}, B_{21}, and B_{12} are the Einstein coefficients. Under 100% efficiency the metastable state is defined with the decay rate provided as $dN_2/dt = -A_{21}N_2 + B_{12}U(\nu_0)N_1 - B_{21}U(\nu_0)N_2 = -dN_1/dt$. The metastable state is further defined through $B_{12} = (g_1'/g_2')B_{21}$, where the RADIATION weights g_1' and g_2' for the energy levels are correlated through $N_2/N_1 = (g_1'/g_2')\exp(-h\nu/k_bT)$. The transitions are confined under the PAULI EXCLUSION PRINCIPLE and the de Broglie orbital restriction. These conditions describe the situation of one-to-one relationship between the stimulated and spontaneous emission under the condition $n < 1$, while $n > 1$ will produce stimulated emission. The fact that the electron orbit is not perfect enhances the broadening of the energy spread line. The final emission linewidth will follow from the ultimate optical configuration of the cavity. Once stimulated emission has been accomplished (by setting the appropriate operational conditions), the photons need to be harnessed for amplification. Placing mirror on opposite side provides a means for amplification in the direction of propagation z: $d\Phi_{phot}/dz = d\Phi_{phot}/cdt = dN/dt = R_{21}N_2 - R_{12}N_1 = \Phi_{phot}\sigma_{21}N_2 - \Phi_{phot}\sigma_{12}N_1 = \sigma\Phi_{phot}\Delta N$, assuming that the cross sections are equal. The critical population inversion based on a cavity with a medium of length ℓ, and mirrors with reflectivity r_1 and r_2 and stimulated condition information, comes to $\Delta N_c = -\ln(r_1r_2)/2\sigma\ell$. The excitation source is required to have a greater energy content than the emitted photons, hence the pump source has either a shorter wavelength of the energy from the electrical current of chemical reaction is substantial within the time frame of the stable excited electron. The PUMP efficiency for laser is only a few percent and the remaining energy will need to be discarded as heat, requiring a cooling mechanism. Lasers are classified based on the medium and the following categories are recognized: chemical, diode, dye, gas, SOLID-STATE, and free-electron laser (FEL). Chemical laser operate based on energy released from either a chemical FLOW of medium with irreversible reaction achieved at MIXING or a reversible chemical reaction. Chemical lasers typically use molecular rather than atomic transitions. One chemical laser, atomic iodine, does operate on atomic level (emission at 1.3 μm), while hydrogen fluoride (HF) and deuterium fluoride

(DF) provide examples of laser operating on molecular level. Due to the low energy content of the chemical reaction, the emission wavelength will be in the INFRARED. The HF laser has broad emission spectrum due to the ill-defined energy content of the molecular chemical reaction, operating in the band 2.6 – 3.3 μm, as do virtually all chemical lasers. The diode laser or semiconductor laser uses the standard semiconductor materials used in diodes and induces light emission at the *pn*-JUNCTION resulting from electrical current, encapsulated by mirrors. The accelerated charge principle is achieved by means of the applied electrical potential and obligatory current, forcefully dislocating electrons and inherent charge recombination with holes. Continuously creating new holes by migrating electrons provides the photon emission. An aluminum–gallium–arsenide (AlGaAs) semiconductor laser, for instance, produces light in a broadband ranging from 760–790 nm, and a gallium–arsenide (GaAs) semiconductor laser, for instance, produces light in a broadband ranging from 807–840 nm. Generally, diode laser are producing low power output, but his is still a developing field. Dye lasers operate on the flow of a CHROMOPHORE in LIQUID form that is excited by an external laser or a flash lamp. Due to the relatively broad emission spectrum, resulting from the broad excitation energy range, dye lasers are commonly tunable, and can be adjusted to the specific needs of the application. One favorite pigment for dye laser operation id the rhodamine chromophore. Dye lasers are popular in tattoo removal just because of the ability to tune the laser for optimal parameters with regard to the tattoo dye, the skin COLOR, and the vascularization in the treatment area. Some dye lasers can be tuned in the spectrum ranging from 360 – 720 nm, with continuous improvements and expansions as technology progresses. Liquid laser may be considered dye lasers, and groups have achieved laser action from their favorite alcoholic substance; for instance, the whiskey laser. GAS lasers use an electrical discharge as the pump mechanism in various noble gases, ranging from argon, to helium–neon and krypton ION. One gas laser operating at a very short wavelength is the Excimer laser (xenon chloride) operating at 308 nm nitrogen laser at 337.1 nm. Due to the temporary nature of the gas discharge these are primarily pulsed lasers. The solid-state laser is where it all started with the ruby crystal. Solid-state lasers generally rely on pumping by means of light sources: other lasers or flash lamp. The ruby laser uses a "dope" to provide the narrow emission excitation process, in this case chromium imbedded in a sapphire LATTICE, emitting at 694.3 nm. Another well-known solid-state laser is the neodymium:yttrium–aluminum–garnet laser, where the neodymium dope provides the wavelength of choice either at the first wavelength of 1064 nm, or the second transition at 1334 nm. A different class of laser is the FEL, which relies on the perturbation of an electron beam to generate light emission, initially emitted as a CATHODE ray. The cathode can be, for instance, a crystal structure of lanthanum hexaboride (LaB_6). The perturbation is referred to as "wiggle," which is provided by an alternating magnetic field B_w. FEL instruments are rather large and are several hundred cubic meters in size. The electrons are traveling at relativistic velocities and produce emissions (λ_L) proportional to the wiggle FREQUENCY (ν_w, respectively wavelength λ_w): $\lambda_L = (\lambda_w/2\gamma_r)\{1/[1+(eB_w\lambda_w/2\pi m_e c^2)]\}$, based on the electron REST MASS m_e and the relativistic correction factor $\gamma_r = (1-\beta_r{}^2)^{-1/2}$, with β_r the relativistic ratio of the electron velocity (v_r) to the speed of light (c): $\beta_r = v_r/c$. Lasers can operate in various modalities: continuous wave (CW), pulsed (on/off), and superpulsed. Examples of superpulse are Q-switched and mode-locked delivery. Lasers are classified based on their wavelength, exposure duration, and power output. The classification is influenced by the accessible emission limit (a laser property) describing the maximum level of laser radiation that the device can generate: luminescent exposure and power (Watt). The classification is generalized as follows: Class 1—safe under reasonably foreseeable operation (not accounting for unsafe operations, such as removal of safety precautions); Class 1M—generally safe, some precautions may be required; Class 2—visible light at low power (< 20 mW), blink limits risks; Class 2M—emission of ULTRAVIOLET or infrared invisible light, generally safe, some precautions may be required; Class 3R(A)—safe for viewing with the unaided EYE (no optical devices allowed); Class 3B—hazardous, diffuse reflection may be safe; Class 4—hazardous under all conditions, hazardous to eyes and skin. Note that the eyes are the most vulnerable and will be protected under most any classification of laser, with the exception of laser pointers. Keep in mind older laser pointers (pre-2005) that are viewed straight on into the laser beam will cause retinal damage (see Figure L.32).

Interaction of electromagnetic radiation and atomic systems-1

- Assume an atomic medium is enclosed in a thermally isolated container at a temperature T
  - The atoms possess only two possible infinitesimally sharp energy states: W_u and W_i
  - Photon transitions occur between level u and i
  - Monochromatic radiation is absorbed between the two energy states, or subsequently emitted at frequency ν_{ui}

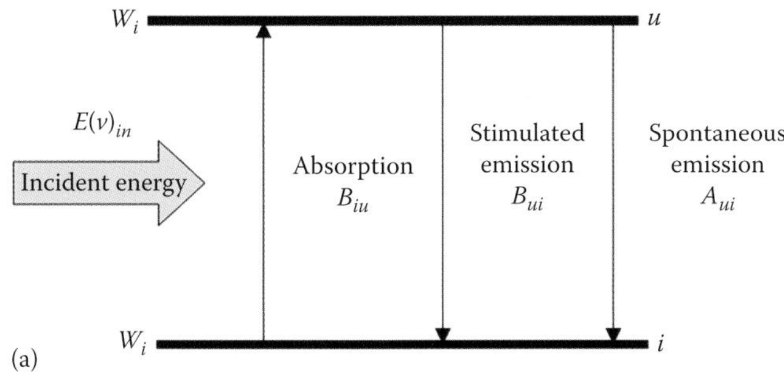

Normal distribution population inversion

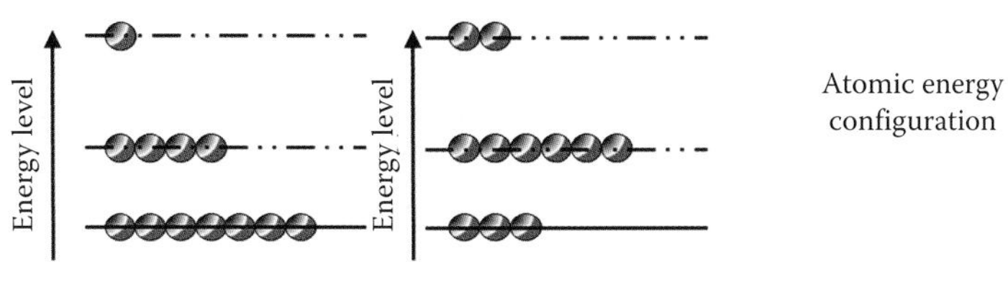

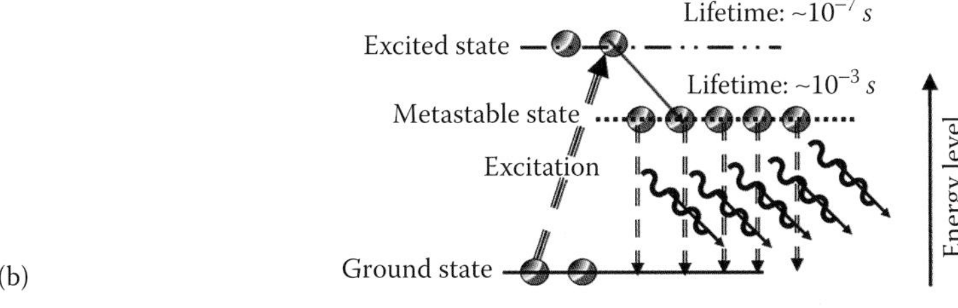

Four-level laser system

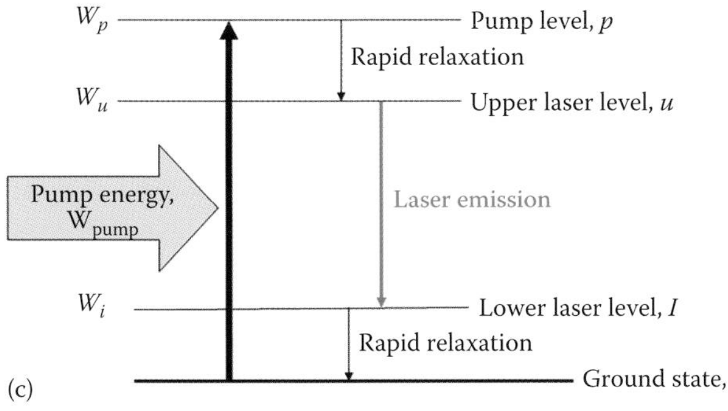

Figure L.32 (a–c) LASER examples and the mechanism of operation. *(Continued)*

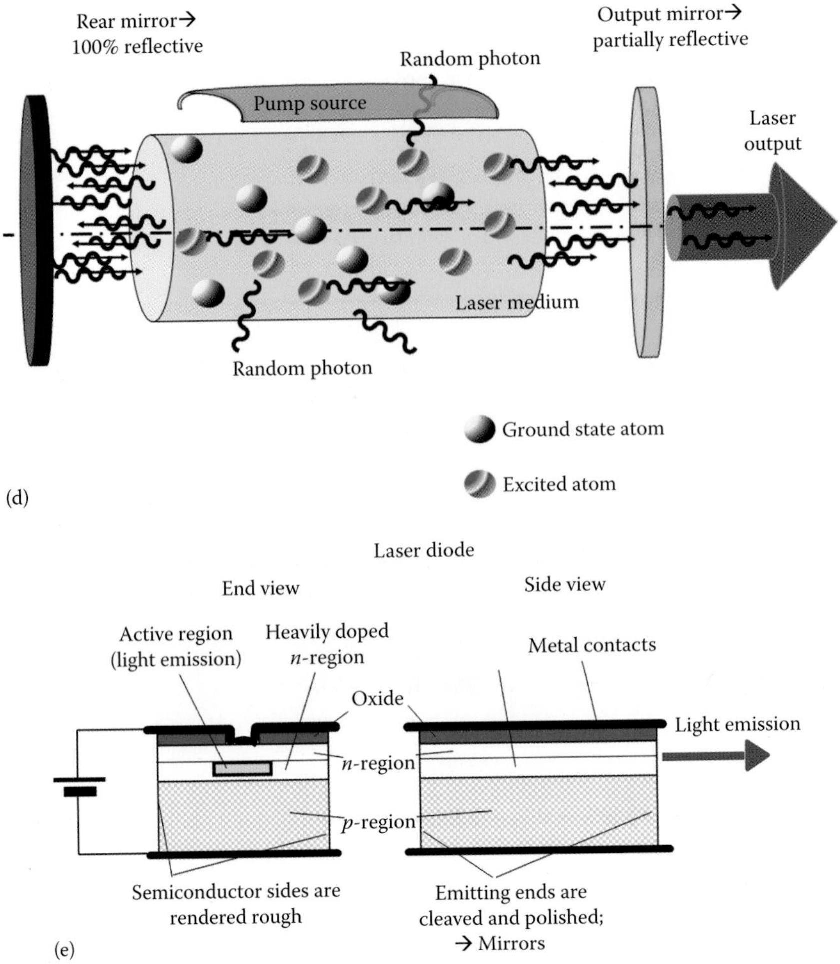

Figure L.32 (Continued) (d–e) LASER examples and the mechanism of operation.

Laser biostimulation

[biomedical, chemical, optics, thermodynamics] Mechanism of action using light to accelerate a biological process, specifically applied to healing of surface wounds. In particular, light is an ENERGY source that can be processed by tissue in similar fashion as found in trees, creating a form of PHOTOSYNTHESIS. Laser biostimulation can be used to induce chemical reactions as a catalyst as well. Also known as light biostimulation, or just biostimulation with reference to light. Additional nomenclature includes low-level laser therapy (LLLT), also known as 3LT, low-level light therapy or photomedicine. The early Egyptians (~100 BC) were aware of the potential for light in clinical use. Further applications were in the thirteenth century when the physician Henri de Mondeville (1260–1320) used RED light in the treatment of smallpox. Since the inception/development of laser, the laser has been tested for every known affliction. It was not until the work of the more systematic approach by the Hungarian physician and surgeon Endre Mester (1903–1984) in 1967, who used ruby and helium–neon (He–Ne) lasers for studies in wound healing, that LLLT became a more established science with verifiable correlation to the use of light with respect to other treatment options and placebo. Methods applied to measuring the influence of light were either phenomenological (rate of cure—“subjective”), chemical (BLOOD or urine analysis), or ACTION POTENTIAL rate/AMPLITUDE based as well as subjectively based on individual PERCEPTION. Light has been verified as a means to induce physiological effects. The most well-known is photosynthesis in plants and the production of vitamin D in mammals (only for the wavelength range: 280–320 nm). The main principle is that specific photons that have the potential for influencing the chemistry or physiology need to be absorbed to achieve a result. This means that the light penetrating into tissue will have a lower probability of inducing effects with greater depth due to attenuation resulting from both absorption and SCATTERING. Additionally, the proper wavelength (-range) needs to be administered in order to obtain the energy conversion appropriate for the desired results. The MAGNITUDE of applied light will also have a crucial impact on the final outcome, too much fluence may cause adverse effects, whereas too little will not achieve any effects. However, most photobiological effects are cumulative, placing the constraints on the exposure duration as well as the radiant fluence. One specific example is that it is safe to irradiate the cellular DNA with "blue" light, since DNA does not have the mechanism to convert this energy (although ULTRAVIOLET light will), while bilirubin is most definitely susceptible to blue light. Blue light changes bilirubin (yellow breakdown product of normal heme catabolism; blood) into a form that the baby can more easily get rid of in his or her stool and urine, a condition affecting approximately 70% of newborns (jaundice). Phototherapy treatments decrease the bilirubin levels in the blood by changing the *trans*-bilirubin into *cis*-bilirubin isomer, which is water soluble. Applied light within the wavelength range 390–470 nm is highly effective, whereas green light (530 nm) is not only ineffective for production of the photoisomer, but capable of reversing the reaction and may hence be considered harmful. The QUANTUM yield of the light irradiation is the product of the PROBABILITY that the light will be absorbed (function of action spectrum) and the probability that the delivered cumulative amount of light will induce a chemical or physiological reaction. The action spectrum provides the relative efficacy of light at certain wavelengths to achieve a biological response. The spectral response depends on the effective chromophores involved. The CHROMOPHORE is required to mediate the energy conversion aspect in any irradiation process, whether this would be chemical or thermal. Mechanism of action. The light interaction with biological media can be classified under four specific mechanisms that rely of unique individual physical, chemical, and physiological principles. The four areas are as follows: (1) The interaction on a cellular level, with the cellular components; split further in metabolic (i.e., cellular components and chromophores) and functional (i.e., membrane; gates/transmembrane potential/cellular communication) interaction. (2) On a tissue structure and function basis, whole tissue effects. (3) Chemopsychological influences. (4) And lastly, psychosomatic aspects. The cellular chromophores responsible for the effect of visible light on mammalian cells, including cytochrome c oxidase (with absorption peaks in the near infrared) and photoactive PORPHYRINS. Mitochondria are thought to be a likely site for the initial effects of light, leading to increased ATP production, modulation of reactive oxygen species, and induction of transcription factors. These effects in turn lead to increased CELL proliferation and migration (particularly by fibroblasts); modulation in levels of cytokines, growth factors, and inflammatory mediators; and increased tissue oxygenation. In the cells the chemical ACTIVITY can be found in the NUCLEUS and the MITOCHONDRIA of cells. Certain proteins, such as NADH-dehydrogenase (i.e., flavoprotein, yellow in COLOR), can work as photoacceptors in a similar fashion to chlorophore. Additional "regenerative" influences involve the stimulation of the fundamental cellular building blocks DNA and RNA into division, increasing the cell multiplication process. Furthermore light-induced serotonin breakdown to alleviate pain can be verified through the excretion of the chemicals resulting from the production of 5-hydroxyindole acetic ACID under irradiation by 632 nm light (helium–neon laser). Specific cellular MEMBRANE gates/channels are influenced on their DIFFUSION rate by irradiation with light. One specific example is the light-mediated diffusion through the PTPV1 membrane gate. For this particular channel, the sensitivity to light has been shown to be very specific, no response under irradiation by either 406 or 635 nm, but only changes due to 532 nm. Additionally, cell signaling, cellular communication by means of light has been documented and also shows potential for light-mediated cellular activity. On a MACROSCOPIC level the interaction between the chemical: nitric oxide (derived through chemical interaction within human digestion from ingredients found in beets) with resulting light-mediated vasodilation aspects are well documented. On a more general platform tissue warming by infrared light is used on a daily basis by radiative heaters such as electric heater coils for whole-house heating as well as by sunlight. Infrared light up to 1900 nm has deep tissue penetration and the potential to be used for deep tissue heating. Infrared lamps used in the prepared meat section of the grocery store and fast-food chains are an example of this as well as heat-lamps used to treat MUSCLE aches. Longer wavelengths are absorbed on surface impact. On a psychological level, mood and behavioral changes have been induced with measurable chemical outcome resulting from irradiation of SKIN areas that were not in the proximity of the EYE, in order to avoid the visual psychological impact. Examples are the "treatment" of "winter blues" and inducing changes to the circadian rhythm, in particular beneficial to long-distance travelers. On the skin surface almost all highly vascularized areas are susceptible to the influence of light to induce modulate behavior (influence the effects of "jet lag") and mood ("depression"), first discovered for the area behind the knee ("popliteal fossa"). Sleep pattern changes under the influence of light have been quantified by REM sleep PHASE occurrence and durations. Research has demonstrated that nighttime light exposure suppresses the production of melatonin, the major hormone secreted by the pineal gland that controls sleep and WAKE cycles. Therefore, a reduction in melatonin at night is associated with subjective levels of sleeplessness. Short wavelength light (446–477 nm) has been linked in particular with a reduction in melatonin. Studies have shown that one hour of moderately bright light exposure (1000 lux) was sufficient to suppress nocturnal melatonin to daytime levels. This also indicates that the exposure to blue light during the day may result in more alert daytime activity. This last statement is underscored by the science behind the selection of room light spectral profile in offices. The psychosomatic effects of light, induced based on visual PERCEPTION, affect the following. Behavioral and mood changes resulting from light within certain wavelength bands when observed by the eye. The color of room lighting is a phenomenon that is directly or indirectly experienced by the observer "mood lighting" versus "blue tone" light when concentration is required. A clear sky has a "color temperature" of approximately 10,000 K, which peaks at 300 nm as defined under Wien's law. Room lighting can be "tuned" to the desired needs based on commercial luminescent bulb selection (see Figure L.33 and Table L.1).

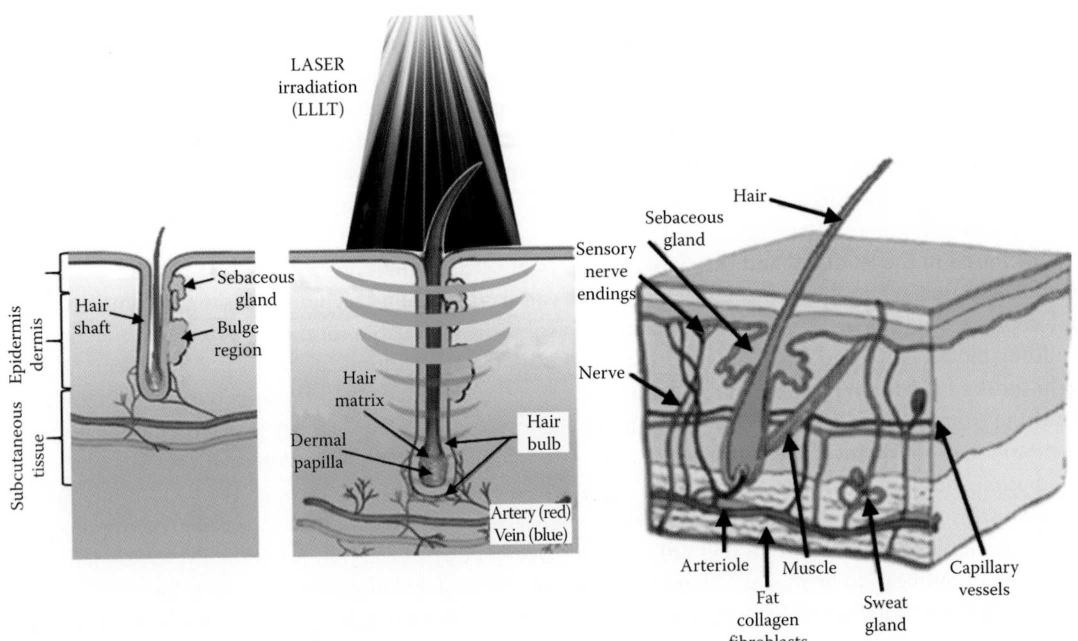

Figure L.33 Examples of laser biostimulation.

Table L.1 **Overview of low-level light therapeutic procedures and the alternatives available to the consumer (e.g., procedure or over-the-counter vs. by prescription)**

APPLICATION	WAVELENGTH RANGE (NM)	COMPETING TECHNOLOGIES
Acupuncture	630, 780	Needle
Alzheimer's	632	Nicotine/medication
Blood flow	410–420 nm, 540–550 nm, and 570–580 nm Pulse pause & 310 nm (with NO)	Capzasin (muscle rub)
Brain function, recovery	665, 808, 910	Exercise
Bone generation	830	Steroids, exercise
Carpal tunnel	830	Steroids/exercise
Circadian rhythm (jet lag)	446–477 nm	Behavioral routines, oxygen, "illicit drugs"
New: Claudication pain	310 + beet juice	Massage
Collagen/cartilage	900; 1064	NA
Dentistry (heal/pain)	632, 660, 830	Tylenol, ibuprofen
DNA genetic aberration	<260 modify DNA (carcinogenic)	X-ray
DNA → cell division	400, 620, 680, 760 and 825 nm	NA
New: Fetus in womb	Red–Near-IR	Music to the baby
Hair growth	635	Rogaine
Jaundice	390–470	NA
Joint (horse)	1064	NA
Laser "acupuncture"	808 nm	Needle acupuncture
Membrane gate (TRPV1)	532	Medication
Memory	632; 1064	NA
Mood (winter blues)	Blue	Medication
Muscle relaxation	808, 810 nm	Ben-gay, massage, sauna
Muscle—Greyhound	808; 810; 830	Massage
Nerve ("pain"/dysfunction)	830	Medication
Oral mucositis	632; 660; 830	Chemotherapy or medication
Osteoarthritis	Several wavelengths; no effect	NA
REM sleep	446–477 nm	Medication
Pain	808; 810; 900	Medication
Peripheral neuropathy	665, 810, 904	Acupuncture
Psoriasis	310, UV	Ointment/medication

(*Continued*)

Table L.1 (*Continued*) **Overview of low-level light therapeutic procedures and the alternatives available to the consumer (e.g., procedure or over-the-counter vs. by prescription)**

APPLICATION	WAVELENGTH RANGE (NM)	COMPETING TECHNOLOGIES
Rhinitis	650	
Spine	(polarized)	Physical therapy
Sport injury (joint)	808, 810 nm	Rest
Tissue warmer (human/pet)	Near-IR, broadband	Electric blanket (conductive)
Vasodilation: blood perfusion	310 (+NO)	Hormones/medication
Vitamin D	280–320	Sun-tan bank, vitamin supplement
Weight loss	635	Exercise/liposuction
Wound healing	632	Steroids (ingested/topical)

Laser Doppler

[biomedical, fluid dynamics, general, mechanics, optics] Due to the coherence of the laser source the wavelength and time are extremely well defined, lending it to the process of INTERFERENCE for diagnostic purposes. DOPPLER shift occurs as a result of the MOTION of the secondary source, which now will be the REFLECTION from a component in the path of the incident laser beam. Measuring the Doppler shift allows for accurate and noninvasive determination of the MAGNITUDE and direction of the velocity of objects, such as checking for the velocity of an automobile by law enforcement or the localized BLOOD flow velocity in an organ, resolved by blood vessel (averaged). Combining the laser Doppler mechanism with coherence TOMOGRAPHY can provide RESOLUTION within the blood vessel to establish a FLOW velocity profile (see Figure L.34).

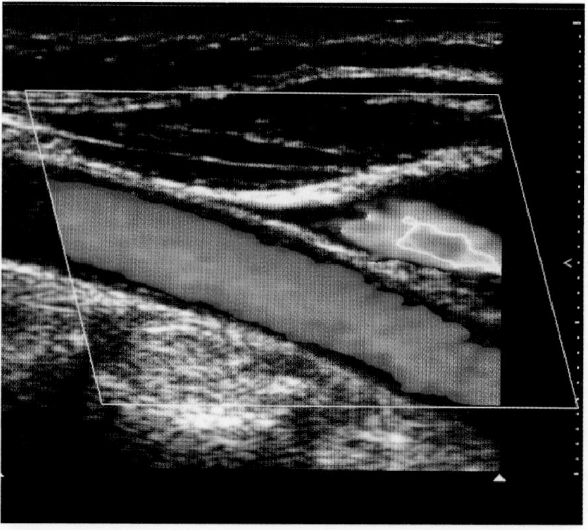

Figure L.34 Application of Doppler velocity measurement in human carotid artery. The velocity magnitude, and respective direction with respect to the probe (positive → "toward"; or negative ← "away") is represented in false color.

Laser Doppler anemometer

[fluid dynamics] As the ANEMOMETER is used to determine the velocity of wind by mechanical means in the location of the device, the use of laser will provide the opportunity to determine the wind direction and velocity at great DISTANCE from the device. The mechanism of action is the basic DOPPLER principles, his time using the DISPERSION in the AIR density resulting from atmospheric flow.

Laser holographic interferometer method

[computational, fluid dynamics, optics] The concept of taking advantage of the WAVE attributes of electromagnetic containing phase (ϕ) information in three-dimensional IMAGE reconstruction was initially suggested in 1948 by the Hungarian scientist DENNIS GABOR (1900–1979). It was not until the introduction of the coherent laser light that phase-sensitive representations could be stored on photographic plate and be used for virtual visual three-dimensional reconstruction. Specifically the coherence of the laser makes it ideally suited to perform the INTERFERENCE pattern construction with a high degree of accuracy. The holographic mechanism recombines scattered light from an object with a reference beam that is generated by splitting a laser beam in two components in an INTERFEROMETER design, such as a MICHELSON INTERFEROMETER. The scattered light will have a phase-shift $L_2 = L_{02}e^{i\phi_2}$ with respect to the incident and reference light $L_1 = L_{01}e^{i\phi_1}$, where the PHASE shift is captured as $\Delta\phi = \phi_2 - \phi_1$, yielding the interference at the converging point of the interferometer (e.g., the PHOTOGRAPHIC PLATE), expressed as the intensity, or respectively the degree of photographic emulsion darkening as $I = 2L'\{1+\cos(\Delta\phi)\}$, assuming little difference in incident and scattered RADIANCE ($L' = L_{01} = L_{02}$), the phase difference is related to the path length traveled as $\Delta\phi = kd(\cos\theta_1 + \cos\theta_2)$, where $k = 2\pi/\lambda$ the wavenumber, with λ the wavelength, d the DISTANCE, and θ_1 and θ_2, respectively, the ANGLE on incidence with the SCATTERING object and the scattering angle of the detected ray, providing positive and negative interference based on the path length difference in multiples of half-wavelength. In reconstruction a broadband source can be used to generate the optical illusion of a three-dimensional object using stereoscopic VISION (*also see* **INTERFEROMETRY**) (see Figure L.35).

(a)

(b)

Figure L.35 (a) Laser holographic interferometer method used during three-dimensional guidance for artificial insemination and (b) holographic image viewing in free-space, futuristic, but not too far away in the future.

Laser scanning confocal microscopy (LSCM)

[biomedical, optics] Scanning laser microscope where both light delivery and detection for a three-dimensional semitransparent object are controlled by means of the focal length of LENS that can be translated to and fro with respect to the object, hence providing a slice algorithm used to section the object in parallel planes. The axial RESOLUTION is a direct function of the NUMERICAL APERTURE of the lens. The LSCM focuses the probing light as well as the imaging plane at a certain level and uses APERTURES to reject the out-of-focus rays in order to enhance contrast and resolution. Scanning in a preset pattern in a single plate provides the digital information to reconstruct each individual plane and form a three-dimensional image. The basis of the scanning microscope is provided by a conventional optical MICROSCOPE, adapted for step-wise scanning in *x*, *y*, and *z* directions by means of servomotor control, or stepper motors. The illumination has been replaced by laser beam to ensure selective and focused illumination of the region of interest. Generally, more than one laser is used to provide spectral-based analysis. Certain aspects of the object may be more visible, higher contrast than other characteristics under narrow band illumination. The use of a dichroic scanning MIRROR allows for wavelength-specific illumination in scanning fashion. Each laser is fitted with the specific dichroic mirror for optimal scanning discrimination. The use of an aperture in line with the imaging lens will reject all out-of-focus light, providing the confocal aspect. The specimen can additionally be tagged with fluorescent probes to identify certain characteristic features, anatomical structures, and chemical signatures. The fluorescent imaging also applies to immunofluorescence imaging, providing the ability to highlight certain proteins. The IMAGE formation is radiance (intensity) based only, at the respective wavelengths. The SIGNAL acquisition uses either a PHOTOMULTIPLIER tube or pin-diode detector for the location-specific radiance. LSCM offers the following advantages: (1) higher resolution images than conventional microscopy (greater than twofold improvement in LATERAL RESOLUTION), (2) higher magnification than conventional microscopy, (3) generation of three-dimensional images, and (4) it minimizes diffraction influences, rejecting stray light due to the small dimension of the illuminating spot and target in the FOCAL PLANE. LSCM is still limited in resolution because this is still linked to the properties of light itself. The confocal microscope offers opportunities for frequent, repetitive (hours or days in between scans) quality control without the need for disassembly of the specimen, as is required for conventional microscopy. The repetitive scanning is in particular useful for biological CELL growth, specifically with respect to regenerative MEDICINE (see Figure L.36).

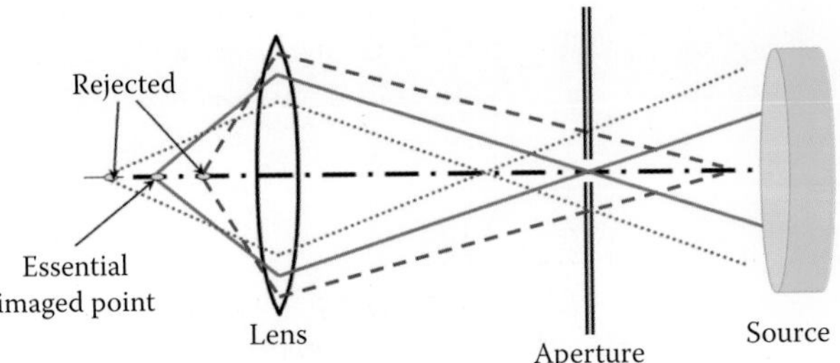

Figure L.36 Laser scanning confocal microscope.

Laser speckle method (LSM)

[fluid dynamics, optics] The scatter/reflection of the coherent laser light from a rough surface generates a granular light distribution pattern called a speckle pattern. The speckle pattern results from the INTERFERENCE of multiple waves with respective random individual phases. The spatial interference pattern observed is a direct function of the laser spot size (D) and the DISTANCE from the object (z) as well as the laser WAVELENGTH (λ) yielding a fringe pattern frequency: $\nu_{fringe} = D/\lambda z$, and respective spacing: $\sigma_{speckle} = 1/\nu_{fringe} = \lambda z/D$ (see Figure L.37).

Figure L.37 Laser scanning speckle surface contour tracing for thirteenth century wood carving. (Courtesy of LASer & Electro optical Research in engineering metrology, Università degli Studi dell'Aquila, L'Aquila, Italy.)

Latent heat

[general, thermodynamics] The heat required to accomplish a PHASE TRANSITION; solid ↔ liquid, liquid ↔ vapor, while the medium remain at constant temperature. The following versions of latent heat are used: latent heat of FUSION (heat released to solidify a LIQUID), heat of sublimation (HEAT TRANSFER to accomplish transfer from solid to VAPOR), and heat of vaporization (ENERGY to vaporize liquid).

Latent heat of fusion (L_f)

[general, thermodynamics] The quantity of HEAT (Q) exchanged per unit mass (m) required to liquefy a solid object while maintained at its melting temperature: $Q = +/- mL_f$. (*Note*: Reversible: +/−) (*also see* **HEAT OF FUSION**).

Latent heat of sublimation

[general, thermodynamics] The quantity of heat exchanged per unit mass required to vaporize a solid object while at its melting temperature (*also see* **HEAT OF SUBLIMATION**).

Latent heat of vaporization

[thermodynamics] The quantity of heat exchanged per unit mass required to change a LIQUID object into VAPOR while at its boiling temperature (*also see* **HEAT OF VAPORIZATION**).

Lateral resolution

[acoustics, optics] The ability to distinguish two points adjacent to each other. In ACOUSTICS, the RESOLUTION to separate two objects that are at a horizontal DISTANCE d is a function of the imaging WAVELENGTH (λ), the APERTURE of the source (D), and the focal length of the acoustic generation mechanism (f): $d = \lambda f/D$. In OPTICS, the discrimination is $d \cong 1.22\lambda f/D$, (the airy disk radius, as generated by the diffraction pattern; the IMAGE of object 2 needs to fall in the first minimum of the diffraction pattern of the INTERFERENCE pattern generated by the imaging system for object 1) which is often defined as the ANGLE (θ_{res}) between the rays emitted to the observer from two adjacent objects: $\theta_{res} \cong 1.22\lambda/D$ (*also see* **RAYLEIGH CRITERION, RESOLVING POWER,** *and* **AIRY DISK**).

Latitude

[geophysics] The angular position of the circumventing indicator on the globe of a PLANET with respect to the meridian/equator, which is half way between the POLES of rotation (North–South). This compared to the longitude, measured with respect to the Greenwich line running North–South, describing the location in the circumference combined yields the means to locate a land mass, ship, or house on a street (*also see* **GLOBAL POSITION SYSTEM**). There are several regions demarcated by latitude, the tropics, subtropics, midlatitude (Europe, Central and northern Asia, North America, Australia), and next to the polar regions (NORTH and South Poles, respectively, on the northern and southern hemispheres). Latitude also applies to marking out the celestial configuration, markedly the Big Dipper is only visible on the northern hemisphere (see Figure L.38).

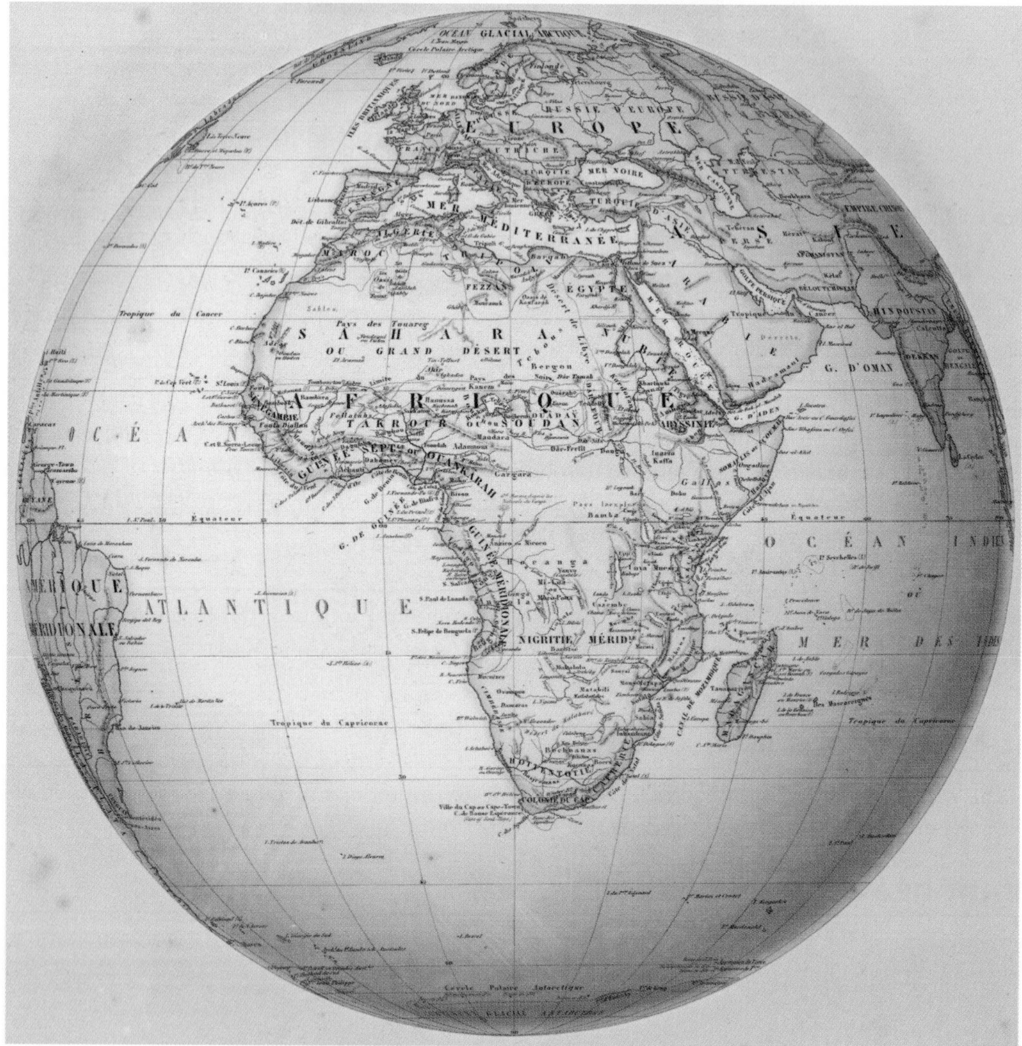

Figure L.38 The geographic latitude of Earth at 15° intervals with respect to the equator in geometric frame of reference.

Latitude effect

[nuclear] The observed cosmic radiation appears to be relatively constant when measuring as a function of LATITUDE. Below a latitude of 50°, moving from the North Pole to the equator there is a sudden decrease, with a minimum at the equator, from where the detected MAGNITUDE increases while scanning the southern hemisphere to level off again at 50° latitude toward the South pole. This observation was made by ARTHUR HOLLY COMPTON (1892–1962) and colleagues, and published in 1930. Later investigations show that there is a reduced cut-off ENERGY for cosmic ray particles toward the POLES, while at the equator the energy cut-off for protons is 15 GeV and at the 50° HELIOGRAPHIC LATITUDE this has been reduced to 2.7 GeV; for perpendicular incident rays. This phenomenon may be correlated to the asymmetry of the MAGNETIC shell (see Figure L.39).

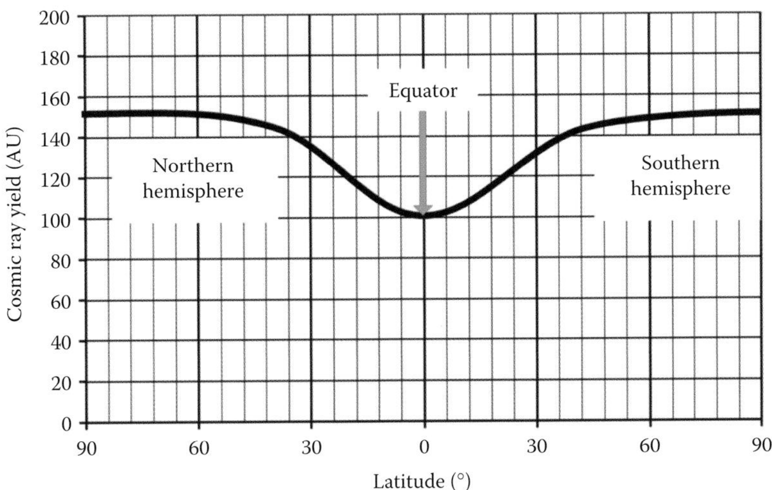

Figure L.39 Quantification of the latitude effect, illustrating the drop-off in cosmic radiation between 15° northern latitude and 50° southern latitude, with a minimum at the earth's equator.

Lattes, César Mansueto Giulio (1924–2005)

[atomic, nuclear] Brazilian nuclear physicist and scientist. Lattes is most know for the team effort in resolving the MUON enigma. In 1947, the discovery of the PION and the derived elementary PARTICLE muon was published by César Lattes with credits to GIUSEPPE OCCHIALINI (1907–1993) and CECIL FRANK POWELL (1903–1969). The observation was made on photographic plates doped with additional boron, tracking the trajectory of the cosmic ray particle path while in the Bolivian Andes mountains at an altitude of 5500 m. In 1947, Lattes managed to produce a pion by colliding ALPHA PARTICLES on carbon atoms in the CYCLOTRON at University of California Berkley (see Figure L.40).

Figure L.40 César Mansueto Giulio Lattes (1924–2005). (Courtesy of Leonado dos Santos Vaz.)

L

Lattice

[atomic, chemical, solid-state] Regular arrangement of ions, molecules, or atoms in a two- or three-dimensional structure with specific chirality (i.e., symmetry). The lattice structure is the result of the chemical bonds between the respective constituents. The grouping results in a crystalline structure outlined by a total of 11 axes of symmetry, five (5) monaxial point groups (0°;180°;120°;90° orthorhombic; 60°) in additional six (6) polyaxial point group sets (4 dihedral set; 1 tetrahedral set; and 1 octahedral set). The crystalline structures available are as follows: ISOMETRIC or cubic, with three orthogonal vectors of equal MAGNITUDE; tetragonal, with three orthogonal vectors only 2 of equal magnitude; orthorhombic, defined by three orthogonal vectors all of unequal magnitude; hexagonal, defined by two equal magnitude vectors at 60° ANGLE with each other and a third unequal in magnitude at perpendicular angle; monoclinic, outlined by three vectors of different magnitudes of which only 2 are perpendicular; trigonal, defined by three equal vectors that are at equal angles with each other however not perpendicular; triclinic, outlined by three vectors of unequal magnitude at angles that are nonconforming between respective pairs (*also see* **BRAGG PLANE** *and* **BRAVAIS LATTICE**) (see Figure L.41).

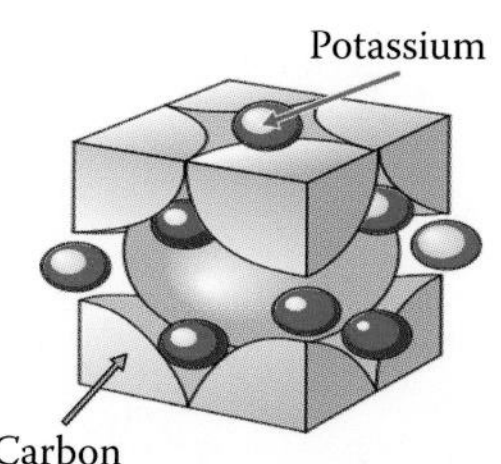

Figure L.41 Lattice structure. Graphene lattice.

Lattice array

[atomic, condensed matter, solid-state] Structural configuration of components, often applied to dipoles, in a repetitive pattern. A very simple lattice array is a triangle.

Lattice constant

[atomic, condensed matter, solid-state] Characteristic length separating two adjacent constituents in a LATTICE structure (see Figure L.42).

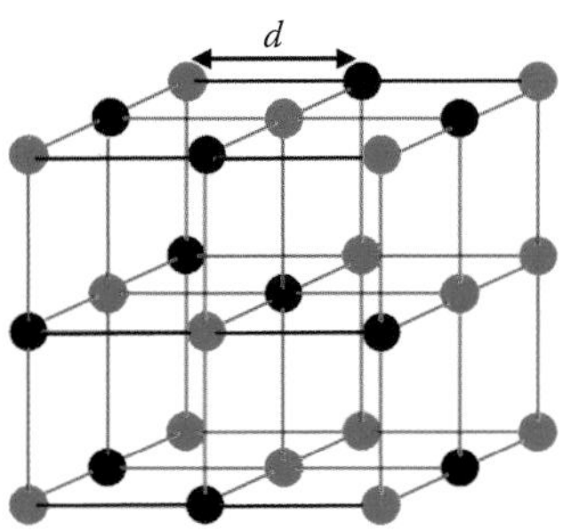

Figure L.42 Illustration of the lattice constant for a lattice.

Lattice factor

[atomic, condensed matter, solid-state] As electrons are scattered while interacting with a LATTICE the equation of MOTION provides a WAVE function (Ψ) for the electron motion resulting from interaction with respective lattice constituents x_i at a random location $\vec{r}$: $\Psi_i(\vec{r}) = \Psi_0 e^{i(\vec{k_i}-\vec{k_f})\cdot\vec{R_i}}$, with intensity $I = |\Psi|^2$, where $\vec{k_i} = 2\pi/\lambda_i$ is the incident wave vector, λ the wavelength, $\vec{R_i} = m_i a_1 + n_i a_2$ the vector outlining the structure of the unit CELL in the lattice with respective lattice constants a_1 and a_2, m_i and n_i constants, and $\vec{k_f}$ the outgoing wave-vector. This results in the following conversion: $I = |\Psi|^2 = |\Sigma_i \Psi_i|^2 = |\Sigma_{j=i\ \mathrm{base}}^{J} \Psi_{0j}|^2 \times |\Sigma_{i=1\ \mathrm{lattice}}^{N} e^{i(\vec{k_i}-\vec{k_f})\cdot\vec{R_i}}|^2$, where the first term represents the summation over all constituents ($|\Sigma_{j=i\ \mathrm{base}}^{J} \Psi_{0j}|^2$, the "structure factor") and the second term is the sum over all the lattice cells, the lattice factor. The lattice factor is the determining factor in the analysis of the projected (single-) scattered electron pattern on the screen.

Lattice plane

[atomic, condensed matter, solid-state] Intersecting plane of a LATTICE that can be duplicated in parallel pattern to describe the three-dimensional lattice structure. Also considered the repetitive structural pattern of connected components at regular intervals, illustrating the symmetry of the pattern of lattice components (see Figure L.43).

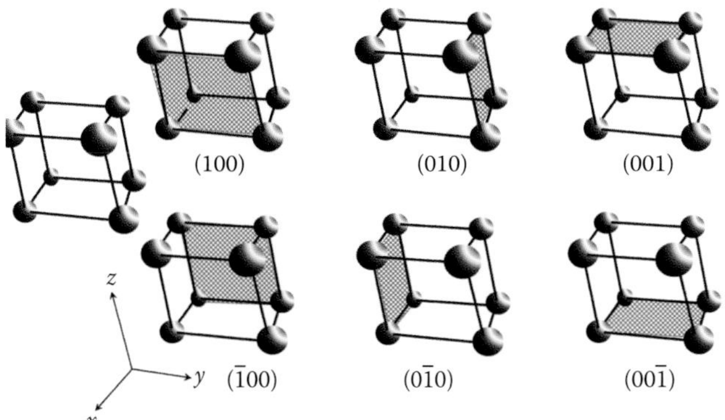

Figure L.43 Definitions for the six specific lattice plane configurations.

Lattice spacing

[atomic, condensed matter, solid-state] *See* LATTICE CONSTANT.

Lattice theory

[computational] Mathematical methods that apply to functions and phenomena with symmetry and order. Lattice theory is often applied in Boolean theory.

Lattice vibration

[acoustics, atomic, condensed matter, solid-state] Vibrations of a lattice structure generating a pressure wave. Due to the strong bonds in the regular pattern the individual MOTION of components is directly coupled to the neighboring components in the LATTICE. The vibrations in a regular lattice under the influence of harmonic forces between components induce, as a normal mode, lattice waves. Due to the potentially anisotropic nature of the crystal the WAVE propagation can be subject to DISPERSION. Lattice wave can range in frequency from several Hertz to above and beyond 10^{13} Hz. Lattice vibrations can have several POLARIZATION directions, depending on the cystalline structure. (see Figure L.44)

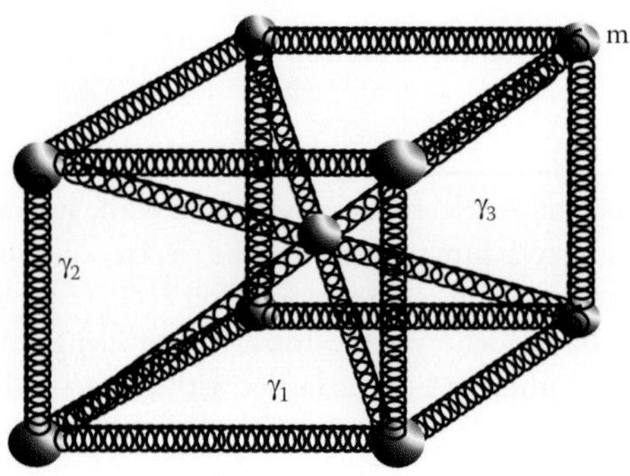

Figure L.44 Outline of the configuration supporting lattice vibrations.

Laue, Max Theodor Felix von (1879–1960)

[general, optics, solid-state] Physicist from Germany. Von Laue discovered X-RAY diffraction by crystal structures supported by the efforts of Walter Friedrich (1883–1968) and PAUL KNIPPING (1883–1935). This research was based on the recognition of X-ray RADIATION by WILHELM CONRAD RÖNTGEN (1845–1923) in 1895 and 1901. This discovery lead to the Bragg GRATING and molecular crystal structure analysis. Max von Laue was awarded the Nobel Prize in Physics for his work in 1914 (see Figure L.45).

Figure L.45 Max Theodor Felix von Laue (1879–1960). (Courtesy of German Federal Archive. http://www.iucr.org/publ/50yearsofxraydiffraction/full-text/von-laue.)

Laue diffraction pattern

[atomic, nuclear, solid-state] *See* **Laue pattern**.

Laue pattern

[imaging, nuclear] Line diffraction pattern generated by X-ray transmission through a crystal. Based on the projected diffraction pattern the three-dimensional crystalline structure and energy configuration can be determined, similar to an optical diffraction pattern such as the dual-slit experiment. The crystal acts as a three-dimensional diffraction grating, specifically under irradiation by an extremely narrow X-ray beam (*also see* **Laue diffraction pattern**) (see Figure L.46).

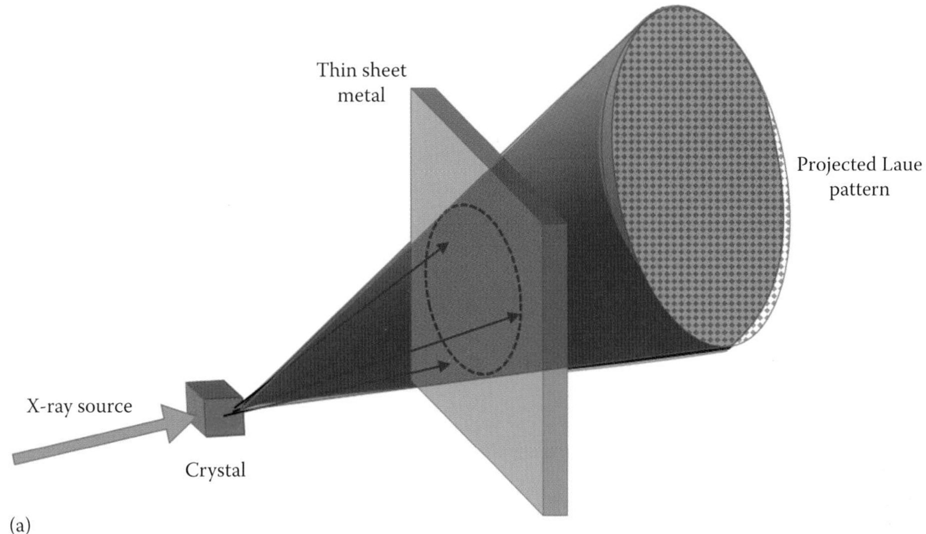

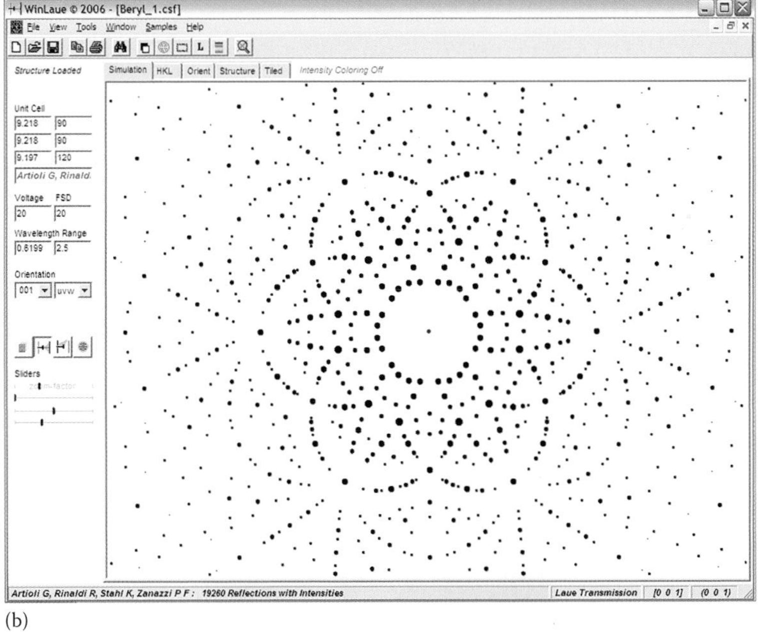

Figure L.46 (a) Experimental design of the collection of the X-ray diffraction pattern using the Laue technique with narrow beam of X-ray photons incident on a thin sheet of metal. (b) X-ray diffraction simulation: Laue pattern. (Courtesy of Steffen Weber with J. Cystal.)

Laue technique

[atomic] X-ray scattering technique as introduced by Max von Laue (1879–1960) using large crystals or crystal-powder for the recording of the Laue X-ray diffraction patterns. The crystals can be vibrated or rotated to induce perturbation for enhanced contrast.

Lauritsen, Charles Christian (1892–1968)

[atomic, nuclear] Physicist from Denmark. Lauritsen's work includes the development of high-energy X-ray emitters used for cancer therapy. A discovery made during bombarding the nucleus of carbon atoms with protons illustrated how gamma rays could be generated artificially (see Figure L.47).

Figure L.47 Charles Christian Lauritsen (1892–1968).

Lauterbur, Paul Christian (1929–2007)

[biomedical] Chemist from the United States. Lauterbur's work involved the development of magnetic resonance imaging, by configuring magnetic fields with gradients in three dimensions in order to create a mechanism for three-dimensional reconstruction, by means of providing spatial encoding. These principles were later refined by Richard Robert Ernst (1933–) by modulating the magnetic fields as a function of time, the basis of modern MRI (see Figure L.48).

Figure L.48 Paul Christian Lauterbur (1929–2007). (Courtesy of Joan Dawson.)

Laval nozzle

[fluid dynamics] Converging–diverging nozzle design introduced by Carl Gustaf Patrik de Laval (1845–1913) in 1893. The throat of the nozzle is designed so that the gas flow reaches supersonic velocities. The concept primarily applies to incompressible fluids (see Figure L.49).

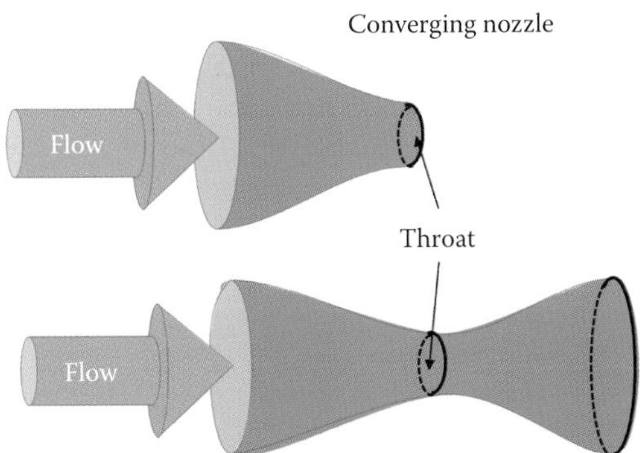

Figure L.49 Laval nozzle.

Lavoisier, Antoine-Laurent de (1743–1794)

[biomedical, chemistry, mathematics] Scientist, chemist, and economist from France (he also studied law) who has been attributed to naming the elements oxygen in 1777 and carbon in 1789. Lavoisier stated the elementary definition of an element as a material that cannot be split into more elementary components with the same unique chemical properties. In total Lavoisier may have verified the existence of roughly 40 elements. The description of oxygen coincides with the work of Jan Ingen-Housz (1730–1779) on photosynthesis. Alternatively, until then carbon was known as graphite, which was used in pencils at the time of the disclosure in 1594 by D.L.G. Harston and A.G. Werner, but had been known for centuries as a marking tool. Lavoisier is often referred to as "the father of modern chemistry." The work of Lavoisier illustrated the regular binding patterns of elements to form products, such as salt, water, and alcohols (see Figure L.50).

Figure L.50 Antoine-Laurent de Lavoisier (1743–1794). (Courtesy of C.E. Wagstaff in 1835.)

Law of angular momentum

[nuclear] The rotation of the electron-spin angular momentum ($\vec{J}$ =) converges for infinitesimal rotations to $\vec{J} \times \vec{J} = i\vec{J}$ (*see* **ANGULAR MOMENTUM**).

Law of atmospheres

[geophysics, general] The PRESSURE (P) as a function of altitude (z) in a planet's ATMOSPHERE can be defined as $P(z) = P_0 e^{-mgz/k_bT}$, where m is the average molecular mass of the gaseous composition, $k_b = 1.3806488 \times 10^{-23}\ \mathrm{m^2kg/s^2K}$ the Boltzmann constant, P_0 the reference pressure, and g the GRAVITATIONAL ACCELERATION. This is also known as the BAROMETRIC LAW (*see* **ATMOSPHERE**) (see Figure L.51).

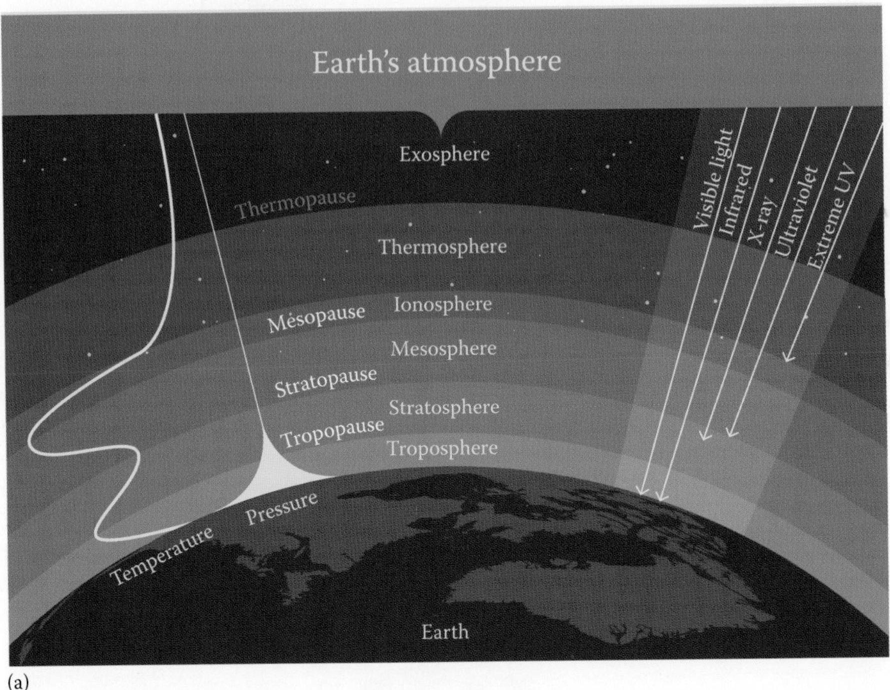

Figure L.51 (a) Graphical representation of the law of atmospheres. *(Continued)*

(b)

Figure L.51 (Continued) (b) atmospheric view of conditions above the mainland England and Ireland, and the western edge of France.

Law of conservation of angular momentum

[general, mechanics, thermodynamics] In a rotational system of particles (e.g., solid as well) where there is no net torque applied will have no loss of the total sum of angular momentum around a fixed point of reference. Note the rate of change in ANGULAR MOMENTUM (L) is equal to the applied net TORQUE (τ): $dL/dt = \tau$ (*see* **ANGULAR MOMENTUM**).

Law of conservation of charge

[energy, general, solid-state] For an ISOLATED SYSTEM charge cannot be created or destroyed. The total charge of closed system will remain the same. This may elude to the fact that the total charge of the UNIVERSE equals zero, but there is currently no mechanism available to verify this hypothesis.

Law of conservation of energy

[fluid dynamics, thermodynamics] In any ISOLATED SYSTEM (i.e., no external forces) the sum of all ENERGY forms remains constant. The forms of energy can, for instance, be work (W), potential energy (U), kinetic energy (KE), CHEMICAL ENERGY (E_{chem}), and electrical energy (E_{elec}). Please note that according to Einstein's theory (ALBERT EINSTEIN [1879–1955]) MASS (m) can be a form of energy as well ($E = mc^2$, where c is the speed of light). The early principles of the concept of CONSERVATION OF ENERGY date back a long time, maybe even old Greek philosophers, but was expressed in a general form by WILLIAM RANKIN (1820–1872) in 1853. In a process the energy contribution of all different thermodynamic properties are included in the balance: kinetic and potential energy of a process, heat, electrical energy as well as chemical energy. Some energy contributions can be on the atomic or molecular scale, and there is a means of conversion between all energy contributions, for instance but not limited to: chemical to kinetic or heat, electrical to mechanical or heat, but the sum of all energy constituents remains constant in any process.

Law of conservation of mechanical energy

[general] This conservation law only focuses on the KINETIC ENERGY (KE) and potential energy (PE) of a process, there is neither heat, electrical energy nor CHEMICAL ENERGY or any other form of energy involved at this point: $KE_1 + PE_1 = KE_2 + PE_2$, where the subscript identifies the state of the process. The general LAW OF CONSERVATION OF ENERGY does, however, include all forms of energy.

Law of conservation of momentum

[general] A system in MOTION will remain in motion at the same velocity when there are no external forces (F). The system will be comprised of units of mass (m_i) with respective velocity (v_i) yielding the momentum $\vec{p} = m\vec{v}$. Any change in momentum (in either MAGNITUDE and/or direction) over TIME (t) will be the result of an external influence, forming the impulse: $\vec{J} = \Delta\vec{p} = \int_{t_1}^{t_2} \Sigma\vec{F}dt$. RENÉ DESCARTES (1596–1650) made the first announcement with respect to conservation of momentum in 1644.

Law of conservation of parity

[atom, nuclear, quantum] Parity is the constraints that apply to a position function, specifically when applying space inversion. When the position function remains unchanged under the transformation the PARITY is considered to be either positive, or even, while if the function changes only in sign (+/–) under the INVERSION from positive to negative coordinates the parity is odd or negative. Other changes are not defined by parity. A system can be described by wave-functions and under conservation of parity there can be no distinction between clockwise and counterclockwise or right and left for any fundamental physical interactions. Elementary, there can be no distinction between a right-handed physical system and a left-handed system.

Law of corresponding states

[energy, fluid dynamics, general, thermodynamics] All gases look and act alike if they initially obey the VAN DER WAALS EQUATION OF STATE when TEMPERATURE (T), PRESSURE (P), and VOLUME (V) are expressed in DIMENSIONLESS quantities ($\hat{\square}$) as $\hat{T} = T/T_c$; $\hat{P} = P/P_c$ and $\hat{V} = V/V_c$, where $\square_c$ defines the Van der Waals conditions at the critical temperature. The constants can be derived from the PT curves. The corresponding states are now defined by $\left[\hat{P}+\left(3/\hat{V}^2\right)\right]\left[\hat{V}-(1/3)\right]=(8/3)\hat{T}$. The LAW OF CORRESPONDING STATES served as a guide to J. Dewar during his experimental efforts in liquefying hydrogen in 1898 and to H. Kamerlingh Onnes leading to the LIQUEFACTION of helium in 1908.

Law of cosines

[computational, general] For a regular triangle the sides (A, B, C) all relate to each other with respect to the ANGLE opposite to the respective ridge (respectively: α, β, γ) are related as $C^2 = A^2 + B^2 - 2AB\cos\gamma$ *see* **PYTHAGORAS**).

Law of definite proportions

[computational, general] In any CHEMICAL COMPOUND the respective constituents will always be present in the same proportions independent of the manner in which the aggregate was synthesized. The criteria resulted from the work performed by ANTOINE-LAURENT DE LAVOISIER (1743–1794). For instance, WATER (H_2O) will always be split into constituents (i.e., ELEMENTS) with 2:1 ratio. The chemical reconstruction was more formally defined by JOHN DALTON (1766–1844) in 1808.

Law of Dulong and Petit

[general, thermodynamics] The raising of the temperature of a specific molecular configuration (i.e., chemical composite) requires a fixed amount of ENERGY that corresponds to the chemical configuration. This means that the SPECIFIC HEAT of a material has a constant value. This EQUIVALENCE PRINCIPLE was experimentally verified and expressed in 1819 by PIERRE LOUIS DULONG (1785–1838) and ALEXIS THÉRÈSE PETIT (1791–1820).

Law of increasing disorder

[general] Generally process that consume ENERGY or produce pollution or will result in an increase in disorder, thereby limiting the validity of the theoretical solution for an idealized process. Additionally, most natural processes are irreversible, they begin from a state of equilibrium which is disturbed by changing boundary conditions, degrading the system, such as a melting ice cube placed in a GLASS of water. The entropy of the frozen water will increase (*see* **SECOND LAW OF THERMODYNAMICS**).

Law of inertia

[general, mechanics] Initially proclaimed by GALILEO GALILEI (1564–1642) around 1638, but later formally defined by SIR ISAAC NEWTON (1642–1727) (*see* **NEWTON'S FIRST LAW**).

Law of inertia, rotational equivalent

[general] A body is compelled to perform a rotation with fixed angular velocity unless an external torque is applied. (*Note*: The initial revolution is the result of an applied torque, which may, for instance, be from physical mechanical interaction, electric or MAGNETIC FIELD, or GRAVITATION.)

Law of interaction

[general, mechanics] To every action there is always an opposite and equal reaction; in other words, force acts in pairs, EARTH pushed back with an equal force (i.e., Normal force) as the force resulting from GRAVITATIONAL ACCELERATION exerted on a mass (*also* **NEWTON'S THIRD LAW, SIR ISAAC NEWTON [1642–1727]**).

Law of large numbers

[computational] Any phenomenon can be defined by a number (n) of random variable-independent events (Ξ_i), each occurring with a certain associated PROBABILITY ($P(\Xi)$). Letting the number of events become large (not necessarily approach infinity) forces the description to converge within the product of the number of events and the respective mean value (μ_{mean}) with respect to the VARIANCE (σ^2). Expressing the phenomenon as a series ($S^e{}_n$) yields $\lim_{n \to \text{large}} S^e{}_n / n = \left(\sum_1^n \Xi_i\right) - n\mu_{\text{mean}} \to 0$.

Law of mass action

[biomedical, thermodynamics] The equilibrium condition for a single chemical reaction, expressed as $\prod_{i=1}^q \left(P_{ii}/P_0\right)^{\mathbb{C}_i} = \exp - \left[(1/RT)\sum_{i=1}^q \mathbb{C}_i V_{cii}\left(T, P_0\right)\right] = K(T)$, where $\mathbb{C}_i$ is the stoichiometric number of the ith constituent of the chemical reaction (defined by $\sum_{i=1}^p \mathbb{C}_i A_i(\text{phase})$, with $A_i(\text{phase})$ the PHASE conditions for the respective constituents; $\mathbb{C}_i$ will be positive for products, negative for reactants, and zero for noncontributing chemical reagents), $V_{cii} = G_{ii}(T, P)$ is the chemical potential for ingredient i (note this equals the Gibbs free ENERGY), P_0 the standard pressure (usually 1 atm), P_{ii} the Partial pressure of the ith component, T is the local temperature, and $R = 8.3144621(75)\,\text{J/Kmol}$ the GAS constant, and $K(T)$ is the "equilibrium constant" at specific temperature for the chemical reaction. (*Note*: $\prod_j^z(\chi)$ is the product operator.) Also referred to as the law of mass action of Guldberg or law of mass action of Guldberg, Waage, van't Hoff, and Horstmann.

Law of Pascal

[fluid dynamics, thermodynamics] When pressure is applied to a confined LIQUID this pressure will extend in all directions with equal MAGNITUDE and equal potential. This principle, for instance, forms the basis for hydraulic lifts, where pressure is translated into force by means of controlling the size of the free-moving surface area. An indirect consequence of this principle is that for a liquid that is in equilibrium under uniform pressure the surface will always assume a horizontal position. Consider the volume of liquids illustrated by figure, where all named points represent segments perpendicular to the surface with unity length. Neglecting the pressure gradient over the height: $h_2 - h_1$ makes the pressure on the surface outlined between the respective edge segments $A_{20} \Leftrightarrow A_{21}$ and $K \Leftrightarrow A_{21}$ uniform. The pressure magnitudes of the respective pressure vectors: $\overrightarrow{A_{21}}$ on the surface outlined by edges $A_{20} \Leftrightarrow A_{21}$, $\overrightarrow{A_{22}}$ on the surface outlined by $K \Leftrightarrow A_{21}$, and $\overrightarrow{A_{23}}$ on the surface outlined by $K \Leftrightarrow A_{20}$ are considered to be in HEART of the respective surfaces and are perpendicular to each surface of the WALL of the reservoir. The vectors intersect in point A_{02} on the wall of the container. Due to the fact of equilibrium (no flow conditions) the pressure triangle (insert 1) is equivalent to the triangle outlined by the respective surfaces, which yields $\left|\overrightarrow{A_{21}}\right| / \text{Area}\left(A_{20} \Leftrightarrow A_{21}\right) = \left|\overrightarrow{A_{22}}\right| / \text{Area}\left(K \Leftrightarrow A_{21}\right) = \left|\overrightarrow{A_{23}}\right| / Area\left(K \Leftrightarrow A_{20}\right)$ meaning the pressure on each surface is equal. The pressure on the respective surface is equal to the product of the surface area times the height of the center of mass of the liquid resting on the center of the surface multiplied by the specific GRAVITY of the liquid.

Law of reflection

[acoustics, general, optics] When an electromagnetic or acoustic beam strikes a reflective surface, or when a ball is thrown at a WALL, the ANGLE of incidence (θ_i) equals the angle of reflection (θ_r); measured in reference with the normal to the surface: $\theta_i = \theta_r$.

Law of refraction

[acoustics, general, optics] A WAVE will travel from one medium ($\square_1$) with respective speed of propagation to another medium ($\square_2$) with a different density (expressed by the ANGLE with respect to the normal θ) and associated speed of propagation and the path of propagation will bend away from the normal to the surface of the second medium when this is more dense and toward the normal when less dense. When exceeding the CRITICAL ANGLE for the incident wave all the WAVE trajectories will be reflected. In OPTICS, the index of REFRACTION represents the optical density, where the speed of propagation (v) is less than for vacuum (c = speed of light): $n = c/v$. The LAW OF REFRACTION for ELECTROMAGNETIC RADIATION is expressed as $n_1 \sin\theta_1 = n_2 \sin\theta_2$. Also referred to as SNELL'S LAW. For ACOUSTICS, this is captured by the acoustic index which is a function of DENSITY (ρ) and ELASTIC MODULUS (E_{el}): $n_{\text{mech}} = \sqrt{(\rho/E_{el})}$, which can be temperature dependent and hence gradual, however for a single medium this can also be the case in optics (*see* **SNELL'S LAW OF REFRACTION**).

Law of similarity

[fluid dynamics] *See* **FROUDE'S LAW OF SIMILARITY.**

Law of sines

[computational, general] For a regular triangle the sides (A, B, C) all relate to each other with respect to the ANGLE opposite to the respective ridge (α, β, γ, respectively) are related as $\sin\alpha/A = \sin\beta/B = \sin\gamma/C$.

Law of the constancy of the speed of light

[general] The speed of light in free space has an invariant value for an inertial system. This entails that the speed of light will be independent of the velocity of the source while in MOTION. This is also Einstein's second postulate.

Law of the lever

[general, mechanics] An object that is subjected to zero total torque (τ_F) will be in rotational equilibrium: $\sum \tau_F = \sum F_i r_i = 0$, where F_i represents the individual forces attached to a point at DISTANCE r_i from a pivotal point of reference (see Figure L.52).

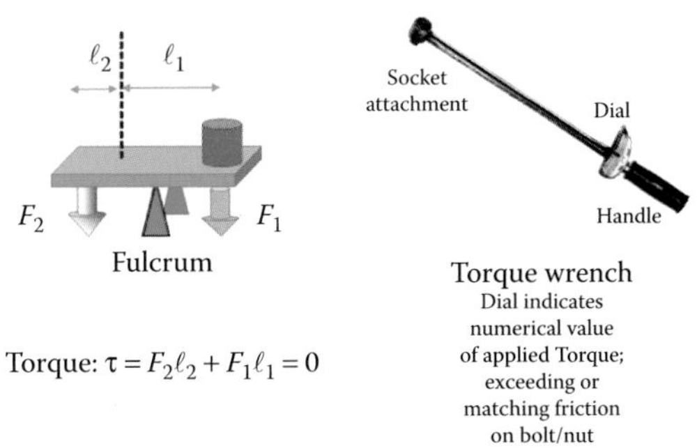

Figure L.52 (a) Law of the lever (b) Dial indicating the torque applied with the lever when attached to a bolt /nut on the top left and a hand pulls up/down on the bottom right; torque applied over the distance separating the two points. Nut will turn when no opposite torque is applied.

Law of universal gravitation

[general] Every object in the UNIVERSE attracts every single other object regardless of size with a MAGNITUDE that is directly proportional to the product of the masses of the two objects (m_1 and m_2, respectively) while inversely proportional to the square of the DISTANCE separating the two objects (r) with a force F defined as $F = G\left(m_1 m_2 / r^2\right)$, where $G = 6.67 \times 10^{-11}\,\mathrm{Nm}^2/\mathrm{kg}^2$ is the universal gravitational constant. (*Note*: The GRAVITATION attraction of an object with arbitrary shape and uniform density is identical to a point source with the same mass at a matching distance to the CENTER OF GRAVITY of the object outside the object.) The asphericity of EARTH will as such have a different GRAVITATIONAL ACCELERATION as a function of the LATITUDE.

Law of viscosity, Newton

[fluid dynamics] The viscous behavior of liquids described by SIR ISAAC NEWTON (1642–1727) under restricted conditions (i.e., Newtonian liquid) defines that the rate of shear stress ($\tau = F/A$) is directly proportional to the rate of shear strain: $\partial v/\partial y$, where y is the DISTANCE with respect to the object under stress for an object or LIQUID under deformation as a result of an externally applied FORCE (F) on the surface with area A. This Newtonian behavior stand is contrast to shear-thickening fluids/materials, shear-thinning fluids/materials and Bingham plastics, for instance. *Note*: In reference, the drag-force (F_d)

on a sphere with diameter d falling in a quiescent liquid cylinder with VISCOSITY η_{visc} expressed as $F_d = 6\pi\eta_{visc}vd$, where v is the velocity of the falling object, this is call the Stoke's law (see Figure L.53).

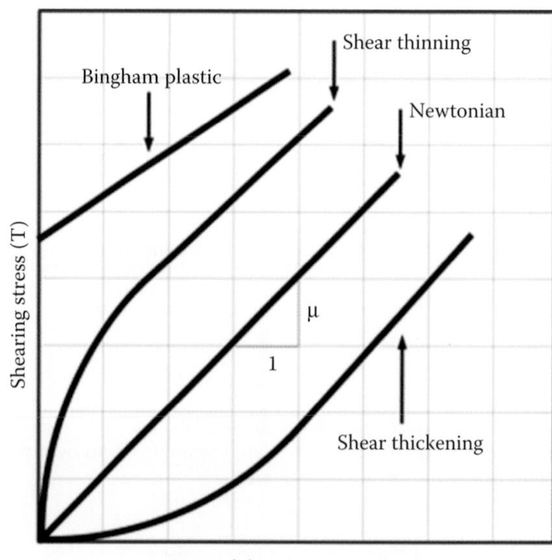

Figure L.53 Newton's law of viscosity.

Lawrence, Ernest Orlando (1901–1958)

[atomic, nuclear] Scientist from the United States. Lawrence's work included the development of the CYCLOTRON used for PARTICLE acceleration (e.g., ALPHA PARTICLE, DEUTERON, and PROTON) and nuclear collision measurements (see Figure L.54).

Figure L.54 Ernest Orlando Lawrence (1901–1958) in 1939.

Lawrence Livermore National Laboratory

[general] Federal research facility in partnership with the University of California, Bechtel, Babcock & Wilcox, URS, the Battelle Memorial Institute as well as Texas A&M University. The facility was founded in 1952 and houses one of the most powerful laser systems, The Nova laser. The principal task is to research on the safety and efficacy of nuclear weaponry (see Figure L.55).

Figure L.55 Aerial photograph of the Lawrence Livermore National Laboratory. (Courtesy of Michael Macor, The *Chronicle*.)

Laws of engineering and physics (as well as mathematics)

[general] The following laws and principles defining phenomena and actions related to the fields of physics, ENGINEERING, and chemistry are AMPÈRE'S LAW, Ampère's circuital law, AMPÈRE–Maxwell law, ARCHIMEDES PRINCIPLE, associative law, AVOGADRO'S LAW, BAROMETRIC LAW, Beer–Lambert law, BIOT–SAVART LAW, BLANC'S LAW, BOLTZMANN DISTRIBUTION LAW, Bouguer law, BOYLE'S LAW, Bragg's law, BREWSTER'S LAW, BUYS–BALLOT LAW, Carnot principle, CASSINI'S LAWS, CHARLES' LAW, commutative law, CONTINUITY EQUATION, COULOMB LAW, CURIE LAW, degenerate GAS LAW, distributive law, DULONG–PETIT LAW, FARADAY LAW, FERMAT PRINCIPLE, FIRST LAW OF THERMODYNAMICS, Fick's law, FIRST POSTULATE OF RELATIVITY, FOURIER'S CONDUCTION LAW, FROUDE'S LAW OF SIMILARITY, GAUSS'S LAW, Gay–Lussac law, GRAHAM'S LAW OF DIFFUSION, GREEN'S LAW, GUTENBERG–RICHTER LAW, HAGEN–POISEUILLE LAW, HENRY'S LAW, HOOKE'S LAW, HUBBLE'S LAW, HUND'S LAW, HUYGENS' PRINCIPLE, JOULE'S LAW, KEPLER'S LAWS, KIRCHHOFF LAWS, KIRCHHOFF'S RADIATION LAW, KIRCHHOFF'S LOOP RULE, KIRCHHOFF'S NODE RULE, LE CHÂTELIER–BRAUN PRINCIPLE, LAPLACE LAW, LAPORTE RULE, LAW OF ANGULAR MOMENTUM, LAW OF CONSERVATION OF ANGULAR MOMENTUM, law of conservation of atomic nuclei, LAW OF CONSERVATION OF CHARGE, law of conservation of electric current, LAW OF CONSERVATION OF ENERGY, law of CONSERVATION OF LINEAR MOMENTUM, law of CONSERVATION OF MASS, law of CONSERVATION OF MASS–ENERGY, LAW OF CONSERVATION OF MECHANICAL ENERGY, LAW OF CONSERVATION OF MOMENTUM, LAW OF CONSERVATION OF PARITY, LAW OF CORRESPONDING STATES, LAW OF COSINES, LAW OF DEFINITE PROPORTIONS,

LAW OF DULONG AND PETIT, LAW OF INCREASING DISORDER, LAW OF INERTIA, LAW OF INTERACTION, LAW OF LARGE NUMBERS, LAW OF MASS ACTION, LAW OF MASS ACTION OF GULDBERG–WAAGE–VAN'T HOFF AND HORSTMANN, LAW OF PASCAL, LAW OF REFLECTION (SNELL), LAW OF REFRACTION (SNELL), LAW OF SIMILARITY, LAW OF SINES, LAW OF THE CONSTANCY OF SPEED OF LIGHT, LAW OF THE LEVER, LAW OF MASS ACTION, LAW OF UNIVERSAL GRAVITATION (NEWTON), LAW OF VISCOSITY (NEWTON), laws of motion, LAWS OF PLANETARY MOTION, LAWS OF THERMODYNAMICS, LENZ'S LAW, LORENTZ FORCE LAW, MOORE'S LAW, MALUS'S LAW, MAXWELL EQUATIONS, MOSELEY'S LAW, MURRAY'S LAW, NEWTON'S FIRST LAW, NEWTON'S SECOND LAW, NEWTON'S THIRD LAW, NEWTON'S LAW FOR FLUIDS, NEWTON'S LAW OF COOLING, OHM'S LAW, PASCHEN LAW, PERIODIC LAW, RADIOACTIVE DECAY LAW, RAOULT'S LAW, SECOND LAW OF THERMODYNAMICS, second postulate of relativity, SNELL'S LAW, STARLING'S LAW, Stefan's law, STOKE'S LAW, superposition principle, TATE'S LAW, Torricelli's law, VAN'T HOFF LAW, AND WORK–ENERGY THEOREM.

Laws of planetary motion

[astrophysics, mechanics] There are THREE LAWS OF PLANETARY MOTION, all derived by JOHANNES KEPLER (1571–1630). KEPLER'S FIRST LAW states that all planets in our SOLAR SYSTEM revolve around the Sun in an elliptical orbit. KEPLER'S SECOND LAW relates to the speed of MOTION with respect to the segment of the orbit. Each line drawn from the Sun to a PLANET will mark of equal areas in the orbital plane for equal time intervals. KEPLER'S THIRD LAW correlates the average Sun-to-planet DISTANCE ($r_{\odot}$, denoting the Sun as the central body) to the period of revolution (T) as a constant: $r_{\odot}{}^{3}/T^{2} = C_{\odot} = 1\,\text{Astronomical unit}^{3}/\text{Earthyear}^{2}$, where Astronomical unit $= 1.5 \times 10^{11}$m and Earthyear $= 31.6 \times 10^{6}$s the time is takes for the EARTH to circumvent the Sun (365.24 days) (*see* **JOHANNES KEPLER [1572–1630]**).

Laws of thermodynamics

[biomedical, energy, general, nuclear, solid-state, thermodynamics] There are three laws of thermodynamics, zeroth, first, and second. The ZEROTH LAW OF THERMODYNAMICS was introduced by JOSEPH BLACK (1728–1799) around 1760. The FIRST LAW OF THERMODYNAMICS was introduced in 1850 by RUDOLF JULIUS EMANUEL CLAUSIUS (1822–1888) and WILLIAM RANKINE (1820–1872). The SECOND LAW OF THERMODYNAMICS was introduced based on the concepts introduced by Rudolf Clausius in 1854, LORD KELVIN (1824–1907) in 1851, and the axiomatic thermodynamics statements from CONSTANTIN CARATHÉODORY (1873–1950) in 1909.

Lay

[biomedical, mechanics] Indication of SURFACE ROUGHNESS. Specifically, the deviation from the established and defined "normal" shape and geometry as created by milling and machining. The "Lay" describes the general direction of a surface treatment resulting from the methods used. Lay can be circular, cross-hatch, multidirectional, parallel, particulate, perpendicular, and radial (see Figure L.56).

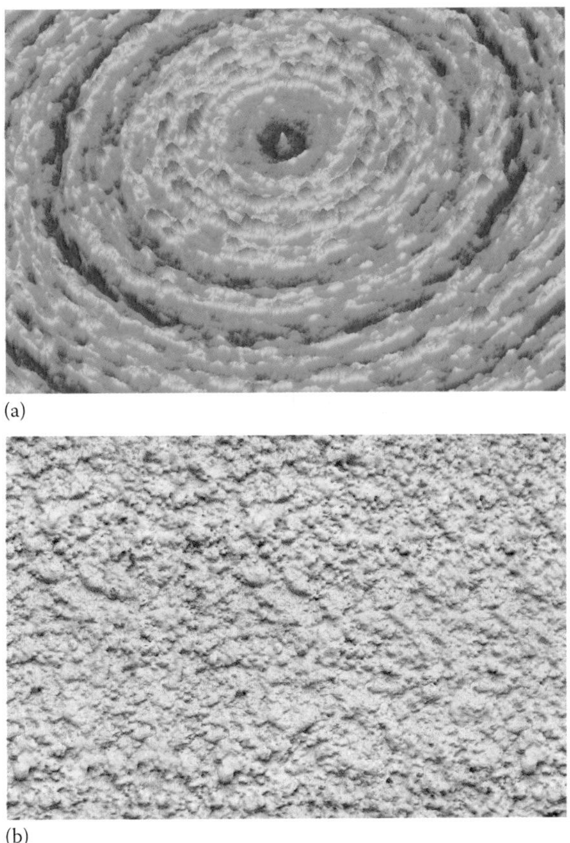

Figure L.56 (a) Microscopic image portraying a diamond turned surface finish measurement (Courtesy of Zygo.) and (b) surface roughness. (Surface standard ANSI B46.1-1962 implemented by the American Society of Mechanical Engineers.).

L-C-R AC network

[electronics, general] Circuit containing an INDUCTOR (L), CAPACITOR (C), and RESISTOR (R), and the way an alternating signal (AC) propagates through according to the "cable equation" (also referred to as the WAVE EQUATION or the TELEGRAPH EQUATION). The circuit may be arranged in parallel and series connections in various combinations. Specifically, the circuit can be designed as a frequency filter, SIGNAL integrator (i.e., "average"), or amplifier. The telegraph equation (derived its name from the early days of wired analog data transmission) is used to derive the electrical potential (U_{pot}), which varies with time, as a function of the propagation path length (dz) as a function of TIME (t) as can be found by solving a one-dimensional differential equation: $(1/LC)(d^2U_{pot}/dz^2)=(d^2U_{pot}/dt^2)+[(R/L)+(\mathbb{R}/C)](dU_{pot}/dt)+(\mathbb{R}R/LC)U_{pot}$, where $\mathbb{R}$ represents the conductivity over a length of schematic (see Figure L.57).

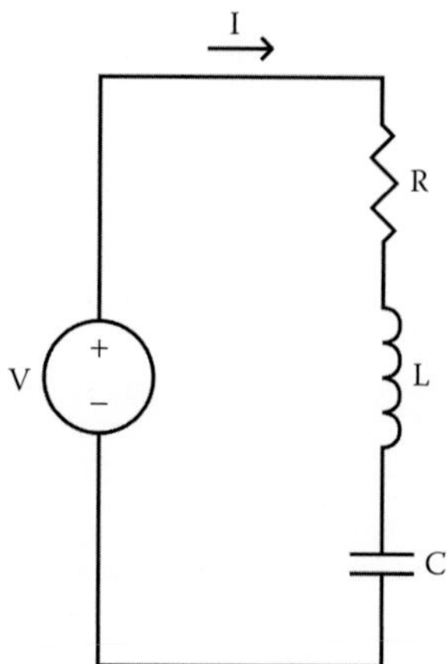

Figure L.57 Representation of the manner in which an alternating signal (AC) interacts with an L-C-R network, circuit containing an inductor (L), capacitor (C), and resistor (R).

Le Châtelier, Henry Louis (1850–1936)

[chemical, thermodynamics] Chemist from France. Henry Le Châtelier is most know for the definition of the boundary conditions of a chemical reaction, and their influence on its process (*also see* **CHÂTELIER–BRAUN PRINCIPLE**) (see Figure L.58).

Figure L.58 Henry Louis Le Châtelier (1850–1936).

Le Châtelier–Braun inequalities

[chemical, thermodynamics] ENERGY constraints for potential energy (or internal energy: U_{pot}) as well as VOLUME (V) as a function of temperature (T, in this case $1/T$) for a number of reagent constituents (n) under certain PRESSURE (P) of a system with entropy (S tied to the Gibbs free energy ($G=U-TS+PV$)) defined as $[\partial(1/T)/\partial U]_{V,n}\leq[\partial(1/T)/\partial U]_{P/T,n}<0$ and $[\partial(P/T)/\partial V]_{U,n}\leq[\partial(P/T)/\partial V]_{1/T,n}<0$. These expressions entail the following; with increasing energy the PROBABILITY for energy release is increasing, equivalently an increase in volume will promote the surrender of volume (hence contradicting the increase: $d(P/T)<0$). This inequality can be rewritten using the link between entropy and internal energy as: $[\partial T/\partial S]_{V,n} \geq [\partial T/\partial S]_{P,n} > 0$ and $-[\partial P/\partial V]_{S,n} \geq -[\partial P/\partial V]_{T,n} > 0$.

Le Châtelier–Braun principle

[chemical, thermodynamics] Chemical equilibrium as described independently by both HENRY LOUIS LE CHÂTELIER (1850–1936) and Karl Ferdinand Braun (1850–1918). The principle confines the response of a chemical system to perturbations, hence subduing the rate of progression and enhancing the stability of equilibrium of the system. The mechanism of action can be traced from the LE CHÂTELIER–BRAUN INEQUALITIES. With respect to a chemical reaction this translates into the fact that when the concentration of one constituent ($[\chi]$) changes the chemical reaction will shift in the direction to counteract this particular change: $a[A]+b[B] \rightleftarrows c[C]+d[D]$ (also Le Châtelier principle; *also see* **HOMEOSTASIS**).

Le Verrier, Urbain (1811–1877)

[astronomy, mechanics] Scientist and mathematician from France, known for his discovery of the PLANET Neptune (see Figure L.59).

Figure L.59 Urbain le Verrier (1811–1877).

Lead storage cell

[general] Charge storage device using lead oxide (PbO_2) and ACID (e.g., sulfuric acid: H_2SO_4) that can release the stored electrical charge as a current under a fixed potential, generally at 2V per CELL. The lead storage cell is commonly used in automobiles and is rechargeable. The lead storage cell or lead-acid BATTERY was invented

by the French physicist Gaston Planté (1834–1889) in 1859. The chemical exchange supporting the ELECTRON (e^-) current is as follows: on the negative (CATHODE) side $Pb + HSO_4^- \rightarrow PbSO_4 + H^+ + e^-$ and on the anode $PbSO_2 + HSO_4^- + 3H^+ + 2e^- \rightarrow PbHSO_4 + 2H_2O$. The current MAGNITUDE can theoretically be derived from the molecular weights of the constituents in the chemical reaction, which equals 642.6. A BATTERY with a mass of 642.6 g of reagent material can theoretically produce 2 Faraday of electrical charge, which equates to $84.3\,\text{AmpH}$ per kilogram, where $1\,\text{Ampere} - \text{Hour} = 3600\ \text{Coulomb}$ (see Figure L.60).

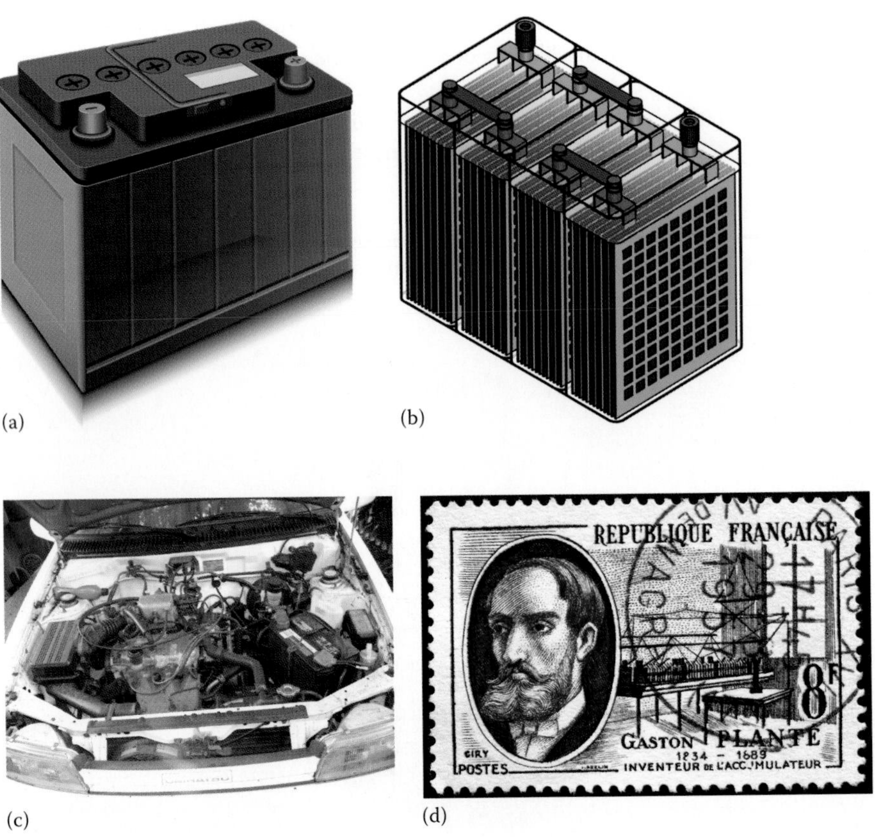

Figure L.60 (a) Outside view of lead-acid battery, (b) diagram of lead plate-configuration in lead-acid battery, (c) lead-acid battery in engine compartment of automobile, and (d) Image of Gaston Plante (1834–1889) from France, the inventor of the lead-acid battery.

Lead zirconate titanate (PZT)

[acoustics, biomedical, mechanics] Ceramic medium that can convert electrical ENERGY into MECHANICAL ENERGY and vise-versa. When applying a zeroth order sinusoidal alternating current to PZT the material will perform a single frequency OSCILLATION at the same rate as the current. This principle is for instance applied in ULTRASONIC IMAGING and FLUID pumps. The generated FREQUENCY (ν_z) is a function of the crystal dimension in the direction of wave propagation (z), a material properties resulting from the manufacturing mechanism ($k^{\nu}{}_z$) known as the "frequency constant," at a specific harmonic (n) of RESONANCE: $\nu_z = n\left(k^{\nu}{}_z / z\right)$. The reverse is applied in STRAIN-GAUGES, measuring contraction and EXPANSION rate of change and MAGNITUDE. PZT is one of the most well-known and oldest materials in this application, however may new materials are developed on an ongoing basis (see Figure L.61).

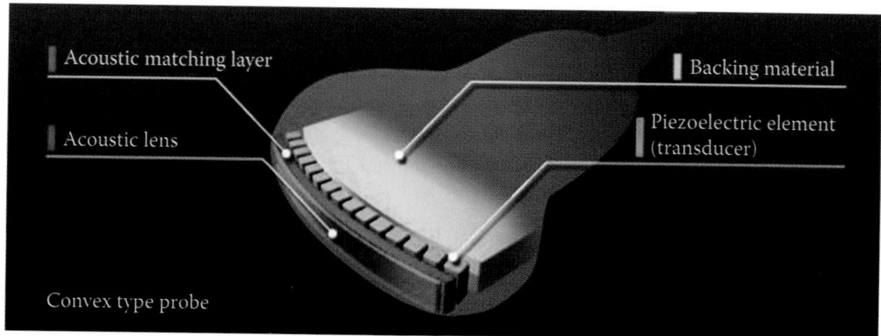

Figure L.61 Image of linear-array lead zirconate titanate (PZT; element lead = Latin *plumbum* [Pb]) ultrasound probe. (Courtesy of Epoxy Set Inc., Lincoln, Rhode Island.)

Leading edge

[fluid dynamics] BOUNDARY LAYER in FLOW that evolves from a point-of-contact: the leading edge, may also be referred to as the point of inception.

Leapfrog method

[computational] Technique used in NUMERICAL methods. In finite ELEMENT or finite step calculations, the values for a specific function are derived through a process where the function is calculated at one point that is relatively easy, the next data point is calculated after a leap over the coordinates to provide the next mid-step values, while the value at the "leapfrog" coordinate can be found through interpolation.

Least squares

[computational] Process used in data fitting, to closely match a well-defined function to a nonconformal range of data with respect to experimental observations. Usually the system is overdetermined and needs to be scaled down for conclusions. The least-squares mechanism can be attributed to the German mathematician CARL FRIEDRICH GAUSS (1777–1855), used in 1795, however, the method may very well have been published prior to this by the French mathematician ADRIEN-MARIE LEGENDRE (1752–1833). The mechanism uses the RESIDUALS (R_i) for a series of data points (ζ_i, i.e., dependent variables) at independent values χ_i providing: $R_i = \zeta_i - f(\chi_i, \varsigma)$, where $f(\chi_i, \varsigma)$ is an approximation or model function that is supposedly a close match, and next minimizes the sum for "smoothing" as described by Sum $= \sum_{i=1}^{\infty} R_i^{\,2}$. Choosing the best fitting function will yield the lowest value for the least-squares. Least square fitting has applications ranging from curve fitting to LINEAR REGRESSION, and is widely used in SIGNAL processing and general statistical methods.

Leclanché, Georges (1839–1882)

[general] Electrical engineer from France. Leclanché invented the first electrical storage device (i.e., the BATTERY), known as the Leclanché CELL (1866), which evolved into the battery we now know as the alkaline cell (see Figure L.62).

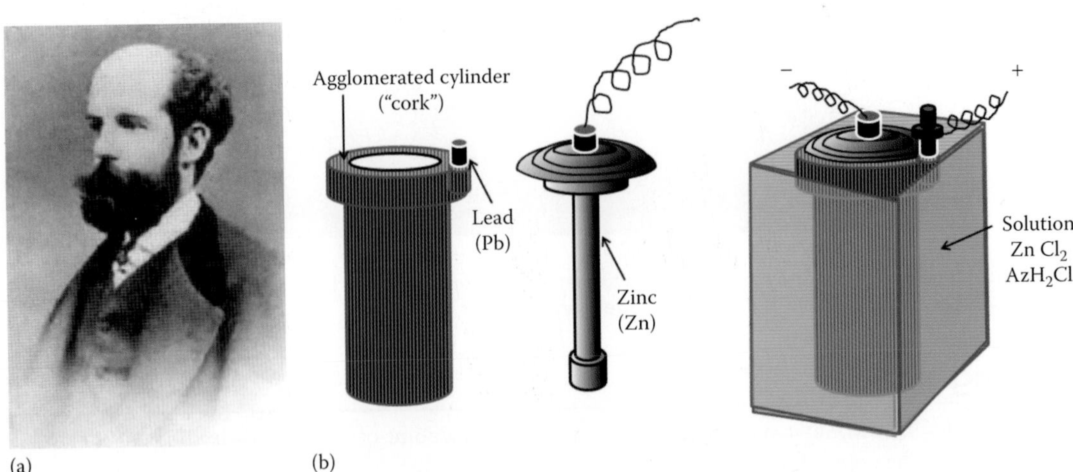

Figure L.62 (a) Georges Leclanché (1839–1882), and (b) Élément Leclanché-Barbier, the first concept of an electric storage device, later evolved into the widely used alkaline cell.

Left ventricular assist device (LVAD)

[biomedical, fluid dynamics] Mechanical pump that is implanted in a patient with reduced HEART muscle contraction, and hence reduced BLOOD volume stroke. The LVAD is usually installed as a SHUNT, bypassing the left ventricle connecting the pulmonary VEIN directly with the AORTA. Note that the work (W) of the PUMP is generally matched to the work of the heart as $W = PV$, where P is the applied pressure or pressure gradient over the system (i.e., device), and V the stroke volume. In case the parallel system does not have equal FLOW, there will be backflow through one of the branches with reduced efficacy (see Figure L.63).

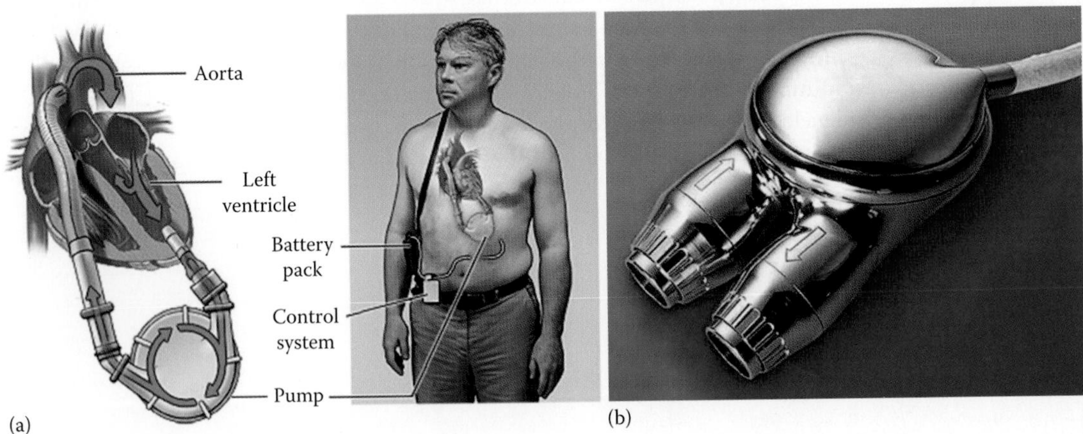

Figure L.63 (a) Left ventricular assist device (LVAD) connected to the heart of a patient. (Courtesy of Healthwise/Thoratec.) (b) Left ventricular assist device (LVAD). (Courtesy of Thoratec.)

Left ventricular pressure

[biomedical, fluid dynamics] The pressure exerted by the left ventricle of the mammalian HEART, pumping BLOOD into the AORTA, crossing the mitral VALVE. The pressure range from diastolic (relaxed) to systolic during full compression. The left ventricular DIASTOLIC PRESSURE will be approximating zero since there is no COMPLIANCE in the system (during the ventricular filling stage the pressure technically turns negative during the EXPANSION phase), compared to the arterial pressure in the arm which has a wind kessel back-up system of the entire vasculature and hence ranges approximately from 30 mm Hg to 160 mm Hg for human SPHYGMOMANOMETER recordings, depending on the personal cardiac and vascular health. The SYSTOLIC PRESSURE will vary with health and exercise history (see Figure L.64).

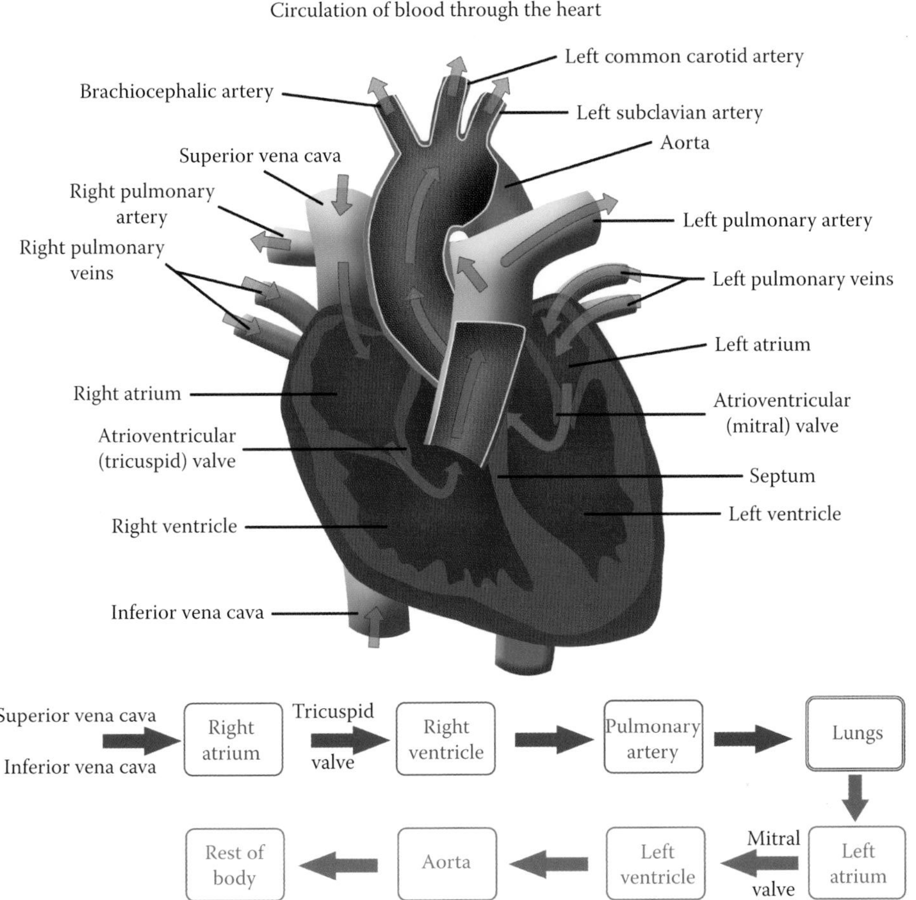

Figure L.64 Left ventricular pressure.

Leg

[biomedical] Anatomical appendage used to provide the mechanism for equilibrium support and translation of a larger biological unit. The leg has a support structure (in mammals consisting of bones) and a

MUSCLE structure to apply a torque, resulting in a pivotal action around a joint. Usually found in even numbers (see Figure L.65).

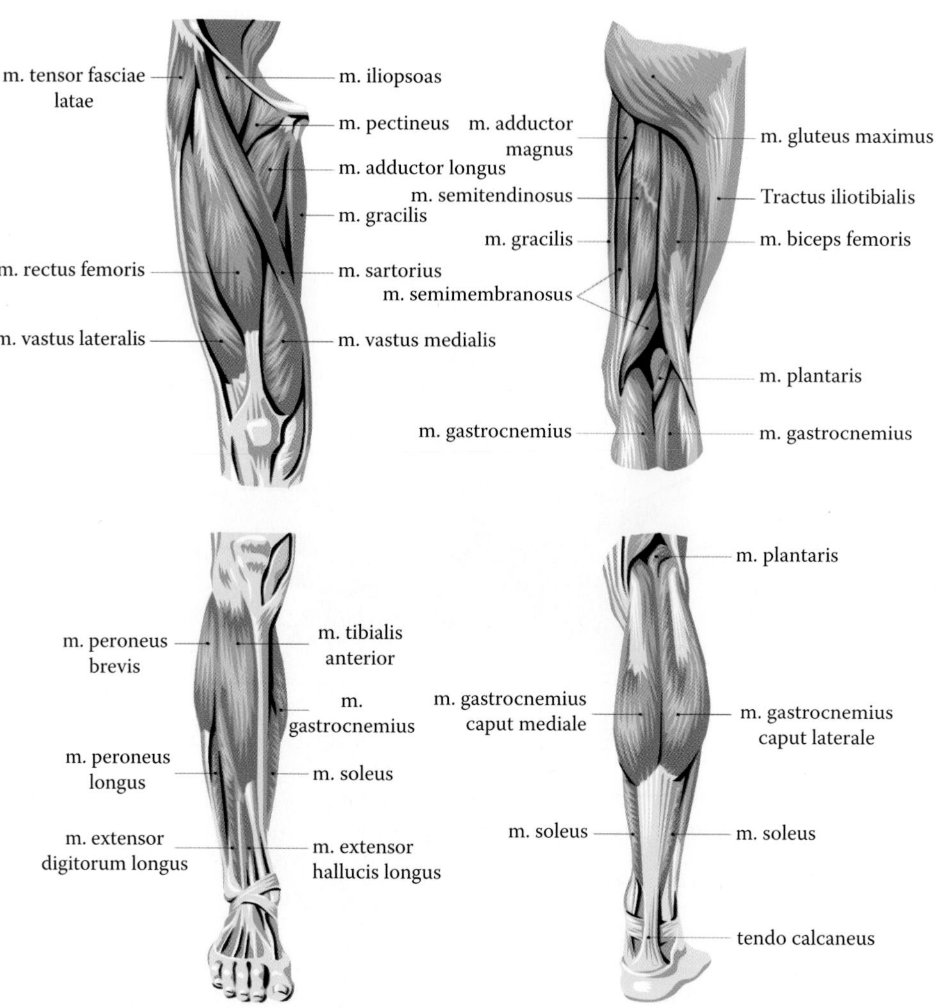

Figure L.65 Representation of the human leg with muscle structure, bone structure, and tendons.

Legendre, Adrien-Marie (1752–1833)

[computational] Mathematician and physicist from France. Legendre is known for his integral transformation as well as polynomial series development of complex functions. The LEGENDRE TRANSFORM is used to solve thermodynamic equations and specifically yield solutions for "enthalpy" and the Gibbs free ENERGY. Legendre also introduced the concept of the LEAST SQUARES method (see Figure L.66).

Figure L.66 Adrien-Marie Legendre (1752–1833), watercolor caricature produced in 1820 by French artist Julien-Leopold Boilly.

Legendre differential equation

[astrophysics/astronomy, computational, quantum] Formulation of an expression devised by ADRIEN-MARIE LEGENDRE (1752–1833) to allow complex equations to be solved by approximation: $d/d\chi\left\{\left(1-\chi^2\right)(d/d\chi)P_\ell(\chi)\right\}+\ell(\ell+1)P_\ell(\chi)=0$, taken in arbitrary direction χ, with the reference frame in spherical coordinates, with as SOLUTION the LEGENDRE POLYNOMIAL power series of orthogonal functions.

Legendre equation

[computational] Basic quadratic equation in three dimensions expressed as $ax^2+by^2+cz^2=0$ in CARTESIAN COORDINATES, which can only be solved is the following products of the coefficients a, b, and c are quadratic residues: $-ab$; $-bc$; and $-ca$.

Legendre function

[computational] This may refer to the LEGENDRE POLYNOMIAL or the LEGENDRE DIFFERENTIAL EQUATION. Generally, this indicates the solutions to the Legendre differential equation, also known as the Legendre polynomials.

Legendre polynomial

[astrophysics/astronomy, computational, nuclear, quantum] The work of ADRIEN-MARIE LEGENDRE (1752–1833) on celestial MECHANICS resulted in series of polynomials that are of general use. A formal description of a phenomenon may be expanded in the DEGREES OF FREEDOM that can be solved independent from each other. The Legendre polynomials solutions are defined as $P_\ell(\chi)=\left(1/2^\ell\right)\sum_{k=0}^{\ell}\binom{\ell}{k}^2(\chi-1)^{\ell-k}(\chi+1)^k$, which is a SOLUTION to the Legendre differential equation. The Legendre polynomials are azimuthally symmetric. In quantum PHYSICS the WAVE function (Ψ) may be expanded in the respective coordinate systems, specifically in spherical coordinates (r,θ,ϕ) and spherical functions: $\Psi=R(r)\Theta(\theta)\Phi(\phi)$. The polynomials are expressed as follows: $\Theta(\theta)=\sum P_\ell(\cos\theta)$ and $\Phi(\phi)=e^{im\phi}$, where $P_\ell(\cos\theta)$ is a polynomial series of ascending powers of trigonometry functions (the NUMERICAL cut-off on the series development {limit ℓ} will introduce an error which will set the accuracy of the approximation, primarily based on the boundary conditions), and ℓ and m are integers (e.g., quantum numbers) under the condition $|m| \leq \ell$. In QUANTUM physics the polynomial series is linked to the TOTAL ANGULAR MOMENTUM $M = \sqrt{(\ell(\ell+1))}\hbar$, and the angular component with respect to the axis of rotation (z) as $M_z = m\hbar$, where $\hbar = h/2\pi$, with PLANCK'S CONSTANT: $h = 6.62606957 \times 10^{-34}\ \mathrm{m^2kg/s}$. Another example of the use of Legendre polynomials is in the section on radiative transfer.

Legendre transform

[atomic, computational] Theoretical algorithm used in function approximations, converting a line as a function of location (x), generally expressed as $y = \alpha x + \beta$ to the location of intercept with the vertical axis (β) where $\alpha = dy/dx$ is the slope of the line. When the line is curved the following approximation can be made: $y = \alpha(x)x + \beta(x)$, which converts into $\beta(\alpha) = y(x) - [dy(x)/dx]x$, where $\beta(x)$ is the Legendre transformation of y. This process can be expanded for a range of variables $(\alpha_1, \alpha_2, \alpha_3, \ldots, \alpha_n)$ to yield: $\beta(\alpha_1, \alpha_2, \alpha_3, \ldots, \alpha_n) = Y(x_1, x_2, x_3, \ldots, x_n) - \Sigma_i [dy(x)/dx_i]x_i$, which transforms the function Y into a series constituted from the slopes of the function at the respective points x_i.

Lehmann, Inge (1888–1993)

[geophysics] Scientist from Denmark who discovered the Earth's inner core in 1929, further explained in separation into an inner and outer core in 1936. The description of the core outline was based on her collection of the velocity of propagation, with subsequent calculation, all based on EARTHQUAKE recording from a multitude of location on the PLANET, in the early 1900s (without the availability of computers). The seismic P-WAVE (compression wave) can travel through LIQUID media (outer core, and layers of the ASTHENOSPHERE), whereas the S-wave (shear wave) cannot. The seismologic work and theoretical description of P-wave propagation offered the essential tools for the modern day monitoring tool for underground (clandestine) atomic detonations (see Figure L.67).

Figure L.67 Inge Lehmann (1888–1993). (Courtesy of B.A. Bolt.)

Leibniz, Gottfried Wilhelm von (1646–1716)

[general] Mathematician and scientist from Germany, then Electorate of Saxony, Holy Roman Empire. Leibniz is known for the introduction of the integral symbol and principles in mathematical description, as well as the concept of differentiation. He also designed the concept of the binary arithmetic system in 1679. Leibniz is often also considered to be the father of the calculus system in scientific approach and engineering (see Figure L.68).

Figure L.68 Gottfried Wilhelm von Leibniz (1646–1716).

Leidenfrost, Johann Gottlob (1715–1794)

[general, thermodynamics] Physician from what is now known as Germany. Known for the formal description of a vapor BARRIER between a LIQUID drop and a hot plate, the LEIDENFROST EFFECT (see Figure L.69).

Figure L.69 Johan Gottlob Leidenfrost (1715–1794).

Leidenfrost effect

[thermodynamics] When a drop of LIQUID is introduced on a hot surface, when the HEAT TRANSFER is high enough, will vaporize the point of contact to form a low-friction BOUNDARY LAYER. The VAPOR barrier simultaneously prevents an effective transfer of heat, leaving the liquid drop virtually intact for an extended period of time. This phenomenon was described by JOHANN GOTTLOB LEIDENFROST (1715–1794), a German physician (see Figure L.70).

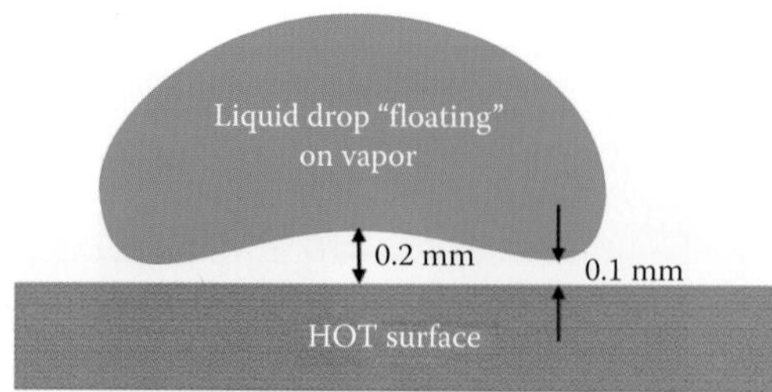

Figure L.70 Illustration of the concept of the Leidenfrost effect, a drop of water appears to "float" above a hot plate.

Lemaître, Monseigneur Georges Henri Joseph Édouard (1894–1966)

[astrophysics/astronomy, atomic, nuclear] Physicist from Belgium, he was also an ordained priest. In 1927 the work of Lemaître was published and revealed what is now known as the Hubble constant. Lemaître was one of the first known people to publish his theory of the EXPANDING UNIVERSE, in this view he proposed the origin of the UNIVERSE, now known as the "BIG BANG THEORY" based on his hypothesis of the "primordial atom." His theory of the expanding universe is often presented as HUBBLE'S LAW. His doctoral studies were performed under CHARLES DE LA VALLÉE-POUSSIN (1866–1962). The work of ALEXANDER FRIEDMANN (1888–1925) is often taken in association with that of Lemaître. Prior to this the general opinion was that the universe is static, specifically pertaining to the SPECIAL THEORY OF RELATIVITY introduced by ALBERT EINSTEIN (1879–1955) introduced in 1905 (see Figure L.71).

Figure L.71 Monseigneur Georges Henri Joseph Édouard Lemaître (1894–1966) in 1933, taken while teaching at the Catholic University Leuven, Belgium. (Courtesy of Katholieke Universiteit Leuven/Université Catholique de Louvain, Leuven, Belgium.)

Lenard, Philipp Eduard Anton von

[atomic, nuclear] Scientist from Slovakia, now Germany (*see* **Von Lenard**).

Length, chord

[fluid dynamics, general, geometry, mechanics] The length of a traced curved path or one-dimensional extend of a real or virtual curved surface (e.g., wing surface in direction of flow) (*see* **chord**).

Length, measurement

[general] France was the first country to commit to a unified system of measures in 1799, using a decimal system, steps/divisions of 10^n, with n = integer, under guidance of emperor Napoleon Bonaparte (1769–1821). The meter as unit of length, was defined as one ten-millionth of the DISTANCE from the at that time accepted location of the North Pole to the equator over the meridian running through Paris, France. Later this was made into a standard that could be used to verify and validate on a universal scale by defining the distance on alloy bar made from platinum and iridium in 1889. Later calibration standards include the definition implemented in 1960 based upon a wavelength of krypton-86 radiation, and the currently (introduction: 1983) accepted distance traveled by light in VACUUM during a time frame of 1/299792458 s. Length can be measured optically by INTERFEROMETER techniques as well as acoustically based on time of flight, and the old stand-by ruler/tape measure, where the later has a high tolerance due to inherent FATIGUE and wear.

Length contraction

[general] An object observed by an eyewitness that holds the object will have a specific length (L_s). When observed from a DISTANCE when traveling parallel to the object while in MOTION with velocity v will make the object appear shorter (L_m) according to the following rule: $L_m = L_s\sqrt{\left[1-\left(v^2/c^2\right)\right]}$, where $c = 2.99792458\times10^8\,\mathrm{m/s}$ is the speed of light with respect to the observation (see Figure L.72).

Figure L.72 Graphical representation of the relativistic concept of length contraction.

Lennard-Jones, John Edward, Sir (1894–1954)

[chemical, computational, electronics] Mathematician and scientist from Great Britain. Lennard-Jones dedicated his work to the understanding of the molecular structure and in particular the role of the VALENCE electron (see Figure L.73).

Figure L.73 Sir John Edward Lennard-Jones (1894–1954).

L

Lennard-Jones potential

[chemical, computational, electronics, quantum] Molecules and atoms that are not part of a chemical structure (i.e., using the exchange of VALENCE electrons) exert a force on ach-other that is repulsive at short DISTANCE and attractive at large distance. The electrical POTENTIAL (V) for the "internuclear" spacing between molecules (r_{inter}) expressed as $V\left(r_{\text{inter}}\right) = 4U_{\in}\left[\left(r_{\sigma}/r_{\text{inter}}\right)^{12} - \left(r_{\sigma}/r_{\text{inter}}\right)^{6}\right]$, where r_{σ} is the intermolecular distance where the potential is zero and $U_{\in}$ the ENERGY in the interatomic attraction (i.e., depth of POTENTIAL WELL). The interatomic/intermolecular energy may depend on DIPOLE and quadruple interaction, but on a larger scale this is attributed to transient electric fields that overlap, even at greater distances. The attractive forces may include Van der Waals forces and London forces, but these do not account for the repulsion between molecules at close separation. The repelling mechanism of action may be attributed to collisions. In the SIR JOHN EDWARD LENNARD-JONES (1894–1954) approach, molecules reach a point where they can be considered as "solid" spheres, resulting from the tight electron configuration of the chemical bounds within the MOLECULE. This principle was considered to offer an explanation for incompressible liquids in the early 1900s (see Figure L.74).

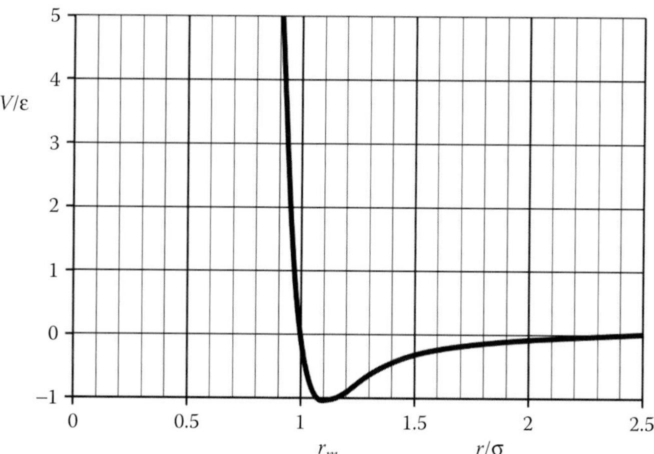

Figure L.74 Graphical representation of the strength of the Lennard-Jones potential with respect to distance.

Lens

[acoustics, biomedical, electromagnetism, general, optics] Device that provides the mechanism of action to change the course of wave-forms: ELECTROMAGNETIC RADIATION, mechanical waves, electric or MAGNETIC fields by themselves, as well as charged particles (technically, also subject to the SCHRÖDINGER WAVE EQUATION). The optical lens mechanism generally falls under GEOMETRICAL OPTICS. Optical imaging with a lens relies on the LAW OF REFRACTION for real or virtual image formation. A set of binoculars or an optical MICROSCOPE uses a set of lenses to form a VIRTUAL IMAGE (as seen by the naked EYE), whereas a CAMERA uses lenses (e.g., zoom lens, fish eye, standard) to project a REAL IMAGE on a PHOTOGRAPHIC PLATE or digital array of CHARGE-COUPLED DEVICE (CCD) elements. Composite lenses can be constructed using various layers of materials, providing physical correction factors for focal length and spectral profiles. Lenses can be symmetric and asymmetric. Examples of asymmetric lenses are cylindrical. The IMAGE forming mechanism (i.e., RESOLUTION) is limited by the diffraction principle defined by the ABBÉ LIMIT, also found as the RAYLEIGH CRITERION. Regular spherical optical lens design can be considered to be carved out by two overlapping spheres, with respective radii, thus forming the basis to the Lens (makers) equation. Spherical lens designs are biconvex, biconcave, planar convex, planar concave, MENISCUS convex, and meniscus concave. Aspherical lens design. In contrast to transmission imaging, mirrors can also form images and have similar design configurations and constraints as well as similar rules apply, but the coordinate system for the image is now reversed. Complex imaging systems use combinations of transmission and reflection, and may also include prisms to shorten the path by means of folding the optical path (e.g., binoculars). In electron beam imaging (TRANSMISSION ELECTRON MICROSCOPE or reflection electron microscope) the electron beam is redirected and collimated to a narrow "focal" point by means of magnetic fields. In an electron microscope the lens is a coil or sets of coils arranged in geometric configurations that produces a well-defined MAGNETIC FIELD that can be adjusted (see Figure L.75).

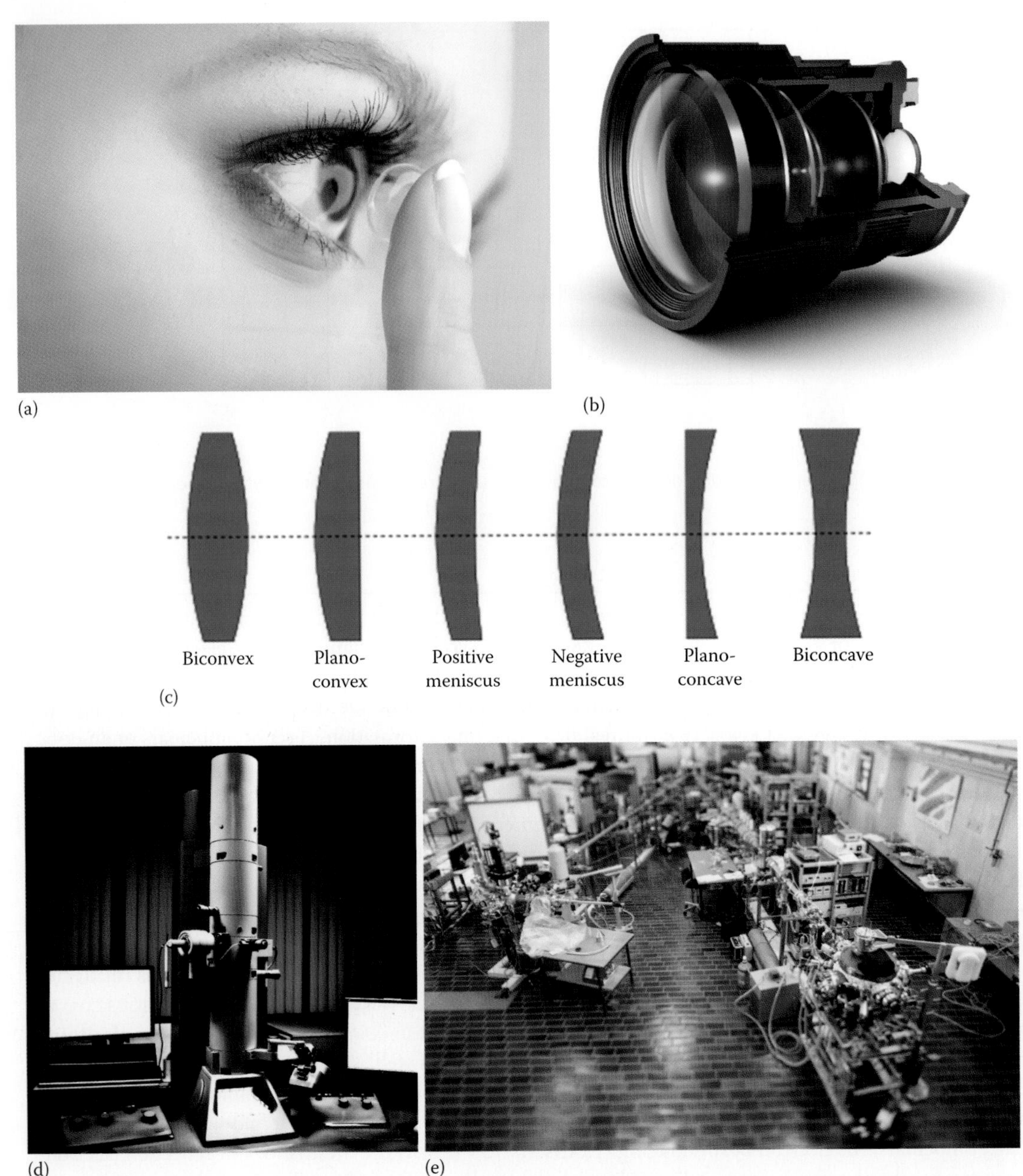

Figure L.75) Assortment of lens designs and applications: (a) contact lens and lens of the human eye and (b) camera lens cross-sectional view, (c) general concepts in optical lens design, (d) electronic lens for electron microscope, and (e) compound lens design for particle accelerator.

Lens, aspherical surfaces

[general, optics] Lens design that does not use the overlapping sphere configuration. The aspherical lens corrects for material properties and associated aberrations. The EYE is an example of an aspherical lens design (see Figure L.76).

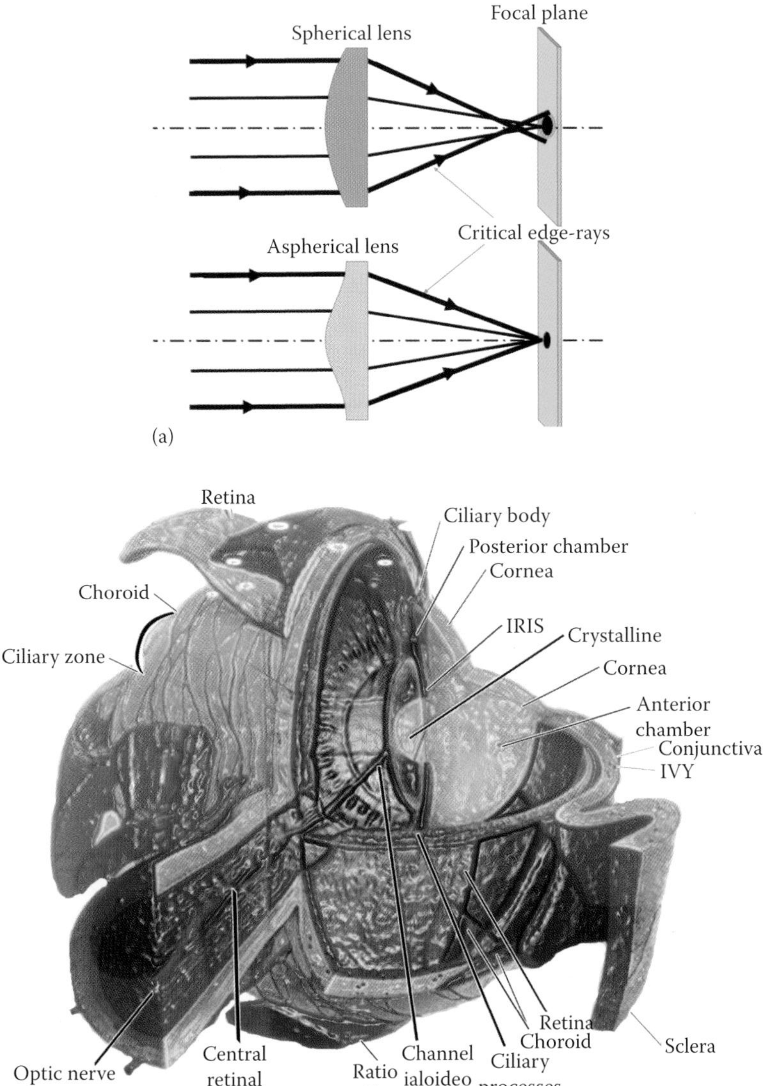

Figure L.76 Aspheric lens design: (a) general design and (b) human crystalline lens.

Lens, Einzel Lens, extended imagery

[general] In charged PARTICLE convergence/divergence with MAGNETIC and electric field LENS design the fields may be contained by hollow disks, CONES or cylinders. In case a hollow cylinder is used that has a set

of two gaps, allowing to form a pair, with TOTAL POTENTIAL difference across the cascading pairs to add to zero is an Einzel lens (see Figure L.77).

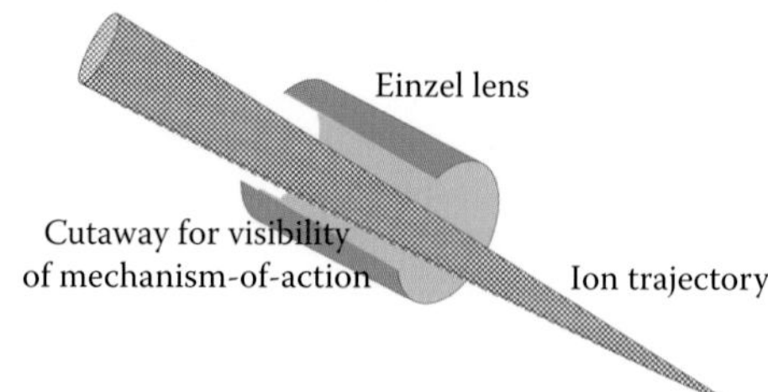

Figure L.77 Einzel lens design for directing charged particles using specific magnetic and electric field configurations.

Lens, focal point and plane

[general] The FOCAL POINT of a LENS will have the rays entering in parallel configuration exit through the focal point. The focal point of the lens is located on the optical axis. The plane perpendicular to the optical axis intersecting in the focal point is the FOCAL PLANE of the lens. Rays passing through a lens from a location that does not intersect with the optical axis will form an IMAGE that does not necessarily coincide with the optical axis, but will fall within the focal plane (see Figure L.78).

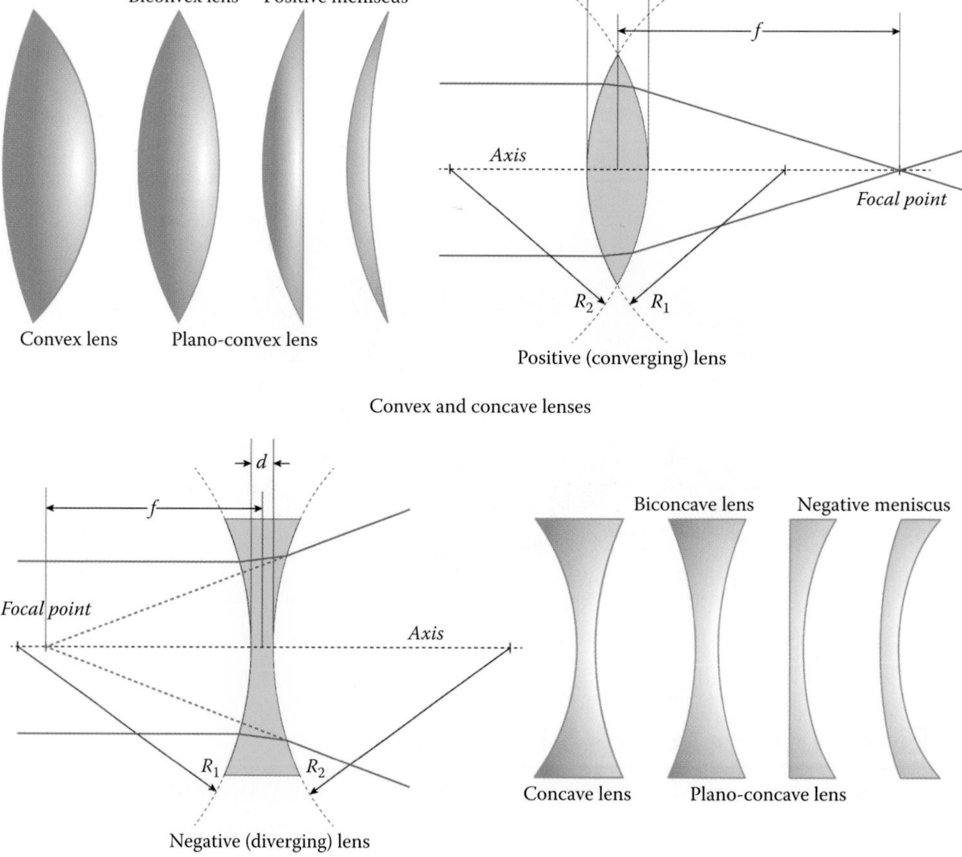

Figure L.78 Focal point and focal plane for a convex and a concave lens design, respectively.

Lens, gravitational

[geophysics] A gravitational LENS describes the influence of a GRAVITATIONAL FIELD on the path of ELECTROMAGNETIC RADIATION. This phenomenon was described by ALBERT EINSTEIN (1879–1955) and was first investigated during a solar eclipse in the year 1919, trying to establish the influence of the sun's own GRAVITATION on the directional emission/propagation of light. The deflection ANGLE (θ_B) induced by a gravitational field with MAGNITUDE proportional to the mass of the object (M) with respect to the incident direction is $\theta_B = 4GM/c^2b$, where $c = 2.99792458 \times 10^8$ m/s is the speed of light, G the gravitational constant, and b an "impact parameter" describing the respective mass influence. This principle may provide the tools to analyze the potential of the phenomenon referred to as "BLACK HOLE." Images obtained by the HUBBLE SPACE TELESCOPE are prone to gravitational lensing due to the immense distances involved in the field of view for this TELESCOPE (see Figure L.79).

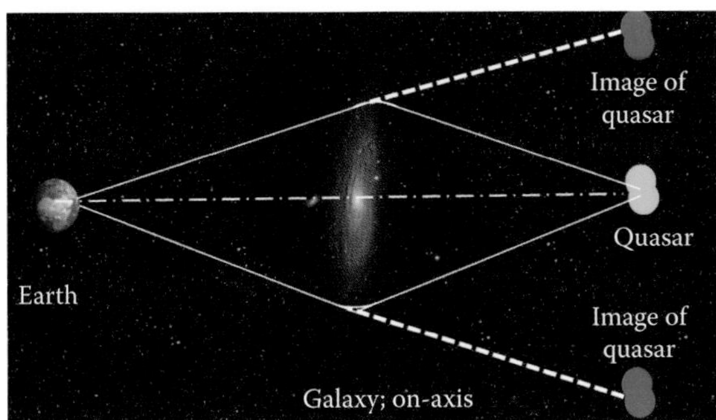

Figure L.79 Diagram of the gravitational lens concept and the practical implications.

Lens, magnetic

[biomedical, general] In charged PARTICLE beam imaging the use of a MAGNETIC multipole (generally quadrupole, in STAR formation with same pole facing each other, opposite POLES adjacent) or discontinuous/asymmetric electric coil. The coil will generate a MAGNETIC FIELD based on the AMPÈRE'S LAW resulting from a current. The magnetic field will interact with the azimuthal component of the velocity of a moving charged particle as well as with the radial component, hence rotating and shifting the IMAGE orientation. One specific example is found in the imaging with positron emission TOMOGRAPHY (see Figure L.80).

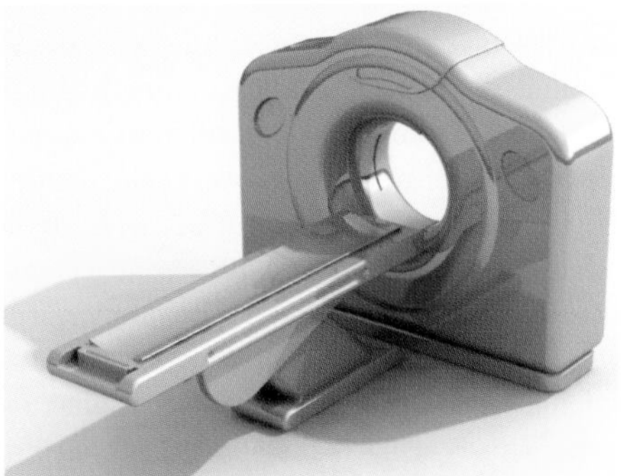

Figure L.80 Illustration of the use of magnetic lenses in the signal collection mechanism of action for a positron emission tomography machine.

Lens, magnification

[general] *See* **MAGNIFICATION.**

Lens, thin lens combinations

[general] In order to provide a correction mechanism for the various LENS ABERRATIONS combining more than one lens, each made of material with specific index of REFRACTION and individual focal lengths can provide the means to eliminate the majority of distortions, leaving only border effects to be discarded. Border effects can easily be eliminated by relying on overfill of the recording mechanism (see Figure L.81).

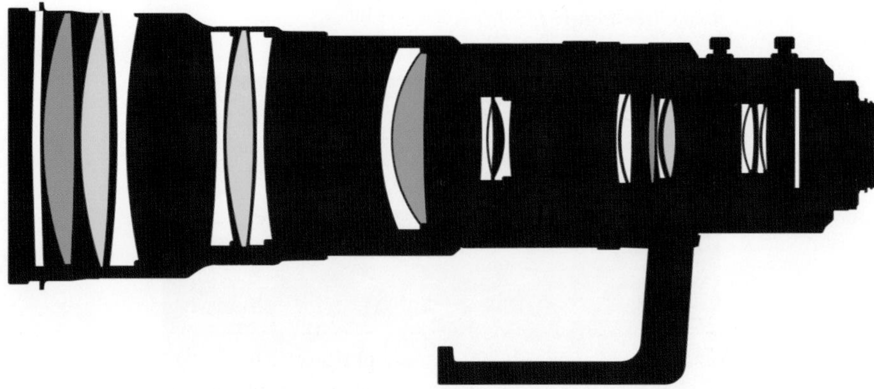

Figure L.81 Representation of thin lens concept in telephoto lens design for the correction of chromatic and spherical aberrations. The "sandwiched" lenses act as single lenses with a convoluted index of refraction as a function of radius.

Lens aberrations

[acoustics, biomedical, general, optics] Image forming distortions created as a result of the limitations of the LENS or the mechanism of data transfer. Several aberration mechanisms can be recognized: ASTIGMATISM, chromatic, coma, distortion, field-curvature, lateral COLOR. Astigmatism is generally the result of a deformation from symmetry in the lens construction, next to boundary effects in a symmetric lens. In astigmatism tangential lines and radial lines may have an IMAGE that is formed at different locations with respect to the DISTANCE to the lens, thus changing the physical configuration of the image. CHROMATIC ABERRATIONS result from the fact that different colors have different focal points for a lens of a single material (compound lenses can resolve this), thus forming separate image locations for different colors. This results in out-off focus images of different colors in one single imaging plane. Coma is the distortion where the various zones of a lens form images at different magnification, which result primarily in radial distortions. Distortion is very similar to coma, however the magnification discrepancy is nonuniform, it can be localized due to material imperfections or surface irregularities. Field curvature is similar to astigmatism with the distinction that the image is formed on a concave or convex surface instead of a flat imaging plane, still perpendicular to the optical axis. Lateral color aberration is the phenomenon where the images of respectively different colors are formed at different size in the same imaging plane. Note that an image is considered to be sharply demarcated. The FRESNEL LENS applies a specific form of lens design that intentionally creates an aberration but this is visually interpreted as continuous (discontinuous lens design based on this principle is for instance the automobile head-light). The Fresnel lens is generally symmetric and is found in light-houses (see Figure L.82).

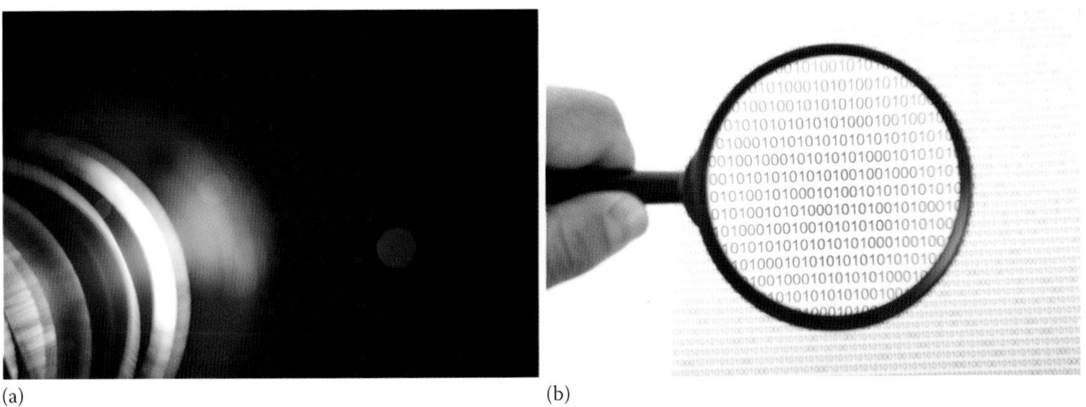

Figure L.82 Lens aberrations: (a) chromatic aberration and (b) spherical aberration.

Lens axicon focusing

[optics] Lens configuration that can provide BESSEL BEAM light propagation. This principle is used, for instance, in the precision alignment for large telescopes as well as in ultrashort laser pulse focusing. Additionally. the bar code scanners found in supermarkets use a LENS axicon for focusing a highly dispersive field resulting from the undefined surface properties (see Figure L.83).

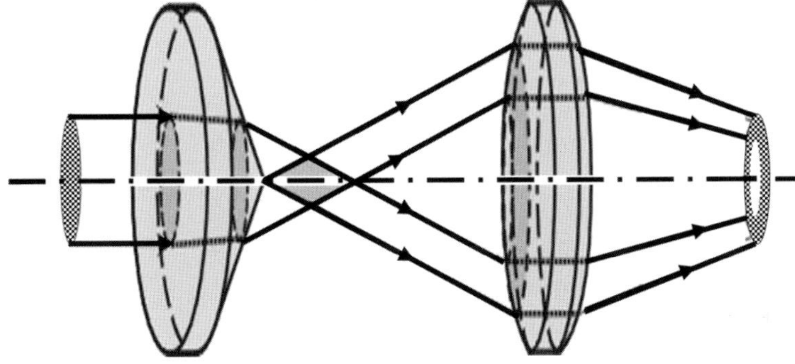

Figure L.83 Outline of lens-axicon focusing.

Lens maker's equation

[general] The equation describing the focal length (f) of an optical LENS as used by as a function of the radius of curvature of the incident surface (R_1) with respect to the exit surface (R_2) for a confined medium with index of REFRACTION n_2 when placed in an environment with index (n_2). For a thin lens this is expressed as $1/f = (n_2 - n_1)/n_1\left[(1/R_1)-(1/R_2)\right] = P_{\text{power}}$, which yields the power P_{power} of the lens, that is, the "strength" of the lens as indicated by the optician making the lens for VISUAL ACUITY. Also known as the lens equation or thin lens formula. This equation was described by RENÉ DESCARTES (1596–1650). For a THICK LENS the refraction on either side of the medium will need to be accounted for, as well as the DISTANCE traveled before intersecting with the next curved surface. The lens maker's equation is derived

from geometry, to be $1/f = (n-1)\left[(1/R_1) - (1/R_2) + (n-1)t/nR_1R_2\right]$, where t represents the thickness distance of the optical path through the refractive medium with index of refraction n (see Figure L.84).

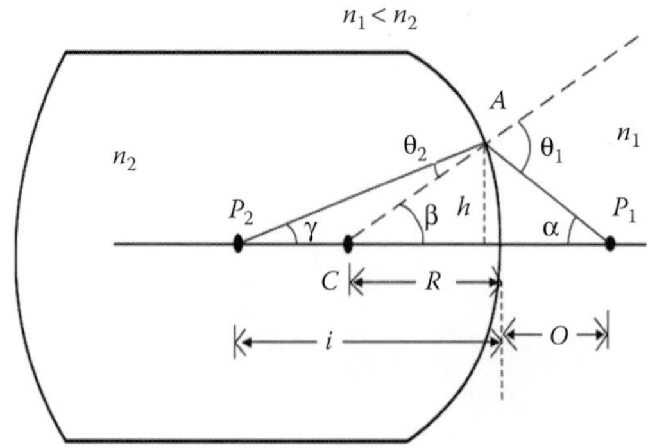

Figure L.84 Lens maker's equation concept.

Lens maker's equation

[general] The lens maker equation uses the REFRACTION concept to describe the formation of an IMAGE in a FOCAL POINT (f) of a system of aspherical surfaces with respective radii R_i using SNELL'S LAW as follows: $1/f = (n_2 - n_1)/n_1\left[(1/R_1) - (1/R_2)\right] = P$, where n_1 is the index of refraction of the surrounding medium, n_2 the index of the refractive medium, and P the power of the LENS expressed in diopters. For a thin lens, the lens maker equation reverts to $(1/f) = (1/i) + (1/o)$, where i is the image DISTANCE to the lens and o is the object distance (see Figure L.85).

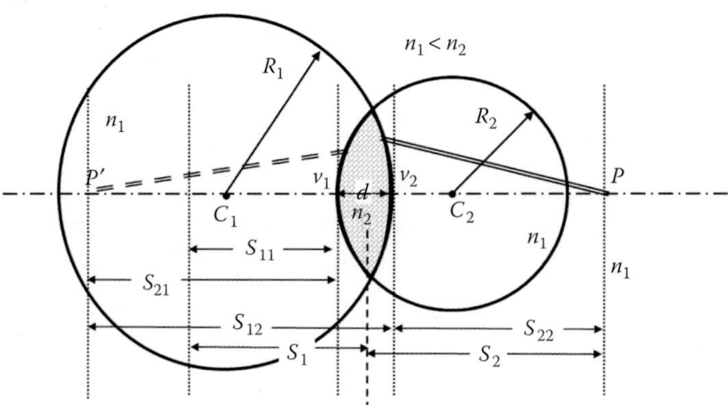

Figure L.85 Diagram representing the concepts used in the lens maker's equation.

Lenz, Heinrich Friedrich Emil (1804–1865)

[electromagnetism, general] Russian scientist with Baltic-German connection (Cyrillic name: Эмилий Христианович Ленц). In 1833, Lenz described the phenomenon that the induced electromotive force, or induced voltage, will produce a MAGNETIC FIELD that is opposite in direction of the change in magnetic field that induces the voltage itself, which introduced the negative sign in the Faraday's law (*see* **Lenz's law**) (see Figure L.86).

Figure L.86 Heinrich Friedrich Emil Lenz (1804–1865).

Lenz–Ising model

[solid-state] Theoretical model describing the PHASE TRANSITION for a uniaxial FERROMAGNET. Named after Wilhelm Lenz (1888–1957) and ERNST ISING (1900–1998). The MAGNETIC phase transition is a second-order phenomenon. The model uses a magnetic spin LATTICE configuration with lattice site Λ with respective spin locations $\square_j$, allowing only "up (+1)" or "down" (−1) spin: $\sigma_{\text{spin}} = \left(\sigma_{\text{spin}}{}^{j}\right)_{j\in\Lambda}$; $\sigma_{\text{spin}}{}^{j} \in \{-1,+1\}$. The model also describes the prevalence for neighboring spins to align, however, opposite alignment of a range of lattice locations can remain order (subcritical) or supercritical disordered state. Adjacent spins (i, j), all within the lattice: $i, j \in \Lambda$ experience an external MAGNETIC FIELD $B_i{}'$, which is defined by an interaction parameter $\mathbb{I}_{ij}$. The total interaction can be described by the Hamiltonian: $H(\sigma_{\text{spin}}) = -\sum_{i,j} \mathbb{I}_{ij}\sigma_{\text{spin}}{}^{i}\sigma_{\text{spin}}{}^{j} - \mu_{\text{magn}}\sum_j B_j{}'\sigma_{\text{spin}}{}^{j}$, where the magnetic moment $\mu_{\text{mag}} = (-e/c)(v/2\pi r)\left(\pi r^2\right)$, where e electron charge in Coulomb, $c = 2.99792458 \times 10^8\,\text{m/s}$ the speed of light and r the radius of the orbit of an electron revolving with speed v. The PROBABILITY dissemination for the SPIN configuration is defined by a BOLTZMANN DISTRIBUTION ($P_{\tau_T}(\sigma_{\text{spin}}) = e^{-\tau_T H(\sigma_{\text{spin}})}/Z_{\tau_T}$, where $\tau_T = 1/k_B T$ with the Boltzmann coefficient $k_b = 1.3806488 \times 10^{-23}\,\text{m}^2\text{kg/s}^2\text{K}$ and temperature T; note $Z_{\tau_T} = \sum_{\sigma_{\text{spin}}} e^{-\tau_T H(\sigma_{\text{spin}})}$ is a NORMALIZATION factor combining the effects of all spins to yield a probability $0 \le P_{\tau_T}\left(\sigma_{\text{spin}}\right) \le 1$). A critical temperature can be identified, below which order will result in net magnetization. The full model cannot be solved analytically, unless severe assumption are made.

Lenz's law

[electromagnetism, general] Pertaining to a CURRENT (I) through a circuit running in loop, resulting from an electric field ($\vec{E}$) providing an ELECTROMOTIVE FORCE (ε_{emf}) with a resulting MAGNETIC FIELD ($\vec{B}$) passing through an area (A, with normal $\vec{n}$) the following equation was defined: $\varepsilon_{\text{emf}} = -(1/c)(d/dt)\int_{S_0} \vec{B} \cdot \vec{n}dA$, where S_0 is the surface, $c = 2.99792458 \times 10^8\,\text{m/s}$ the speed of light, all with respect to time (t). Named after

HEINRICH LENZ (1804–1865) who introduced the concept in 1834. This is closely related to the Faraday's law (see Figure L.87).

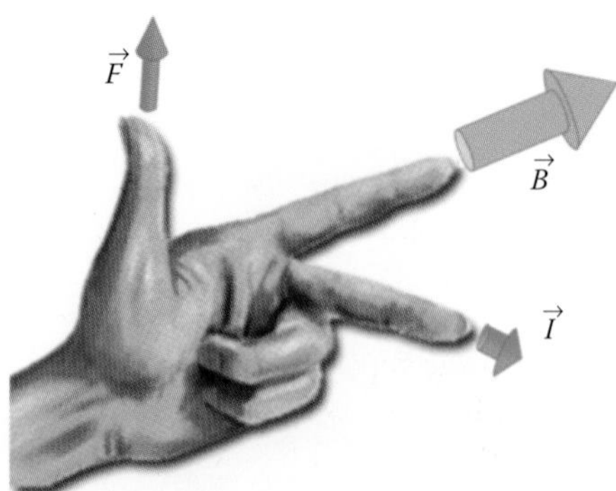

Figure L.87 The configuration of the orientation of the force on a moving charge (i.e., current) under the influence of a magnetic field under Lenz's law.

Leonardo da Vinci (1451–1519)

[fluid dynamics, general, mechanics] *See* **DA VINCI, LEONARDO**.

Leonards, Jack Rack (1919–1978)

[biomedical, chemical, fluid dynamics] Inventor and scientist from Canada. Leonard designed and verified the workings of a parallel plate dialysis machine in 1948 in collaboration with LEONARD T. SKEGGS (1918–2002). This type of artificial KIDNEY is different from the device developed by WILLEM JOHAN KOLFF (1911–2009) in the manner that it does not require a BLOOD pump.

Lepton

[astrophysics/astronomy, atomic, energy, general, nuclear, quantum, thermodynamics] Class of elementary PARTICLE generally without intrinsic net charge, except for the electron. Lepton are not subjected to the STRONG NUCLEAR FORCE, in contrast to the MESON, and hence does not bind in the nucleus. Examples of leptons are electron, MUON, tau particle, and NEUTRINO. Leptons have an intrinsic SPIN of $1/2$ and hence obey the Fermi–Dirac definition.

Lepton, angular momentum of

[atomic, general, solid-state] Leptons have a small angular momentum that is measured in multiples of $h/4\pi$, where $h = 6.62606957 \times 10^{-34}\ \mathrm{m^2kg/s}$ is Planck's constant.

Lepton number (*L*)

[astrophysics/astronomy, atomic, energy, general, nuclear, quantum, thermodynamics] CONSERVATION OF CHARGE designation for ELEMENTARY PARTICLES indicating the fact that for each Lepton (e.g., electron, MUON, tau) the equivalent charge must add up to same charge value on either side of the equation. For instance, for the following PARTICLE transition: $\mu^- \rightarrow e^- + \overline{\nu}_e + \nu_\mu$, where μ^- indicates a muon, e^- represent an electron, $\overline{\nu}_e$ is an electron anti-neutrino and ν_μ a muon NEUTRINO; the lepton number for the respective breakdown is represented as follows: L_μ: $1 = 0 + 0 + 1$ and L_e: $0 = 1 - 1 + 0$.

Leucippus (fifth century BC)

[general] Scientist from ancient Greece, who in approximately 450 BC introduced the concept of the ATOM as the first documented entry of an elementary PARTICLE that contains all the characteristics of the object that consists of a multitude of these particles and is indivisible. The Greek word atomos (ατομοσ) means "that what cannot be cut further."

Lever

[general, mechanics] A device used to provide torque by means of converting the force applied to one side of a bar that is hinging on a FULCRUM with respective DISTANCE to the same force in the opposite direction with a different distance to the fulcrum on the opposing site of the fulcrum. The radius pivoting on the elbow joint supported by the humerus while a force is applied by the biceps is a well-known example, as well as cranes hoisting equipment for construction (see Figure L.88).

Figure L.88 Lever on slot machine.

Levinthal's paradox

[biomedical, computational, thermodynamics] Proteins are long chains of molecules (i.e., MACROMOLECULES, generally containing hundreds of atoms) that will configure themselves to establish a condition of MINIMUM ENERGY and entropy. Considering that a protein consisting of 2000 atoms will have 6000 degrees of freedom, 2/3 due to rotation and the remaining resulting from relative bond angles. Generally the protein structure may not appear to have an organized structure but the polypeptides do in fact have a structure as derived from X-RAY diffraction studies. The local amino acid sequences will most likely form stable interactions and will act as NUCLEATION points in the folding process. The regularity in the folding process, creating relatively fixed relative bond angles can be derived in Fourier space from the X-ray diffraction spectral analysis.

Levitation

[electromagnetism] The act of suspending an object in free space without anything attached, using a remotely operating force ($\vec{F}$). MAGNETIC LEVITATION can be achieved by means of electrical current which generates a magnetic field ($\vec{B}$) according to LENZ'S LAW ($\vec{F} = m \cdot \nabla \vec{B}$), which can, for instance, counteract gravitational attraction (on a mass: m), provided there is enough symmetry to avoid lateral net forces. ELECTRIC CHARGE and MAGNETIC FIELD can exert a force without the requirement for direct contact. Levitation can be used to provide a low-friction interaction between two objects, for instance, in train transport. A mechanical suspension by means of AIR flow through a rail at closely separated interval is technically not considered to fall under levitation since there is a direct contact force involved resulting from the air flow (see Figure L.89).

Figure L.89 The concept of levitation, as a result of an external magnetic field, maglev train in Shanghai, with velocity exceeding 500km/h, respectively mainland China.

Lewis, Gilbert Newton (1875–1946)

[electromagnetism, general] Physicist and chemist from the United States, who is best known for his introduction of the word "PHOTON" for ELECTROMAGNETIC RADIATION in 1926. Lewis also worked on the definition of VALENCE electrons and introduced the concept of chemical bonds known as the covalent bond, and created the "Lewis symbols" used to describe ways in which atoms bond until this day. Lewis was the first to produce "HEAVY WATER" in the early 1930s with double-weight hydrogen atoms. The discovery of heavy water was essential in the experimental design for ATOMIC ENERGY (see Figure L.90).

Figure L.90 Gilbert Newton Lewis (1875–1946). (Courtesy of The Chemists' Club, New York.)

Lewis number ($Le = \kappa / D_{AB} = Sc/Pr$)

[fluid dynamics, thermodynamics] Dimensionless number indicating the ratio of the thermal DIFFUSION to the molecular diffusion, where κ is the thermal diffusion coefficient; D_{AB} the molecular diffusion coefficient for the constituent AB, as used in the FICK'S EQUATION; Sc the Schmidt number; and Pr the Prandtl number. Named after Warren K. Lewis (1882–1975).

Leyden jar

[electronics, general] Also known as the Leiden jar (Leyden being the old Dutch vernacular for the university city in the Netherlands now known as Leiden), dated for its use around 1745. A glass-jar device filled with a quantity of water, with a CONDUCTOR on the inside and on the outside of the container used in the early days of investigations in the collection of "electric fluid." The Leyden jar conductors were attached to the Leyden jar forms the precursor to the modern day CONDENSER or CAPACITOR, as well as provided basic scientific evidence of storage of electrical charge leading to the invention of the BATTERY. The ELECTRIC CHARGE build-up (static ELECTRICITY) was accomplished by FRICTION of various materials. The first static electricity charge GENERATOR was developed by OTTO VON GUERICKE (1602–1682) in 1650 (see Figure L.91).

Figure L.91 Drawing of the original concept of the Leyden jar.

Libration point

[computational, general, geophysics] *See* **LAGRANGIAN LIBRATION POINT.**

Lifetime (τ)

[biomedical, nuclear] Average time of existence for RADIOACTIVE ISOTOPE. Tie over which the number of isotopes DECAY to e^{-1}: $\tau = \int_0^{\infty} t N_0 e^{-\lambda_{1/2} t} dt \big/ N_0$, where $\lambda_{1/2}$ is the decay constant, t time, and N_0 the original quantity of isiotipes (*also see* **MEAN LIFE**).

Lifshitz–Kosevich theory

[electromagnetism, quantum, solid-state] The RESONANCE component of an electrodynamic potential in the interaction on electrical RESISTANCE during CONDUCTOR exposure to an oscillatory MAGNETIC FIELD. The MAGNITUDE of the electrodynamic potential is defined as $\Phi_{osc} = 2V_k T \left(eB/\hbar c\right)^{3/2} \left(\partial^2 S/\partial k_N{}^2\right)_{km}^{-1/2} \sum_{j=1}^{\infty} \left\{\left[\exp\left(-2\pi^2 j k_B T_D/\beta' B\right)/\sinh\left(2\pi^2 j k_B T_D/\beta' B\right)\right] * \cos\left[\left(j\hbar e S_m/eB\right) - 2j\pi\gamma \pm (\pi/4)\right] * \cos\left(j\pi g m_c^*/2m_0\right)\right\}$, where S defines the cross-sectional surface of the Fermi area, $\beta' = e\hbar/m_c^* c$ is the Bohr double magneton, $m_c^* = \hbar^2 \left(\partial S/2\pi\partial E\right)_{E_F}$ the CYCLOTRON effective mass, E_F the Fermi ENERGY, B the magnetic field strength, and E the energy on the FERMI SURFACE. This has relevance with respect to k-SPACE orbit electrons, specifically in perpendicular direction to the magnetic field. One specific application is in the theoretical description of the functionality of MOSFET SEMICONDUCTORS.

Lift

[fluid dynamics] Force resulting from flow that provides the mechanism to raise an object subjected to fluid flow: $F_L = (1/2)\rho v_{flow}{}^2 AC_L$, where ρ is the FLUID density (e.g., accounting for altitude), A the surface area of the AIRFOIL (i.e., WING, or sail [horizontal force]), v_{flow} the relative AIR velocity (net velocity with respect to the wing, including for instance air flow and wing speed). This lift force describes the conditions for an airfoil to remain afloat during flight. Lift is a function of the density of the air, the FLOW velocity, next to the air's viscosity and compressibility, and the device parameters: the shape of the body, the surface area over which the fluid flows, and the inclination of the geometry of the body with respect to the flow. The influences resulting from geometric body shape, respective surface inclinations, fluid viscosity, and compressibility is a complex system. The lift coefficient designated can be used to account for the boundary conditions, providing a relatively simple equation. Lift on a rudimentary level is a direct result of the BERNOULLI'S EQUATION, where the path for fluid flow on the top is longer that the flow on the bottom of the object subjected to flow and resulting increased flow velocity on top, hence creating a pressure gradient in the upward direction, with effective lift force. At the position of the irregular object at the critical ANGLE with respect to direction of flow the lift will be maximized, also called angle of attack. Generally, a wing will have adjustment options (extension segments) that can change the angle of attack, while the wing itself remains fixed. The same will apply in a horizontal manner for a sail of a sailboat. The sailboat can adjust the angle of attack. Another example of an airfoil is a ski jumper. When the angle of attack grows, the separation point of the flow on the upper surface moves forward from the trailing edge toward the LEADING EDGE. On most airfoil shapes when the critical angle of attack is reached, the upper surface flow is more separated and the airfoil, sail or wing will produce the maximum lift coefficient. With increasing angle of attack, the upper fluid flow becomes more and more fully separated with a dramatic reduction in lift coefficient. When the airfoil wing angle exceeds the critical angle of attack, a condition with respect to airplanes results called stall, or lift stall. Also note that an airfoil can be symmetric and still maintain lift, specifically due to the lift-angle, which artificially increases the path length on the upper side. Airplanes can hence fly upside-down depending on the wing symmetry and lift angle. Even for symmetric objects (round, square, etc.) a situation can occur that produces lift due to CIRCULATION vortices that result in a condition of zero flow velocity at a point in the proximity of the surface of the object, with resulting Bernoulli pressure gradient: $\Delta P = -\int_0^{2\pi} P\sin(\theta)\, a d\theta = \rho\kappa_{circ} v_{flow}$, where κ_{circ} represents the cyclic constant defining the circulation and a is a constant. The cyclic constant is linked to the VELOCITY POTENTIAL (ϕ) as $\phi = \kappa_{circ,0}\omega + \kappa_{circ,1}\omega' + \kappa_{circ,2}\omega'' + \cdots$, where ω' defines the CIRCULATION FUNCTION in a specific location, a specific circuit. The circulation function is not the "CIRCULATION" related to vortices (see Figure L.92).

Figure L.92 Lift on an object (i.e., plane) subjected to flow.

Lift, stalling angle

[fluid dynamics] The ANGLE of the wing (moveable WING or angle of ascent of the plane) for AIRFOIL shapes when the critical angle of attack is reached. At this point, the upper surface flow is more separated and the airfoil has surpassed its point of maximum LIFT coefficient. Increasing angle of attack beyond the stalling angle will cause the upper FLOW pattern to detach with a dramatic reduction in lift coefficient. Beyond this angle the lift will reduce and the plane will not elevate. The stalling angle of lift (stalling angle of attack; attack angle) for most airfoils has a characteristically value of approximately 15°. Another example of an airfoil is a ski jumper. The ski jumper quickly reduces in velocity due to the AIR DRAG that the whole-body experiences (see Figure L.93).

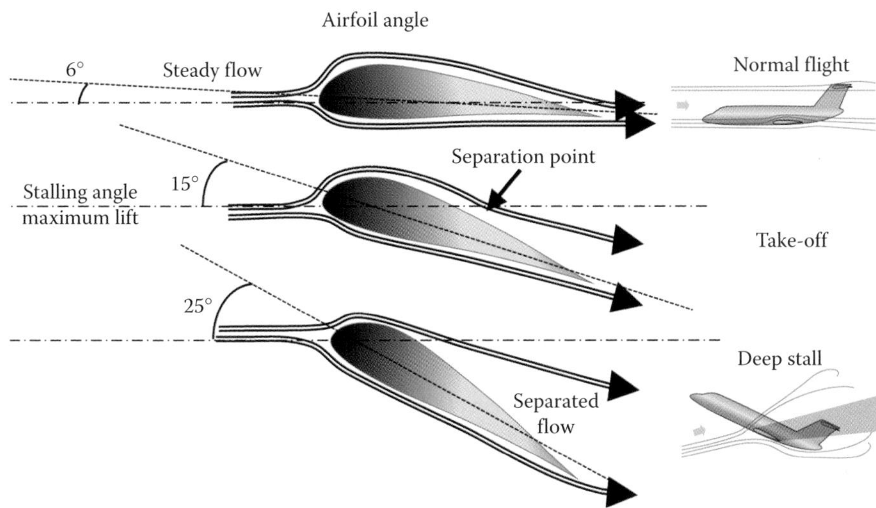

Figure L.93 Illustration of the effect of airfoil angle with respect to fluid flow; stalling angle for Lift.

Lift coefficient (C_L)

[fluid dynamics, general] Number used to account for the impact on LIFT of all of the complex dependencies of curvature, shape, as well as particular FLOW conditions. This number follows from rearranging the lift equation. Coefficient in an equation that describes the threshold limit for airborne lift force (F_L) of an object outfitted with wings, as described in the following equation: $F_L = (1/2)\rho v^2 AC_L$, where ρ is the FLUID density (e.g., accounting for altitude), A the surface area of the AIRFOIL (i.e., WING), v the AIR velocity (net velocity with respect to the wing, including for instance air flow and wing speed). This lift force describes the conditions for an airfoil to remain afloat during flight. The lift coefficient is defined as a function of the ANGLE of incidence, or the wing angle with respect to the airflow in addition as a function of MACH NUMBER and REYNOLDS NUMBER, describing the local fluid conditions (e.g., HUMIDITY and fluid mixture: RAIN). At a specific altitude, the velocity needs to exceed the ORBITAL VELOCITY to remain in lift, the point at which the flight velocity equals the orbital velocity is called the Kármán line. The lift coefficient is defined as $c_\ell = 2F_L/\rho v^2 A$, where F_L is the lift for the wing with surface area A, under relative flow velocity v (see Figure L.94).

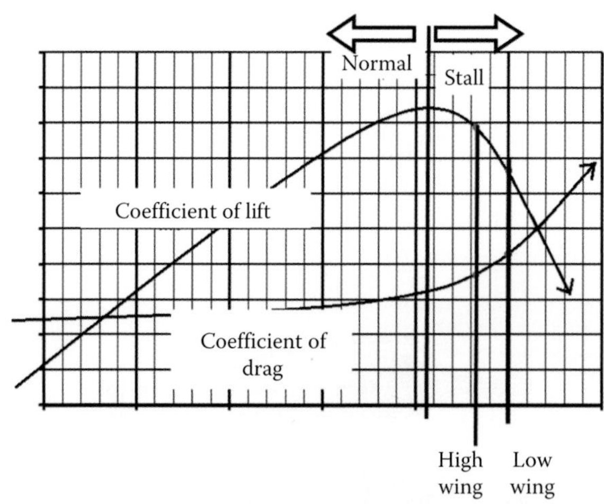

Figure L.94 Lift coefficient and lift–drag ratio.

Lift–drag ratio

[fluid dynamics] Amount of lift (L) experienced by an AIRFOIL, divided by the viscous DRAG (F_{drag}) generated by the FLUID it moves through. The ratio of the LIFT force with respect to the drag RESISTANCE is a scaling marker of the aerodynamic efficiency of for instance an airplane. Under normal conditions, the optimal conditions are described as $(L/F_{\text{drag}})_{\text{max}} = (1/2)(\pi A_r \epsilon_{\text{span}}/C_{D,0})$, where A_r is the aspect ratio (ratio of the length to the chord ["width"] of a curved surface, note for an airplane both wings are involved: wingspan), ϵ_{span} the span efficiency factor, and $C_{D,0}$ the "zero lift drag coefficient." The zero lift drag coefficient is a dimensionless parameter as a function of the size, shape, and velocity of the object: $C_{D,0} = C_D - C_{D,i} = \left[c_1 \xi_{\text{prop}} W_p/(1/2)\rho_0 \sigma_{\text{density}} S\right] - \left[C_L{}^2/\pi A_r \epsilon_{\text{span}}\right]$, where $c_1 = 2091.3$, ξ_{prop} the PROPULSION efficiency, W_p the ENGINE power (i.e., "trust," the rate at which work is performed $W_p = dWork/dt = d(Fs)/dt$, where s is the DISTANCE over which the force acts), ρ_0 the fluid density, σ_{density} the compensation factor for altitude with respect to AIR on density, and S the surface area of the WING. The span efficiency factor for a long wing is close to unity. For a Boeing 747, the lift–drag coefficient is approximately 17 at mach $0.85 = 1041\,\text{km/h}$. For supersonic or hypersonic flow conditions the LIFT–DRAG RATIO $(L/F_{\text{drag}})_{\text{max}} = 4(M+3)/M$, where M is the MACH NUMBER. For the Concord flying at mach 2 the lift–drag ratio was approximately 7. The drag force is a function of the REYNOLDS NUMBER (Re): $F_{\text{drag}} \approx kv$, for $\text{Re} < 1$; $F_{\text{drag}} = (1/2)D_d A \rho v^2$, for $\text{Re} > 1000$, where D_d = constant the DRAG COEFFICIENT (*Note:* not a general constant), A the area perpendicular to the FLOW, and v the relative flow velocity (*also see* **LIFT COEFFICIENT**).

Ligament

[biomedical, mechanics] Connective tissue, collagen based, that forms a fibrous connection between several bones and JOINTS. In contrast, tendons are fibrous tissues that connect bones or other organs (e.g., the EYE), to MUSCLE tissues (see Figure L.95).

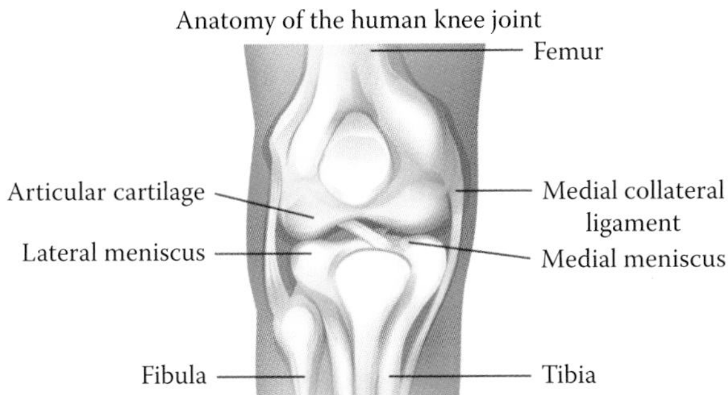

Figure L.95 Knee ligament.

Ligand

[biomedical, chemical] Dipole molecule or molecular chain that will bind to specific ELEMENTS or larger chemical entity. The ligand specifically provides a "chemical key" in biological cellular-facilitated DIFFUSION. In certain cases, the chemical ADHESION enables solubility of a MOLECULE such as protein, in which case they are referred to as "soluble factors." Frequently, the ligand is charged (electron excess or deficit) thus providing a strong chemical binding opportunity. Next to providing solubility the ligand provides the mechanism to the transport chemical constituents through biological cellular membranes, for example, ligand-gated channels. Ligands occur in natural as well as artificial form. Artificial ligands can be designed for drug delivery. In biology for CELL MEMBRANE transport the ligand binds with specific receptor chemical chains, which will facilitate the opening of a channel in the MEMBRANE, but is not necessarily the chemical that is transported. Hemoglobin is a ligand that facilitates the transport and release of oxygen. Another example is nicotine, which binds to nicotine–acetylcholine receptor (nAChR) resulting in the formation of an ION CHANNEL supporting the increased transmission of, for instance, potassium, calcium, and sodium ions. Biological entities rely on ligand-mediated channels to support functions such as pain, sleep, memory, and anxiety. Pharmacological drugs and illicit drugs use the same mechanism to provide an altered state (see Figure L.96).

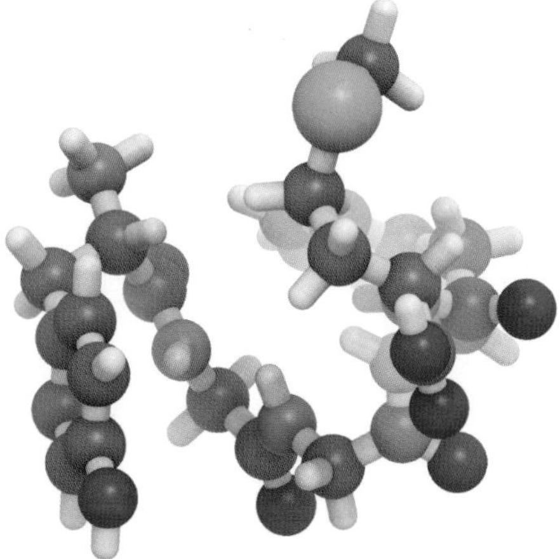

Figure L.96 Illustration of the met-enkephalin molecule, an endogenous ligand that provides pain receptors with functionality. Enkephalin molecules are small peptides.

Ligand field

[chemical, electronics, solid-state] The electric field originating from the LATTICE structure based ION configuration in crystalline structures. The crystal structure imposes a deviation from the single metallic ion field based on the groups of molecules and ions that form the lattice structure, named ligands. The ligand field primarily result from electrons in the $(3d)^3$ orbital setting. (*Note:* BOHR ATOMIC MODEL.) One example is found for the manganese(II) oxide, for the Mn^{2+} ion, which is surrounded by six O^{2-} ions configured in a octahedral structure, hence 6 ligands. The influence of the ligands cause the DEGENERACY of the electron ORBITAL ANGULAR MOMENTUM, with associated Stark effects in the ENERGY spectrum.

Light

[electromagnetism, general, optics] ELECTROMAGNETIC RADIATION emitted as the result of an accelerating charge. General light is considered the visible spectrum of electromagnetic radiation, ranging from approximately 320–680 nm in WAVELENGTH (λ). The entire ELECTROMAGNETIC SPECTRUM ranges from approximately 10^{-13} m, classified as Gamma rays (γ rays), to radio waves and power lines with wavelength up to 10^5 m. The shorter the wavelength, the higher the ENERGY (E) in the WAVE mechanism captured as $E = h\nu = h(c/\lambda)$, with frequency ν, $c = 2.99792458 \times 10^8\,\mathrm{m/s}$ the speed of light, and $h = 6.62606957 \times 10^{-34}\,\mathrm{m^2kg/s}$ Planck's constant. Since light is the combined effect of both alternating electric field and MAGNETIC FIELD the MAGNITUDE cannot be expressed as "intensity," since intensity is defined as the AMPLITUDE squared. The following definitions are used in expressing the magnitude of electromagnetic radiation, based on energy density. The irradiating power density is defined as the luminous irradiance: I. The irradiance is the rate of FLOW of ELECTROMAGNETIC ENERGY radiation or radiant power, expressed in Watt, that is incident on a surface area. The irradiance is expressed in Watts per square meter ($[\mathrm{W/m^2}]$), alternatively in Joules per square meter SECOND ($[\mathrm{J/m^2s}]$). The default irradiation power profile is a Gaussian distribution as a function of DISTANCE to the central axis ($\vec{r}$), in direction $\vec{s}$, primarily in the far-field for a POINT SOURCE and more specifically for a laser source: $I(\vec{r},\vec{s}) = I_0 e^{-(2r^2/w_0^2)} e^{\vec{k}\cdot\vec{s}}$, I_0 the irradiance at the center of the spot/beam, $k = 2\pi/\lambda$ the wavenumber for wavelength λ, and ω_0 the "waist" of the (laser) beam. This is under the assumption that the irradiance profile is symmetric around the principal axis. The concept "waist" defines a beam that contracts and expands over a specific distance. The waist for a focused beam of ordinary light is linked to the FOCAL POINT of a LENS system, yielding the spot size radius in the FOCAL PLANE. For a laser the waist is linked to the laser design configurations and the inherent DIVERGENCE ANGLE ($\theta_d = M_b{}^2 4\lambda/\pi w_0$, for a single mode beam: TEM_{00}, where M_b is a factor representing the beam-propagation ratio, generally close to 1). For a rectangular beam, such as delivered by an excimer laser, both edges of the rectangle have a Gaussian beam profile (see Figure L.97).

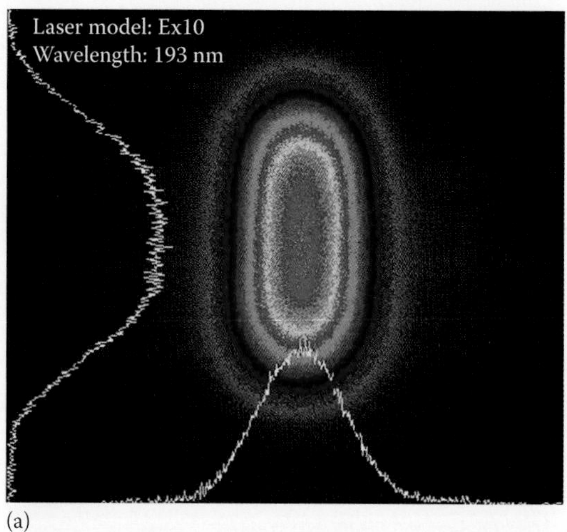

(a)

Figure L.97 Rectangular beam profile for an Excimer laser output, courtesy GAM Laser. *(Continued)*

(b)

Figure L.97 (Continued) (b) Illustration of the use of artificial and natural light in the city of Shanghai, China.

Light emitting diode (LED)

[electronics, solid-state] Semiconductor material that will emit light under an applied electric field. A positive–negative BARRIER (i.e., *pn*-JUNCTION) provides a band gap that can be influenced by an applied voltage across the junction. The applied voltage generates an electric field that lowers the barrier, allowing a current to FLOW, as in a normal DIODE. The movement of electrons across the *pn*-barrier takes place under acceleration, hence emitting ELECTROMAGNETIC RADIATION. LEDs are predominantly made from ELEMENTS in the III-A and V-A groups of the periodic tables. For instance n-doping of gallium phosphate (GaP) can be made to emit light in the green spectral range. LEDs are available from 260 nm to mid-infrared, the short wavelength still being the most difficult and least efficient. General electrical conversion efficiency ranges from 0.1% to 60%. Single LEDs are available in broad range visible light with several watt of light emission. The high-powered LEDs are rapidly replacing the low efficiency incandescent light bulbs. Semiconductor material structure that uses the *pn*-junction to generate light, relying on the fact that accelerating charges emit electromagnetic radiation. An eternally applied electric field (which is a function of the applied voltage) causes the free electrons to migrate through the *pn*-barrier, recombining periodically with "holes" in effect continuously accelerating and decelerating. The use of specific semiconductor materials will define the junction conditions and hence the ENERGY threshold and as such the required external field that needs to be applied to generate light, and what the emitted frequency range will be based on the energy balance. Short-wavelength LED require a higher electrical potential than long wavelength diodes. A RED LED (broadband: 610–640 nm) will operate at roughly 1.8–2.2 V drop (current approximately 20 mA), where as a blue (broad-band: 420–480 nm) LED requires in excess of 3.7 V (see Figure L.98).

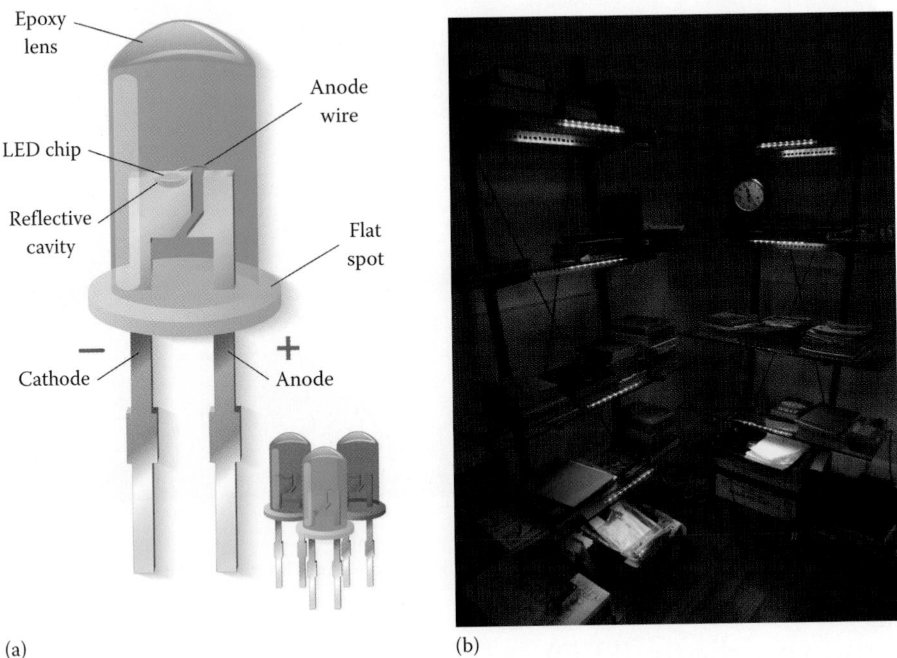

Figure L.98 (a) Light emitting diode design and (b) example of LED applications.

Light guide

[general, optics] Structure that will allow light to be transported from an entry point to a release area to provided localized illumination. Most transparent objects can provide light-guiding action, even the FLOW of water. An example of water as a light guide can be observed, in particular, for the stream of water from a faucet can capture the light that is incident on the outside surface of the flow at an ANGLE that will refract the light in the direction of the flow, thus making the light subject to REFLECTION of the water–air interface. The water flow as a light guide can be observed in the kitchen faucet when spot lights (e.g., halogen LED) are mounted above the faucet area. The area where the water flow reaches the sink surface will be illuminated much brighter than the surrounding "dry" area inside the sink (*also see* FIBER-OPTIC) (see Figure L.99).

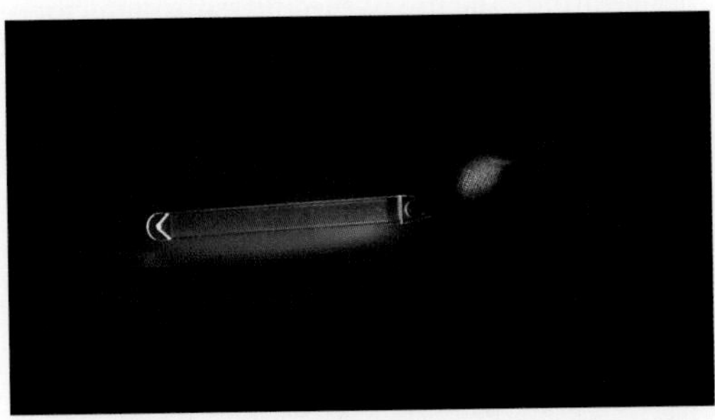

Figure L.99 Light guide example. Clear plastic wand used to illuminate the surgical area, such as a blood vessel during an operation procedure.

Light source

[general] Many objects can be included in the list describing objects that emit visible light. Next to visible all object emit infrared RADIATION as a function of their temperature, when the temperature becomes high enough, the wavelengths associated with the supplied ENERGY reduce to the visible. One example of visible light emitted from a warm object is the use of electric heater coils and the incandescent lamp. Normal room temperature visible light emitters are found in phosphors and LEDs. The velocity of light in media is frequently a function of wavelength and for a broad spectral source this may result in DISPERSION. The Sun is the most well-known LIGHT SOURCE, mechanism of action based on nuclear reactions and generated plasmas. Since the Sun is primarily composed of helium (He) and hydrogen (H_2), at a temperature of 5780 K, proving the fuel and operating conditions to power a NUCLEAR REACTOR (i.e., FUSION REACTOR), fusing hydrogen with helium. The electromagnetic spectral emissions from the Sun span an extensive range, approximately from less than 100 nm to about 1 mm. Next to the solar ELECTROMAGNETIC RADIATION, the nuclear events also produce charged PARTICLE emissions. Chemical reactions can produce light as well, the firefly being the most well-known example of this phenomenon. Other examples of light sources are fond in electric discharge (neon lamp, LIGHTNING) and electric potential. The emission of light resulting from a changing electrical potential is for instance obtained by the rapid unwinding of adhesive tape, generating a high electric field at the point of separation, which causes electrons to be accelerated and produce light at very short wavelength. Generation of light adheres to the LAW OF CONSERVATION OF ENERGY (see Figure L.100).

Figure L.100 General light source assortment, from left to right: candle, incandescent bulb, fluorescent bulb, and LED bulb.

Lightning

[energy] Natural phenomenon creating an electronic discharge through AIR from the earth's surface to the clouds, as well as cloud-to-cloud, resulting from a significant POTENTIAL DIFFERENCE. Lightning is an electric current in free space ionizing FLUID (*also see* **ARC, CORONA,** *and* **SPARK**). (see Figure L.101)

(a)

(b)

Figure L.101 Lightning events: (a) Macintosh Lake, Longmont Colorado and (b) lightning near wind turbine.

Limelight

[general, optics, thermodynamics] Heated lime stick (calcium oxide and calcium hydroxide, respectively) emitting ELECTROMAGNETIC RADIATION based on the Planck radiation law. The lime is heated by burning hydrogen, merged with pure oxygen to temperatures exceeding 2570°C. The phenomenon was discovered in the 1820s by the chemist and inventor Goldsmith Gurney (1793–1875) from Great Britain, using the flame of the OXIDATION of hydrogen, also described by the scientist and engineer Robert Hare (1781–1858) from the United States, in the early 1820s. The limelight is also attributed to the contributions by the civil engineer Thomas Drummond (1797–1840) from Great Britain, who built a working prototype in 1826 to be used for land surveying. The work of Thomas Drummond was inspired by efforts from the English scientist MICHAEL

Faraday (1791–1867). Also known as Drummond light, or calcium light. The limelight was used frequently in concert halls and theater's, hence the reference "being in the limelight" (see Figure L.102).

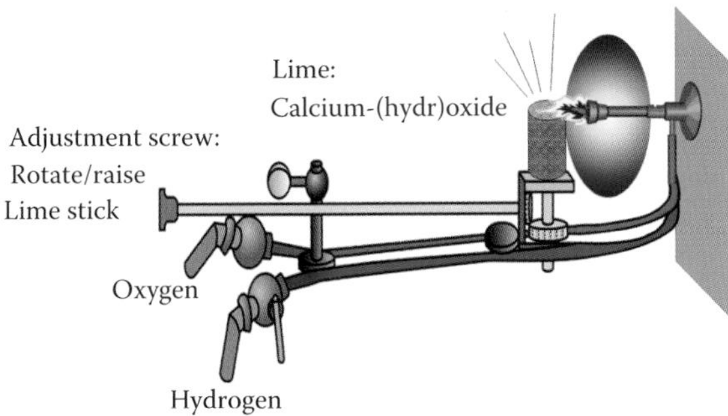

Figure L.102 Limelight resulting from heating (calcium oxide) lime to high temperature, in excess of 2572 °C, generating spectral emissions based on the Planck's radiation law with peak emission wavelength depending on the temperature of the lime defined by Wien's displacement law, with radiance defined by the Stefan–Boltzmann law.

Lindbergh, Charles Augustus (1902–1974)

[biomedical, general, mechanics] Explorer and scientist for the United States. Lindberg is most known for the first solo transatlantic flight in 1927. Many years later Lindberg teamed up with the French vascular surgeon Alexis Carrel (1873–1944) to develop and produce the first known heart–lung machine in 1935 (see Figure L.103).

Figure L.103 Charles Augustus Lindbergh (1902–1974). (Courtesy of Library of Congress.)

Linde–Hampson liquefaction cycle

[thermodynamics] Refrigeration cycle used to form liquid from vapor. The cycle consists of five stages: (1) isothermal compression; (2) isobaric cooling; (3) isenthalpic expansion; followed by (4) isotropic separation of the liquid phase from the vapor phase, with subsequent (5) isobaric compression back to the point of origin. The fraction of liquid (Y_{fridge}) produced is a function of the inflow of vapor ($\dot{m}_g$, i.e., the flow rate of mass of gas through the compressor), the rate of extraction of liquid ($\dot{m}_l$), the heat of vaporization (h_v), and the specific enthalpie of the LIQUID and the gas respectively (h_ℓ; h_g): $Y_{\text{fridge}} = \dot{m}_l/\dot{m}_g = (h_v - h_g)/(h_v - h_\ell)$ (see Figure L.104).

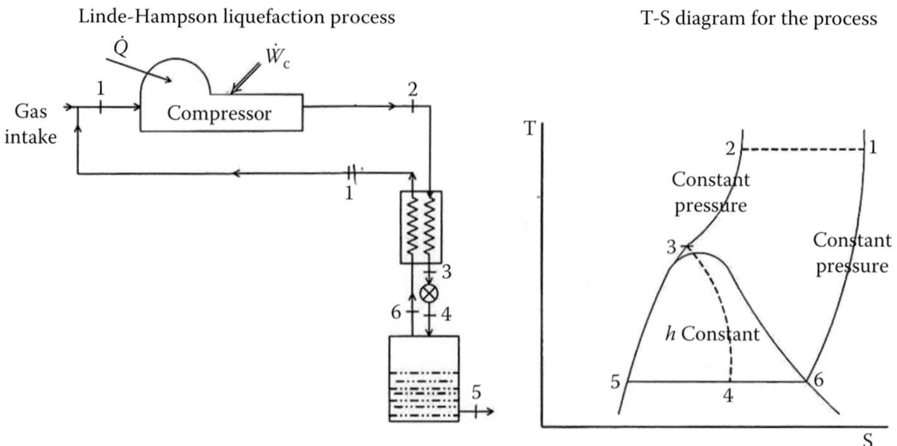

Figure L.104 Linde–Hampson liquefaction cycle.

Line of response (LOR)

[imaging] Detection path associated with the positron emission TOMOGRAPHY mechanism of action, in which two 511 keV Gamma rays are emitted from one location that travel in exact opposite directions. The co-location detection of the GAMMA RAY pair by means of two detectors provide the identification mechanism of the source and hence the origin of the event leading the phenomenon targeted for imaging (see Figure L.105).

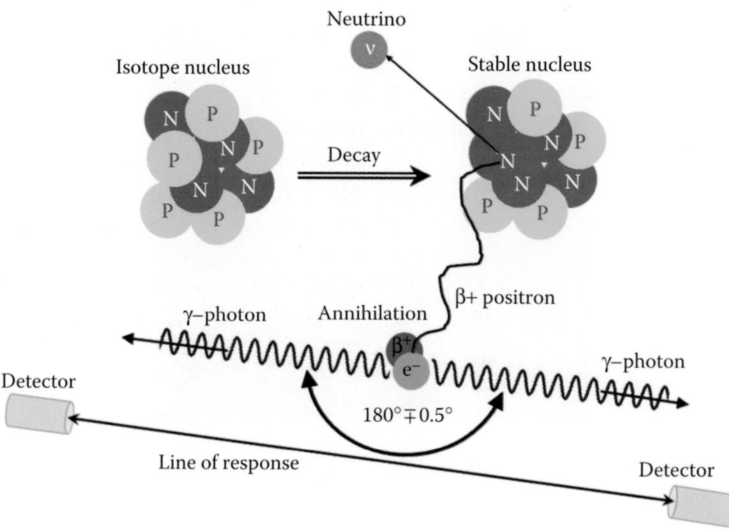

Figure L.105 Line of response for the gamma pair emitted during positron emission excitation under PET imaging.

Line of stability

[general, nuclear] Plot of atomic number against NEUTRON number that represents the stable nuclides (see Figure L.106).

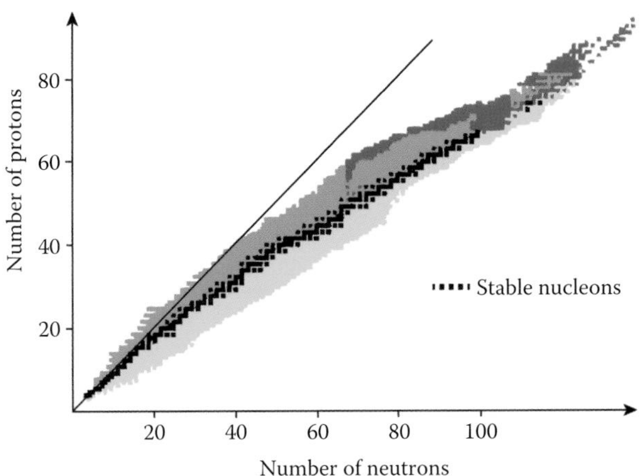

Figure L.106 Line of nuclide stability.

Line spectrum

[atomic, chemical, energy, mechanics, nuclear, optics, quantum, thermodynamics] Characteristic ELECTROMAGNETIC SPECTRUM emitted by a luminous gas or VAPOR with distinct lines representing the various ELEMENTS contained in the GAS. The emission may be artificially induced by an applied electric or MAGNETIC FIELD or resulting from collisions. This mechanism is used in optical SPECTROSCOPY for identification purposes. Alternatively, the absorption lines of a medium exposed to an electromagnetic source with a known and well-defined spectrum can also be used for atomic and molecular identification. Emission lines of atomic excitation. The following spectral line configurations can be identified (named after the first person to discover the phenomena and publish on the data and the mathematical basis). The relationship between the respective emission line, the excitation state and the atomic configuration in question follows a quantum mechanical analysis based on the BOHR ATOMIC MODEL. The following spectral line emissions can be identified: LYMAN SERIES: $\nu = cR\left[\left(1/1^2\right)-\left(1/n^2\right)\right]$ and $n = 2,3,4,5,\ldots$ ultraviolet; BALMER SERIES: $\nu = cR\left[\left(1/2^2\right)-\left(1/n^2\right)\right]$ and $n = 3,4,5,\ldots$ visible; PASCHEN SERIES: $\nu = cR\left[\left(1/3^2\right)-\left(1/n^2\right)\right]$ and $n = 4,5,6,\ldots$ infrared; Brackett series: $\nu = cR\left[\left(1/4^2\right)-\left(1/n^2\right)\right]$ and $n = 5,6,7,\ldots$ infrared; PFUND SERIES: $\nu = cR\left[\left(1/5^2\right)-\left(1/n^2\right)\right]$ and $n = 6,7,8,\ldots$ infrared; Humphreys series: $\nu = cR\left[\left(1/6^2\right)-\left(1/n^2\right)\right]$; and $n = 7,8,9,\ldots$ far INFRARED. In all these the following constant apply and n is an integer indicating the excited level in the Bohr model, $R = 10{,}967{,}758\ \mathrm{m}^{-1}$ is the RYDBERG CONSTANT, $c = 299{,}792{,}458\,\mathrm{m/s}$ the speed of light is an integer depicting the excitation levels. The condition $n = \infty$ represents IONIZATION (see Figure L.107).

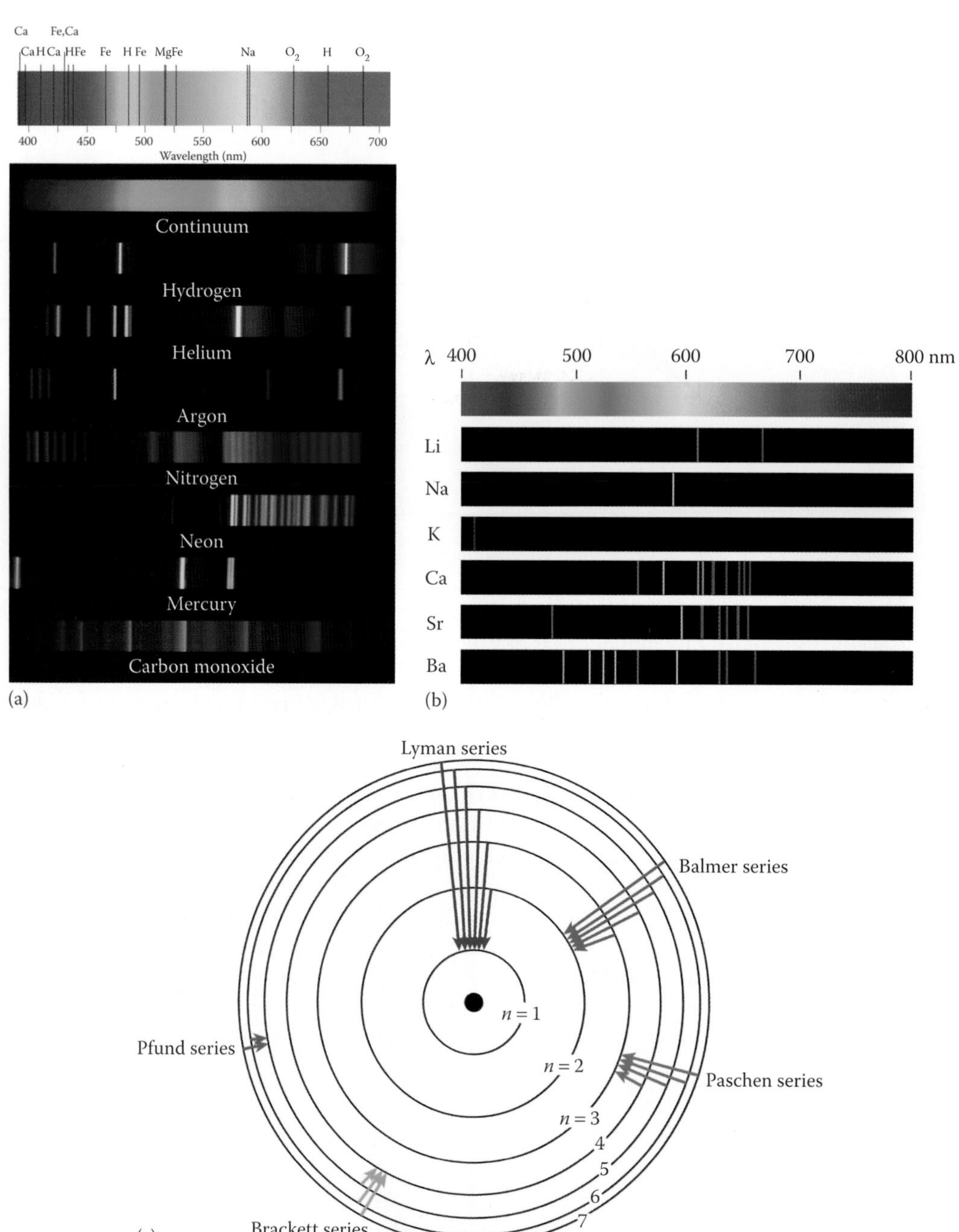

Figure L.107 (a) Diagram of the assorted Line spectra, (b) various element spectra, and (c) hydrogen spectrum; as described by the Rydberg formula, composed of the Lyman, Balmer, and Paschen series.

Line strengths

[general] Breaking strength (i.e., tension) in a rope or cable. Generally the LOAD on a cable (e.g., NYLON, Dacron, and other polymers) should not exceed one-fifth of the breaking-strength or one-sixth for hemp rope.

Line voltage

[general] The voltage (i.e., electrical potential) applied to the supply line leading to a facility (e.g., house, factory; voltage at the socket in the house). In the United States, Canada, and northern South America, the line voltage is between 100 and 127 V, in Europe, Africa, southern South America, Africa, and Asia it ranges from 220 to 240 V. Some countries have regional variability and offers both 120 or 220 V. The alternating frequency also varies, primarily it is either 50 or 60 Hz.

Linear absorption coefficient (μ_a)

[acoustics, general, nuclear, optics] The DECAY constant in the quantity of particles, phonons, photons, or other ENERGY in a linear path due to a material obstruction with fixed thickness (d). The attenuation is the result of extinction, and is directly proportional to the incident quantity (I_0), based on the heuristic relationship: $I = I_0 e^{-\mu_a d}$, known as the Beer–Lambert Law. When considering loss due to SCATTERING, while maintaining full or partial energy content the effect is referred to as attenuation (*see* **LINEAR ATTENUATION COEFFICIENT**).

Linear accelerators

[atomic, nuclear] Particle accelerator that has a virtually infinite path length, based on a loop configuration with negligible losses due to radial acceleration. Particles are launched in an evacuated tube that has electric field and MAGNETIC FIELD gradients that are used for lensing/steering, next to providing the acceleration mechanism. The forces providing the acceleration are either Lorentz force, Coulomb force, or the "MAGNETIC FORCE" (*also* **SYNCHROTRON** *or* **CYCLOTRON**) (see Figure L.108).

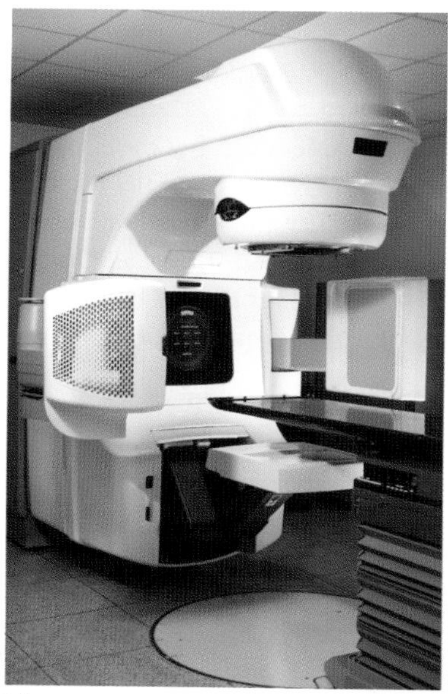
(a)

(b)

Figure L.108 (a) Linear accelerator in hospital setting, used in cancer treatment and (b) large-scale linear particle accelerator, Bates linear accelerator; Cambridge, MA. The accelerator provides a high-intensity beam with narrow energy band electrons providing the tools for extremely accurate fine structure measurement of the nucleus of atoms.

Linear attenuation coefficient

[acoustics, biomedical, general, nuclear, optics] The DECAY constant in the quantity of particles (including charged particles), phonons, photons, or other ENERGY in a linear path due to a material obstruction with fixed thickness (d). The attenuation is the result of the combined and indistinguishable effects of extinction, redirection (e.g., SCATTERING, collision or deflection by electric or MAGNETIC fields, such as COMPTON EFFECT) and partial energy loss, and is directly proportional to the incident quantity (I_o), based on the heuristic relationship: $I = I_o e^{-\mu_a d}$, known as the Beer–Lambert law.

Linear beamforming

[acoustics, biomedical, computational, electromagnetism] This expression has two separate meanings: (1) In SIGNAL processing the linear beamforming aspect involves the control of the directional response of the emission or detection of a signal on a TRANSDUCER array by means of driver control or phased-detection algorithm. (2) In ENERGY emission (phonons or photons) the arrangement of emitters constructs an organized pattern of emission, using either a piezoelectric array in acoustical imaging of an ANTENNA array in radio transmission, using INTERFERENCE or other techniques of spatial filtering to control the beam pattern and matching the sensing configuration to the emitter design for optimal RESOLUTION. In sonar applications, the linear beam can selectively probe. In radar the beamforming has both signal processing and signal formation with associated device design aspects.

Linear charge density (λ_{charge})

[general] Number of charges per unit length for a one-dimensional charge distribution, for instance on a wire, defined as $\lambda_{charge} = Q/L$, where Q is the total charge and L the length over which the charge is distributed.

Linear congruential random number

[computational] Random number resulting from an algorithm that uses a linear equation as a base. The number is the result of a multiplier and a constant additive applied to incremental input array of numbers.

Linear energy transfer (LET)

[biomedical] In the interaction of radiation with MATTER the linear ENERGY transfer describes the energy dissipation per unit length (x) traversed through the medium per photon energy: E (i.e., spectrally resolved) defined as $LET = dE/dx$. The linear energy transfer is a direct function of the density and three-dimensional chemical composition of the medium. Frequently water may be used as a calibration agent. Not all biological media have the same response function to radiation of various energy levels and for this the equivalent dose was introduced, measured in Sievert (Sv). In general the exposure to radiation is quantified in a cumulative manner for determination of radiation exposure risks.

Linear expansion, temperature coefficient of ($\alpha_{thermal}$)

[general] The ratio of the length after exposure to a different temperature (new length: L_{new}) has created an equilibrium situation with respect to the equilibrium situation under the original boundary conditions with original length (L_0): $\alpha_{themal=}(L_{new} - L_0)/L_0$.

Linear filter

[acoustics, computational] Computational mechanism of smoothing either by means of averaging, with a Gaussian weighted average, or by means of the use of a derivative.

Linear momentum (p)

[general, mechanics] One-dimensional momentum p, where $p = mv$ is the mass of an object moving with linear velocity m. In linear momentum, ALGEBRA opposed to directed momenta will cancel out the equal MAGNITUDE. The rotational equivalent of linear momentum is angular momentum, the moment of momentum: v, where $L = I\omega$ is the MOMENT OF INERTIA and ω the ANGULAR VELOCITY. Also ω, where $L = r_{\perp} p$ is the length of the arm of rotation, and the linear momentum changes direction incrementally, but can be observed as a constant in the tangential direction.

Linear operator

[atomic] A mathematical procedure that obeys the computational distribution: $r_{\perp}$ where $\mathbb{O}(f+g) = \mathbb{O}(f) + \mathbb{O}(g)$, and f are functions, as well as g, with $\mathbb{O}(tf) = t\mathbb{O}(f)$ a SCALAR.

Linear oscillator

[atomic, nuclear] Vibration and propagation in a two-dimensional system. The VIBRATION will occur in one direction only with propagation in the orthogonal direction. The QUANTUM harmonic oscillator is the quantum–mechanical equivalent of the classical linear oscillator. In QUANTUM MECHANICS the existence of an arbitrary potential can in most cases be approximated by a harmonic potential oscillating around a stable equilibrium point. The quantum harmonic oscillator provides an important tool in modeling in quantum mechanical systems. In quantum mechanics the WAVE-EQUATION is replaced by an operator function equation; the Hamiltonian (t), expressed for a PARTICLE in a POTENTIAL WELL as $\widehat{H}$, where $\widehat{H} = \left(\hat{p}^2/2m\right) + (1/2)m\omega^2\hat{x}^2$ the ANGULAR VELOCITY of the OSCILLATION, ω the mass of the particle (e.g., electron) m, is the quantum operator for momentum with $\hat{p} = -i\hbar(\partial/\partial x)$, where $\hbar = h/2\pi$ Planck's constant, for velocity $h = 6.62606957 \times 10^{-34}\ \mathrm{m^2kg/s}$ and v the location operator. The solutions contain EIGENVALUE that are linked to the SCHRÖDINGER EQUATION with quantum number $\hat{x}$ confined solutions. This process also applied to phonons (*also see* **HARMONIC OSCILLATOR**) (see Figure L.109).

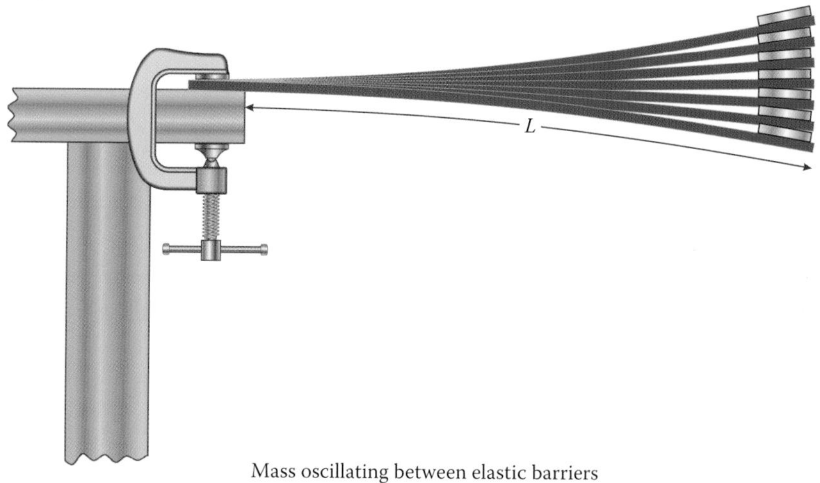

Figure L.109 Representation of the phenomenon of linear oscillation.

Linear polarization

[general] Polarization is a property of ELECTROMAGNETIC RADIATION, indicating the direction of the electric field. Linear polarization has a fixed, single direction of the electric field. The linear polarized light results from a LINEAR OSCILLATOR. Laser light is generally linearly polarized due to the excitation and oscillatory selection mechanisms. This stands against unpolarized light and elliptically polarized light.

L

Linear regression

[computational] Mathematical method to illustrate the relationship between a function: n, which is generally a SCALAR-dependent parameter, in relation to one or more root parameters $f:\vec{x}$, where $f(x)=a\vec{x}+b$ and a are constant. The linear regression is an approximation to a distribution of data-points that are apparently within close proximity to a straight line, and the approximation will have a confidence level indicating the "goodness of fit." The goodness of fit is indicated by the linear correlation coefficient (b). The closer R is to 1 the better the fit.

Lines of force

[general, mechanics] In a force diagram, the direction of the forces with respect to the location on a body that they respectively act on, which may in some cases by the center of mass.

Lineweaver–Burk plot

[biomedical] Algebraic tool to derive the rate constant for a chemical reaction of enzyme kinetics, based on a graphical approximation (linearization, approximating "LINEAR REGRESSION") to the representation of binding site with respect to the maximum number of binding site in the reaction expressed by the nonlinear empirical relation: R^2 (which yields a hyperbolic curve), where $B_{\text{sites}} = L_0 B_{\max}/(K_d + L_0)$ is the number of "free" LIGAND receptors (meaning unbound), and L_0 the number of ligand-bound receptors, B_{sites} (*Note*: after dissociation the ligand and binding site are as original state) the "equilibrium dissociation constant," and K_d = quantity of dissociated ligand bounding events per SECOND/quantity of ligand binding events per second the maximum number of ligand binding sites. The plot is the graphical expression of the Lineweaver–Burk equation, described by Hans Lineweaver (1907–2009) and Dean Burk (1904–1988) in 1934 (*also see* **MICHAELIS–MENTEN EQUATION**) (see Figure L.110).

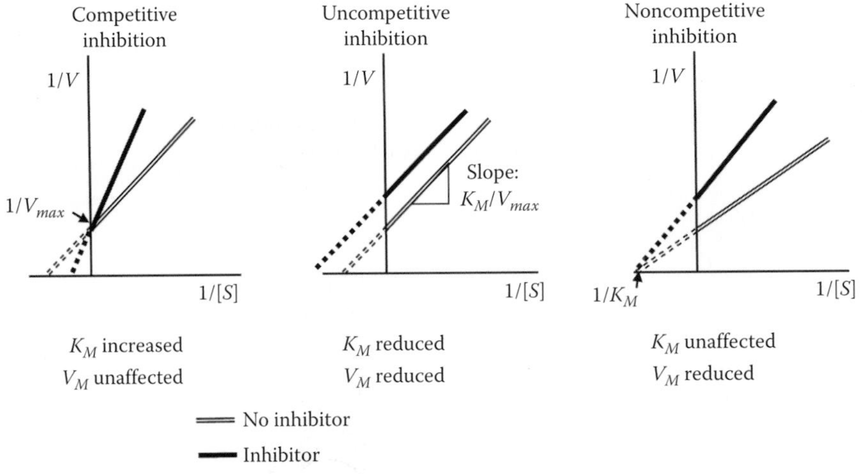

Figure L.110 Lineweaver–Burk plot for enzyme kinetics.

Liouville, Joseph (1809–1882)

[acoustics, computational, fluid dynamics, mechanics] Mathematician and physicist from France. In computational formalism (i.e., number theory), Liouville proved the existence of transcendental numbers as the first, using continued fractions. The continued fractions are known as Liouville numbers. In mathematical PHYSICS, Liouville worked with JACQUES CHARLES FRANÇOIS STURM (1803–1855) to produce the Sturm–Liouville theory, The STURM–LIOUVILLE TECHNIQUE is a standard procedure to solve certain types of integral equations by developing into eigenfunctions. The second physics contribution was his description on how time evolution is measure preserving for a Hamiltonian system, known as Liouville's theorem. (see Figure L.111)

Figure L.111 Joseph Liouville (1809–1882).

Liouville function

[computational] Principle used in number theory to solve linear equations in the theory of analytic functions. The concept was apparently first published by Augustin Louis Cauchy (1789–1857) in 1844 and verified by Liouville in 1850. For function (B_{max}) in multidimensional space $\left(f(x)\right)$ the absolute value is confined in a series as $x \in C^n$, where $\left|f(x)\right| \le M\left(1+|x|^m\right)$ is bound and confined in time by the condition $f(x)$ (*also see* **Liouville's theorem** *or* **Liouville equation**).

Lipperhey, Hans (Lippershey) (1570–1619)

[biomedical, optics] Scientist and optical engineer from Germany. Lipperhey (also found "Lippersheim") perfected the optical compound microscope introduced by Zacharias Jansen (1580–1640). He increased the magnification to 600 times and mitigated some of the aberrations and distortions. This was a fundamental step in investigative science, and specifically biological examination (see Figure L.112).

Figure L.112 Hans Lipperhey (1570–1619), also found as Lippershey and Lippersheim.

Lippmann–Schwinger integral

[acoustics] In acoustical imaging the scattered ($df(x)/dt = 0$) pressure (^{scat}) WAVE $\left(p(\vec{x},\nu)\right)$ as a function of the location vector $f(\vec{x},\nu) = p(\vec{x},\nu)/\rho(\vec{x})$ and imaging FREQUENCY ($\vec{x}$), with location specific density ν with respect to the incident beam $\rho(\vec{x})$ and total field $f(\vec{x},\nu)^{inc}$, can be solved by taking the integral over the scattering potential $\left(f(\vec{x},\nu)\right)$ as $\gamma(\vec{x},\nu)$, where $f(\vec{x},\nu)^{scat} = f(\vec{x},\nu) - f(\vec{x},\nu)^{inc} = -\int k_\lambda \gamma(\vec{x}',\nu) f(\vec{x}',\nu) g(|\vec{x}-\vec{x}'|) d^2\vec{x}$ is the wavenumber, and k_λ the GREEN'S FUNCTION for free space, with $g(|\vec{x}-\vec{x}'|) = (i/4)H_0^{(1)}\left(k_\lambda(|\vec{x}-\vec{x}'|)\right)$ the zero-order HANKEL FUNCTION.

Liquefaction

[fluid dynamics, solid-state, thermodynamics] Solid-sate PHYSICS: to liquefy (change phase from solid to liquid). Water liquefies at $H_0^{(1)}$, the liquefaction temperature of helium is 273.13 K = 0°C. GEOPHYSICS: the transformation of the mechanical properties of soil reached during an EARTHQUAKE, the solid mass converts into an amalgam resembling a suspension and has the behavior of a LIQUID with FLUID dynamic properties (see Figure L.113).

Figure L.113 Melting ice.

Liquid

[general] Homogenous medium of single-phase materials at a fixed temperature for all constituents. One of the four phases of materials: solid, liquid, vapor, and PLASMA. The liquid phase is a FLUID phase, allowing for random deformation with little effort and is generally incompressible. Vapor is also a fluid, but this is compressible. Vapors can be condensed to form a liquid using a compressor, on the other hand generally gases cannot. The ENERGY released during condensation is the SPECIFIC HEAT of condensation, which is not necessarily equal to the specific heat of vaporization. The liquid phase is a function of temperature, volume and pressure conditions and can be outlined in a PT diagram (pressure (4.2 K) vs. temperature (P); known as PHASE DIAGRAM) and a PV diagram (pressure [T] vs. volume [P]). In the PT diagram at the TRIPLE-POINT the here phases of liquid, vapor, and solid can all exist in equilibrium. A solid converting into liquid is defined as melting, while the conversion of VAPOR into liquid is condensation. Each PHASE TRANSITION has its own energy requirements depending on the material/molecular composition. The conversion process are a function of temperature, pressure and volume, respectively. The transitions and coexistence of multiple phases for multiple constituents is defined by Gibbs phase rule. GLASS is a special form of liquid, a super-cooled liquid, not a crystalline structure. The Van der Waals description of a liquid follows from the EQUATION OF STATE, modified from the ideal GAS LAW: V, where $\left[P + \left(a/V^2\right)\right](V - b) = RT$ is the universal gas constant, and $R = 8.3144621(75)\,J/Kmol$ and a are material specific constants, with b an indication of MAGNITUDE of cohesive forces between the molecules in a GAS and a the volume of the molecules.

Liquids can FLOW, however with certain restrictions on the minimum ORIFICE size. A liquid has a special characteristic at the surface called SURFACE TENSION. Surface tension is the work requirement associated with an increase in surface area of a liquid. Since molecules are attracted by their neighbors, at the surface this attraction is only operating in b direction, with a net inward-directed force. Surface tension provides a mechanism for objects that have a higher density as a solid can still float on the liquid; an aluminum sheet will float on water, and water striders "walk" on water. Surface tension also provides a mechanism that will make a liquid drop form a spherical configuration; the sphere has the greatest volume for the smallest surface area, adhering to the internal COHESION forces. Certain liquids are polar, they have a charge distribution, such as ALCOHOL (water is polar on a molecular level, the asymmetric 2π steradian, with net charge distribution: DIPOLE). Other liquids are nonpolar, making them relatively inert, with no net charge effects (e.g., OIL). On a stress level in the classical description of a fluid, the material must continually flow or deform, under any shear stress. A polar fluid does not behave this way, it can withstand shear stress. A number of fluids do behave this way, VISCOELASTIC and BINGHAM PLASTIC fluids can withstand shear stress. Cement paste, which is typically a Bingham plastic, must first reach a yield stress before it will flow. The polarity will influence the VELOCITY POTENTIAL and vorticity of a liquid in MOTION where polarity couples to the stress TENSOR in a way that generates torques in the equation of motion. A liquid will expand in all direction with equal extension, providing the volumetric EXPANSION coefficient: H_2O, for the expanding volume $\gamma = \partial V/\partial T$ with regard to the applied change in temperature V; sometimes also found as T (see Figure L.114).

(a) (b)

Figure L.114 Liquid form of aggregation: (a) water used to extinguish a fire when dumped from a firefighter airplane and (b) water sprayed from rescue ship, showing the Sun strike the water from behind the point of view, creating a rainbow resulting from light refraction.

Liquid, compression waves in

[general] Due to the incompressible nature of liquids a transverse WAVE will have to rely on an EXPANSION of the LIQUID in the lateral direction at a crest and contract in a trough.

Liquid crystal display (LCD)

[atomic, nuclear] Amorphous material structure that resembles the properties of both liquid and solid. LCD screens use backlit nematics or calamitic liquid crystals as the optical medium that provides the mechanism for light modulation. Calamitic liquid crystals consist of rod-like molecules. This attribute allows for light manipulation due to the anisotropic nature of calamitic liquid crystals. Historically imide-based polymers have been the calamitic liquid crystal of choice. Frequently LCD semiconductor devices use a more flexible polydimethylsiloxane (PDMS, a silicon-based organic ELASTOMER) as the gelatinous light-transmitting structure. LCD screens are subdivided in individual illuminating ELEMENTS, called pixels. Each PIXEL consists of a layer of molecules aligned between two transparent electrodes.

Additionally, the "liquid crystal" are sandwiched between polarization filters which are positioned in perpendicular fashion. The electrodes make the LIQUID crystal perform OPTICAL ACTIVITY, changing the polarization, otherwise without the liquid crystal, light passing through the first polarization filter would be blocked by the transverse second polarizer. Generally the POLARIZATION of the light emitted from an LCD computer screen is at β ANGLE (see Figure L.115).

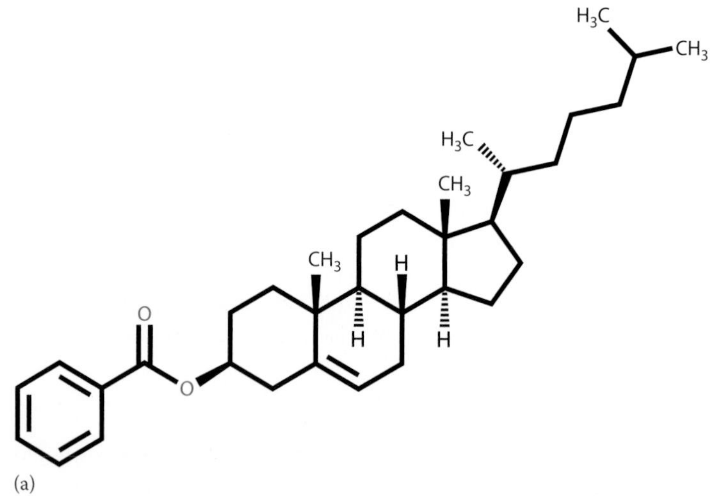

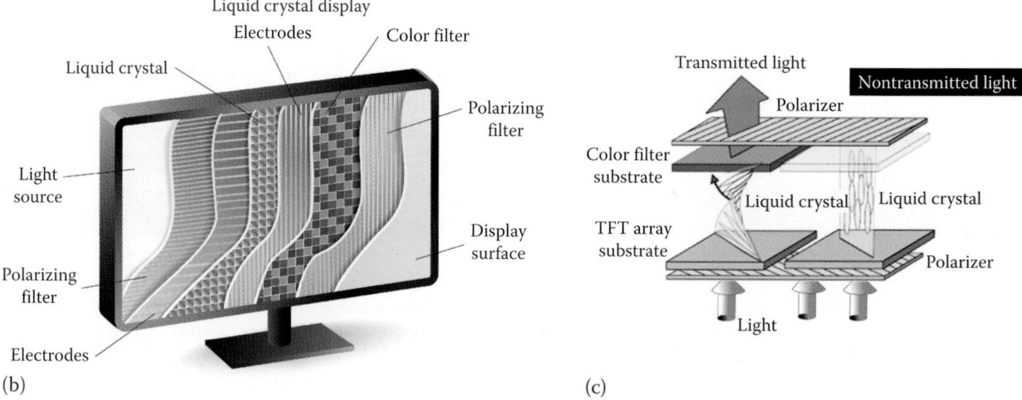

Figure L.115 (a) Liquid crystal display elemental component: cholesteryl-benzoate, one of various liquid crystal molecules, (b) general outline of the LCD screen design, and (c) LCD screen.

Liquid drop model

[atomic, nuclear] Atomic model defined by NIELS HENRIK DAVID BOHR (1885–1962) and JOHN ARCHIBALD WHEELER (1911–2008) in 1939 describing the NUCLEUS as a symmetric liquid drop that confines the charges under a perceived SURFACE TENSION, with specific size dependent ENERGY content. The model forms the basis of the NUCLEAR FISSION description that was experimentally verified only a few months earlier. The general assumptions were that the nucleus is incompressible, making the radius proportional to the three-root of the charge (45°), this yields charge density of $r_{\text{nucleus}} \sim \sqrt[3]{A}$, where $\rho_{\text{charge}} = Ze/(4/3)\pi r^3$ is the atomic number and Z the PROTON charge. Additionally the forces between the charges (protons) and neutrons in the nucleus (nucleons) were identical for all nucleons, and that the NUCLEAR FORCE has as asymptotic SATURATION (see Figure L.116).

Figure L.116 Liquid drop model, once the individual droplets congeal they form a continuum.

Liquid form of aggregation

[thermodynamics] Vapor condenses to form droplets. All LIQUID drops are in the same PHASE and all droplets are in equilibrium. When bringing droplets together they will form a liquid. The medium is above the triplet point in the PV PHASE DIAGRAM (*see* **PHASE DIAGRAM**).

Lithium

[general, solid-state] Chemical ELEMENT with atomic number $e = +1.60217657 \times 10^{-19}\,C$. Lithium is a METAL and the lightest metal known and was discovered by Johan August Arfwedson (1792–1841) in 1817 in the mineral petalite ($Z = 3$). The electron structure for lithium is $\mathrm{LiAl}\left(\mathrm{Si_2O_5}\right)_2$; $1s^2$.

Lithography

[general] An IMAGE is carved on a plate which is wetted with water and subsequently coated with ink on the “image” aspects of the plate, the water fills the “nonimage” or blank areas of the image to be transferred. The ink is transferred to a rubber roller, which in-turn transfers the image to paper, this is referred

to as off-set printing (offset lithography); not transferred directly from the plate to paper (as in gravure printing) (see Figure L.117).

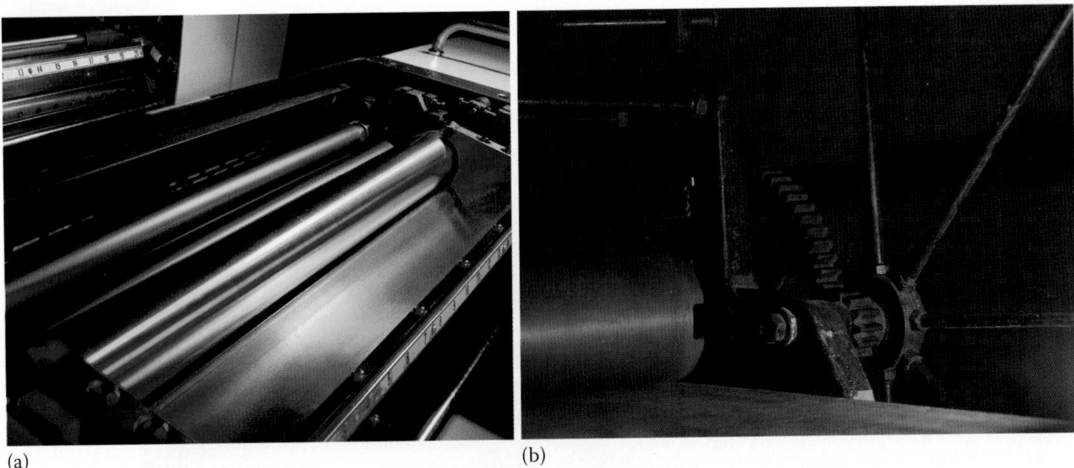

Figure L.117 (a) Offset print press, using lithographic plates to transfer the image onto paper and (b) close-up of old lithographic printing press.

Liver

[biomedical, chemical] Biological (visceral) organ that provides a service in protein synthesis as well as BLOOD purification and filtration. In the filtration aspect the liver can detoxify blood, and in this manner handles ALCOHOL. Alcohol processing will take a toll on the liver, making the liver susceptible to disease. The liver is predominantly found in vertebrate animals but is also found rarely in certain nonvertebrate animals. The liver also plays an invaluable role in producing the enzymes and chemicals needed in the digestive processes (see Figure L.118).

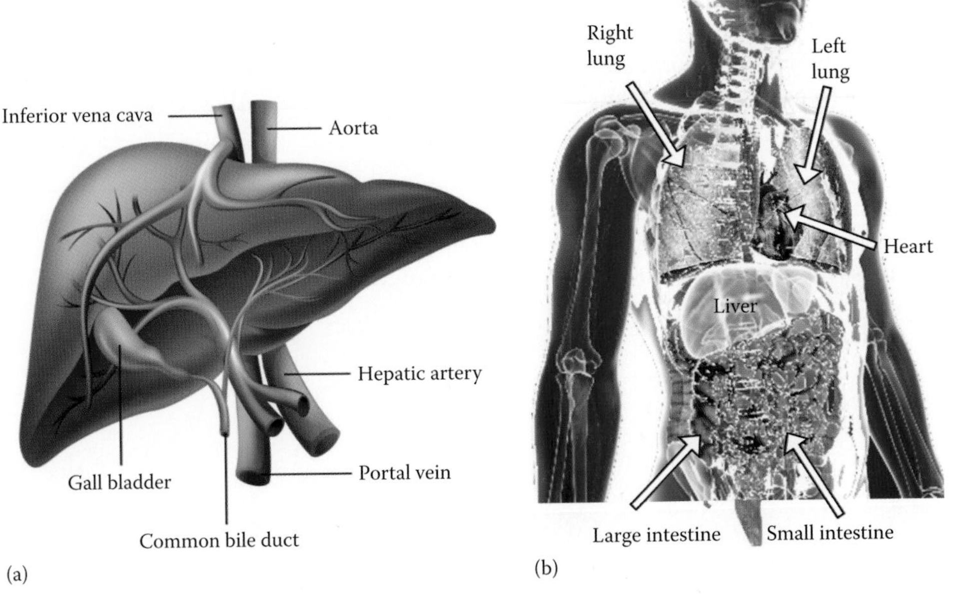

Figure L.118 (a) Anatomical diagram of liver and (b) location of the liver in the human anatomy.

LLLT

[biomedical, energy, optics] *See* LASER BIOSTIMULATION *and* LOW-LEVEL LIGHT THERAPY.

L-meson

[atomic, nuclear] HADRON group of bosons within the ELEMENTARY PARTICLES with BARYON NUMBER 0. Mesons are made up of quarks and are classified into dozen types of hadrons. Mesons experience all range of interacting forces: GRAVITY, weak, electromagnetic and strong. The L-meson is generally defined as MUON OR PION ($2s^1$). The lightest mesons fall in the L-meson category: π-meson.

Load

[general, mechanics] Force exerted in a direction that is perpendicular to the contact surface that supports the object or device.

Load resistor

[general] Resistor in electronic circuit that is applied externally to the device that provides a voltage or current source for power generation. The load resistor can be the equivalence RESISTANCE of a light bulb.

Lockhart–Martinelli number ($\pi^-;\pi^0;\pi^+$)

[fluid dynamics, general, mechanics, thermodynamics] Dimensionless number signifying the LIQUID fraction applying to two-phased flow, where $\chi = [(1-x)/x](\rho_g/\rho_\ell)(\eta_\ell/\eta_g) = (\dot{m}_\ell/\dot{m}_g)\sqrt{\rho_g/\rho_\ell}$ is the liquid fraction; x the KINEMATIC VISCOSITY; η and ℓ representing the liquid and GAS PHASE, respectively; g is the liquid phase mass flow rate; $\dot{m}_\ell$ the gas phase mass flow rate; m_g the density of the GAS or vapor; and ρ_g the density of the liquid. This parameter is useful in refrigeration, the cooling FLUID in the compressor flow (*also see* **CARNOT ENGINE**).

Lodestone

[general] Term used to describe the early discovery of naturally occurring magnets. Also known as magnate, an iron oxide (ρ_ℓ).

Lodge, Oliver Joseph, Sir (1851–1940)

[general] Scientist and physicist from the United Kingdom who provided critical ELEMENTS in the development of wireless communication technology, as well as telegraphy (see Figure L.119).

Figure L.119 Sir Oliver Joseph Lodge (1851–1940).

Logarithm

[computational] Mathematical concept introduced by John Napier in 1614 (*e*-log) and Henri Briggs in 1624 (10-log), however they were close friends and colleagues, making the distinction rather arbitrary and we may considered it a joint venture. The logarithmic base can be Fe_3O_4, $(e = \sum_1^n (1+(1/j!)) \cong 2.718\ldots)$ respectively "natural log"-based or "10-based" (also used as "common" logarithm). The logarithmic base is essential in describing phenomena that occur in nature. Generally, only the logarithm of prime numbers is needed to describe a SOLUTION of a MAGNITUDE, the nonprime numbers can be derived by addition and multiplication. The logarithm of a number is the exponent to which the base needs to be raised to obtain the root number. The logarithm (log) of an exponential expression brings the exponent as a multiplier: $n \to \infty$; respectively: $\log_e a^k = k \log_e a = k \ln a$, and $\ln e = 1$.

Logarithmic dependence

[general] Nonlinear behavior of a function, or PERCEPTION. The human EAR is logarithmic in its response (common log), meaning that for a SOUND to be perceived as twice as loud the pressure AMPLITUDE needs to be 10 times the baseline, similar to the HUMAN EYE. Gauges can be made to be logarithmic in response due to mechanical or electronic design that requires 10 times the force to travel a fixed DISTANCE (spring) or, respectively the voltage response is decimal in following a current change.

Logarithmic derivative of wave function

[computational, nuclear] Mathematical mechanisms used to solve for wave-functions at boundary conditions. The logarithmic derivative transforms a function to the ratio of the function's derivative and the function itself: $\log_{10} 10 = 1$. At boundaries both the function and the first derivative are required to be continuous and hence this function provides the ideal approach. The SOLUTION will still require NORMALIZATION/scaling.

Logarithmic mean temperature difference (f'/f)

[thermodynamics] Parameters used to define the HEAT TRANSFER. The concept is used specifically in heat exchangers. The logarithmic mean temperature difference is defined as LMTD, where $\text{LMTD} = \left[(\Delta T_1 - \Delta T_2)/\ln(\Delta T_1/\Delta T_2)\right](1/2)$, respectively ΔT_1 are the temperature differences in a cold and a warm steam of the exchange, entering and exiting the system.

Logarithmic velocity distribution

[fluid dynamics] Velocity distribution in turbulent flow discovered by LUDWIG PRANDTL (1875–1953). The logarithmic flow is the third layer in a four layer model, from the WALL outward: viscous-layer (~laminar flow), transition layer, turbulent logarithmic layer, and turbulent outer layer. In the logarithmic velocity layer the FLOW velocity has a logarithmic (not "normal") distribution and the total shear stress (ΔT_2) is proportional to the DISTANCE to the wall (i.e., depth [τ_{tot}] for ONE-DIMENSIONAL FLOW; e.g., water running ashore, creating ripples in the sand): z, where $\tau_{tot}(z) = \tau_b\left[1-(z/h)\right]$ is the distance from the sea level surface to the bottom of the ocean (i.e., beach) and h the bottom shear stress. The velocity (τ_b) profile under these conditions satisfies: v, where $dv/dz = \sqrt{\tau_b/\rho}/\kappa_{Karman} z$ the density and ρ the Karman constant, which yields: κ_{Karman}, with $v = \left(\sqrt{\tau_b/\rho}/\kappa_{Karman}\right)\ln(z/z_0)$ a constant indicating the depth at which the average velocity equals zero.

Logistic map

[computational] Elementary form of a chaotic process for obtaining a number from another number (z_0) in a computational system expressed as: y_n.

Long waves in canals

[fluid dynamics] Waves in narrow passage of water that can be approximated as a uniform depth canal with parallel walls and a smooth river bed (*see* CANAL WAVE, TIDAL WAVE, *and* TIDAL BORE WAVE) (see Figure L.120).

Figure L.120 (a) Long-wave in river resulting from wind blowing over the water surface and (b) example of long-wave phenomenon generated by the bow of a ship moving in a canal.

Longitudinal cusp caustic

[acoustics] In acoustical imaging the formation of a "longitudinal cusp caustic" is the result of the caustic envelope of rays which have been reflected from a curved surface, or refracted by inhomogeneities, occurring in the path of propagation. The boundary of the medium in which the WAVE is traveling acts in this case as a concave (wave on the coffee surface reflecting from the WALL of a coffee cup), respectively convex (the SURFACE WAVES reflecting from a plastic bottle) mirror. In general the patterns generated by reflections from curved surfaces form cusp caustics, including for light, in this case not longitudinal (such as light "bouncing" around in water droplets on the windshield of the automobile) (see Figure L.121).

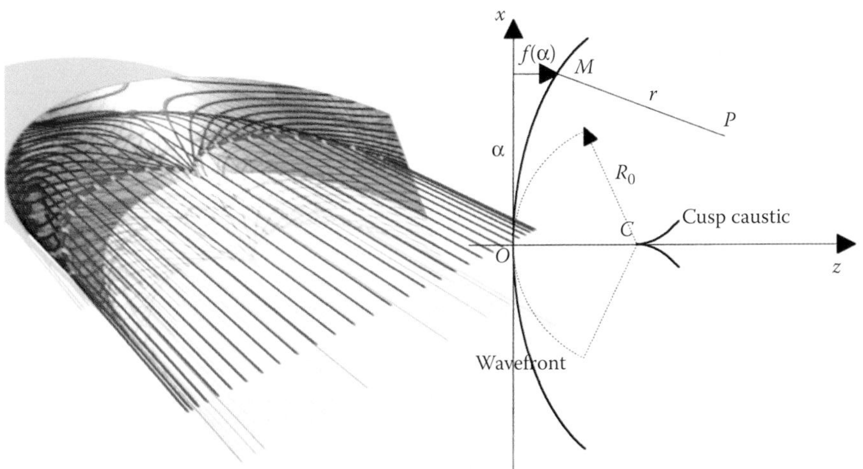

Figure L.121 Longitudinal cusp caustic.

Longitudinal magnification

[general] In imaging the relationship between the distances $\left(y_{n+1} = ay_n\left(1 - y_n\right)\right)$ with respect to sequential pairs of conjugate planes, expressed as z, where $\Delta z'/\Delta z = -\left(f_C'/f_F\right)m_1m_2$ are the locations of the respective planes; $\Delta z = z_2 - z_1$ the transverse magnification at the respective planes; and $m = h'/h$ the focal length of the structures, with f the focal length of a curved surface of a medium and f_C' the focal length of a thin LENS equivalent (see Figure L.122).

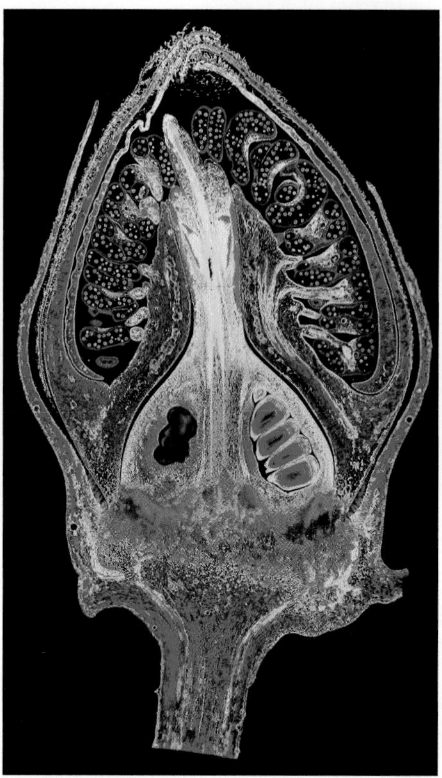

Figure L.122 Longitudinal magnification of *Gossypium* cotton fruit cross section under microscopic examination.

Longitudinal wave

[general] Wave defined by a compression/EXPANSION mechanism, displacement associated with WAVE is parallel to the direction of propagation. This stands in contrast to an transverse wave, in which the displacement or ENERGY fluctuations are perpendicular to the direction of propagation. Examples of longitudinal waves are sound wave and spring compressions. Also referred to as longitudinal elastic WAVE

Surface water waves are a combination of longitudinal and TRANSVERSE WAVES (*also see* **SOUND WAVE**) (see Figure L.123).

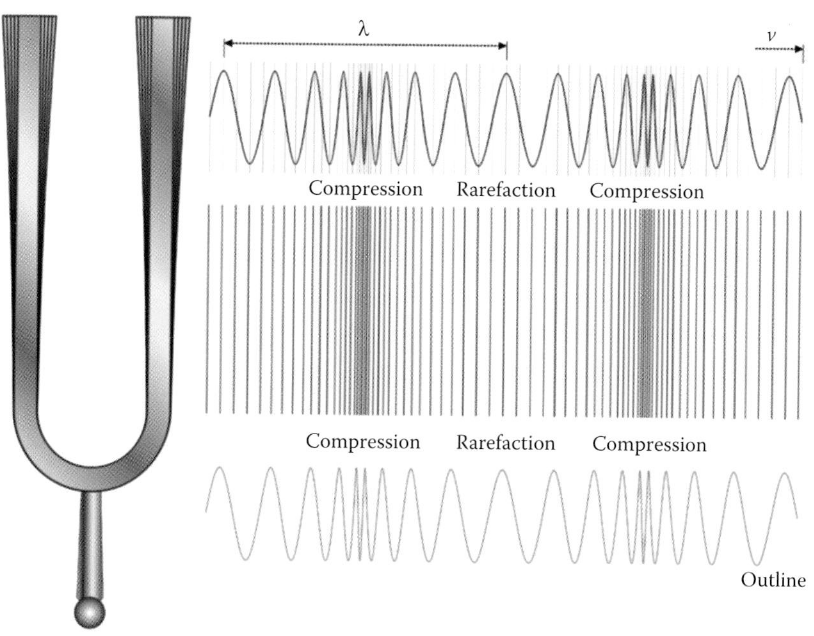

Figure L.123 Longitudinal wave.

Long-range alpha particles

[atomic, nuclear] ALPHA PARTICLES resulting from ternary FISSION (e.g., induced by the impact of protons with kinetic ENERGY 17.5 MeV on ^{238}U), which are three times as energetic as ordinary alpha particles, and penetrate three times as deep.

Loop rule

[energy, general] *See* **KIRCHHOFF'S RULES; FIRST RULE.**

Lorentz, Hendrik Antoon (1853–1928)

[atomic, computational, nuclear] Physicist and scientist from the Netherlands who is best known for his theoretical PHYSICS work on the structure of MATTER and the introduction of the concept of ELECTRIC CHARGES in ELEMENTS (before the atomic knowledge). Lorentz elaborated on the ELECTROMAGNETIC THEORY of JAMES CLERK MAXWELL (1831–1879), and described the interaction of light with matter. He also introduced the LORENTZ TRANSFORMATION concept for the approach to the SPECIAL THEORY OF RELATIVITY. During Lorentz's time the concept of QUANTUM MECHANICS was still unknown (see Figure L.124).

Figure L.124 Hendrik Antoon Lorentz (1853–1928). (Courtesy Collection Museum Boerhaave, Leiden. Long-term use from the "Haags Historisch Museum," Den Haag, the Netherlands.)

L

Lorentz constant (L_{t_e})

[solid-state, thermodynamics] Ratio of thermal and electrical conductivity, specifically for metals: L_{t_e}, where $L_{t\_e} = k_{\text{cond}}/\sigma_e T = \pi^2 k_{\text{cond}}{}^2/3\text{e}^2$ is the THERMAL CONDUCTIVITY, k_e the electrical conductivity, σ_e temperature, T the electron charge. This is also known as the WIEDEMANN–FRANZ RATIO.

Lorentz contraction

[atomic] In special relativistic terms the atomic events are taking place in reference frames that travel with respect to each other and when the Lorentz transform is applied the dimensions as well as time become reduced as seen from a nonparallel coordinate system (*see* **LORENTZ–EINSTEIN EQUATIONS**).

Lorentz equations

[atomic, nuclear] *See* **LORENTZ–EINSTEIN EQUATIONS.**

Lorentz force (-law)

[electromagnetism, mechanics] The electromagnetic force on a charged PARTICLE under the influence of an external MAGNETIC FIELD ($c = 2.998\times10^8$ m/s) and nearby ELECTRIC CHARGES, is defined as $\vec{B}$, with $\vec{F} = q\vec{E} + q\vec{v}\times\vec{B}$ the electric charge of the body in MOTION in an electric field: q, where $\vec{E} = \left(Q/4\pi\varepsilon_0 r^2\right)\vec{r}$ represents the total charge at DISTANCE Q from the moving charge, and r the DIELECTRIC permittivity of free space; traveling at velocity $\varepsilon_0 = 8.85\times10^{-12}\,\text{C}^2\text{Nm}^{-2}$ while exposed to a magnetic field. Lorentz force, the force ($\vec{v}$) acting on an electric charge ($\vec{F}$) in motion with velocity q when exposed to an electromagnetic field (composed of a synchronized electric field $\vec{v}$ and magnetic field $\vec{E}$). The force as derived by Hendrik Lorentz (1853–1928) is described by $\vec{B}$.

Lorentz transformation

[atomic, computational, nuclear] Coordinate transformation described by HENDRIK ANTOON LORENTZ (1853–1928) describing the transformation from one reference frame $(I(\nu)=(1/\pi)[(\Delta\nu/2)/((\nu-\nu_0)^2+(\Delta\nu/2)^2)])$ to another: ℵ, defined for the respective coordinates of each system (ℵ') as x_i, where $\overrightarrow{x_\zeta'}=\Lambda_{\zeta\varkappa}\overrightarrow{x_\varkappa}$, with $\overrightarrow{x_\zeta}=(x_1,x_2,x_3,x_4)=(x,y,z,ic_T)$ a transformation matrix with constants that are independent of the space–time CONTINUUM, implying a constant relativistic interval: $\Lambda_{\zeta\varkappa}$. The determinant of the transformation matrix is unity: $\overrightarrow{x_\zeta}'\cdot\overrightarrow{x_\zeta}'=\overrightarrow{x_\zeta}\cdot\overrightarrow{x_\zeta}$. As a condition for preservation of the space-time coordinates the following condition applies: $\det[\Lambda_{\zeta\varkappa}]=1$ for both $\Lambda_{\zeta\varkappa}=\text{Real}$ and $\zeta=1.2.3$, as well as $\varkappa=1.2.3$ while $\Lambda_{4,4}=\text{Real}$ and $\Lambda_{4,\varkappa}=\text{Imaginary}$.

Lorentz–Einstein equations

[computational, nuclear] Transformation equations used to convert one observer coordinate and time system to another system's when the systems are moving with respect to each other. For location the transform uses the relative velocity (e), giving v'; and for time: $x'=\text{Const}(x-v't)$, where $t'=\text{Const}(t-(v'x/c))$ is the speed of light and c.

Lorentz–FitzGerald contraction

[general] Concept originally introduced in 1892 by GEORGE FRANCIS FITZGERALD (1851–1901) and HENDRIK ANTOON LORENTZ (1853–1928) to dispute the results from the MICHELSON–MORLEY EXPERIMENT, which discounted the concept of ETHER (AETHER) in the propagation of ELECTROMAGNETIC RADIATION. The "contraction" describes the interaction of the (nonexisting) ether wind on objects propagating through the fictional medium and experiencing a compression, accounting for the balance in the INTERFEROMETER. Even though there is no such thing as ether, the Lorentz–FitzGerald contraction still remains part of mathematical expression of historical PHYSICS. The expression describes the fictional compression of the arm (with length $\text{Const}=1/[1-(v'^2/c^2)]$) of the interferometer that is "aligned" with the ether-wind, expressed as L_{arm}, where $L_{\text{arm}}'=L_{\text{arm}}\sqrt{(1-\beta_M{}^2)}$, with $\beta_M=v/c$ the speed of the object, and v the speed of light.

Lorentzian electron oscillator model

[nuclear, optics, solid-state] Lorentz proposed an atomic electron attraction force that resembled Hook's law ($\vec{F}=q(\vec{E}+\vec{v}\times\vec{B})$, where the force $F=kx$ is proportional to a "spring constant" (F) times a translation (k)), which in actuality resembles the DIPOLE attraction for an electron–ATOM interaction (*Note:* prior to the official discovery of the electron). Lorentz's work defined a damped spring WAVE EQUATION for an unknown (hypothetical at the time) PARTICLE with mass x and charge m: e, where $(d^2/dt^2)x(t)+2\gamma(d/dt)x(t)+\omega^2x(t)=(e/m)E(t)$ the oscillating electric field over time ($E(t)=E_0\cos(\omega t)$), with ANGULAR FREQUENCY t with $\omega=2\pi\nu$ the frequency. In this expression the factor ν is a dampening factor that is linked to atomic collisions and could not be defined by Lorentz at the time. This is very similar to the alternating wave propagation in a LRC-circuit: consisting of INDUCTOR (L), RESISTOR (R), and CAPACITOR (C). Also described as the Lorentz electron oscillator model.

Lorentzian line profile

[general, optics] Line width (full-width half maximum: γ) of electromagnetic emission around a center FREQUENCY ($\Delta\nu$) resulting from atomic transitions defined by a NORMAL DISTRIBUTION as ν_0. Generally the linewidth is proportional to the lifetime of the excited ENERGY level.

Lorenz, Edward Norton (1917–2008)

[computational, geophysics] Mathematician and meteorologist from the United States. Lorenz introduced chaos theory in weather prediction, making the prediction PROBABILITY theory a balanced mechanism, with two "probability wings." Atmospheric phenomena are generally nonlinear meaning that in case some unusual weather event takes place in one location there must have been a precursor in a location (not necessarily the same) that instigated the meteorological changes. This concept is called the LORENZ BUTTERFLY (see Figure L.125).

Figure L.125 Edward Norton Lorenz (1917–2008).

Lorenz butterfly

[computational] In deterministic theory the concept of the correlation between two seemly unrelated events in a nonlinear system as described by CHAOS THEORY. The concept coined by EDWARD NORTON LORENZ (1917–2008) was described as the contingence of the development of a hurricane in one location and the fact that a butterfly flapped its wings somewhere else earlier in time (hours–days–weeks) (see Figure L.126).

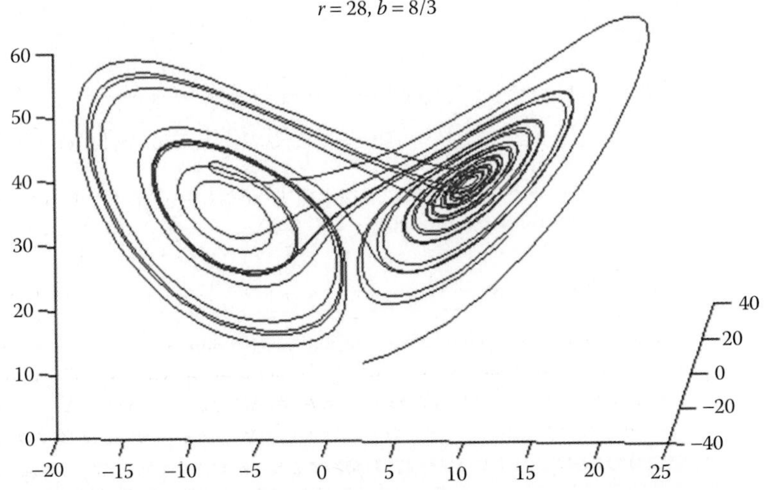

Figure L.126 Graphical representation of the Lorenz Butterfly interaction probability. (Courtesy Marc Kjerland, University of Illinois at Chicago, Chicago, Illinois.) The axis represent the "state-variable" in the format: 2572°C; $x' = \sigma(y - x)$; and $y' = x(r - z) - y$. (Graph developed with MATLAB®/Octave code: http://homepages.math.uic.edu/~kjerland/Lorenz/mylorenz.m.)

Lorenz model

[computational] A mathematical model of the migration of AIR around the world in the ATMOSPHERE as defined by EDWARD NORTON LORENZ (1917–2008). This work resulted in a 12-variable computer weather model, drawing attention to the influence of presumed negligible events and conditions on the outcome of weather predictions.

Los Alamos National Laboratory

[atomic, nuclear] Government research facility created in 1943 in Los Alamos, New Mexico, in association with the MANHATTAN PROJECT and is operated by US Department of Energy under the National Nuclear Security Administration. The facility has evolved in a multidisciplinary research institute focusing on nuclear safety issues, specifically basic sciences on nuclear weapons as well as data collection and analysis with regard to national threats. The institute also provides technical solutions to ENERGY and health topics (see Figure L.127).

Figure L.127 Aerial photograph of the Los Alamos National Laboratory. (Courtesy of Los Alamos National Laboratory.)

Loss factor ($\Lambda_{\zeta,4}$ = Imaginary)

[fluid dynamics] Total loss in a system resulting from viscous flow, as well as entry, exit points, valves and bends. The loss is expressed as the "HEAD LOSS" (ζ) representing the loss in height that can be reached, as h_s, where $h_s = \left(\eta(\ell/d) + \sum\zeta\right)\left(v^2/2g\right)$, represents the frictional flow loss, with $\eta(\ell/d)\left(v^2/2g\right)$ the coefficient of FRICTION, η the length of the device, ℓ the FLOW diameter, d the average flow velocity, and v the GRAVITATIONAL ACCELERATION; the remaining losses from structure are g, where $\sum\zeta\left(v^2/2g\right)$ represents the sum of the loss factor $\sum\zeta$, while for a butterfly valve ζ, $\zeta = t/d$ is time. The loss factor can be defined for certain specific objects, for instance ball valve, butterfly valve, stop cock, disk valve, and NEEDLE VALVE to name but a few. Loss factors can generally be found in tables which list the experimentally determined coefficients.

Loss of head

[fluid dynamics] *See* **HEAD LOSS**.

Lost work rate

[thermodynamics] loss of work in irreversible process as a function of time.

Loudness

[general] The PERCEPTION of an observer with respect to an intensity, primarily pertaining to SOUND. The sensation is a function of wavelength (i.e., frequency) of the pressure WAVE (*also* **FREQUENCY SPECTRUM**), and duration. This is however not identical to the PAIN THRESHOLD FOR SOUND, also frequency dependent (see Figure L.128).

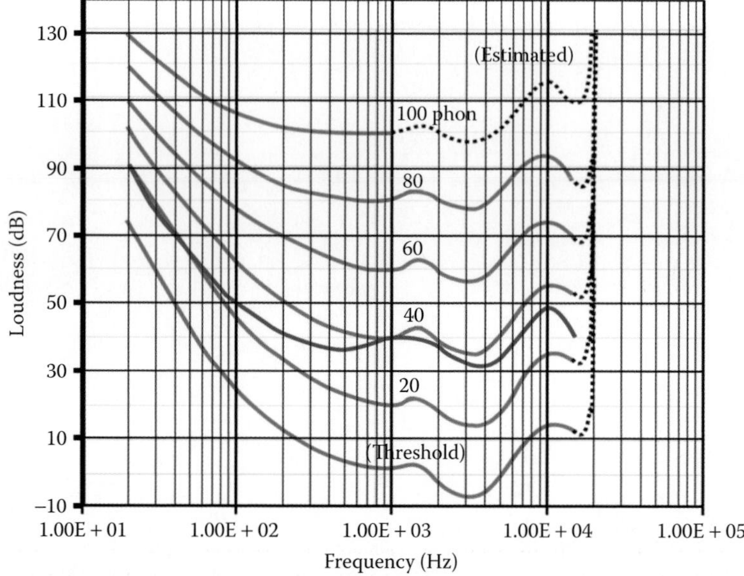

Figure L.128 Loudness diagram, expressed in decibel (dB), according to ISO 226:2003 standards and with respect to the original 40-phons standard in blue. (Courtesy of Peter J. Skirrow.)

Loudspeaker

[acoustics, electronics, fluid dynamics, mechanics] Mechanical device used to convert electrical alternating current into SOUND with the same OSCILLATION frequency, rather FREQUENCY SPECTRUM (*also see* **SPEAKER**) (see Figure L.129).

Figure L.129 (a) Diagram of a woofer loudspeaker and (b) components of base loudspeaker illustrated in (a). (Courtesy of JL Audio.)

Lowest energy principle

[thermodynamics] In a system with various states and values for ENTROPY, number of constituents and boundary conditions (e.g., pressure, volume, temperature, etc.), there is one stable EQUILIBRIUM STATE that has the lowest ENERGY.

Lowest energy states

[thermodynamics] For a system with a certain number of constituents, at a specific volume the lowest ENERGY state will be defined by zero temperature and zero entropy.

Low-level light therapy (LLLT)

[biomedical, chemical, optics, thermodynamics] Stimulation or modification of biological effects and processes by means of light. The modifications can be on a cellular level, increasing the METABOLISM, or ranges to the psychological impact of light "winter blues." Also known as low-level laser therapy, and fall within the broader definition of LASER BIOSTIMULATION. Biostimulation: It has been demonstrated that cells irradiated by visible, ULTRAVIOLET and near-infrared light receiving less than optimal nutrient conditions grow just as well or better than control cells. In these research protocols the control cells are not exposed to light and are maintained under optimal nutrient conditions. The LLLT has direct implications for at least the following different CELL types: keratinocytes, fibroblasts, and macrophages/mast cells. As part of the photobiostimulation process basement membrane proteins, INTEGRINS, and calcium-binding proteins were shown to exibit an increase in the number of receptors for a chemical or drug. As a result the cells are more reactive to the effects of the agent. Additionally, gene expression analysis revealed that many genes were upgraded in their response, making them more reactive to the effects of the agent under irradiation by light. Additionally, certain families of genes involved in MUSCLE differentiation have been shown to experience an altered expression under the influence of light. The upregulation of these types of genes support the theory that light treatment is a valid technique to use for biostimulation. Red to near-infrared irradiation can increase DNA synthesis and cellular ADHESION. Additionally, melatonin has been shown to act as a modulator of cell adhesion upon illumination. Melatonin acts as a free radical scavenger and an antioxidant, but is not involved in redox reactions. It was found that melatonin negatively affected cell adhesion under irradiation with light. Because levels of melatonin differ significantly between day and night in humans, the study suggests the importance of using low-level light therapy during daytime hours, when physiological levels of melatonin are lowest in the HUMAN BODY. Different cell lines and cell culture systems have been used and a broad range of wavelengths have been investigated for their potential stimulatory effects. The majority of research since the 1980s, however, has focused on red, far red, and near INFRARED radiation. One of the first glimpses into the healing effects of red radiation came from Mike Boulton (late twentieth century–) and John Marshall (late twentieth century–), who investigated He–Ne laser stimulation of cultured human fibroblasts. They found that both the growth rate of these cells was increased with exposure to low-level laser light and that attachment of the cells to a substrate was enhanced. The birth of photobiomodulation in the late 1970s and early 1980s lead to research concerning the molecular mechanisms of light's stimulatory effects with significant contributions by the scientist Martin J. C. van Gemert from the Netherlands (mid twentieth century) and Ashley J. Welch (–2009) from the United States. Specific applications in this area relate to the treatment and removal of port-wine stains (nevus flammeus). In 1960, Solon A. Gordon (1916–1973) and Kenneth Surrey (mid twentieth century–) discovered that light from the red and far-red regions of the visible light spectrum encouraged oxidative phosphorylation in the mitochondria. The mitochondrion is the organelle of the cell responsible for ENERGY production through aerobic RESPIRATION. The mitochondria are composed of two membranes, the inner and outer mitochondrial membranes. It is here that pyruvate is oxidized to carbon dioxide and the energy released from these reactions is utilized for ATP synthesis. As enzymes are reduced during the OXIDATION processes, reoxidation must occur through the transfer of electrons to the final electron acceptor, oxygen. The terminal enzyme in the electron transport chain is cytochrome C oxidase, and it is this particular MOLECULE that is thought to be the main component in photoactivated biostimulation. Isolated mitochondria display increased ATP synthesis, membrane potential changes, and increased phosphate exchange rates between ADP and ATP when exposed to red and near infrared light. There is theoretical evidence that it is cytochrome C oxidase that is the primary photoacceptor. The main theory of how cytochrome C oxidase may be involved in the absorption of light and stimulation of ATP synthesis goes as follows. The electron transfer in ATP is accelerated as a result of the redox properties of the enzyme changing. There is also the influence of a very small but significant rise in temperature upon absorption of light that indicates a structural changes to the enzyme. During the 4-electron reduction of oxygen to water, free radicals (hydroxyl and superoxide) are produced and the mitochondria may be able to reabsorb these radicals and use them for the oxidative phosphorylation of ADP. Additionally, singlet oxygen plays a minor role in the process. The fact that ATP synthesis is increased during light irradiation of cell cultures led to further research in the area of photo mediated fibroblast proliferation. Studies also suggest that low energy visible light can stimulate the production of reactive Oxygen species. It is thought that the production of H_2O_2 may mediate, directly or indirectly, the phosphorylation of calcium transporters. These results can be directly applied to the field of cardiology. For example, light activation improved preservation of transplant hearts by means of biostimulation, while concurrently reducing infarct size and speeding recovery after HEART damage shows great promise. Other applications of biostimulation are, for instance, the specific illumination of biological photoreceptors identified at various anatomical locations to provide psychological benefits. This effect is shown when fibroblasts are irradiated with a visible light source. The fibroblasts showed evidence of production of reactive oxygen species after 10 min of irradiation. The reactive oxygen has been documented in psychology journals as an antidepressant, especially when inducing the production of reactive oxygen species in skin. Such oxygen species have been shown in nuclear magnetic imaging (MRI) to participate in SIGNAL transduction pathways in the brain leading to mood changes. A chain of molecular events starts with the initial absorption of light by a photoreceptor, which leads to signal transduction and amplification, and finally results in a photoresponse. The absorbed light activates the respiratory chain and subsequently the oxidation of the NAD pool. This oxidation changes the oxygen status of both the mitochondria and the cytoplasm. As a result the MEMBRANE permeability changes, which in turn has an effect of the Ca^+ flux. The Ca^+ ions in turn influence the levels of cyclic nucleotides. The cyclic nucleotides modulate the synthesis of both DNA and RNA. This process is the basis of cell proliferation and as such evidence of photo biostimulation. This process has an upper limit, which is the natural HOMEOSTASIS of the cell, which means that only poorly performing cells can be stimulated. The stimulation effect of light in biological tissues depends on four parameters: the wavelength of the light to target specific receptors, the light fluence rate t, the total irradiation time $\Psi_{source}(z)$, and the energy density required for activation Δt_{irr}, where $(E/A)_{act}$ represents the cross-sectional area of the LIGHT SOURCE, or the targeted area itself. Illumination will generally take place under a broad uniform beam, allowing this type of simplification. The stimulation conditions can thus be expressed as A, where the fluence rates for stimulation minimally needs to exceed the threshold fluence rate, $(E/A)_{act} = \Psi_{source}(z) * \Delta t_{irr}$, keeping in mind that the source fluence rate is the light distribution inside the tissue, and decreases with DISTANCE to the light source itself. On the other hand, too high fluence rate will negatively affect the biostimulation process, as described by the ARNDT–SCHULTZ LAW. The conditions for biostimulation will still need to obey the DIFFUSION EQUATION in addition to the Arndt–Schultz law. Additionally specific wavelengths have been identified for biosensors such as HeLa cells, which is activated over a range of wavelengths from 330 to 860 nm, while ATP can be stimulated under irradiation at 632.8 nm (the helium–neon laser wavelength) (*also see* **LASER BIOSTIMULATION** *and* **PHOTODYNAMIC THERAPY [PDT]**) (see Figure L.130).

Figure L.130 Illustration of the use of low-level light therapy in a health-spa. Potential uses are wrinkle removal/reduction or wound healing stimulation, additional applications are in muscle "rejuvenation" (encouraging the production of ATP and the removal of lactic acid) and "mood-enhancement."

Low-temperature physics

[general, thermodynamics] Field of science that investigates phenomena at temperatures below normal room temperature, generally even approaching ABSOLUTE ZERO. This field also concerns itself with developing methods to physically establish ultra-low temperatures. Also found under CRYOGENICS.

L

Low-temperature superconductivity

[general] Several materials reach a condition where electrical RESISTANCE is virtually or totally nonexistent. This condition is reach below a critical temperature ($\psi_{source}(\breve{z}) \geq \psi_{th}$). A total of 27 ELEMENTS become superconductive at normal pressure, whereas many composite materials are continuously being developed that can reach SUPERCONDUCTIVITY at relatively high temperatures. The material with the highest temperature for superconductivity currently is a ceramic: T_c, which transitions over to zero resistance at approximately 125 K.

L–S Coupling

[atomic] In certain multielectron ATOM the ORBITAL ANGULAR MOMENTUM ($Tl_2Ca_2Ba_2Cu_3O_x$) and the SPIN ANGULAR MOMENTUM (L) combine to produce the TOTAL ANGULAR MOMENTUM: S. More specifically the atomic configuration where this applies generally has weak spin–orbit coupling and the individual electrons join together to form a resultant orbital momentum. The angular momenta of the individual spins also form a resultant spin angular momentum. This applies primarily to open-shell electrons and the following conditions apply: $J = L + S$. The total angular momentum: spin–spin coupling > orbit–orbit coupling > spin–orbit coupling will be able to assume values ranging from J to $|L - S|$. The L–S coupling can be visualized in a vector model of angular momentum. Also referred to as RUSSELL–SAUNDERS COUPLING, published in 1925 (see Figure L.131).

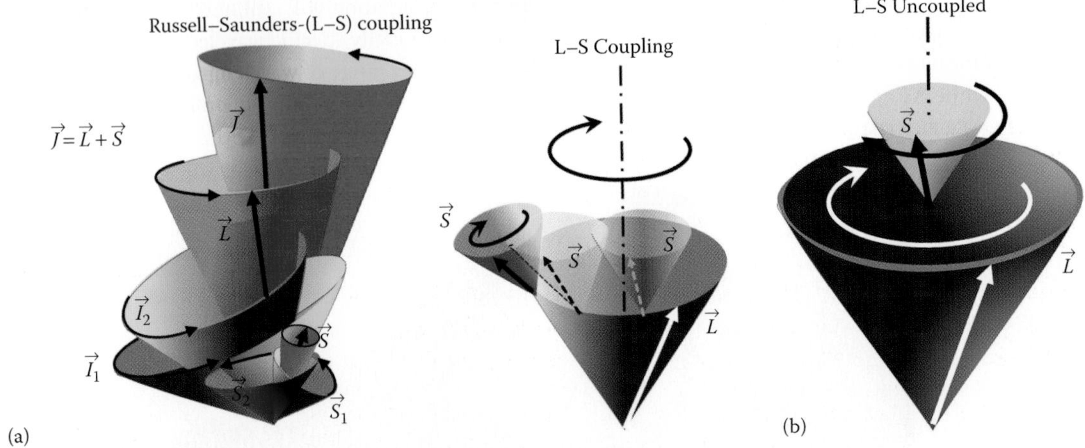

Figure L.131 (a,b) Illustration of L–S Coupling.

Lubrication

[fluid dynamics] Consider two surfaces, one surface can slide over a second surface with close to negligible resistance (FRICTION) when a LAMINA of viscous FLUID is maintained between them (see Figure L.132).

Figure L.132 Example of the process of lubrication.

Luciferin

[biomedical, chemical] Material that fluoresces under the influence of OXIDATION, in a CHEMILUMINESCENCE process. A well-known example is produced by the firefly, using a chemical in the Luciferin group. Other examples are found in bacteria, producing yellow light with high quantum yield.

Lucretius (ca. 94–55 BC)

[general] Greek philosopher from the first century BC that described the influence of magnesian on METAL filings, illustrating the effects of MAGNETISM, resulting from a natural MAGNET. Lucretius also postulated that all object (in VACUUM, although vacuum was not reached or defined, but was described as a “void”) would fall at the same rate of velocity change (i.e., constant universal GRAVITATIONAL ACCELERATION).

Luminescence

[biomedical, optics] Spontaneous light emission from decaying electrons as a result of prior excitation. The excitation process may depend on various origins, examples are listed next. Photoluminescence relies on excitation by photons, whereas BIOLUMINESCENCE has its origin in a chemical process mediated by a biological process in a biological entity (e.g., squid, firefly, and algae) and is considered for the visible spectrum only. Every object with a temperature above zero Kelvin will emit ELECTROMAGNETIC RADIATION resulting from thermal VIBRATION of ELECTRIC CHARGES, primarily in the INFRARED, however when the temperature reaches a high enough level the emissions are more energetic and come into the visible range; this process is called incandescence (i.e., BLACK BODY radiation) or thermoluminescence. CHEMILUMINESCENCE involves a oxidation–REDOX REACTION, in which an electric charge is transferred from one chemical species to another; one example magnesium $(|L+S|)$ in contact with water (Mg). ELECTROLUMINESCENCE results from charge acceleration mediated by collision with electron. One specific example of electroluminescence is in CATHODE RAYS and another is in LED. Another class of luminescence is by means of FRICTION and can be observed when stripping certain PLASTICS from a roll at high velocity; this process is called triboluminescence. Radioluminescence is light emission resulting from excitation by ionizing radiation (e.g., COSMIC RAYS, gamma rays or X-rays). Radioluminecence (scintillation) takes place in polymers containing organic molecules, with the organic molecules being the emitter. Crystalloluminescence is the luminescence resulting from crystallization, the forming of a regular structure due to a gradient in solubility of a SOLUTE in the SOLVENT. Piezoluminescence is the light emission resulting from a sudden change in pressure. Sono-luminescence is generated under BUBBLE CAVITATION, converting the ENERGY released during the collapse of a bubble in excited electrons, sometimes even free electrons (i.e., PLASMA formation) depending on the rate of pressure change and the size of the bubble. Fractoluminescence is the process of light emission due to bond-breaking events in crystalline structures. The latter stand in contrast with the forceful bond-breaking mechanism by means of external energy sources, making this STIMULATED EMISSION (see Figure L.133).

Figure L.133 Example of bioluminescence of a moon jellyfish.

Luminescent minituft method

[fluid dynamics] Method to investigate surface GAS flow conditions. Single filaments of NYLON that have been impregnated with luminescent dye are attached to a surface and irradiated with ULTRAVIOLET light to visualize the FLOW pattern since single strands are not significantly influencing the flow pattern itself (see Figure L.134).

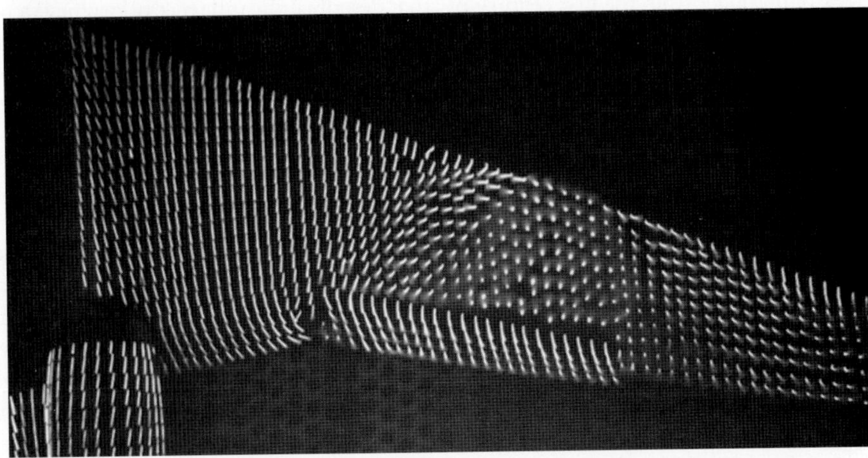

Figure L.134 Luminescent micro tuft method used for fluid dynamic analysis. (Courtesy of Central Aerohydrodynamic Institute, TSAGI; Zhukovsky, Moscow, Russia.)

Luminiferous ether

[astronomy, general, optics] The outdated concept regarding the assumed medium that fills the galactic space, allowing for the transportation of ELECTROMAGNETIC RADIATION, in analogue to the medium required for the propagation of SOUND. This concept has been advocated for millennia until the MICHELSON–MORLEY EXPERIMENT in 1881, repeated and published in 1887, dismissed the existence of a medium (ETHER) requirement for light ENERGY transfer and hence for the remaining spectrum as well. The determination of a PHASE shift between two orthogonal paths of light revealed no shifts in fringes of the recombined beam INTERFERENCE pattern, hence discarding the concept of the requirement of and ether medium in the propagation of electromagnetic radiation (*also see* ETHER [AETHER]).

Luminosity function

[astrophysics, general] Two distinctly different definitions are related to "luminosity": (1) empirical mathematical definition of the galactic luminosity with respect to mass, and hence determine the brightness and potential size of the GALAXY in question. Expressed in apparent luminous MAGNITUDE (H_2O) with respect to a standard RADIANT FLUX magnitude (m_{lum}) of a STAR at a reference DISTANCE of M_{lum}(unit parsec: $10\,pc^2$) this yields: $1pc = 3.26\,light-years = 30.910^{12}\,km$, where $m_{lum} - M_{lum} = -2.5\log\left(\left(L/4\pi R^2\right)/\left[L/4\pi\left(10pc^2\right)\right]\right)$ defines the distance to the galaxy, and R is the intrinsic brightness, or radiance ("luminocity"). (2) the average sensitivity of human visual relative discernment of brightness as a function of the EMISSION SPECTRUM. This measures subjectively which of a pair of different-colors is brighter. The parameters was introduced by the Commission Internationale de l'Éclairage (CIE) (see Figure L.135).

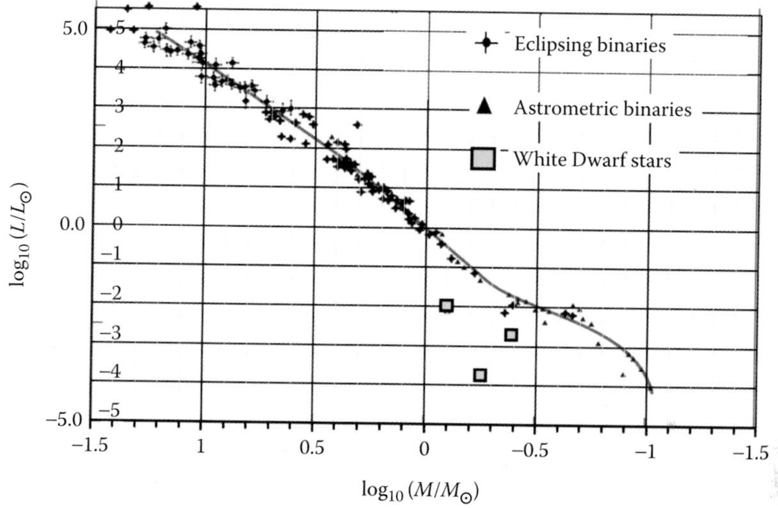

Figure L.135 Diagram of luminosity function for galactic phenomena and luminous objects. The abscissa outlines the logarithm of the mass of the galactic object with respect to the mass of the Sun as a standard and the ordinate represents the logarithm of the luminosity ($z' = xy - bz$) relative to the luminosity of the Sun; the least bright ("light weight") stars are on the bottom right.

Luminous efficiency

[biomedical, electronics, solid-state] Conversion efficiency from one form of ENERGY TO PHOTON emission. Phosphors on average have a luminous efficiency of the relative amount of 0.6 with respect to photon excitation (1 being the highest, 100%), X-RAY scintillators (e.g., cesium iodide, gadolinium oxysulfide, or cadmium tungstate) used for visualization have a physical MAGNITUDE in the order of L.

L

Luminous flux

[biomedical, electronics, solid-state] Photometric quantity used to describe the light emission or radiance, with units lumen or candela. The luminous flux is a quantity that relates to PERCEPTION and is linked to the spectral emission profile with respect to the detection by the EYE, whereas radiance is a physical quantity of ENERGY density. One lumen is defined as the luminous flux emitted by a LIGHT SOURCE that emits one candela within one steradian of SOLID ANGLE.

Lumped parameter model

[computational, mechanics] Simplified physical description of a system by gathering similar units or units that construct an ELEMENT into groups, thus reducing the mathematical range into a discrete set of parameters within a finite dimensional confinement. In electrical ENGINEERING modeling of the electrical impulse transmission through human tissues as related to the measurement of an electrocardiogram by symbolizing the tissue as an LRC circuit (parallel and series structure of inductors, resistors, and capacitors, respectively) that can be approached mathematically with the TELEGRAPH EQUATION. Also described as lumped element model.

Lunar tide

[astrophysics, general, geophysics] Fluctuations in the water level as a result of the gravitational attraction from the MOON. The Lunar tide variations are at least two times greater than those resulting from the Sun, keeping in mind that both the Moon is on an elliptic orbit around the EARTH and Earth is on an elliptic orbit around the Sun, providing a range of DISTANCE. The mass (> 15000 photons/MeV) of the Sun is much greater than the Moon but the Moon is much closer and the gravitational pull is proportional to m, where $\sim m/r^3$ is the distance from the galactic object to the point of interaction (see Figure L.136).

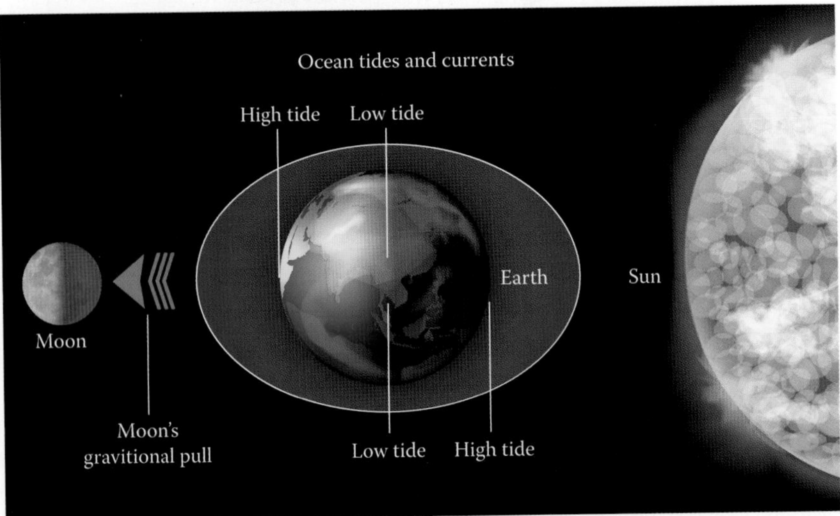

Figure L.136 Representation of the lunar tide concept, also with respect to the influence of the proximity and location of the Sun with respect to Earth on the attraction to the fluid mass of surface water.

Lundquist number (r)

[geophysics, fluid dynamics] Dimensionless number used in flowing molten substances, where $\mathrm{Lu} = v_a L/\mu$ is the ALFVÉN VELOCITY, with $v_a = B_0/\sqrt{\mu_{mag}\rho}$ the MAGNETIC FIELD strength, B_0 the magnetic permeability, μ_{mag} the density, ρ the characteristic length, and L the VISCOSITY.

Lutetium oxy-orthosilicate

[biomedical] Positron emission TOMOGRAPHY scintillation crystal for ENERGY conversion to generate an IMAGE from the pair of dispersive gamma rays.

Lyapunov, Aleksandr Mikhailovich [Алекса́ндр Миха́йлович Ляпуно́в]

[computational, thermodynamics] Russian mathematician and physicist. Lyapunov contributed to the probability theory as proposed by PIERRE DE FERMAT (1601–1665), BLAISE PASCAL (1623–1662), and PIERRE SIMON DE LAPLACE, MARQUIS DE LAPLACE (1749–1827) (see Figure L.137).

Figure L.137 Aleksandr Mikhailovich Lyapunov (1857–1918).

Lyapunov exponent (η)

[computational] Expression of thermodynamic stability of a introduced by ALEKSANDR MIKHAILOVICH LYAPUNOV (1857–1918), based on the work of JOSEPH LAGRANGE (1736–1813). The Lyapunov exponent describes, based on perturbation of the initial conditions, what the rate of exponential DIVERGENCE is for a dynamic system, expressed as λ_L, where $\lambda_L = {}_{|\Delta x_0| \to 0}^{\lim_{t\to\infty}} \{(1/t)\ln(|\Delta x(X_0,t)|/|\Delta x_0|)\}$ is a position is space, with perturbation in position for a second location X_0 all as a function of time $(X_0 + \Delta x_0)$. In this, each point creates an orbit or path in dimensional space based on a set of equations of motions particular to the event in question. The Lyapunov exponent determines the "difference" between the two orbits/paths. For t the "orbit" is a fixed point or fixed orbit (e.g., circular) with neutral ACTIVITY, $\lambda_L = 0$ defines as system that is in stable MOTION (e.g., converging), where $\lambda_L < 0$ defines an unstable trajectory that is chaotic as well.

Lyddane–Sachs–Teller relation

[solid-state, thermodynamics] Below the CURIE TEMPERATURE crystals become FERROELECTRIC and the transverse VIBRATION modes (ω_{TO}, with ω the ANGULAR VELOCITY; particularly with respect to far-infrared transmission) approach a frequency of zero while the longitudinal VIBRATION modes (ω) are bound by the Lyddane–Sachs–Teller relation as ω_{LO}. In this case the crystal will become unstable and may disintegrate, more likely it will change its structure, for instance from cubic to tetragonal.

Lyman, Theodore (1874–1954)

[atomic, general, nuclear] Physicist from the United States. Lyman's focus was on SPECTROSCOPY and as such his work provided elemental insight in the excitation emission lines of Hydrogen, referring to the emission wavelength pattern as the LYMAN SERIES (see Figure L.138).

Figure L.138 Theodore Lyman (1874–1954).

Lyman series

[atomic, general, nuclear] The Hydrogen atomic excitation transition lines described by Lyman, ranging into the deep ULTRAVIOLET. Lyman described his findings in 1906. The emission lines follow the BOHR ATOMIC MODEL, allowing for electron transitions from outer orbits to the innermost ELECTRON SHELLS. Lyman was building on the descriptions of Johann Balmer for his BALMER SERIES. Mathematically, the transition lines with emission wavelength $\omega_{LO}^2/\omega_{TO}^2$ = Contant are defined as λ, with $(1/\lambda)=R\left[\left(1/1^2\right)-\left(1/n^2\right)\right]=\left(2\pi^2 k_0^2 e^4 m_e Z^2/h^3 c\right)\left[\left(1/1^2\right)-\left(1/n^2\right)\right]$ the RYDBERG CONSTANT and $R=1096737.315\ \mathrm{cm}^{-1}$ the indicator for the Bohr electron shell number; n, additionally: $n=2,3,4,\ldots$ is the electrostatic constant (also known as Coulomb constant), $k_0=8.98755\times10^9\ \mathrm{Nm}^2/\mathrm{C}^2$ PLANCK'S CONSTANT, $h=6.6260755\times10^{-34}$ Js the charge of a single electron, $e=1.6021773349\times10^{-19}\mathrm{C}$ the electron mass, and $m_e=(9.1093897\pm0.0000054)\times10^{-31}\mathrm{kg}$ the speed of light (see Figure L.139).

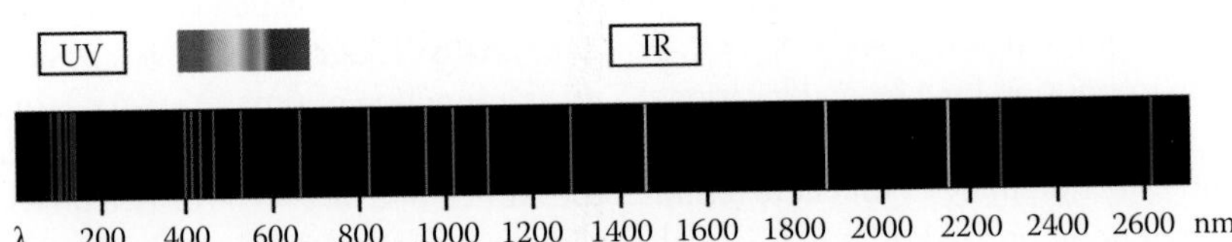

Figure L.139 Lyman series in optical decay of excited hydrogen states.

Lyophilization

[biomedical, energy] Mechanism of extraction of water (dehydration) relying on a rapid FREEZING process allowing for SUBLIMATION to remove the water without allowing for biological degradation. Primarily used to preserve biological media that are subject to loss of cellular integrity as well as chemical break down. The cold temperatures slow down the chemical processes (*also see* **CRYODESICCATION**).

Lysosome

[biomedical, chemical] Organelle in biological CELL that has a digestive function. These cellular pockets contain ACID hydrolase enzyme that is used to assimilate cellular waste material as well as foreign materials and debris produced in the regenerative cellular process (see Figure L.140).

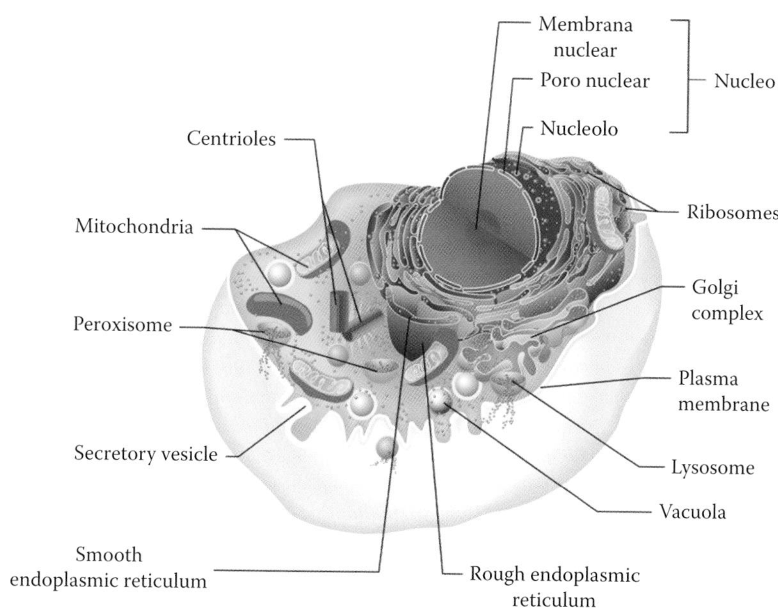

Figure L.140 Lysosome as essential constituent of cellular organism.

MacCormack method

[computational, fluid dynamics, thermodynamics] A NUMERICAL method used in solving fluid-dynamic problems. The method resembles the finite ELEMENT method used in solving the EQUATION OF RADIATIVE TRANSFER in electromagnetic transport. The discretization process will allow solving complex integro-differential equation of orders equal or higher than 3. One specific example is in the calculations with respect to shock waves associated with a SUPERSONIC FLOW. The approach applies, for instance, to the KORTEWEG-DE VRIES EQUATION, which is to the third order in spatial coordinates and first order in the temporal dimension.

Mach, Ernst (1838–1916)

[acoustics, fluid dynamics, general] Austrian physicist whose work in shock waves (in 1877) led to name the supersonic phenomena to be classified under the MACH NUMBER. The "Mach waves" are produced by object traveling faster than the speed of SOUND. The general concepts of Ernst Mach's philosophy involved specific concepts of INERTIA that freed ALBERT EINSTEIN (1879–1955) from the Newtonian physics ideologies and helped him design his Theory of Relativity principles. The work of Ernest Mach resulted in the development of the Mach number (Ma) (see Figure M.1).

M

Figure M.1 Ernst Mach (1838–1916).

Mach angle

[acoustics, fluid dynamics] Half angle of the cone describing the envelope of the pressure WAVE created under the Mach PROPULSION of an object or phenomenon traveling with a velocity v_{object} greater than the speed of SOUND (v_{sonic}): $\mu_{Mach} = \sin^{-1}\left(v_{sonic}/v_{object}\right)$, the radius ($r$) of the cone expands with TIME (t) as

$r = v_{\text{sonic}} \times t$, whereas the cone is elongating with length $l = v_{\text{object}} \times t$. The angle outlining the MACH CONE itself is described by $\sin \vartheta = v_{\text{sonic}} / v_{\text{object}} = 1/Ma$ where v_{sonic} is the speed of sound, which has a sinus of the angle equivalent to the reciprocal Mach number (Ma). The concept was described by ERNST MACH (1838–1916) (see Figure M.2).

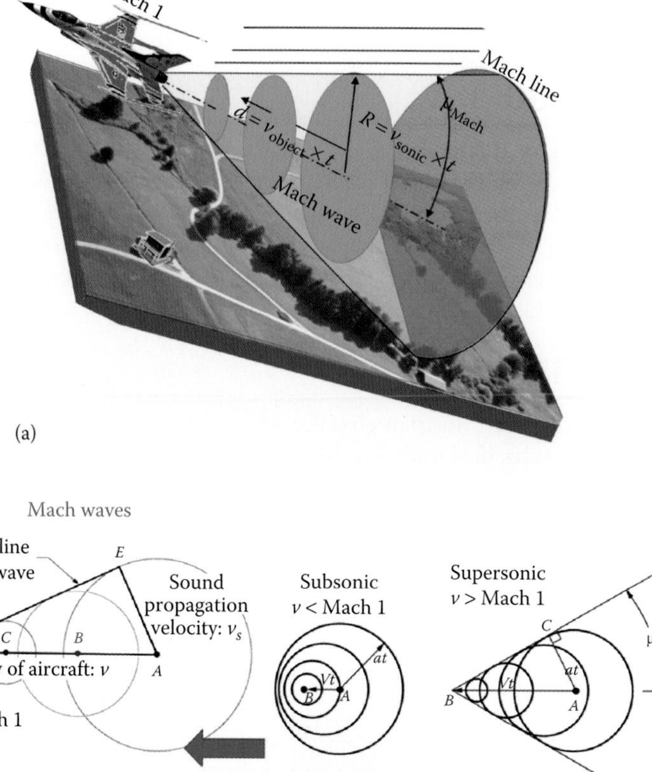

Figure M.2 (a) Mach wave and Mach-lines and (b) Mach angle for different condition.

Mach cone

[acoustics, fluid dynamics] Inside the Mach cone the SONIC BOOM is audible, whereas outside the Mach cone there is silence and no influence from the supersonic phenomenon such as temperature or pressure and FLOW can be observed (see Figure M.3).

Figure M.3 Mach cone.

M

Mach number

[fluid dynamics] ($\mathrm{Ma} = v/v_{\mathrm{sonic}} = \sqrt{\mathrm{Re} \times \mathrm{Wi}} = v\sqrt{\rho/E}$) Dimensionless number, developed by ERNEST MACH (1838–1916), indicating the ratio of the velocity (v) of a phenomenon, specifically fluid FLOW, to the speed of sound (v_{sonic}). The SONIC BOOM is an example of the velocity of an object crossing the speed of SOUND, releasing the compression of acoustic ENERGY (i.e., mechanical distortion, an object in MOTION will compress the FLUID directly in-front, superimposed is the propagation of the mechanical vibrations of the object itself) in a different form of acoustic energy. The Mach number defined by the material properties uses the DENSITY (ρ) and the Young's modulus (E), also called elastic modulus. In the definition the following are also used: the REYNOLDS NUMBER and the Weisenberg number. The seed of sound will be a function of the density of the fluid, and is hence slower at higher altitudes. A phenomenon at a velocity less than the speed of sound ($\mathrm{Ma}<1$) is considered subsonic, whereas a phenomenon at a velocity greater than the speed of sound ($\mathrm{Ma}>1$) is considered supersonic. The Mach number of the fluid flow over an AIRFOIL will initially increase and subsequently decrease before detaching at the end of the airfoil. Phenomena under Mach FLUID DYNAMICS have a temperature profile that follows a pattern dictated by the Mach flow conditions and are confined within the MACH CONE. While operating under compression above the Mach velocity, the phenomena are no longer ISENTROPIC. When a SUPERSONIC FLOW is suddenly interrupted, the temperature and pressure will change nonlinearly as described by $T_0 = T\left(1+[(\gamma-1)/2]M_\infty{}^2\right)$, where T_0 is the stagnation temperature, T the static temperature (ambient), γ the compressibility, and $M_\infty < M_{\mathrm{crit}}$ is lower than the critical Mach number M_{crit}, which indicates the initiation of supersonic flow at a velocity less than the Mach speed. Under the same conditions, the pressure correlates the stagnation pressure P_0 to the static pressure P (ambient) as $P_0 = P\left(1+[(\gamma-1)/2]M_\infty{}^2\right)^{\gamma/(\gamma-1)}$, where for AIR the exponent is $\gamma/(\gamma-1) = 3.5$. The Mach number is associated with various context applications of laws of similarity, defining the ratio of forces or parameters in dynamic phenomena by means of a dimensionless number. The laws of similarity correlate the boundary conditions and conditions such as length, time, and mass;

specifically expressed by INERTIA, transform to another similar case, ensuring that the equations remain invariant; acting as "scaling laws" (see Figure M.4).

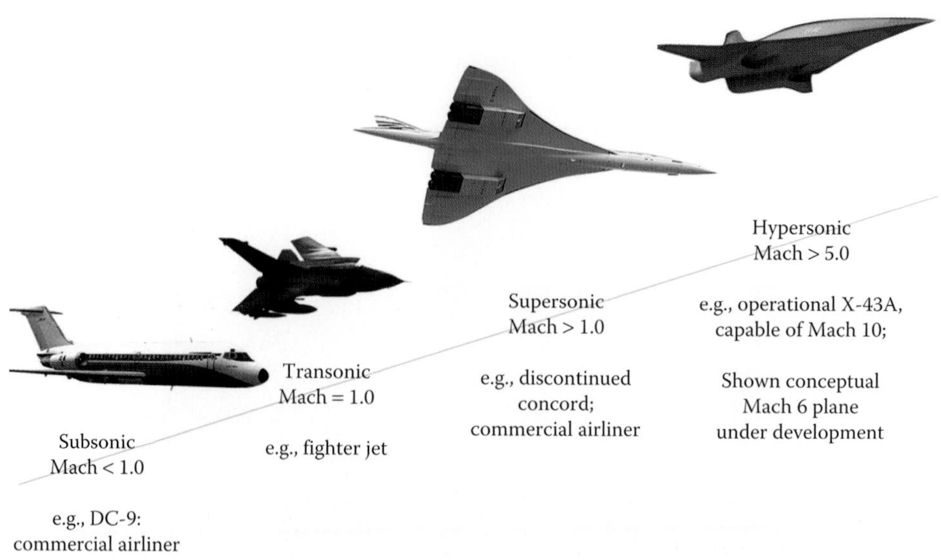

Figure M.4 Illustration of various objects traveling within certain Mach-number ranges.

Mach number, magnetic

[fluid dynamics] *See* MAGNETIC MACH NUMBER.

Mach number, sonic flow

[fluid dynamics] *See* SONIC FLOW.

Mach number, subsonic flow

[fluid dynamics] *See* SUBSONIC FLOW.

Mach number, supersonic flow

[fluid dynamics] *See* SUPERSONIC FLOW.

Mach wave

[fluid dynamics] Pressure WAVE generated by an object exceeding the speed of SOUND (Mac one; "sound BARRIER"), reaching supersonic velocity. The pressure wave results from the fact that the compression density EXPANSION or compression (i.e., FLOW) perturbation initiated by the moving object (sound wave) is overcome by the MOTION of the object, changing the direction of flow by an infinitesimally small ANGLE. The motion in the direction of the emitted sound wave is resulting in a compacting fluid due to VISCOSITY effects. Also referred to as "SONIC BOOM." The Mach wave outlines the pressure OSCILLATION emitted by the moving object (e.g., fighter jet; expanding CAVITATION BUBBLE such as the one that is generated under ultrafast laser irradiation) connecting all crests that are in PHASE, forming a cone with the angle $\mu_{\mathrm{Mach}} = \arcsin(1/Ma) = \arctan(v_n/v_{\mathrm{sonic}})$, the MACH ANGLE, with Ma the MACH NUMBER. The Mach-wave flow direction in the angular expression (θ_{Mach}) is the differential of the Mach angle, and yields the PRESSURE (P) pattern $dP/d\theta_{\mathrm{Mach}} = -(\gamma Ma^2/\sqrt{(Ma^2-)})P$, with γ the compressibility of the FLUID in which the motion takes place. The flow angle is derived from the Euler equation as $d\theta_{Mach} = (v_{sonic}/v^2)dv_n$, with v_{sonic} = constant (the speed of sound), v the propagation velocity of the object introducing the perturbation, and v_n the velocity normal to the WAVEFRONT with respect to the WAVE propagation; assuming ISENTROPIC turbulent flow (see Figure M.5).

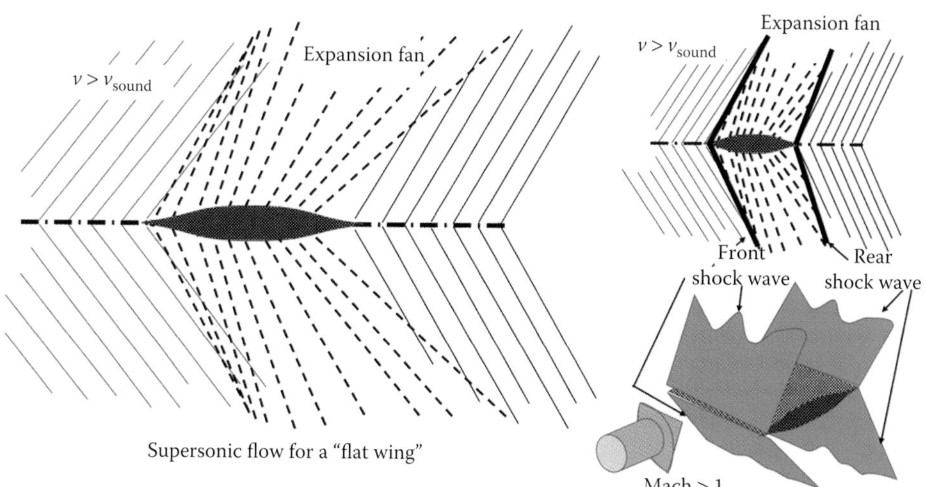

Figure M.5 Mach wave concept: side-view of the calculated flow distribution with respect to "characteristic" Mach waves in the supersonic velocity regime around an aerofoil with lenticular profile. The accumulation of lines representing equal flow-velocity provide an indication of location that will generate shockwaves.

M

Mach's principle

[fluid dynamics, general] Hypothesis pertaining to the fact that all INERTIA in the UNIVERSE is the result of the interaction between all MATTER in the universe, proposed in 1872. This "invisible web" of interaction is also referred to as the "graviton particle," the PARTICLE that ORBITS all mass to provide the gravitational COHESION between objects, stretching out to the interaction between galaxies. Named after ERNST MACH (1838–1916).

Mach–Zehnder interferometer method

[fluid dynamics, optics] Optical investigational mechanism devised by ERNST MACH (1838–1916) and LUDWIG ZEHNDER (1854–1949) based on INTERFERENCE, using a particular "by-pass" loop INTERFEROMETER design that is different from the established MICHELSON INTERFEROMETER of the time. Any interferometer uses a mechanism to split the path of a coherent source, such as a laser, to probe the material properties of a medium in one of the two paths. The difference in PHASE of the electromagnetic WAVE is a direct indication of the RELATIVE index of REFRACTION of the medium under investigation. The Mach–Zehnder interferometer uses transmission for the determination of the DIELECTRIC properties of the medium. In comparison, other interferometers such as the Fabry–Perot and Michelson interferometers use the backscattered or reflected light from a specimen (see Figure M.6).

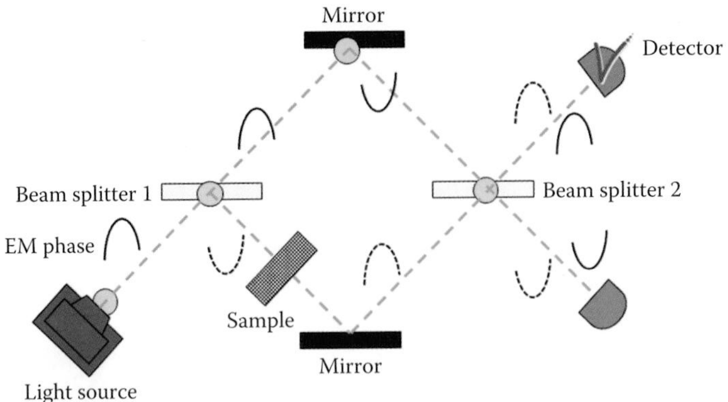

Figure M.6 Mach–Zehnder optical interferometer.

Machine, perpetual-motion

[general, mechanics, thermodynamics] *See* PERPETUAL MOTION.

Machines

[general, mechanics] Mechanical device designed to perform work. Machines are used to make repetitive and heavy activities less strenuous due to the introduction of an external ENERGY source that can perform a set number of ACTIVITY either under electronic or computer control or by means of mechanical gears or hydraulic FLOW. Geared machines use a toothed connection between axles to reduce the applied force to achieve the required force at the location of the desired action by means of torque, the force multiplied by arm length. The torque transfer between gears is directly proportional to the ratio of the teeth on the sprockets applied in the gear. In hydraulic and pneumatic machines, the force is reduced based on PRESSURE (P) applied to an area (A), where the final force ($F = PA$) is inflicted by an area that is larger than the area of fluid on the side where pressure build-up is introduced: $F_1/F_2 = A_1/A_2$, whereas the pressure is equal on both sides based on the COMMUNICATING VESSELS law (see Figure M.7).

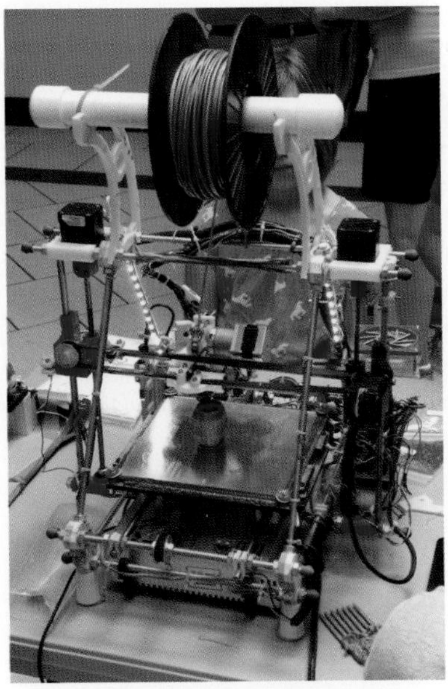

Figure M.7 Rapid prototyping machine constructed from bars and joints and fully functional, once attached to a microprocessor/computer system.

Maclaurin, Colin (1698–1746)

[astrophysics/astronomy, computational, fluid dynamics, mechanics] Mathematician from Scotland. In ALGEBRA, his contribution was a specific series derived from the Taylor series named the Maclaurin series. Additional geometric and calculus-based phenomenological work by Colin Maclaurin was with respect to the shape of rotating bodies presented in 1742 *A Treatise on Fluxions*. In this work, he described the ellipsoidal shape of the EARTH and how this would become more flattened in case the angular momentum increased. The contradictory realization in Maclaurin's work was the description that there will be an optimal configuration. Increasing radius as a result of increasing ANGULAR VELOCITY (ω) will in fact result in bringing the rotation to a halt based on the fact that the ANGULAR MOMENTUM (L) cannot strive for infinity; $L = \omega I$ when the MOMENT OF INERTIA I increases with increasing radius (r), where an infinite radius will define a flat Earth. The optimum will be attained when the earth's radius is approximately 20% greater than its current equatorial radius, with a matching angular velocity of $2.604 \times 10^{-4}\,\pi$ rad/s, 11 times our current rotation, decreasing the day to 2 h and 8 min (see Figure M.8).

Figure M.8 Colin Maclaurin (1698–1746).

Maclaurin ellipsoid

[astrophysics/astronomy, fluid dynamics, mechanics] Based on the *Treatise on Fluxions* published in 1742 by COLIN MACLAURIN (1698–1746), a deformation of a round object will run into an energetic dilemma with an increasing angular velocity. The deformation in a round object while spinning around its axis, where the ellipsoidal shape is assumed to increase its primary radius under a continuously advancing angular velocity, with an inherent increasing angular momentum. There is however an energetic constraint that will limit the increase in angular velocity once the optimal angular momentum has been exceeded, from where the ellipsoid will decrease in angular velocity, while the radius would continue to increase. The expression for the shape of the ellipsoid is defined as $h = (\cos\theta/\sin^3\theta)\left[\theta\left(1+2\cos^2\theta\right)-3\sin\theta\cos\theta\right]$, $h = \omega^2/2\pi G\rho$ (ρ density; G the gravitational constant; ω the ANGULAR VELOCITY for the rotating PLANET), $\cos\theta = c/a$, $0 < \theta < (\pi/2)$ (see Figure M.9).

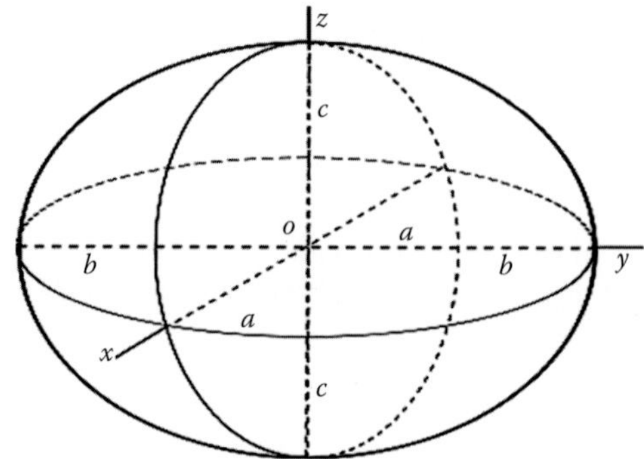

Figure M.9 Maclaurin ellipsoid.

Macromolecules

[biomedical, chemical] Molecules with a high molecular mass. Several POLYMER molecules will qualify as macromolecules, as many biological molecules, including the MOLECULE responsible for radiance VISION (gray scale, in RODS) Rhodopsin: molecular weight 35,200 ± 1200. Other examples are PLASTICS, graphene, carbohydrates, and DNA. The term macromolecule was introduced in the early 1920s by the German chemist Herman Staudinger (1881–1965) for molecules with in excess of 1000 atoms (see Figure M.10).

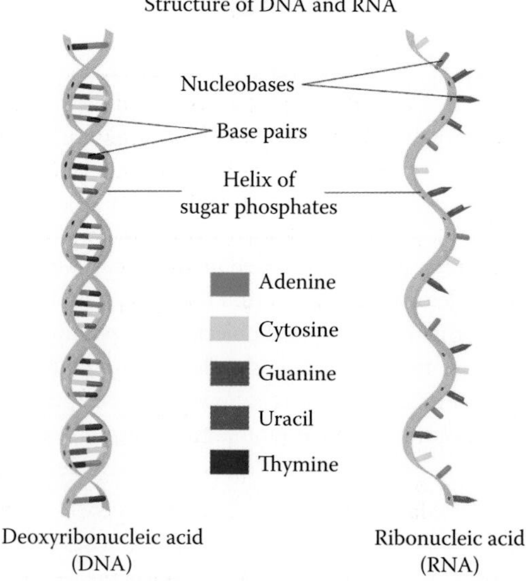

Figure M.10 Graphical representation of the biological DNA macro molecule (Deoxyribonucleic acid), encoding the genetic make-up of biological entities.

Macrophage

[biomedical] Cells that form the first line of attack in infections with the name derived from Greek meaning "large eater." The macrophage performs an active mechanism of encapsulating bacteria or viruses and rendering each individually inactive. The macrophage is approximately three-times the size of a red BLOOD CELL (see Figure M.11). The macrophage is a biological single cell organism that performs active invagination ("consumption" through the CELL MEMBRANE). During this process the SURFACE TENSION is locally modified.

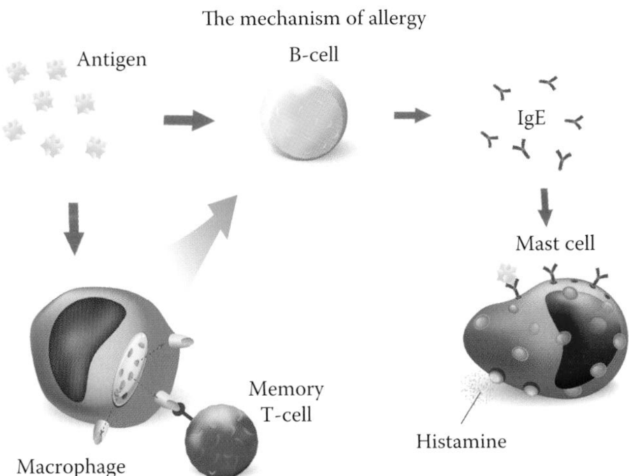

Figure M.11 Macrophage mechanism, in this case as it applies to an immune response.

M

Macroscopic

[biomedical, chemical, general, solid-state] Either directly visible by the naked EYE, requiring no additional visual aids to identify the characteristics; or larger in scale than atomic or molecular level, identifying the mechanical and/or fluid-dynamic features of a constituent.

Magic nucleus

[nuclear, solid-state] The NUCLEAR FORCE holding the NEUTRON and protons together appears to be saturable, leaving distinct numbers of nuclides to have a stable configuration due to the fact that each bond NUCLEON interacts only with a few of its nearest neighbors. Magic nuclei have a certain (magic) number of neutron (N) or protons (Z): 2, 8, 20, 28, 50, 82, and 126, which are more tightly bound than nuclei that do not possess nuclides in magic number format. The nuclear magic number performs a similar function as the atomic number for noble gases; pertaining to atomic PHYSICS. The magic number represents a closed (full) PROTON of the neutron shell (*also see* **BINDING ENERGY** *and* **SHELL MODEL**).

Magnet

[astrophysics/astronomy, biomedical, energy, quantum, solid-state] Device or object with two POLES that form MAGNETIC FIELD lines connecting from one "positive" pole to a "negative" pole. The magnetic mechanism of action is the result of molecular-sized eddy currents that generate a magnetic field as described by AMPÈRE'S LAW, either molecular- sized eddy currents or larger MACROSCOPIC currents in well-defined conductors. A magnet by definition can only have two balanced poles (i.e., both poles are equally strong to ensure that all magnetic field lines are closed), whereas electric field lines can be produced from a single charge concentration. There are three classes of magnets: (1) permanent magnets, (2) electromagnets (e.g., solenoids), and (3) temporary magnets. A special class of magnet is the QUANTUM MAGNET. Permanent magnets have a constant magnetic field over a finite life-time, which may be extensive in duration. The

EARTH has a magnetic field and is classified as a PERMANENT MAGNET, other permanent magnets are ferromagnetic metallic structures as well as ores. Permanent magnets can lose the magnetic attribute resulting from exposure to high temperatures (random vibrational MOTION will disrupt the alignment of the individual magnetic fields generated by the localized eddy currents), mechanical shock (mechanical vibrations, will miss-align the eddy currents in the medium) or exposure to another external magnetic field. Electromagnets derive the magnetic field from a current applied to a conductive circuit that forms the magnetic field only when the current is flowing. One powerful example of electromagnets is the SOLENOID. Electromagnets are for instance used in MEDICINE for MAGNETIC RESONANCE IMAGING (MRI) as well as in electron microscopes for beam-steering next to MAGNETIC LEVITATION for transportation purposes. In consumer applications, magnets are used for door-closer (both permanent magnets [passive] and electromagnets [active]) as well as in compass for directional orientation. Temporary magnets are forming magnetic capabilities based on the confluence of several phenomena that all need to be present at the same time, and will disappear voluntarily as well. A relatively new class of permanent magnets is the "rare-earth magnet," identified by the relatively high magnetic field strength per unit mass. The rare-earth ELEMENTS can be magnetized because their four "f" electron orbitals (as described in the BOHR ATOMIC MODEL) are not filled. The orbitals are the subpart of the shell that in turn is the subpart of the shells. Shells are grouped and named as follows: K, L, M, N, O, P, and Q. The subshells are named as s, p, d, f, and g. In the Bohr atomic model, the f shell may contain a total of 7 pairs of electrons, 14 in total, each with spins pointing in one direction, in accordance with HUNDS' RULE. Having these electrons aligned gives rise to stronger magnetic fields. Rare-earth magnets are made from rare-earth elements, which entails primarily costly resources, not directly occurring in small quantities, rather only obtainable or produced in small quantities (e.g., Nd-Fe-B and Sm-Co). Typically these are compounds or composites that have IRON (Fe) as part of the matrix.

Magnetic

[astrophysics/astronomy, energy, nuclear, solid-state] The phenomenon and condition of possessing MAGNETIC FIELD lines, more specifically, being a MAGNET. (*see* MAGNETIC FIELD) (see Figure M.12).

Figure M.12 Magnet used in scrap yard (i.e., electromagnet), hauling junk metal.

Magnetic axis

[electromagnetism, geophysics] The axis connecting the earth's MAGNETIC NORTH POLE to the MAGNETIC SOUTH POLE. This is not the same axis that connects the GEOGRAPHIC NORTH pole to the GEOGRAPHIC SOUTH pole. The magnetic axis is not fixed, and has switched 180° several times over the past millions of years. Based on geological findings, there is evidence suggesting that the NORTH and south poles may have totally switched positions more than 65 times over the past 600 million years. See PALEOMAGNETISM *and* POLES (see Figure M.13).

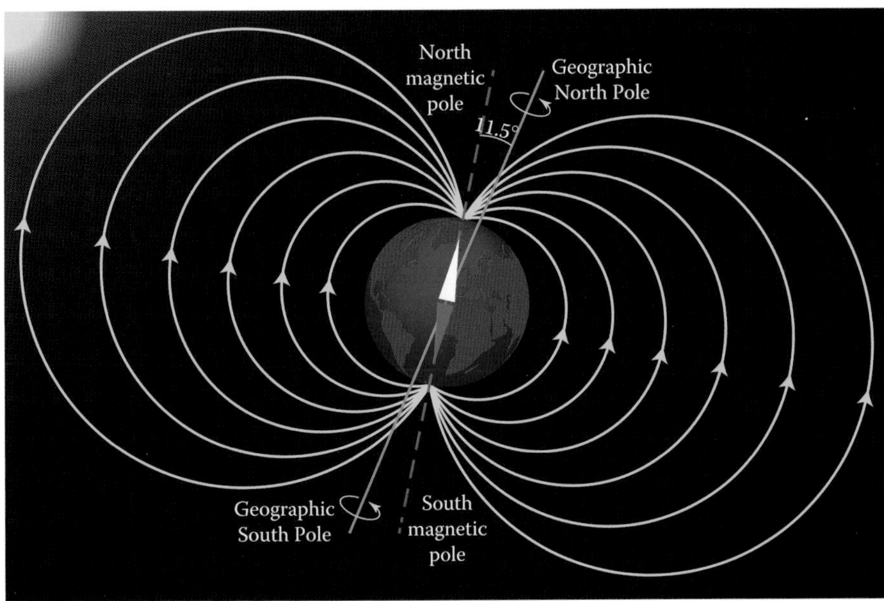

Figure M.13 Magnetic axis versus the geographic axis of the Earth.

Magnetic buoyancy

[astrophysics/astronomy, energy, geophysics] Due to a gradient in magnetic flux-tubes in the solar structure, the MAGNETIC FIELD at the solar surface will be smaller than on the interior, as will be the associated magnetic pressure. Based on the application of the GAS LAW, the density will be less inside the FLUX tube than in the main volume of the Sun. The internal magnetic field can make portions of compressible FLUID less dense than its surroundings, resulting in an upward FLOW under the influence of GRAVITY, the denser "heavier" medium surrounding the less dens medium is pushed out by gravitational buoyance. This mass imbalance creates a hydrostatic pressure with resulting flux tubes, providing the mechanism of action for eruptions resulting from magnetic buoyancy (e.g., solar flare) (see Figure M.14).

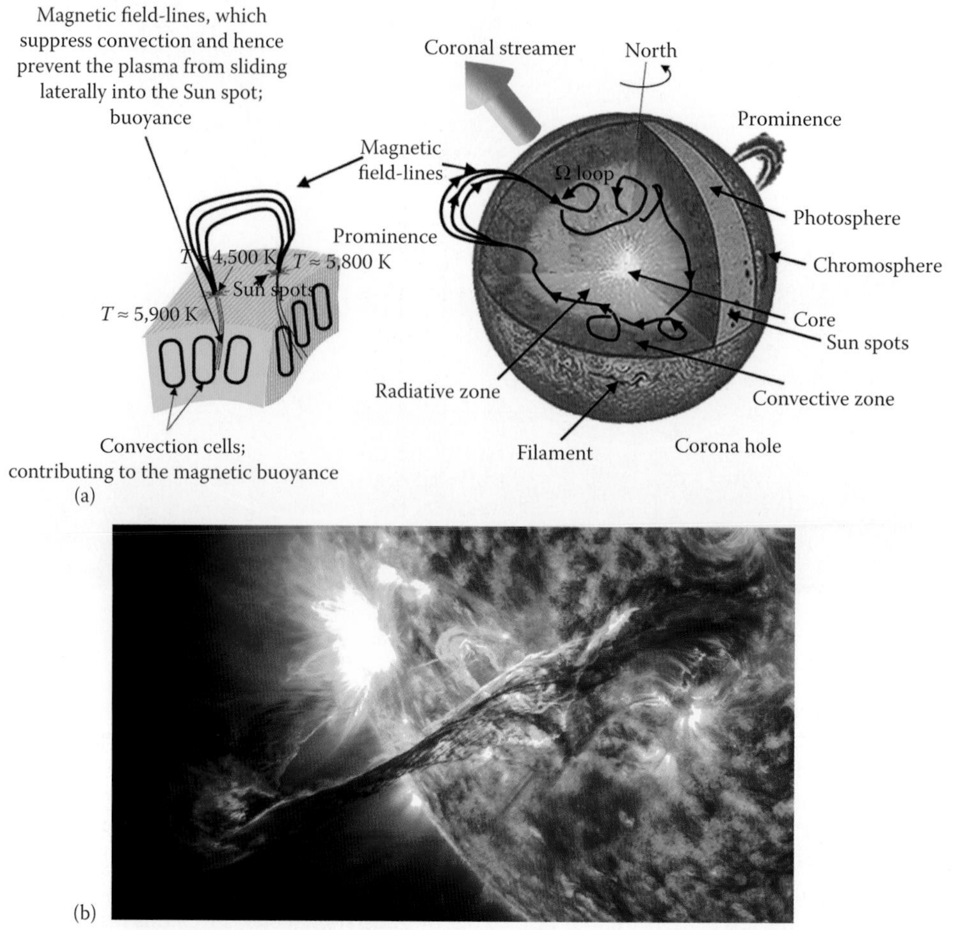

Figure M.14 (a) Magnetic buoyancy in the plasma layers within the sun's volume and (b) solar flare.

Magnetic cooling

[atomic, nuclear] At extremely low temperatures (especially below $T = 1\,K$), it becomes difficult to decrease the temperature of a medium by ordinary means. The use of adiabatic magnetization has been successful for both paramagnetic salts and nuclear cooling, introduced by the chemist William Francis Giauque (1895–1982) from the United States in 1933 for salts, and by means of NUCLEAR MAGNETIC MOMENT in 1955 for cooling of the atomic core by the physicist Nicholas Kurti (1908–1998) from Hungary and by PETER DEBYE (1884–1966) from the Netherlands. The phenomenon was however observed prior to this in 1917 by the physicist Pierre-Ernest Weiss (1865–1940) from France, and the physicist A. Piccard (1884–1962) from Switzerland in 1917. For salts, the ENTROPY (S) can be controlled by an externally applied magnetic field (B) based on the TOTAL ANGULAR MOMENTUM (with quantum number J) as $S = R\ln(2J+1)$, with $R = 8.3144621(75)\ \mathrm{J/Kmol}$ the universal GAS constant. Similarly, for the NUCLEUS, the NUCLEAR ANGULAR MOMENTUM is I, with entropy $S = R\ln(2I+1) - (1/2)\Lambda(B/T)$, where Λ is the Curie constant. For the nuclear cooling, the temperature reduction, starting at an initial temperature $T_i \propto mK$ (specifically $T_i < 20\,mK$) under ADIABATIC DEMAGNETIZATION by means of ISENTROPIC reduction of the applied MAGNETIC FIELD from B_i to B_f, yields: $T_f = T_i/B_i\sqrt{(B_f^{\,2} + b_m^{\,2})}$, with b_m the internal magnetic field of the nucleus of the ELEMENT or alloy (e.g., for copper nuclei: $b_m = 0.3\,mT$). Another form of magnetic cooling that applies to the free electrons in a CONDUCTOR (with temperature T_e), with respect to the nuclear SPIN temperature T_n, yields: $T_e/T_n - 1 = \mu_0 \kappa_K [\dot{Q}_e / \Lambda(B^2 + b_m{}^2)]$, where κ_K is the Korringa constant and $\dot{Q}_e$ is the rate of heat exchange due to the freely moving electrons. Additional mechanisms of nuclear cooling by means of magnetic field involve the use of polarized magnetic field, and the change of direction of POLARIZATION with respect to the nuclear alignment, next to cooling in cascaded stages with different DOPING materials for a specific medium (see Figure M.15).

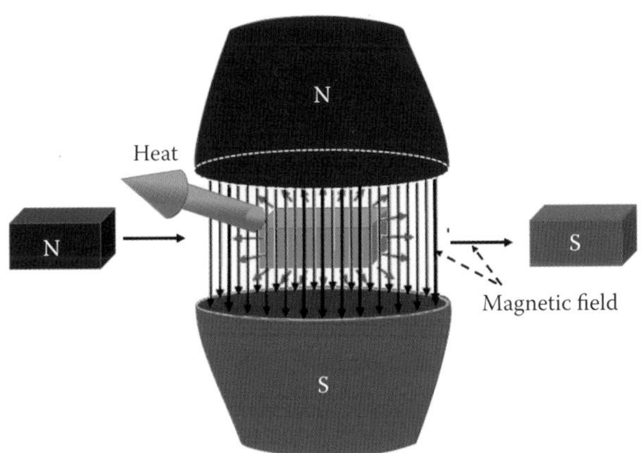

Figure M.15 Outline for the concept of magnetic cooling.

Magnetic dipole

[electromagnetism, general] Two POLES of equal and opposite MAGNITUDE at a fixed DISTANCE. A prime example is the BAR MAGNET. An ATOM can also form a magnetic dipole based on the angular momentum of the electrons, and more specifically when the atomic structure has unpaired electrons. The magnetic dipole is characterized by a magnetic dipole moment. The electrons in the atomic structure act as current loops, however without a fixed orientation (not providing a SOLENOID configuration). In electric circuits, a closed current loop, that generates a MAGNETIC FIELD perpendicular to the plane of the loop in a direction based on the right-hand rule. The current loop will generate a torque ($\vec{\tau}$) when exposed to an external magnetic field ($\vec{B}$) expressed as $\vec{\tau} = \overrightarrow{M_{\text{current}}} \times \vec{B}$, where $\overrightarrow{M_{\text{current}}}$ is the magnetic dipole moment of the current loop (see Figure M.16).

Figure M.16 Magnetic dipole: Earth with the central magnetic portrayed as a bar magnet; magnetic field lines encapsulating Earth in equimagnetic concentric toroidal shells. *Note:* the earth's magnetic north pole is on the geographic south side.

Magnetic dipole moment ($\overrightarrow{M_{current}}$)

[general] The potential of a current loop to express itself with a torque, defined as $\overrightarrow{M_{current}} = NIA\vec{n}$ where I is the current in the loop, N is the number of loops in the device carrying the current, A is the area outlined by the loop, and $\vec{n}$ is a unit vector in the direction perpendicular to the plane of the loop; the direction can be found by applying the right-hand rule.

Magnetic field

[biomedical, electromagnetism, geophysics] {use: imaging (MRI), guidance (compass), actuation}—An electric current generates a magnetic field according to AMPERE'S LAW: $\mathbf{B} = \mu_0(I/2\pi r)$, with μ_0 the magnetic permeability of the medium, and r the DISTANCE to the current. The magnetic field direction can be derived using the "right-hand rule," where the fist of the right hand illustrates the current in the direction of the thumb and the fingers the direction of the produced magnetic field. The direction of the magnetic field lines is by convention from the *north* to the *south* pole, and magnetic field lines are always closed, which means they will in certain cases pass through the device generating the magnetic field. For a coil, the magnetic field strength is generated by a loop current and is $\mathbf{B} = N\mu_0(I/2r)$, with N the number of coil revolutions. The magnetic field lines for a coil are shown in the figure. Similarly the EARTH has a magnetic field that is generated by the FLUID core, which is FERROELECTRIC. The geological North Pole of the Earth is actually the pool indicated by the north pole of a compass MAGNET, and is as such truly a MAGNETIC SOUTH POLE. The earth's magnetic field is influenced by the SOLAR WIND, which deforms the magnetic field lines as shown in the illustration. The magnetic field lines on a global (close to the surface) level are influenced by geological phenomena and follows patterns as shown by the magnetic field line diagram in the following illustration using data from 1922 as published in "Westphal, W.H., Physik, Ein Lehrbuch für Studierende; Juliu Springer, Berlin 1928." The earth's magnetic field also attracts charged particles, specifically those released from the Sun during a solar flare. The charged particles attracted by the earth's magnetic field are accelerated as they approach the pools and accelerating charges produce ELECTROMAGNETIC RADIATION, which is visible by the "NORTHERN LIGHTS" or AURORA BOREALIS as well as the AURORA AUSTRALIS ("Southern Lights"). Magnetic field can also be used for magnetic imaging when modulated by a RADIO-FREQUENCY (RF) pattern as in MAGNETIC RESONANCE IMAGING: MRI and fMRI. Another application of magnetic field attraction is in MOTION control, such as a VOICE COIL in a loud SPEAKER. Animals also use magnetic fields to orient themselves and locate prey as outlined in ELECTRORECEPTION (see Figure M.17).

(a)

Figure M.17 (a) Close-up of ferromagnetic fluid flowing between two adjacent magnets under the influence of the magnetic field-lines, as portrayed by the fluidic spikes. *(Continued)*

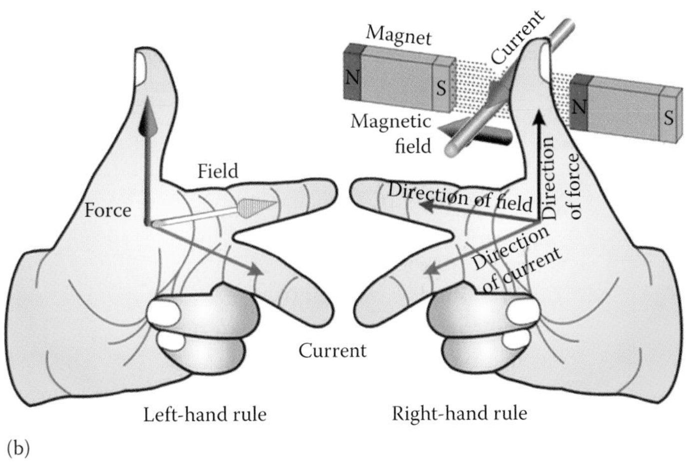

Figure M.17 (Continued) (b) Representation of the force relationship to the magnetic field using the right-hand rule, respectively, the left-hand rule.

Magnetic flowmeter

[biomedical, fluid dynamics] Flow of conductive media or charged particles will induce an electromotive force when exposed to an external MAGNETIC FIELD, hence allowing for noninvasive FLOW rate determination. The voltage generated is proportional to the MAGNITUDE of the magnetic field, the average flow rate, the density of the FLUID flow, as well as the length of the conducting medium flow tube. The measurement of the average flow velocity is based on the FARADAY LAW for electromagnetic induction. Magnetic flowmeters are used in fixed positions on conduits as well as in the format of a clamp-on for temporary flow verification. In medical applications, this type of flowmeter is used to measure the BLOOD flow locally in surgically exposed vessels for diagnostic purposes (see Figure M.18).

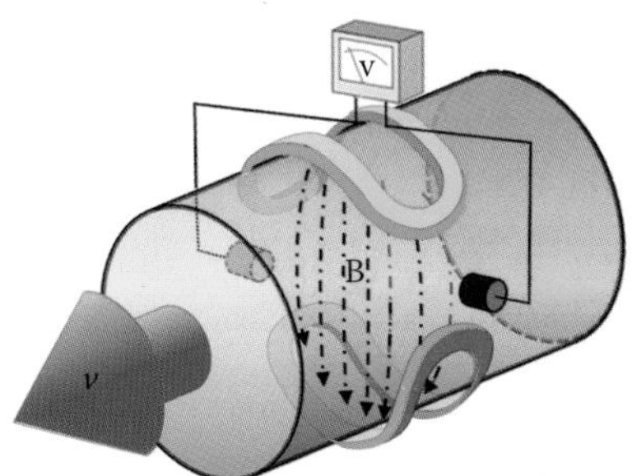

Figure M.18 Magnetic flowmeter principle, using the perceived flow of charges represented as a current.

Magnetic flux (Φ_M)

[general] The magnetic field-line density for a MAGNETIC FIELD ($\vec{B}$) taken perpendicular to an area $\vec{A}$ as $\Phi_M = \vec{B} \cdot \vec{A} = |\vec{B}||\vec{A}|\cos\theta$. The units for magnetic flux are tesla per square meter, which is weber (in honor of a magnetic pioneer from Germany: WILHELM EDUARD WEBER [1804–1891]) $1\,(T/m^2) = 1\,Wb$.

Magnetic force (F_M)

[general] The force exerted on charged particles by a MAGNETIC FIELD ($\vec{B}$) treats the moving particles with charge q and velocity $\vec{v}$ as a current under ANGLE θ with the applied field: $F_M = q\vec{v} \times \vec{B}$. The direction of the force follows the "right-hand rule." For a confined current ($\vec{I}$) in a wire with length ℓ, the force becomes:

$F_M = \ell \vec{I} \times \vec{B}$. This is the force that provides the mechanism-of-action for the formation of the AURORA BOREALIS, the charge stream emitted from the Sun under the earth's magnetic field (*also see* **LORENTZ FORCE** *and* **AMPÈRE'S LAW**).

Magnetic levitation

[electromagnetism, mechanics] Several versions are available, but the main principle remains the induction of a current in coils mounted in a wagon that produces an inherent MAGNETIC FIELD that is opposite to the inducting magnetic field applied from the outside, resulting in repulsion. The induction is based on the FARADAY LAW (described by the English physicist MICHAEL FARADAY [1791–1867] in 1831) and LENZ'S LAW (as introduced by the Russian/Baltic/German physicist HEINRICH FRIEDRICH EMIL LENZ [1804–1865]). The external magnetic field is generated by means of coils mounted in a track that supports the wagon, the LEVITATION coils. The coils in the wagon are ideally superconductors to minimize the resistive loss of current. The PROPULSION of the wagon is achieved by a second set of coils, in a separate location, such as the sides of the track. The propulsion coils are energized in a WAVE pattern along the length of the track, creating a temporal magnetic gradient, providing the magnetic force to move the wagon in the direction of the gradient. The wagon will "float" under the magnetic field repulsion, providing conditions of minimal FRICTION, apart from the AIR resistance during movement. As a fail-safe, there are wheels mounted underneath the wagon in cases when there is no external magnetic field (also found as maglev) (see Figure M.19).

Figure M.19 The concept of magnetic levitation applied to train transport.

Magnetic Mach number

[electromagnetism, fluid dynamics] In magneto-hydrodynamics, the forces are distributed based on origin, when the Lorentz forces are relatively equivalent to the inertial forces, this results in a relative equilibrium between the magnetic ENERGY and the kinetic energy. The LORENTZ FORCE (F_L) resulting from an external MAGNETIC FIELD ($\vec{B}$) $F_L = \vec{j} \times \vec{B}$, where $\vec{j} = \text{curl}\left(\vec{B}/\mu^*\right)$ is the associated current density, with μ^* the DIELECTRIC permeability. The inertial force (F_i) density is represented by the fluid DENSITY (ρ) and the velocity ($\vec{u}$) vector distribution described as $F_i = \rho\vec{u} \cdot \nabla\vec{u}$. The equilibrium in forces yields a Magnetic Mach number of approximately 1: ${A_{\text{Mach}}}^2 = [((1/2)\rho u^2)/(B^2/2\mu^*)] \sim 1$. This is sometimes also referred to as the ALFVÉN NUMBER.

Magnetic materials, permeability of

[general] Material property that is representative of the MAGNETIC behavior of the medium. The magnetic permeability of VACUUM has been established as $\mu_0 = 4\pi \times 10^{-7}\ H/m$, where the magnetic permeability of a medium can be referenced in relation to the permeability of vacuum by means of the RELATIVE PERMEABILITY $(0 \leq \mu_r \leq 1)$ or as its own permeability $\mu_{\text{material}} = \mu_r\mu_0$. Ferromagnetic media generally have a relative permeability greater than 1, AIR and water can be described by $\mu_r \cong 1$ (deviation in the five decimal position or less), while for diamagnetic materials $\mu_r < 1$; $\mu_{\text{material}} < \mu_0$. For ferromagnetic materials, the magnetic permeability may not be constant, rather be a function of the applied MAGNETIC FIELD as well as a function of temperature.

Magnetic moment (μ_{mag})

[general, nuclear] The moment (compare with torque [τ] from mechanical force [F] applied over an arm attached to a hinge point with length [ℓ]: $\tau = Fd$) resulting from a magnetization $(\overrightarrow{m_{\text{mag}}})$ that is induced by a current loop $(\vec{J})$ in a volume of medium (dV) expressed as $d\mu_{\text{mag}} = \overrightarrow{m_{\text{mag}}}dV = (1/c)\vec{J}d\vec{S}$, where c is the speed of light and $d\vec{S}$ is the vector normal to the surface of the volume ELEMENT. The MAGNITUDE of the magnetic moment is $\mu_{\text{mag}} = (-e/c)(v/2\pi r)\left(\pi r^2\right)$, where e is the electron charge in Coulomb, $c = 2.99792458 \times 10^8$ m/s (the speed of light), and r is the radius of the orbit of an electron revolving with speed v. Alternatively $\overrightarrow{\mu_{\text{mag}}} = -g_e\beta_m\vec{s}$, where $g_e = 2.0023...$ the Landé facor, the Bohr magnetron $\beta_m = \hbar|e|/2m_e$ ($m_e = 9.10939 \times 10^{-31}$ kg the electron mass), and the spin $\vec{s} = \hbar s$ (in this case specifically for an electron with the SPIN quantum number s and where $\hbar = h/2\pi$, which is PLANCK'S CONSTANT $h = 6.626 \times 10^{-34}$ J/Hz divided by 2π). The electron will also have an orbital angular moment $\gamma_J = \mu_{\text{mag}}/\hbar J$, with J an integer. The current loop can be isolated in a small volume with neighboring volumes having a random orientation of the respective magnetization. While exposed to an external MAGNETIC FIELD or other influence, they may all line up to make the entire object a MAGNET (e.g., IRON). Object and media that are paramagnetic cannot be fully magnetized, only a fraction of the internal magnetic moments will line up under an applied filed, increasing the total magnetic field strength, but marginally. Substances that are ferromagnetic can be magnetized (made to act as a magnet), and this is the result of the fact that the substance has a MAGNETIC SUSCEPTIBILITY. Although a diamagnetic medium has no internal MAGNETIC DIPOLE moment, it will have an effective magnetic field of its own in the opposite direction of an applied external magnetic field. Magnetic moments result from various currents such as orbital electrons, spin, and deuterons as well as ions to name a few.

Magnetic monopole

[general] The theoretical hold-out in the Gauss' law for MAGNETISM that relies on the fact that MAGNETIC FIELD lines have a starting point and an end point. In case the magnetic monopole would exist (so far no theoretical or experimental indication to the contrary is provided), the integral in Gauss' law will not render zero, right now it still holds for the integral over a surface (S) with surface area ELEMENTS da and normal vector $\vec{n}$ enclosing a magnetic field (B): $\oint_S \vec{B} \cdot \vec{n}da = 0$.

Magnetic north pole

[astrophysics/astronomy, general, geophysics] The pole on the earth's globe where the MAGNETIC FIELD lines originate, located near the GEOGRAPHIC SOUTH Pole. The magnetic field lines terminate at the magnetic south

M

pole, from where the magnetic field continues through the EARTH as a magnetic CONDUCTOR to re-emerge on the magnetic north pole, since per definition magnetic field lines form closed loops (see Figure M.20).

Figure M.20 Ions emitted from solar flares drawn in by the magnetic field pointing into the "North Pole" (*Note:* the geographic North Pole is the magnetic south pole). The resulting effect is expressed by the magnetic force accelerating the ions, hence generating the emission of electromagnetic radiation (i.e., the critical aspect of accelerated charge).

Magnetic poles

[general, geophysics] The locations on a MAGNETIC medium from where the MAGNETIC FIELD lines originate, respectively, are terminated, and continue through the material to form a closed loop. Solid state magnets are available in various shapes and sizes, most familiar shapes are the BAR MAGNET, horse-shoe magnet next to the solenoid ELECTROMAGNET. The EARTH acts as a bar magnet with a NORTH and south pole, providing a three-dimensional magnetic field loop. The magnetic field of the Earth is presumably the result of the rotational MOTION of the IRON inner core, acting as a current loop, as defined by AMPÈRE'S LAW, in close similarity to a SOLENOID. The POLES of the Earth's magnetic field are not fixed and continue to "wander." The earth's magnetic field has changed orientation by 180° many times in the history of the Earth, the last time approximately 780,000 years ago. The magnetic field lines in the Earth's ATMOSPHERE do not follow perfectly straight lines due to influences from magnetic media, such as granite, large bodies of water, and geographical topography (mountain ridges, valleys). A compass will align with the local magnetic field lines, hence providing a mechanism for identification of the locations of the magnetic poles. A compass indicating the magnetic poles can be used for orientation purposes and planning a travel route, in comparison to the "global positioning system" that uses a chain of geo-synchronous orbit satellites to provide triangulation (see Figure M.21).

Figure M.21 Magnetic poles of bar magnets and horse-shoe magnet, "north" attracting "south."

Magnetic quantum number

[nuclear] *See* QUANTUM NUMBER.

Magnetic resonance

[atomic, nuclear] Protons have a MAGNETIC moment, similar to a BAR MAGNET, that can be guided by an external MAGNETIC FIELD. A magnetic moment will precess around the externally applied continuous (steady-state) magnetic field with a frequency that is proportional to the magnetic field strength: the Larmor frequency. When applying an additional oscillating magnetic field that has an orientation perpendicular to the steady-state magnetic field, the magnetic moment can be "persuaded" to flip direction between SPIN states ("up" or "down") when the OSCILLATION of the external field matches the LARMOR PRECESSION frequency. This principle specifically applies to a very simple magnetic moment: the proton. The proton's magnetic orientation resonance ENERGY is emitted in the form of ELECTROMAGNETIC RADIATION in the RF spectrum. The RF spectrum can be detected externally, by applying a gradient in the magnetic field the Larmor frequency for the protons will be location specific, with associated differences in RESONANCE conditions. In this manner, the location specific magnetic resonance can be used for three-dimensional location specific SIGNAL collection. The use of several detectors will provide the line of intersect for each instantaneous RF signal, hence yielding the origin of the PROTON spin. The process of reconstruction based on the multiple lines of intersect and location specific magnetic field strength allows for three-dimensional imaging.

This magnetic resonance process is used apropos in magnetic resonance imaging (MRI), also referred to as nuclear magnetic resonance imaging (NMR imaging) (see Figure M.22).

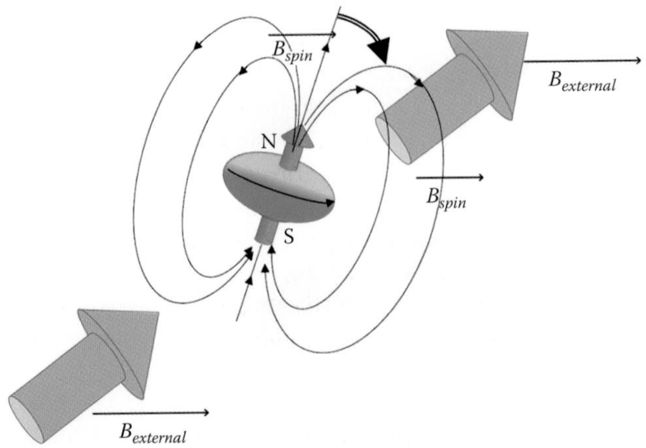

Figure M.22 A charged particle with nonzero spin will act as a magnet that will align with an external applied magnetic field, in particular it will continuously align with a changing external magnetic field and will be in sync with the frequency of the applied changing field, in resonance.

Magnetic resonance imaging (MRI)

[biomedical, electromagnetism, general, nuclear, quantum] Tomographic mechanism of action that generates images of imbedded physical and chemical properties by measuring the NUCLEAR MAGNETIC RESONANCE (NMR) signal emitted by individual and specific atomic and molecular structures with certain ENERGY configurations. The principle of NMR was first described in 1946 by FELIX BLOCH (1905–1983) and EDWARD MILLS PURCELL (1912–1997). It was not until 1973 that MR imaging was made feasible by Paul C. Lauterbur (1929–2007) and Sir Peter Mansfield (1933–), resulting in the implementation of the first clinical scanners by the beginning of the 1980s. The mechanism of action for MRI relies on nuclear excitation and subsequent electromagnetic emission of an inhomogeneous body of material, either biological or solid state by means of irradiation with electromagnetic waves in the range of RF. MRI is most known for its applications in MEDICINE for diagnostic screening. The photonic energy of the ELECTROMAGNETIC RADIATION is much less than what is used in ionizing radiation, such as X-RAY imaging and computed TOMOGRAPHY. The NMR phenomenon is fundamentally quantum PHYSICS. The phenomenon relies on the fact that all atomic nuclei possess an angular momentum with associated respective spins. Nuclei that have an odd number of protons, neutrons, or both have a discrete angular momentum. Hydrogen is one ELEMENT with those properties and is available in abundance in the biological entities such as the HUMAN BODY. The nuclear SPIN can be manipulated as if it were a tiny MAGNET due to the fact that a spinning charged PARTICLE creates an ELECTROMAGNETIC FIELD. When no external MAGNETIC FIELD is applied, the spins are oriented in a random fashion, hence canceling each other, with subsequent zero net magnetization. When an external magnetic field (B_0) is applied, the respective nuclear spins align themselves in the direction of the applied field as a function of time. Slightly more than half the spins align parallel to the direction of B_0 (the z-direction), while the remaining align in the opposite direction (down or antiparallel). The resulting net magnetization (M) points in the B_0 direction (longitudinal direction). The MR imaging concept relies on the fact that the local induced magnetic orientation will recoil to the base state once the external magnetic field is removed, or changes direction. Faraday's law mandates that a changing magnetic field induces an electric current that takes place in the detection mechanism in a receiver coil oriented perpendicular to the MAGNETIC field. The magnetization vector (M) is designed to oscillate and under external coercion will tip within the transverse xy plane. The spin axis will form PRECESSION around the z-axis with the Larmor frequency ω_{Larmor}, which is specific to the medium and the applied field as $\omega_{\mathrm{Larmor}} = \gamma B$, where γ is the GYROMAGNETIC RATIO and B is the magnetic field strength. Thus, the transverse magnetization component M_{xy} induces a SIGNAL in the receiver coil.

RF excitation

The magnetization M is tipped into the transverse plane using an RF excitation pulse, which generates an external weak MAGNETIC FIELD (B_1) perpendicular to M, for example, in the x-direction. It should be noted that the B_1 field is not stationary; it is rotating in the xy plane around the z-axis with a Larmor frequency, ω_0, in the same direction as SPIN precession, which creates the RESONANCE condition. During the period of time when B_1 is on, M lies under the influence of two magnetic fields: a strong stationary field (B_0) in the z-direction and a weak rotating field (B_1) in the xy plane orthogonal to B_0. This results in M simultaneously precesses quickly around the z-direction with a Larmor frequency ω_0, and slowly around the x-direction with a frequency ω_1, where $\omega_0 = \gamma B_0$, and $\omega_1 = \gamma B_1$. This results in a spiral MOTION of M from the z-direction toward the xy plane. Because $\omega_1 \ll \omega_0$, M ends up tipped toward the xy plane with flip ANGLE depending on the RF pulse strength and duration. Excitation RF pulses are referred to with the angle by which the magnetization vector is tipped: for example a 45° RF pulse tips the magnetization vector half way into the transverse plane, while a 90° RF pulse tips the magnetization vector all the way into the transverse plane.

Bloch Equation

The Bloch equation describes the magnetization vector behavior under the NMR phenomenon: $dM/dt = M \times \gamma B$, where M = magnetization vector, B = magnetic field, t = time, and γ is the GYROMAGNETIC RATIO. The operator × (i.e., cross-product) in this case represents vector multiplication (see Figure M.23).

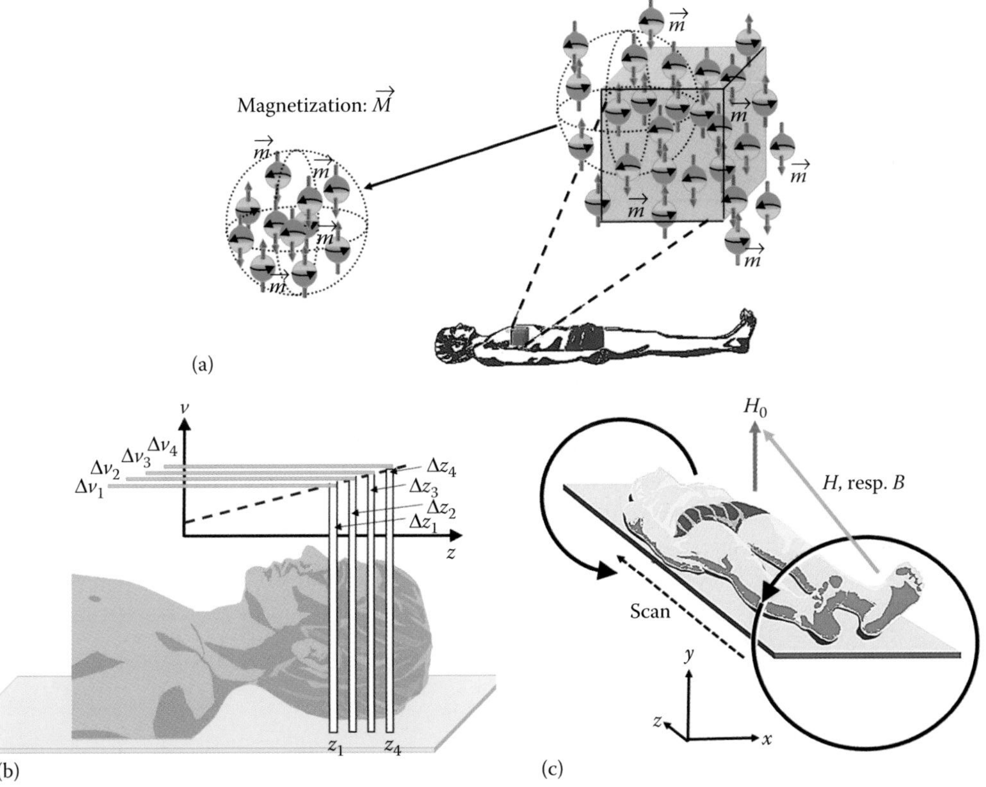

Figure M.23 (a–c) Concepts of magnetic resonance imaging. (Courtesy of Joint Base Langley-Eustis Newport-News, VA, USA.) *(Continued)*

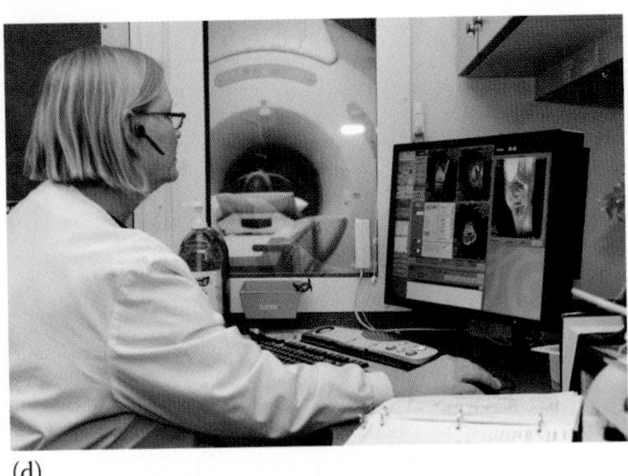
(d)

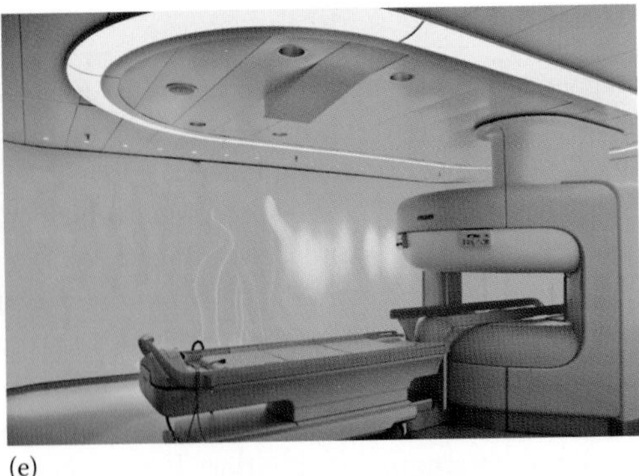
(e)

Figure M.23 (Continued) (d) MRI machine with patient and image reconstruction of magnetic resonance features associated with anatomical structures. (e) Open MRI unit. (Courtesy of Joint Base Langley-Eustis Newport-News, VA, USA.)

Magnetic Reynolds number

[computational, hydrodynamics, magnetism] *See* **REYNOLDS NUMBER, MAGNETIC.**

Magnetic South Pole

[general, geophysics] Physical terminal point for MAGNETIC FIELD lines on the EARTH as a MAGNET, located near the GEOGRAPHIC NORTH pole (northern hemisphere).

M

Magnetic spectrometer

[nuclear] Selective isolation of moving charged particles based on their kinetic ENERGY ($KE = (1/2)mv^2$, based on MASS (m) and velocity (v); using single value charges, the ELECTRIC FIELD (E) based acceleration will yield a uniform velocity potential) when exposed to an external magnetic field that causes the trajectory of the PARTICLE to curve due to the Lorentz force. The force on the CHARGE (q) results in an acceleration that provides a final velocity when the charge emerges from the ANODE of the accelerator potential with acceleration in the direction of the applied gradient in ELECTRIC POTENTIAL (V): $\vec{a} = q\vec{E}/m$. The loss in electric potential energy equates to the gain in kinetic energy as $q(V_2 - V_1) = (1/2)mv_2^2 - (1/2)mv_1^2$, providing the final velocity as a function of mass. The radius of curvature for the path of the moving charged particle exposed to a homogeneous, uniform, steady state MAGNETIC FIELD (B) is expressed by $r = nv/qB$. The terminal location of the particle on a linear sensor array is hence an indication of the mass of the particle. Using this principle, the chemical composition of an unknown material (constructed from a multitude of chemicals) can hence be deciphered, as well as the chemical structure and composition of

specific molecules, next to the analysis of SUBATOMIC PARTICLES in a CYCLOTRON. Also known as mass spectrometer (*see* **BUBBLE CHAMBER** *and* **CLOUD CHAMBER**) (see Figure M.24).

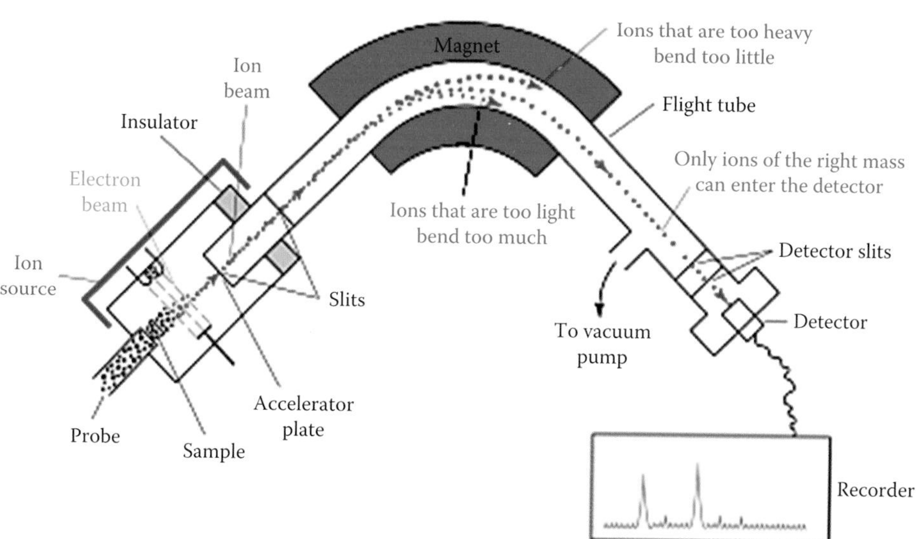

Figure M.24 Magnetic spectrometer, also known as mass spectrometer.

Magnetic susceptibility (χ_{mag})

[atomic, general, nuclear, solid-state] The tendency of individual MAGNETIC DIPOLE moments (μ_{mag}) within a substance to line up with an externally applied MAGNETIC FIELD as thermal agitation (at temperature T) will continue to miss-align the moments, expressed as $\chi_{mag} = \mu_0 N \mu_{mag}{}^2/3kT$, where $\mu_0 = 4\pi \times 10^{-7}$ Tm/A is the DIELECTRIC permeability of VACUUM, N is the number of magnetic dipoles per unit volume and $k = 1.380658 \times 10^{-23}$ J/K is the Boltzmann constant. The principle was described by PAUL LANGEVIN (1872–1946).

Magnetism

[astrophysics/astronomy, energy, general, solid-state] The phenomena created by the MAGNET, more specifically by the MAGNETIC FIELD lines from a magnetic object (*see* **MAGNET**). The concept of magnetic field lines was illustrated in 1269 by Pierre de Maricourt (thirteenth century scientist; often quoted by his friend the English philosopher and friar ROGER BACON [1220–1292]), who shaped a LODESTONE into a sphere and placed IRON splinters on its surface and the METAL slivers aligned themselves with the magnetic field lines running from pole to pole, while at the pole they would stand erect, while the meridian circle would converge at the respective opposing POLES.

Magnetoencephalography (MEG)

[biomedical, imaging] Noninvasive imaging mechanism to study the ACTIVITY of the brain as a function of location in three-dimensional format. DEPOLARIZATION of single nerves creates a MAGNETIC FIELD in a similar fashion to an electric current in a wire (AMPERE'S LAW). The application of state-of-the-art magnetic sensors can detect the emerging magnetic field as a function of location in a tomographic imaging setting using the intersect of lines of detection for multiple sensor units. Magnetic sensors can detect a field strength as small as $1.0 \times 10^{-15}\,T$. Magnetoencephalographic imaging can provide high RESOLUTION details about the stimulated or spontaneous neural activities in the brain. Stimulated activation imaging provides significant details about potential damage to the brain as well as distinguishing from a mismatch in data communications to the brain (e.g., neurological damage to the main neurons leading to the brains such as the optic nerve and the auditory nerve). Generally the MEG imaging technique relies on arrays of SQUIDs (superconducting quantum INTERFERENCE devices) (see Figure M.25).

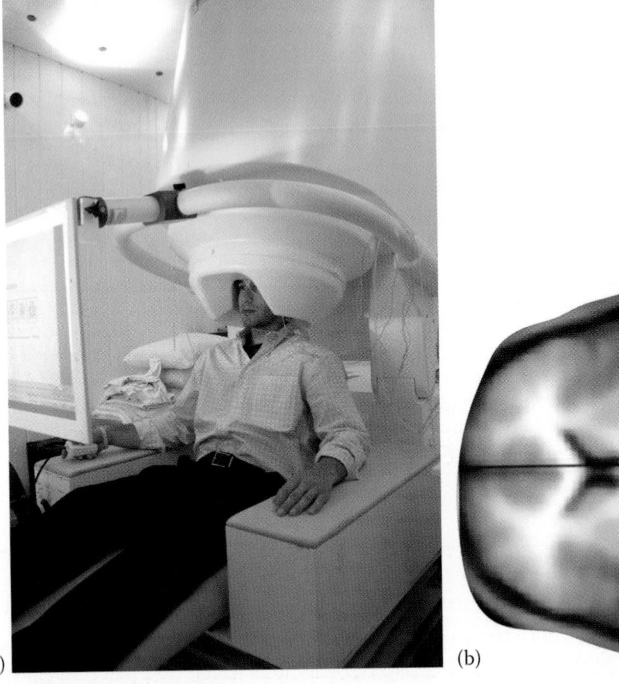

Figure M.25 (a) Magnetoencephalography machine used to image the brain activity. (b) MEG of a person performing mental tasks (frontal lobe activity).

Magnetohydrodynamics

[electromagnetism, general, mechanics] The FLOW of charged particles in any medium, ranging from PLASMA to ionic solutions. Seawater has a substantial electric conductivity due to its SALT content. The conductivity of seawater is $\sigma \cong 3.2\ \mathrm{S/m}$. As a result of AMPÈRE'S LAW and Maxwell's revisions, the flow of electric particles in the earth's MAGNETIC FIELD generates a magnetic field of its own, expressed as $[\partial\vec{B}(r,t)/\partial t] = \nabla \times \left(\vec{u}(r,t) \times \vec{B}(r,t)\right) + \eta\nabla^2\vec{B}(r,t)$, where $\vec{B}(r,t)$ is the FLUX density of the magnetic field, $\vec{u}(r,t)$ is the FLOW velocity of the FLUID, and $\eta \equiv (\mu_0\sigma)^{-1}$ is the magnetic DIFFUSIVITY, with μ_0 the magnetic permeability. One boundary condition follows from the fact that by definition there are no magnetic charges, and $\vec{B}(r,t)$ is solenoidal: $\nabla \cdot \vec{B}(r,t) = 0$. The Swedish electrical engineer and physicist Hannes Olof Gösta Alfvén (1908–1995) has been attributed to be the founder of this particular field of physics (*also see* magnetic Mach number).

Magneton

[atomic, nuclear] Expression for magnetic dipole moment resulting from a spinning spherical particle. This hypothetical spherical particle can be represented either by electrons in an orbit around the nucleus next to the nuclear magnetic moment as an independent phenomenon. The electron magnetic dipole moment, the Bohr Magneton, is expressed as $\mu_B = e\hbar/2m_e c$ where, $\hbar = h/2\pi$ with $h = 6.62606957 \times 10^{-34}$ m^{2}kg/s the Planck's constant, m_e the electron mass, $e = 1.60217657 \times 10^{-19}\,C$ the electron charge, and c the speed of light. The nucleus considered as a "solid" sphere has a nuclear magnetic moment $\mu_N = e\hbar/2m_p c$, where m_p is the proton mass.

Magnetosphere

[energy, geophysics] The earth's magnetic field is inclined with respect to the earth's rotational axis at an angle of approximately 11°. The magnetosphere interacts with the ionic and electromagnetic events and in the ionosphere this will create interference with communication in addition to the occurrence of the aurora events (see Figure M.26).

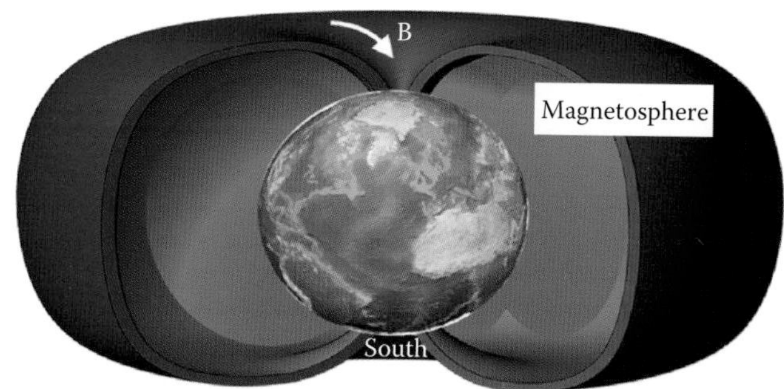

Figure M.26 Illustration of the earth's magnetosphere, and the influence of the sun's magnetic field.

Magnetostriction

[imaging, solid-state] Change in the shape of an oscillating magnet under the influence of an external magnetic field. The magnet's shape change can be orchestrated by rearranging the molecular structure. Magnetic devices however appear to be limited to an upper modulation frequency of 500 kHz. This phenomenon can be applied for general sound generation as well as ultrasound generation.

M

Magnetotactic bacterium

[biomedical, general] Bacteria that use MAGNETISM as a means to guide their path, the bacterial organism contains a chain of magnetite crystals, which create a functional compass needle. The magnetotactic bacteria were discovered in 1975 by Richard P. Blakemore (1950–) (see Figure M.27).

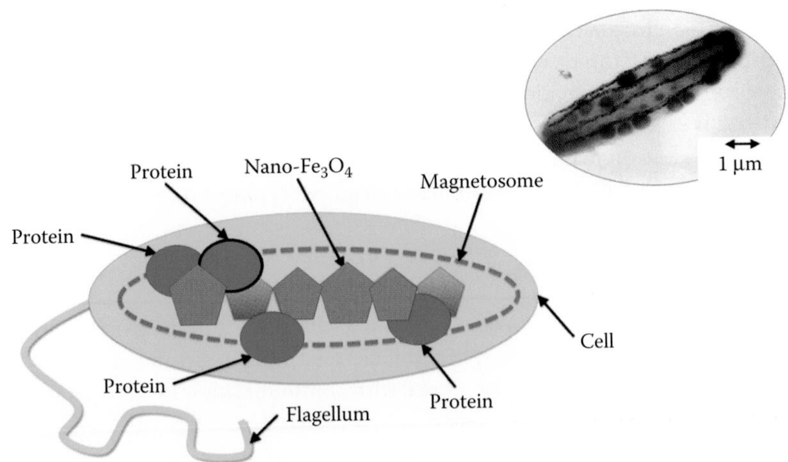

Figure M.27 Configuration of the mechanism-of action for Magnetotactic bacteria. Inset: Magnetotactic bacterium specimen.

Magnification (M_{mag})

[general, optics] The perceived increase (whole integer magnification) or decrease (fractional magnification) in size or details in an IMAGE formed with ELECTROMAGNETIC RADIATION, or electron beam. The EYE forms a real image on the RETINA that is smaller in size than the original object. A magnifying GLASS, microscope, or X-RAY machine forms an image that has a greater spatial resolution than can be observed with the naked eye. Generally, the RESOLUTION or RESOLVING POWER of an imaging system is a direct function of the probing WAVELENGTH (λ), limiting what can be distinguished is at minimum half the wavelength, or more formally the resolving power is defined by the APERTURE (D) of the device as $P = D/1.22\lambda$ (*also see* **RALEIGH CRITERION** *and* **ABBE CONSTANT**). The maximum resolution that is useful in a MICROSCOPE is on the order of $0.1\ \mu\text{m} = 10^{-7}\ \text{m}$ at a magnification of $M_{mag} = 600$ times (although with artificial means $M_{mag} = 2000$ can be made efficient for diagnostic purposes), where the spatial separation of the RODS and CONES forms the limit factor in what can be discriminated to the lower level, next to the wavelength, usually taken on the average of the visible spectrum at $\lambda = 530\ \text{nm}$. An ELECTRON MICROSCOPE uses an image forming mechanism based on the "DE BROGLIE WAVELENGTH" ($\lambda_{deBroglie} = h/p$) that involves electrons that can probe on molecular level and provide an extremely high spatial resolution better than $0.1\ \text{nm} = 10^{-10}\ \text{m}$ with a magnification of the order of $M_{mag} = 10^6$; for instance at 10^5 V acceleration potential, the de Broglie wavelength of the electrons is $\lambda_{deBroglie} = 4\ \text{pm} = 4 \times 10^{-12}\ \text{m}$ (see Figure M.28).

Figure M.28 Example of Magnification, using a magnifying glass.

Magnification, angular

[general] *See* ANGULAR MAGNIFICATION.

Magnitude

[general] Length of vector, NUMERICAL value of parameter/tensor, signal strength, or reactiveness of chemical reaction.

Magnus, Heinrich Gustav (1802–1870)

[computational, fluid dynamics] Scientist and chemist from Germany. Heinrich Magnus provides a significant insight into the phenomenon of LIFT with respect to objects in flight, specifically the deviation from a trajectory for bullets (see Figure M.29).

Figure M.29 Heinrich Gustav Magnus (1802–1870) in 1841.

Magnus effect

[fluid dynamics] Lift force explained by HEINRICH GUSTAV MAGNUS (1802–1870) in 1852. The LIFT applies to finned projectiles (wings may be a consideration, but the Magnus effect applies to vortices) as well as to other objects specifically when a form of rotation or VORTEX is involved (yawing or spinning projectiles), such as a ball or bullet, and also applies to a rotating fan. The lift on a ball for instance is a function of the surface area (configuration, SURFACE ROUGHNESS, and size A), geometry (e.g., GOLF BALL), the inherent velocity (v), the orientation of the ball, as well as the rotation and the density of the FLUID medium (ρ). Magnus hypothesized that lift was derived from nonsymmetrical FLOW separation within the BOUNDARY LAYER of the PROJECTILE. The lift force, using a coefficient of lift (C_L), is defined as $F_L = (1/2)C_L\rho A v^2$. The Magnus effect is distinguishably noticeable for large objects, such as a volleyball being struck during a serve, making the ball float and suddenly visibly lift in an unpredictable trajectory (see Figure M.30).

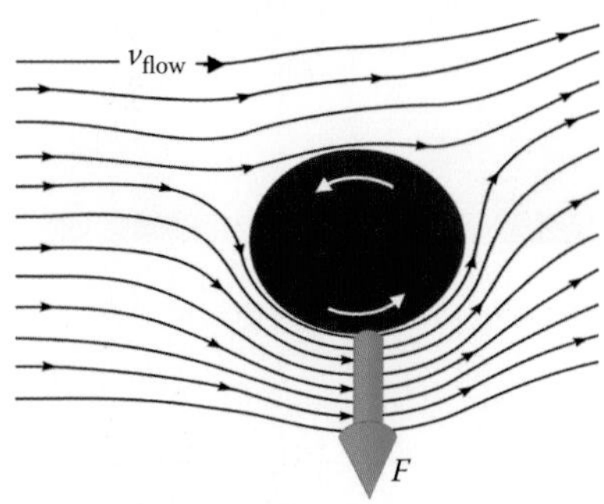

Figure M.30 Representation of the Magnus effect.

Magnus force

[computational, fluid dynamics] Force associated with vortices around a body in a FLOW (*see* **MAGNUS LIFT**).

Magnus lift

[fluid dynamics] "Lifting force" acting on rotating PROJECTILE bodies. A rotating body will provide an increase in pressure where the surface MOTION is in the opposite direction of the FLOW (according to Bernoulli's law) causing disruption of the BOUNDARY LAYER, and lower pressure on the surface area that moves in the same direction as the flow, forming an eddy. The force vector on an object with a boundary layer vortex resulting from external flow conditions is $\overrightarrow{F_{\text{Magnus}}} = \kappa_i \left(v_{\text{vortex},i}, -u_{\text{irrotational},i}\right)$, where $v_{\text{vortex},i}$ is the vortex flow velocity in the ith segment on the surface and $u_{\text{irrotational},i}$ the irrotational velocity resulting from neighboring vortices (derived from the VORTICITY $\overrightarrow{\omega_v(\vec{r},t)} = \nabla \times u(\vec{r},t)$), and κ_i is the VORTEX "strength" of the ith vortex on the surface derived from the BIOT–SAVART LAW. Also known as KUTTA LIFT (see Figure M.31).

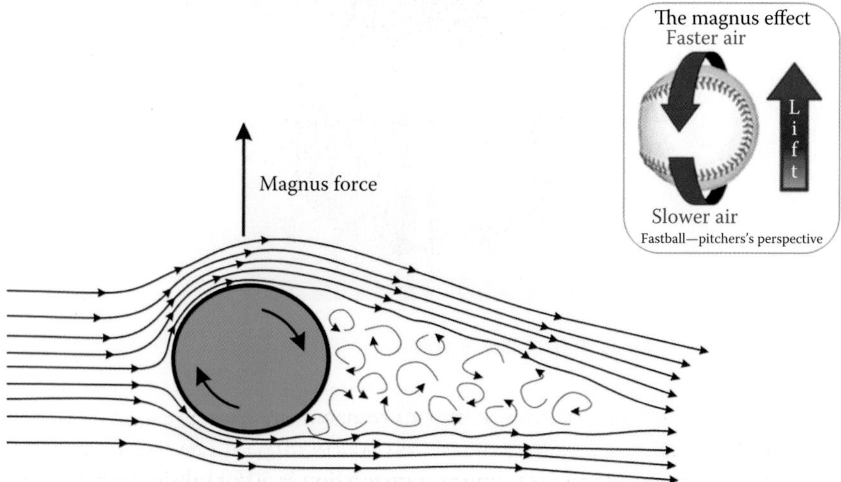

Figure M.31 Illustration of Magnus lift, with insert of the lift of a rotating base-ball, thrown by the pitcher.

Maiman, Theodore Harold (1927–2007)

[optics] American physicist, most known for constructing the first operational laser known, where laser is the acronym for light amplification by STIMULATED EMISSION of radiation. The laser made by Maiman was what is referred to as a ruby laser, made with chromium oxide crystal Cr_2O_3. The invention of the laser is still under dispute between Maiman and GORDON GOULD (1920–2005) (see Figure M.32).

Figure M.32 Theodore Harold Maiman (1927–2007).

Malus, Étienne Louis (1775–1812)

[general] Physicist from France. In 1808, Étienne Malus, an engineer in Napoleon's army, discovered the POLARIZATION OF LIGHT waves. Malus was one of JEAN BAPTISTE JOSEPH FOURIER's (1768–1830) pupils at the Ecole Polytechnique in Paris, France (see Figure M.33).

Figure M.33 Étienne Malus (1775–1812).

Malus's law

[general, optics] The radiance of unpolarized light (Ψ) transmitted through two polarizers on the same optical path with the relative ANGLE of the POLARIZATION direction between the two polarizers Θ expressed as $\Psi = \Psi_0 \cos\Theta$, where the minimum transmission is accomplished when the two polarizers are crossed, with the angle of polarization perpendicular. This was described by ÉTIENNE MALUS (1775–1812) in 1809.

Manhattan project

[atomic, nuclear] Code name for the development of the ATOMIC BOMB headed by Lieutenant General Leslie Richard Groves, Jr. (1896–1970), including the following scientists: NIELS BOHR (1885–1962), JAMES CHADWICK (1891–1974), Otto Frisch (1904–1979), ENRICO FERMI (1901–1954), and RICHARD PHILLIPS FEYNMAN (1918–1988) under the direction of ROBERT OPPENHEIMER (1904–1967) (see Figure M.34).

Figure M.34 Leader of the Manhattan Project: Lieutenant General Leslie Richard Groves, Jr. (1896–1970). (Courtesy of the US Department of Energy.)

Manning, Robert (1816–1897)

[fluid dynamics] Scientist and engineer from Ireland. Manning is known for his contributions to FLOW descriptions in rivers and canals (see Figure M.35).

Figure M.35 Robert Manning (1816–1897).

Manning equation, open channel

[fluid dynamics] Open channel flow description introduced by ROBERT MANNING (1816–1897) in 1889 as an alternative to the Chezy equation. The Manning equation defines the FLOW (Q) as a function of flow area (A), the slope of the bottom of the channel (S_{slope}), as well as the ROUGHNESS of the walls and bottom (defined by the Manning roughness coefficient M_R listed in tables for various configurations), and the flow velocity as v: $Q=(1/M_R)AR_H{}^{2/3}\sqrt{S_{slope}}$, with R_H the hydraulic radius (the ratio of the cross-sectional area of flow to the perimeter of the wetted area, that is, the combined length of all the borders that are touching the LIQUID) (see Figure M.36).

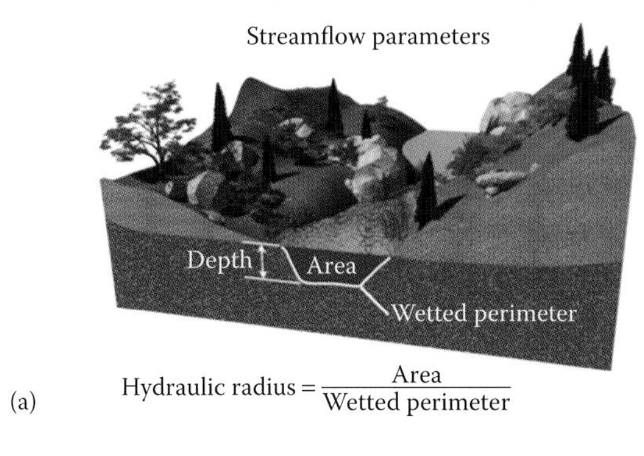

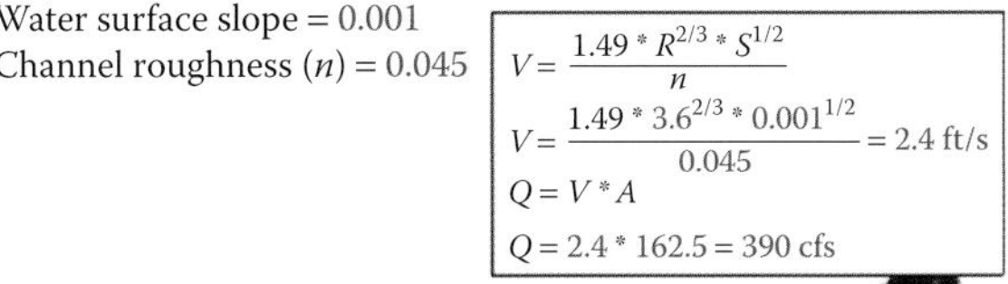

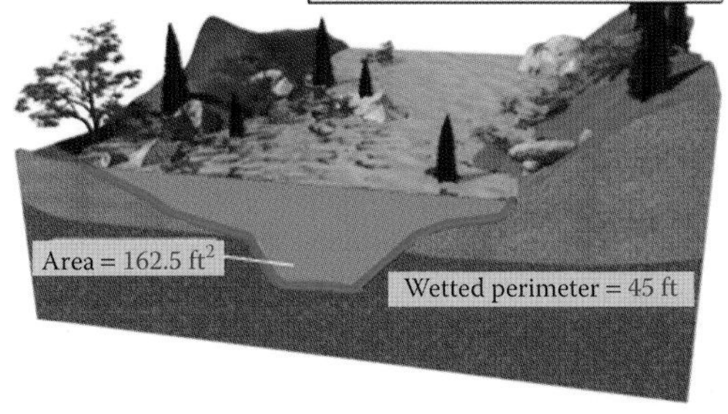

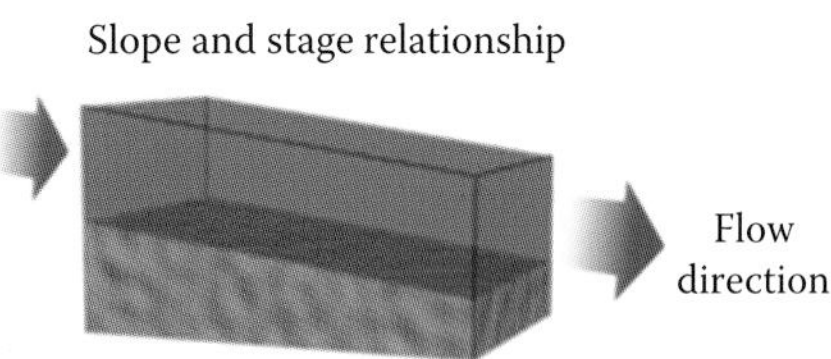

Figure M.36 (a–c) Examples of the implications of the Manning equation, based on simulations produced by The COMET® Program. (Courtesy of the University Corporation for Atmospheric Research (UCAR), and National Oceanic and Atmospheric Administration (NOAA), https://www.meted.ucar.edu/about_legal.php.)

Manometer

[fluid dynamics, general] Device designed to measure volumetric PRESSURE (P).

Pressure gauge

Used as a dial meter or as a liquid column. The height of a column (h)of LIQUID provides generally the mechanism of action to establish the pressure based on COMMUNICATING VESSELS transferring the force applied by pressure on a surface area (A) into a gravitational force (GRAVITATIONAL ACCELERATION g) of a cylinder of a liquid with mass $m=\rho V=\rho Ah$, with density ρ, eliminating the surface area to accommodate for pressure using $F=PA=mgh$, or $P=\rho gh$. A special manometer is used for the determination of BLOOD PRESSURE. An arm band is inflated by pumping AIR into a cuff and the cuff pressure is measured with a mercury (Hg) column in mm Hg. Blood pressure is used to check for arteriosclerosis and deviations in the pump function of the HEART itself. The pressure in the blood vessels (artery in the elbow of the arm) is measured by listening for blood seeping through the constricted vessel as it opens up when the pressure in the cuff is slowly released. The sounds in the periodic FLOW pattern are referred to as KOROTKOFF SOUNDS. The arm pressure is roughly equal to the pressure at the heart since it is at level altitude, any deviation in height needs to be corrected for by the Bernoulli equation (see Figure M.37).

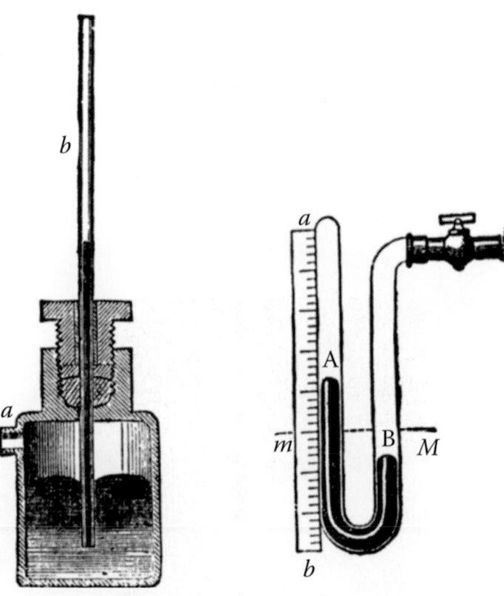

Figure M.37 Liquid-column Manometer.

Marangoni, Carlo Giuseppe Matteo (1840–1925)

[fluid dynamics, general] Scientist from Italy. Marangoni provided research on the effects on SURFACE TENSION due to spatial variations in a BUBBLE shape (e.g., pear, donut, and sphere) in 1865. The tangential (shear) forces at the surface due to influences from wind on a falling droplet or material inhomogeneities (e.g., dissolved chemicals) as well as temperature effects are referred to as Marangoni forces. One expression of a Marangoni surface tension force for a bubble (e.g., soap bubble) is the tangential force (T_s) as a function of the bubble WALL thickness (SKIN thickness τ_d) and local bubble layer density (ρ_s) as a function of the polar ANGLE (θ) with the reference frame at the "center" of the bubble with average radius R_0 (which may not be spherical), as a function of location in the reference frame ($\vec{r}$) expressed as $dT_s/d\theta = -(1/2)\rho_s\left(\vec{r}\right)R_0\tau_d\left(r\right)g\sin\theta$, where g is the GRAVITATIONAL ACCELERATION. Note that the skin of the bubble has two surfaces where forces are acting (see Figure M.38).

Figure M.38 Carlo Giuseppe Matteo Marangoni (1840–1925).

Marcacci, Arturo (late 1800–early 1900)

[biomedical, optics] Scientist from Italy. Arturo Marcacci used his discovery of the toxicity of cinchonamine and quinine (generally alkaloids) in animal and plant cells when exposed to light to perform the first recorded photochemical procedure in BIOMEDICAL OPTICS in 1888.

Marconi, Guglielmo (1874–1937)

[electronics] Italian physicist. Marconi is best known for the development of the first operational RADIO transmitter in 1895. Based on his work in Great Britain, Marconi provided radio transmission between England and France in 1899, and had a company called the Wireless Telegraph and Signal Company, now named the Marconi Company, Ltd. (see Figure M.39).

Figure M.39 Guglielmo Marconi (1874–1937).

Maricourt, Pierre de (1220–1290)

[general] A.k.a. Petri Pergrinus, scientist from France who used needles made of MAGNETIC material to map out the patterns of MAGNETIC FIELD lines of naturally occurring magnetic materials. However, naturally occurring MAGNETISM (i.e., PERMANENT MAGNET) was supposedly already known in or before the tenth century before Christ (1000 BC) in our calendar. The MAGNET was named after the city in Greece called Magnesia where iron oxide was mined and its magnetic properties discovered. The official development of the compass is attributed to WILLIAM GILBERT (1540–1603) (see Figure M.40).

Figure M.40 Statue of Pierre de Maricourt (1220–1290).

Marine geophysics

[general, geophysics] *See* **HYDROLOGY.**

Mariner

[astrophysics/astronomy, general] Several spaceships launched from 1962 to 1972 by the United States; Mariner-2: 1962, trip to VENUS; Mariner-2: 1964, trip to Mars; Mariner-5: 1967 close range fly-by of Venus; Mariner-6 and 7: 1969, trip to the MARS polar regions; Mariner-9: 1971, orbit around Mars; Mariner-10: 1973–1975, trip to Mercury. The Mariner spacecraft series was followed by the Viking series in the 1970s (see Figure M.41).

Figure M.41 Spaceship mariner, Mariner-9 launched in 1971. (Courtesy of the National Aeronautics and Space Administration [NASA].)

Mariner

[geophysics] Nautical entrepreneur, sailor. Person associated with marine life in respect of traversing the globe on the water.

Mariner's astrolabe

[computational, general, geophysics] Instrument used by sailors in the seventeenth century for navigation at sea. The Mariner's astrolabe measures the altitude of the Sun as a function of the time of day to derive the location of the vessel. The Mariner's astrolabe was developed by the Portuguese. The Mariner's astrolabe was replaced by the SEXTANT in the late seventeenth century (see Figure M.42).

Figure M.42 Mariner's astrolabe.

Markov, Andrey Andreyevich (1856–1922)

[computational] Mathematician from Russia (see Figure M.43).

Figure M.43 Andrey Andreyevich Markov (1856–1922).

Markov chain

[computational, thermodynamics] Mathematical process that is subject to changes due to changes in boundary conditions or changes in state, primarily based on statistical PROBABILITY and sequence (next state is the direct result of the previous state). The mathematical system is named after the Russian mathematician ANDREY ANDREYEVICH MARKOV (1856–1922). The Markov chain applies in particular to Monte Carlo methods and simulations in computational PHYSICS.

Markov chain mixing time

[computational, thermodynamics] The rate of convergence to a stationary process with respect to a finite MARKOV CHAIN. The mixing time is typically defined as the initial time frame (τ) over which the process distribution falls below a threshold that is small enough to result in a negligible error in the calculation (acceptable to the process), such as $1/e^2$ measured in "DISTANCE" or the MAGNITUDE between the sequential distributions Θ^1 (and more generally, Θ^p for a mixed system) at time τ and the stationary distribution.

Markov process

[computational, thermodynamics] *See* **MARKOV CHAIN.**

Mars

[astrophysics/astronomy, general, geophysics] Fourth planet from the Sun in the Earth's SOLAR SYSTEM at a DISTANCE of 2.491×10^{11} m at its greatest distance (oval orbit, *also see* **KEPLER**). Mars has an equatorial diameter of 6794×10^3 m. The axial rotation of Mars is on average 24 h 37 min and 22.6 s, the revolution around the Sun is 686.980 earthdays. The PLANET Mars is also known as the "Red Planet" due to its colored appearance resulting from blowing red-dust clouds. Mars was visited by the US NASA program spacecraft, the Pathfinder, in 1997, next to a passing visit of the Mariners series and the Viking series of spacecrafts (see Figure M.44).

Figure M.44 The planet Mars.

Marsden, Ernest (1889–1970)

[atomic, nuclear] Scientist from the United Kingdom. Coworker of JOHANNES GEIGER (1882–1945) and contemporary and colleague of ERNEST RUTHERFORD (1871–1937) who worked on experimental determination of the ENERGY content of ALPHA PARTICLES around 1910. The experiment used thin METAL foils bombarded by alpha particles to observe the SCATTERING pattern, and most alpha particles went straight through, indicating their size to be smaller than the LATTICE structure of the atoms in the foil. The backscattered alpha particles had to encounter same charge particles with a greater mass, later discovered as the NUCLEUS. (*Note*: the charge of the alpha particle was at the time known to be twice that of the electron and positive.) Based on the experimental observations of Marsden and Geiger, Rutherford proposed his model for the atomic nucleus in 1911 (see Figure M.45).

Figure M.45 Ernest Marsden (1889–1970) in 1921.

Marshak, Robert Eugene (1916–1992)

[atomic, computational, nuclear] Physicist from the United States. Marshak developed a theoretical description of the development and evolution of shock waves under the conditions of extremely high temperatures. One specific application of this field of research is in a nuclear explosion. The shock waves generated as the result of an ATOMIC BOMB are called "Marshak waves." This explanation was the subject of a renewed interest a few years ago because it helped describe the consequences of a SUPERNOVA explosion. During his time at Los Alamos, Marshak worked with a select renowned group of physicists such as HANS ALBRECHT BETHE (1906–2005), NIELS BOHR (1885–1962), ENRICO FERMI (1901–1954), RICHARD PHILLIPS FEYNMAN (1918–1988), and ROBERT OPPENHEIMER (1904–1967) (see Figure M.46).

Figure M.46 Robert Eugene Marshak (1916–1992). (Courtesy of the Los Alamos National Laboratory.)

Marshak wave

[atomic, computational, nuclear] Shock WAVE generated during a nuclear explosion, also referred to as a THERMAL WAVE, or radiation DIFFUSION wave. The theoretical formulation was developed by ROBERT MARSHAK (1916–1992). Nuclear explosions are associated with RADIATION conduction, which is facilitated by photons traveling at the speed of light. The physical bounding velocity of thermal waves is much higher than ordinary explosions facilitating classical kinetic heat conduction, which is restricted by the speed of SOUND. The temperature profile of a thermal wave is markedly different from the GAUSSIAN DISTRIBUTION of linear heat conduction. In a nuclear thermal wave, the temperature in the heated zone is fundamentally constant everywhere radiating out from the source of the explosion, whereas near the front it rapidly drops to zero (see Figure M.47).

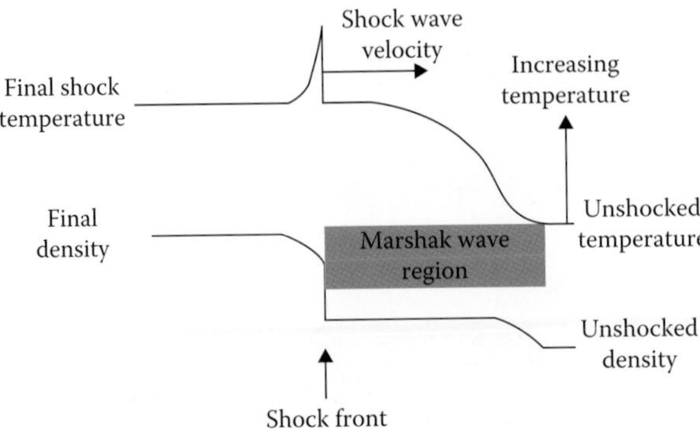

Figure M.47 Temperature profile for a Marshak wave.

MASER

[atomic, electromagnetism] Device that produces amplified MICROWAVE radiation by means of STIMULATED EMISSION (i.e., RESONANCE) phenomena in the host medium, developed approximately in 1954 by CHARLES HARD TOWNES (1915–2015) and ARTHUR SCHAWLOW (1921–1999) with their team at Columbia University in New York, NY and at the Lebedev Institute in Moscow by Nicolay G. Basov (1922–2001) and Aleksandr M. Prokhorov (1916–2002). All four received the Nobel prize for their efforts. Acronym for Microwave Amplification by Stimulation Emission of Radiation. The concept is based on the principle of stimulated emission introduced by ALBERT EINSTEIN (1879–1955) in 1917. Later this concept was found to work at shorter wavelengths using appropriate media, creating the LASER (see Figure M.48).

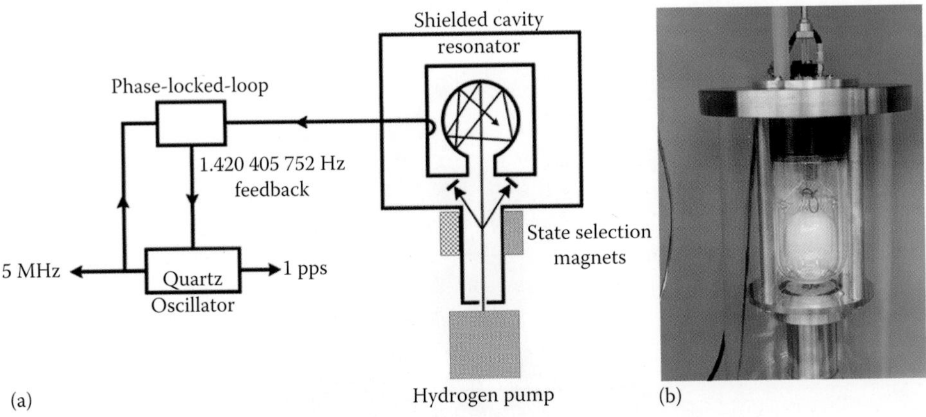

Figure M.48 (a) outline of the MASER oscillation principles, (b) Sealed glass tube used to confine a discharge in hydrogen at radio frequency, representing one of the fundamental elements inside a hydrogen maser. (Courtesy of Smithsonian Astrophysical Observatory; Jet Propulsion Laboratory (JPL)—Frequency Standards Laboratory/ National Aeronautics and Space Administration [NASA].)

Mass (m)

[general, nuclear] Measure of the INERTIA of a volume of substance of media, the physical presence irrespective of GRAVITATIONAL ACCELERATION. The weight of an object on the other hand takes GRAVITY in consideration. Also, the amount of MATTER consisting of atoms and/or (solely) elementary particles. The atomic standard with respect to mass uses the "unified atomic mass unit" u defined as $1\ \text{u} = 1/12\left({}^{12}\text{C}\right)$, one-twelfth of the mass of a standard carbon ATOM (${}^{12}\text{C}$). Mass operational definition relies on the derived quantity of matter (m) based on the measured weight (force "F") and the known gravitational acceleration (a) at the location of the measurement, leading to the mass by applying NEWTON'S SECOND LAW: $F = ma$.

Mass (mu)

[atomic, nuclear] A unit of mass based on the elementary atomic building blocks, using 1/16 of the mass of an oxygen ATOM, where the oxygen atom has a mass of 16.00000 mu. Abbreviation: mu, also found as "atomic mass unit," amu.

Mass absorption coefficient

[nuclear] *See* **MASS ATTENUATION COEFFICIENT.**

Mass attenuation coefficient (μ/ρ)

[biomedical, energy, nuclear] Measurement of the DECAY in PHOTON stream for an ELEMENT, chemical species, or substance (e.g., SOLUTE) due to annihilation or SCATTERING of ELECTROMAGNETIC RADIATION at a particular wavelength; defined per unit mass (based on density $\rho = m/V$, where m is the mass of the substance with V; note gaps in the substance will reduce the PROBABILITY of interaction with EM waves and hence reduced density results in lower attenuation) for a single mixture or element.

M

Mass balance

[thermodynamics] *See* **CONSERVATION OF MASS.**

Mass balance equation

[thermodynamics] Expression that states that the quantity of all species in a medium (solid, LIQUID, and SOLUTION) containing a particular ATOM (in stable or ionized state or bound as molecules or group of atoms) must equal the quantity of that constituent (e.g., ions or group of atoms: molecules) that has been delivered to the medium. This can be expressed in moles or grams. In a chemical reaction, the mass balance equation defines the quantities of the species involved in the reaction, for instance $2H_2 + O_2 \rightarrow 2H_2O \rightleftarrows 2H^+ + 2OH^-$.

Mass balance for a work, heat, and bulk-flow process

[thermodynamics] Kinetic process with respect to the relative MOTION of chemical constituents of various species with respect to each other (i.e., separation and mixing processes). The end result is driven by concentration gradients, which are represented by the entropy of the imbalance in chemical potential. Fluid flow without mass transfer falls under FLUID mechanics, and is not part of the field of mass transfer. Mass transfer theory closely resembles HEAT TRANSFER, as described by the pioneering work of Lewis and Whitman in 1924. The mass transfer in analogy uses a mass transfer coefficient h_m, equivalent to the thermal convection coefficient h. DIFFUSION theory may only be applied for molecular mixtures; PARTICLE size ($d < 10^{-8}\ m$). Under colloid solutions and suspensions (particle size ranging: $10^{-8}\ m < d < 10^{-5}\ m$) the Brownian theory applies. For larger particles ($d > 10^{-5}\ m$), the movement/migration is described by NEWTONIAN MECHANICS. Rewriting Fick's law for mass diffusion (without phase changes or chemical reactions), this provides for the constituent i: $(\partial\rho_i/\partial t) + \nabla\cdot\left(\rho_i\vec{v} + \rho_i\overrightarrow{v_{di}}\right) = (\partial\rho_i/\partial t) + \nabla\cdot\left(\rho_i\vec{v}\right) - D_i\nabla^2\rho_i\vec{v} + \rho_i\vec{v}_{di} = \vec{w}_i$, where ρ_i is the density of the respective species (in the thermodynamic equivalent the density can be replaced by a temperature parameter), $\overrightarrow{v_{d,i}}$ the diffusion velocity for constituent i, $\vec{v}$ the convection velocity, D_i the respective DIFFUSIVITY for the constituents ($[(dn_{di}/dt)/A]\vec{n} = -D_i\nabla c_i$, where n_{di} is the mass diffusion FLUX of species i, A the cross-sectional area of mass transfer, c_i the respective concentrations for the chemical constituents [mol/m^3], and $\vec{n}$ the normal to the surface area), and $\vec{w}_i$ the FLOW rate (particle flux).

Mass damper

[general, mechanics] Dampening pod attached to a moving mass, for example a SHOCK ABSORBER. Also known as a "harmonic absorber," based on the capacity of changing the AMPLITUDE and RESONANCE FREQUENCY of a FORCED OSCILLATION. The mass damper usually includes a spring for ENERGY conversion purposes. The damper is usually attached to a solid structure to reduce the dynamic response of the oscillating structure. The frequency of the damper can be tuned to a particular oscillation frequency to optimize the dampening efficiency. Tuning to specific structural frequency can be accomplished by the FRICTION forces applied within the dampener as well as the spring constant. Dampening can be accomplished by means of FLOW constraints of a liquid filled piston system or by means of surface contact friction. Mass dampers are used in tall buildings, especially in earthquake-prone zone, to reduce the vibrations from wind and tremors and preserve the integrity of the structure (see Figure M.49).

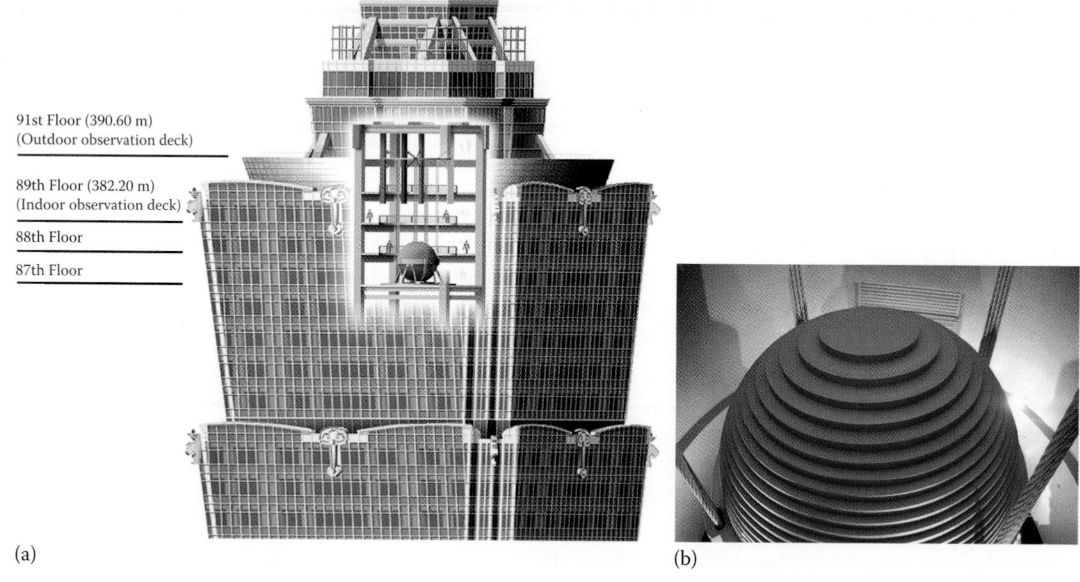

Figure M.49 (a) Tuned Mass damper in sky-scraper in Taipei; Taipei 101 and (b) detail of the Taipei AMss damper. (Courtesy of Guillaume Paumier.)

Mass defect

[chemical, general, nuclear] In chemical and atomic systems this relates to the mass change in bound systems (primarily decrease), particularly with respect to atomic nuclei. The mass nuclear defect can be expressed as $\Delta m = Z(m_p + m_e) + (A - Z)m_n - m_{\text{atom}}$, where m_{atom} is the mass of the primary nuclide, A the mass number (representing the number of nucleons), Z the atomic number (representing the number of protons), m_p, m_e, and m_n, respectively the PROTON, electron, and NEUTRON mass.

Mass density (ρ)

[solid-state] MASS (m) per unit volume (V): $\rho = m/V$, also DENSITY.

Mass energy

[nuclear] Concept that the MASS (m) of an object or system has an ENERGY (E) equivalent: $E = mc^2$, where $c = 2.99792458 \times 10^8$ m/s is the speed of light. Additionally, adding for instance 180 megajoules (180 MJ) of a variety of energy formats to an object will increase the mass by 2 μg. Conversely, mass can be converted into energy, such as with the ATOMIC BOMB or nuclear power generators.

Mass energy absorption coefficient

[biomedical, energy, thermodynamics] The X-RAY energy (keV–MeV range) absorbed per unit mass as described in RADIATION THERAPY treatment, also referred to as mass–energy attenuation (μ_{en}/ρ). The mass–energy attenuation coefficient cannot directly be derived; however, it relies on the theoretical conversion with respect to the mass attenuation coefficient provided by an efficiency factor f_s; after Stephen M. Selzer (1940?–) who provided the heuristic proof of the relationship between the radiation MASS ATTENUATION COEFFICIENT (μ/ρ) and the MASS ENERGY transfer coefficient (μ_{tr}/ρ): $\mu_{en}/\rho = (\mu_{tr}/\rho)(1-g_r) = f_s(\mu/\rho)(1-g_r)$, where the average ratio of kinetic energy of particles ionized during radiation interaction and lost due to deceleration with inherent emission of PHOTON (i.e., radiative DECAY) is represented by g_r.

Mass excess

[nuclear] Expression of the BINDING ENERGY between nuclides (i.e., NUCLEAR BINDING ENERGY), in relative measure to the binding energy within the carbon-12 ATOM characterized per nucleon. In a nuclide, this represents the difference between the actual mass of the nuclide with respect to the mass number expressed in atomic mass units.

Mass flux

[general] The FLOW rate of mass per unit area. The following symbols are used in different fields of science and ENGINEERING: φ, Φ, j, J. One specific example is the current density (electron flow rate per cross-sectional area, but as positive particles) often shown as j or J.

Mass number (A)

[atomic, chemical, general, nuclear, solid-state] The number of nucleons in the NUCLEUS of an ATOM. Symbol: A.

Mass of the neutron

[nuclear] Neutral charge nuclide with mass $m_p = 1.674929 \times 10^{-27}$ kg $= 1.00866$ u.

Mass spectrograph

[atomic, general, solid-state] *See* MASS SPECTROMETER *and* MAGNETIC SPECTROMETER.

Mass spectrometer

[atomic, general, solid-state] Device used to separate accelerated ions with respect to their respective CHARGE (q) to MASS (m) ratio: q/m. Charges are first accelerated under an applied electric field (E as the result of a POTENTIAL DIFFERENCE over a fixed DISTANCE, providing a Coulomb force $F_{Coulomb} = qE$) and are next sent through a velocity (v) filter (based on sending accelerated ions through a MAGNETIC FIELD (B); $qE = qvB$, yielding: $v = E/B$) that provides a uniform velocity profile, irrespective of charge or mass. The ions with specific mass (m) and CHARGE (q) will be diverted by means of an external uniform magnetic field (B_0), providing a radius of curvature ($R_{Mass\text{-}Spec}$) of the circular trajectory under the right-hand rule resulting from the magnetic force $F_{mag} = q\vec{v} \times \vec{B}$: $q/m = E/BB_0R_{Mass\text{-}Spec}$. Generally the ions have a single charge (positive or negative; $q = |e| = 1.60217657 \times 10^{-19}\,C$), but not necessarily. The spectroscopic position of the detection plate (including the detector slit configuration, "mechanically" providing a final filtration mechanism) for the respective particles with respect to the undeflected ION is $\Delta y = -a_1(\Delta(mv^2)/m_0v_0^2) + a_2(\Delta(mv)/m_0v_0)$, where $m = m_0 + \Delta m$, $v = v_0 + \Delta v$, and a_1 and a_2 are characteristic constants with respect to the design and functionality of the mass spectroscopy instrument.

Mass spectroscopy

[atomic, biomedical, solid-state] Detailed measurement of the MASS (m) of isotopes by a device (MASS SPECTROGRAPH or mass spectrometer) introduced by Francis William Aston (1877–1945) in 1919. Charged particles are performing a curved trajectory with radius depending on their charge and mass. The defection is based on $qE = mv^2/2$, CONSERVATION OF ENERGY, where q is the net ISOTOPE charge, E is the applied electric field, and v is the achieved velocity of the accelerated PARTICLE under the influence of the force. A MAGNETIC deflector separates the particles based on their trajectory and are sent through slits, providing a discrete location of the various isotopes with respective masses. The RESOLVING POWER of the device is defined by the design and the focusing ability of the spectrometer (see Figure M.50).

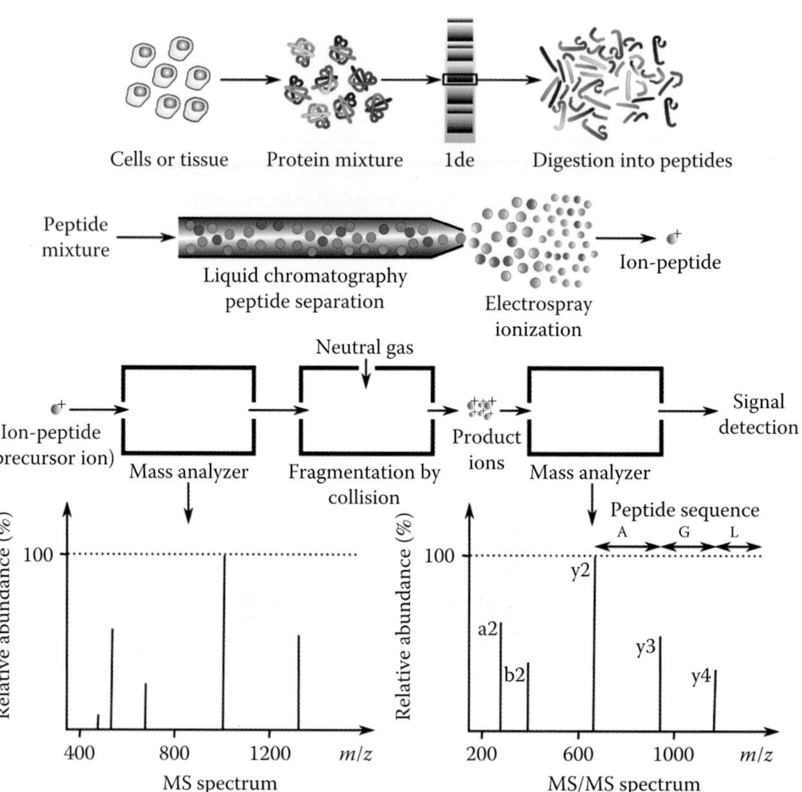

Figure M.50 Mass spectroscopy.

Mass–spring system

[acoustics, biomedical, general, mechanics, nuclear] {use: energy conversion, actuation, imaging} There are many mass–spring systems, some even dampened. To name but a few: shock absorbers on an automobile, woofer (loud SPEAKER), gong/bell, tooth brush, and many more. Generally a simple mass–spring system obeys FICK'S LAW. A dampened mass–spring system uses some form of COMPLIANCE with a phenomenological constant identifying the level of "RESISTANCE" ($C_{\text{Compliance}}$) to dampen the MOTION. Examples of dampened motion are shock absorbers, woofer loud speaker cone, and keys on a PIANO. Several motions are repetitive with a constant frequency and are considered damped OSCILLATIONS, other movements are single pulse. All motions rely on an external force or driving mechanism to initiate the motion. The force expression for a damped spring motion is $F = F_{\text{external}} - C_{\text{compliance}}v - kx = ma$, where v is the VELOCITY of the mass. The external force resulting from a blow (SHOCK ABSORBER or piano) is the change in MOMENTUM P_m: $F_{\text{external}} = (dP_m/dt) = m(dv/dt)$, or it can be a driving mechanism based on ELECTRICITY or MAGNETISM with a preset frequency (e.g., VOICE COIL), another application is in ULTRASOUND imaging using piezoelectric or other mechanisms of driving the OSCILLATION (*also see* **OSCILLATION**) (see Figure M.51).

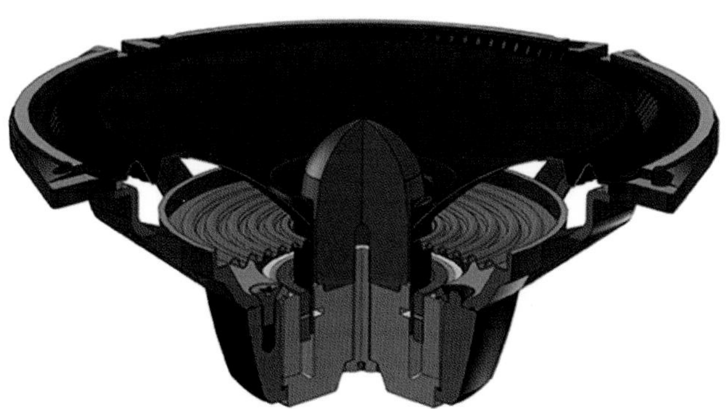

Figure M.51 Mass-spring system that is, loud speaker.

Mass transfer Biot number (Bi_{mass})

[fluid dynamics] Ratio of diffusive to reactive, respectively convective mass transfer resistance: $Bi_{\text{mass}} = k_t L/D_{\text{solid}} = h_D L/D_{\text{solid}}$, where k_{th} is the THERMAL CONDUCTIVITY, D_{solid} is the DIFFUSION coefficient, L is the characteristic length, and h_D the mass-transfer coefficient. The Biot mass transfer number determines the uniformity of constituent concentration in solids.

Mass transfer Fourier number

[thermodynamics] *See* **FOURIER NUMBER, MASS TRANSFER.**

Mass transformation equation

[atomic] Relativistic MASS (m) of an object traveling with velocity v in the observer's frame: $m = m_0\left(1/\sqrt{\{1-(v^2/c^2)\}}\right)$, where $c = 2.99792458 \times 10^8$ m/s is the speed of light in vacuum and m_0 is the REST MASS (classical mechanics). The coefficient $\left(1/\sqrt{\{1-(v^2/c^2)\}}\right)$ is defined as the mass transfer coefficient.

Mass absorption coefficient

Massieu, François Jacques Dominique (1832–1896)

[thermodynamics] Scientist and engineer from France. Massieu is known both for his introduction of the "characteristic function" of a FLUID body, the MASSIEU FUNCTION, and the initial thermodynamic concept of the MASSIEU POTENTIAL, defining the free entropy of a system (see Figure M.52).

Figure M.52 François Jacques Dominique Massieu (1832–1896).

Massieu function

[thermodynamics] Description of the entropy of a system based on a coordinate system with a number (n) of axes {cumulative: (x_i, y_j)} that correlate to the respective variables of the system: $[\Psi] = \Psi(X_1, X_1, \ldots, X_i, Y_{i+1}, \ldots, Y_n)$, introduced in 1869 by FRANÇOIS MASSIEU (1832–1896) (*see* **MASSIEU POTENTIAL**).

Massieu potential

[thermodynamics] Entropic thermodynamic potential defined as $\Phi = S - (1/T)U$, where $S = (U/T) + (PV/T) + \sum_{i=1}^{n}(-\mu_i(N_i/T))$ represents the entropy of a system, T the temperature, U the internal ENERGY, P pressure, V the volume of the system, μ_i the chemical potential chemical constituent i, and N_i the quantity of items (particles, atoms, ions, etc. expressed in MOLE) of chemical component i. The concept of free entropy as introduced by FRANÇOIS MASSIEU (1832–1896) in 1869. The Massieu potential and free energy predate the Gibbs's free energy, which was introduced in 1875 by JOSIAH WILLARD GIBBS (1839–1903). It was shown that the free entropy follows from the LEGENDRE TRANSFORM of the true entropy of a system or process. The Massieu potential is based on the fact that the state of a body is completely defined when two of the three parameters that represent the volume of the system, the temperature of the system, as well as the pressure on its surface are known. Also known as Helmholtz free entropy.

Material fatigue

[general, mechanics] Localized gradual structural damage to a composite or metallic structure or material resulting from cyclic or infrequent repetitive loading. The FATIGUE results from applied nominal maximum stress below the ultimate TENSILE STRESS of the material, and generally less than the yield stress limit. When a certain stress threshold is exceeded, on a MICROSCOPIC level, certain threshold, cracks will form, weakening the integrity of the structure on a macroscopic scale. The continued exposure to the forces involving the implementation of material fatigue will eventually result in breakage (*also see* METAL FATIGUE) (see Figure M.53).

Figure M.53 The impact of Material Fatigue on the structural integrity of the Tacoma Narrows Bridge in 1940, constructed of metal, concrete, and asphalt. The bridge was destroyed only weeks after the official opening due to the vibrations on the suspension cable (Aeolian sound wave) providing the resonance frequency of the road-surface section aspect of the bridge with the associated natural frequency based on elastic moduli, characteristic lengths, and persistence in driving wind (direction and magnitude).

Matter

[general, nuclear, solid-state] Compilation of the physical properties of a medium that define its response to external influences, specifically force. Matter is congealed from a mixture of ELEMENTS for which the atoms and molecules are held together by short- and long-range forces such as gravitational attraction and van der Waals attraction. Matter can be found in various states, or phases: GAS/VAPOR, LIQUID, solid and PLASMA. Mass is a quantity of MATTER, one of the fundamental dimensions, next to thermal properties and volume (incorporating the dimensions of all directions within the frame of reference), and hence density. The thermal properties are internal ENERGY and heat, next to the SPECIFIC HEAT with respect to phase transfers, the change of phase and the pattern in which this takes place, heat exchange with neighboring bodies, conduction, convection, and radiation next to THERMAL EXPANSION. Additional mechanical properties of matter are deformation, COMPLIANCE, and MOMENT OF INERTIA, depending on the mass distribution and applicable LATTICE and/or crystalline structure (see Figure M.54).

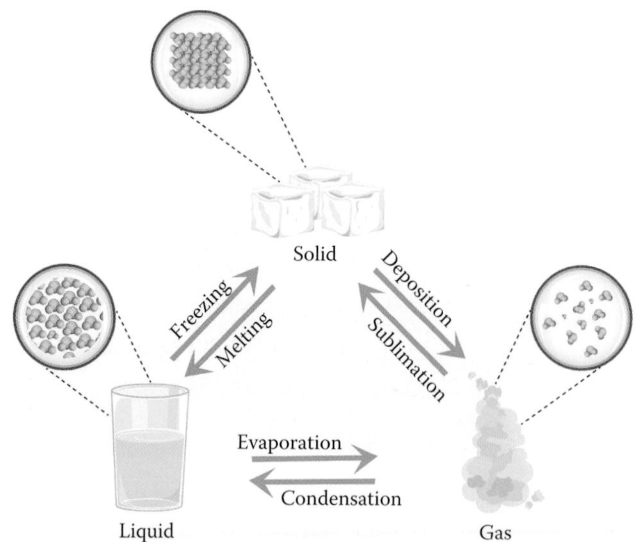

Figure M.54 Matter concepts.

Matter wave

[acoustics, general] Wave propagation based on mechanical disturbance of particles in a medium. Also referred to as a MECHANICAL WAVE, primarily pertaining to ACOUSTICS and FLOW (crest of waves on beach). The VIBRATION of a string on an instrument is a transverse matter wave, and the SOUND of a VOICE in AIR is a longitudinal matter wave (*also see* **De Broglie**) (see Figure M.55).

Figure M.55 Matter wave in flag.

Maupertuis, Pierre Louis Moreau de {Pierre Louis Moreau de Maupertuis} (1698–1759)

[computational, general] French mathematician and physicist. Maupertuis formulated the rudimentary principle of the path of least RESISTANCE to conserve ENERGY (see Figure M.56).

Figure M.56 Pierre Louis Moreau de Maupertuis (1698–1759).

Maupertuis principle

[computational, general] Integral equation describing the path of a PARTICLE in MOTION, following the path of "least action," that is, path of least RESISTANCE; introduced by PIERRE LOUIS MOREAU DE MAUPERTUIS (1698–1759). The integral defines the condition of the extremum (maximum, minimum, saddle point, or stationary point) for a system with N generalized coordinates $\vec{\chi} = (\chi_1, \chi_2, \ldots, \chi_N)$ between two states referenced as $\overrightarrow{\chi_1}$ and $\overrightarrow{\chi_2}$, both as a function of location, conditions (outlined by the conjugate momenta at the generalized coordinates of the system: $\vec{p} = (p_1, p_2, \ldots, p_N)$) and TIME ($t$) by means of the action functional using the path as a function to define the location of the extremum, that is, the condition of the function describing the system: $S_0\left[\vec{q}(t)\right] \stackrel{\text{def}}{=} \int \vec{p} \cdot d\vec{q}$ which yields a SCALAR as a solution, where $p_i \stackrel{\text{def}}{=} [\partial L(\vec{\chi}, \dot{\vec{\chi}}, t)]/\partial \dot{\chi}_i$, $L(\vec{\chi}, \dot{\vec{\chi}}, t)$ the Lagrangian of the system, describing the first-order perturbations of the system. The perturbation does generally not exceed the second-order changes in the "path" $S_0\left[\vec{q}(t)\right]$.

Maximum occupation number

[high-energy, quantum, solid-state] Ground-state ENERGY EIGENVALUE configurations per unit volume for a FERMION collective in a medium (i.e., condensate) consisting of millions of atoms. The primary difference between fermions and bosons is that fermionic energy states have a maximum occupation number of 1. Bosons, on the other hand, in theory have unlimited occupation states. The Pauli principle for the constituent fermions would practically limit the BOSON occupation number. The maximum occupation number is expected to be proportional to the "volume" available to the bosons, divided by the volume occupied by the number of fermions constructing one boson (see Figure M.57).

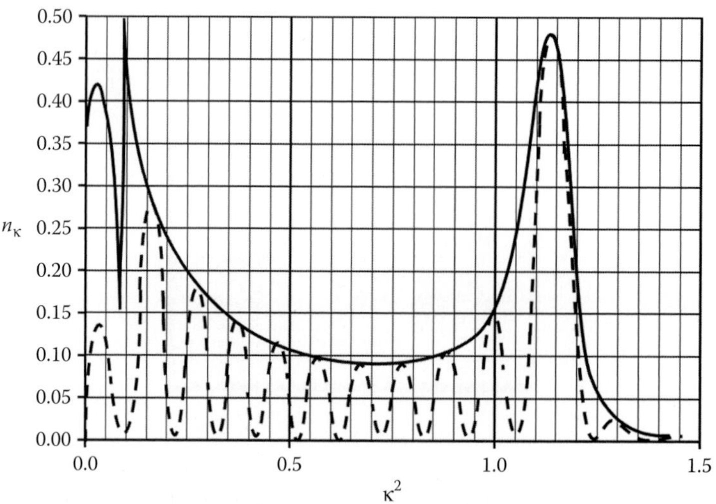

Figure M.57 The maximum occupation number is outlined by the contour of the actual occupation numbers (n_κ) (dotted line) in the excitation band of fermions excited ("pre-heated") to $\lambda\phi^4$ –inflation (ϕ the oscillation) at resonance under the condition $q \equiv (h^*/\lambda) = 1$, λ the oscillation wavelength. The boundary conditions are defined by the Fermi sphere with radius $\kappa_F = q^{1/4} m_\phi$, m_ϕ the inflation mass of the system, $q = h^{*2}\phi_0/m_\phi^2$, h^* the coupling between the inflation and the fermions (Yukawa type—coupling) and ϕ_0 the amplitude of the inflation oscillation. The resonance in this case has 10 background oscillations.

M

Maxwell, James Clerk (1831–1879)

[electromagnetism, general] Scottish scientist and physicist who developed a rigorous relationship between changing MAGNETIC phenomena and the resulting varying electric manifestations such as the induced electromotive force electric potential in a closed circuit, or an alternating electric field in a more general concept. The work of Maxwell was based on the efforts by the American scholar JOSEPH HENRY (1797–1878), the English scientist MICHAEL FARADAY (1791–1867), as well as inspired by CHARLES WHEATSTONE, WILLIAM THOMSON (i.e., Lord Kelvin), the work by CARL FRIEDRICH GAUSS (1777–1855), and ANDRÉ MARIE AMPÈRE'S (1775–1836) circuital law, compiled shortly after his graduation from the University of Cambridge in 1854 (see Figure M.58).

Figure M.58 James Clerk Maxwell (1831–1879).

Maxwell equations

[energy, optics] philosophical extension of the concepts of Faraday's law pertaining to the interaction of a varying MAGNETIC FIELD and the ensuing alternating electric field and, when appropriated, the associated electromotive force. In the 1820s, the efforts of both the English scientist MICHAEL FARADAY (1791–1867) and the American scholar JOSEPH HENRY (1797–1878) independent of each other provided the theoretical support for JAMES MAXWELL CLERK (1831–1879) to develop theoretical expressions linking magnetic field variations to electric field changes developing several theories of electromagnetic WAVE propagation and in the process underwriting the propagation of electromagnetic waves at the speed of light. The Maxwell equations are the following:

ORIGIN	DIFFERENTIAL EQUATIONS IN VACUUM	INTEGRAL EQUATIONS IN VACUUM
Gauss's law	$\nabla \cdot \vec{E} = 4\pi\rho_e$	$\oint_S \vec{E} \cdot \vec{n} dA = -4\pi \oiint_V \rho_e d^3 r = Q_{in}/\epsilon_0$
Gauss's law for magnetism	$\nabla \cdot \vec{B} = 0$	$\oint_S \vec{B} \cdot \vec{n} dA = 0$
Faraday's law	$\nabla \times \vec{E} = \partial \vec{B}/\partial t$ $\partial \vec{E}/\partial z = 0$	$\oint_S \vec{E} \cdot \vec{n} d\ell = -(1/c)(\partial/\partial t) \oiint_V \vec{B} \cdot \vec{n} dA$
Ampère's law	$\nabla \times \vec{B} - \varepsilon_0\mu_0(\partial\vec{E}/\partial t)$ $= \nabla \times \vec{B} - (1/c^2)(\partial\vec{E}/\partial t)$ $= (4\pi/c)\vec{J}$	$\oint_S \vec{B} d\ell = -\oiint_V \left((4\pi/c)\vec{J} + (1/c)(\partial\vec{E}/\partial t)\right) \cdot \vec{n} dA$

Where $\vec{E}$ is the electric field, ρ_e the charge density per unit volume V, t is time, $\vec{J}$ is the current density, $c = \sqrt{\varepsilon_0\mu_0}$ the speed of light, $\vec{n}$ the normal to the surface A of the enclosed space, S the perimeter of the enclosed surface, ℓ the length of the loop enclosing the charges, respectively, $d\ell$ the segment of the tangent length to the curve of the loop, r the radius of the loop, $\mu_0 = 1.2566 \times 10^{-6}(\text{Wb/A.m})\ (\text{N/A}^2)$ the DIELECTRIC permeability for VACUUM, $\varepsilon_0 = 8.8541878 \times 10^{-12}(\text{C}^2/\text{Nm}^2)$ the dielectric permittivity for vacuum, Q_{in} the enclosed net total charge, ϵ_0 the dielectric permittivity of vacuum, and $\nabla = \partial/\partial x_i$ is the Laplace operator with respect to all DEGREES OF FREEDOM x_i. Analogously for a magnetic field ($\vec{B}$), the ELECTROMAGNETIC FIELD parameters are related by the Lorentz force on a moving point charge q: $F_\ell = q\left(\vec{E} + (v/c) \times \vec{B}\right)$, with v the velocity of the moving charges. The current density is connected to the charge change rate as $(\partial\rho_e/\partial t) + \nabla \cdot \vec{J} = 0$.

Maxwell–Boltzmann distribution (f(X))

[fluid dynamics, general, mechanics] Distribution of physical property (e.g., velocity and ENERGY) based on the theoretical work by JAMES CLERK MAXWELL (1831–1879) and LUDWIG EDUARD BOLTZMANN (1844–1906) defined as follows. For the Maxwell energy distribution $N_i/N = g_i e^{-(E_i/k_b T)} / \sum_j g_j e^{-(E_j/k_b T)}$, where i represents a specific MICROSTATE (e.g., QUANTUM STATE), E_i represents the energy of a specific isolated microstate, T the temperature, $k_b = 1.3806488 \times 10^{-23}\ m^2kg/s^2K$ is the BOLTZMANN CONSTANT, g_i a factor that defines the number of microstates with the same energy (DEGENERACY factor), N_i the number of molecules in one equilibrium microstate, and N the total number of molecules this yields: $f(E)dE = 2(1/k_bT)^{3/2}\sqrt{(E/\pi)}e^{-(E/k_bT)}dE$. For the momentum ($p = mv$) (i.e., velocity) this writes as $N_i/N = g_i e^{-((p_{i,x}^2+p_{i,y}^2+p_{i,z}^2)/2mk_bT)} \Big/ \sum_j g_j e^{-(E_j/k_bT)} = (1/Z)\,exp[-((p_{i,x}{}^2 + p_{i,y}{}^2 + p_{i,z}{}^2)/2mk_bT)]$ where m is the molecular mass for the respective constituent of the GAS with distribution function $f(p)dp = (1/(2\pi mk_bT))^{3/2}\, e^{-((p_x^2+p_y^2+p_z^2)/2mk_bT)}dp$ (see Figure M.59).

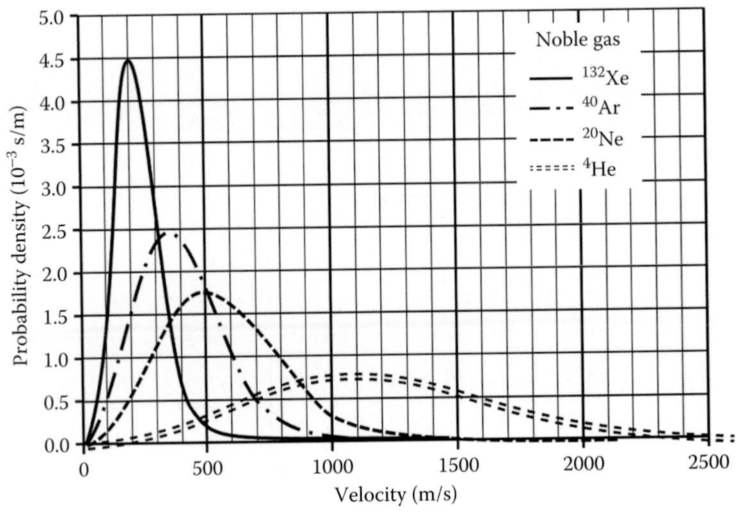

Figure M.59 Outline of the Maxwell–Boltzmann distribution.

Mayer, Julius Robert von {Julius Robert von Mayer} (1814–1878)

[general, nuclear, thermodynamics] Physicist and physician from Germany, pioneer in thermodynamic relations (*see* **VON MAYER, JULIUS ROBERT**) (see Figure M.60).

Figure M.60 Julius Robert von Mayer (1814–1878).

Mayer, Maria Goeppert (Göppert) (1906–1972)

[atomic, computational, general, nuclear] Mathematician, scientist, and physicist from Germany at the time, now Poland. Maria Goeppert-Mayer provided pivotal elaborations on the BOHR ATOMIC MODEL for which she received the Nobel prize in 1963. Maria's contemporaries and friends included her teacher MAX BORN (1882–1970) and friend NIELS BOHR (1885–1962). Additional work of Maria included uranium ISOTOPE separation during the Second World War. Also known as Goeppert-Mayer, Maria (see Figure M.61).

Figure M.61 Maria Goeppert-Mayer (1906–1972).

Mayer relation

[nuclear, thermodynamics] Correlation between the SPECIFIC HEAT under constant pressure (c_p) to that under constant volume (c_v), derived by JULIUS ROBERT VON MAYER. The relationship is a function of the coefficient of isothermal compressibility (κ_T) and the coefficient of isobaric expansion (α_P) next to the TEMPERATURE (T) and VOLUME (V) as $c_p = c_v + (T\alpha_P{}^2V/\kappa_T)$.

Mclean, Jay (1890–1957)

[biomedical, fluid dynamics] Physician, chemist, and scientist from the United States. The collaborative efforts of Jay McLean and his professor William Henry Howell (1860–1945) resulted in the definition of the anticoagulant properties and the clinical and hemodynamic impact of heparin in 1916 (see Figure M.62).

Figure M.62 Jay McLean (1890–1957). (Courtesy of the US National Library of Medicine; donation by Dr. Brockbank 1956.)

Mclennan, John Cunningham, Sir (1867–1935)

[atomic, nuclear] Scientist and physicist from Canada. Colleagues and collaborators John McLennan and Eli Franklin Burton (1879–1948) discovered a new form of radioactivity, consisting of man-made radiation (produced in a vacuum tube with an electron beam, creating metallic origin radioactivity) that had a high-penetration ability and was ionizing in nature in around 1902. Additional pioneering work by Sir Mclennan was in the liquefaction of helium (see Figure M.63).

Figure M.63 Sir John Cunningham McLennan (1867–1935) in 1935. (Courtesy University of Toronto, Toronto, Canada.)

Mean free path

[atomic, computational, fluid dynamics, mechanics, nuclear, optics] The average DISTANCE of the resultant vector that describes the path that a particle or ENERGY unit (i.e., PHOTON) moves between interactions that alter the vector magnitude and or direction (e.g., collisions): $\delta = \sum_N \ell_i / N$, for a GAS $\text{mfp} = \lambda_{\text{mfp}} = RT/(\sqrt{2})\pi d^2 N_A P$, $R = 8.3144621(75)\,\text{J/Kmol}$ the universal gas constant, T = temperature, d = diameter of vessel/container (i.e., characteristic length), $N_A = 6.02214129(27) \times 10^{23}\,\text{mol}^{-1}$ (Avogadro's number), and P the pressure of the gas. Also, the mean distance (i.e., PROBABILITY of the occurrence of traveling this hypothetical distance, expressed by the resultant vector) a photon traverses between optical interactions of either SCATTERING (e.g., atomic resonance) or annihilation (absorption). Abbreviation: mfp, symbol, δ (see Figure M.64).

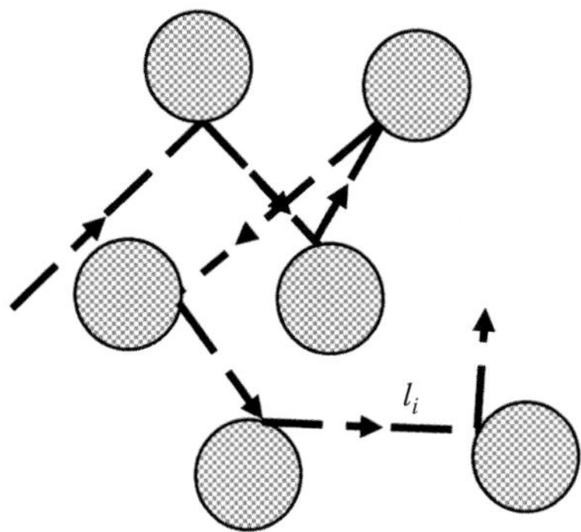

Figure M.64 Representation of the mean-free-path in multiple interactions.

Mean life (τ_{decay})

[atomic, nuclear] *See* **MEAN LIFETIME.**

Mean lifetime (τ)

[general, nuclear] Mathematical average lifetime of the state of an ISOTOPE in a medium consisting of radioactive material. Also, the exponential constant that defines the DECAY of isotope defined as the reciprocal of the decay constant expressed as $\tau_{\text{decay}} = 1/\lambda_{\text{decay}}$, where $dN/dt = -\lambda_{\text{decay}} N$ with N the number of radioactive isotopes, yielding $N(t) = N_0 e^{-t/\tau_{\text{decay}}}$. This expresses the fact that τ_{decay} is the time in which the quantity of isotopes reduces to $e^{-1} = 0.3679$, or 37% (*also see* **HALF-LIFE**).

Mean Speed Theorem

[general] *See* **MERTON MEAN SPEED THEOREM.**

Mean value of potential over a spherical surface

[computational, electromagnetism, fluid dynamics] In electric applications, this pertains to the surface charge on a spherical CONDUCTOR. Note that the charge will be equally distributed over the surface (S) of the conductor with surface charge density σ_{charge}. The sphere will have a radius $r > 0$. The total charge is defined as $q_{\text{electric}} = A\sigma_{\text{charge}} = 4\pi r^2 \sigma_{\text{charge}}$. Since this is a symmetric condition, the electric field is directly proportional to the DISTANCE to the origin of the sphere R. The electric potential is derived from the Coulomb law: $V(R) = \oint_S (\sigma_{\text{charge}}/4\pi\varepsilon_0 r')dr'$, where ε_0 is the DIELECTRIC permittivity of VACUUM. Additionally GAUSS'S LAW provides $V(R) = q_{\text{electric}}/4\pi\varepsilon_0 R$. Equating the two potentials yields that the potential outside the sphere is equal to the potential at the center of the sphere: $V(R) = q'_{\text{electric}}/4\pi\varepsilon_0 r$, where q'_{electric} is the total enclosed charge, assuming the sphere is the only charged volume in the space under consideration. In FLUID DYNAMICS, the potential pertains to the VELOCITY POTENTIAL (ϕ_{flow}; *Note*: $v_x = \partial\phi_{flow}/\partial x$, etc. and $v_R = \partial\phi_{flow}/\partial R$) expressed by $M(R) = (1/4\pi r^2)\oint_S \phi_{flow} dS = (1/4\pi)\oint_0^{4\pi} \phi_{flow}(r,\omega)d\omega$, where ω represents the SOLID ANGLE over the surface of the sphere. Incompressible fluids can be described as having potential flows that are solutions of the NAVIER–STOKES EQUATIONS. In solving for the potential flows, one can apply the HELMHOLTZ DECOMPOSITION principle, which states that every solution of the NAVIER–STOKES equations can be decompartmentalized in respective rotational parts and irrotational components, each satisfying LAPLACE'S EQUATION. The irrotational part will satisfy the boundary conditions, whereas the rotational velocity will generally not.

Measurement

[general] Acquisition of data pertaining to an event, phenomenon, or object (dimensions, weight, etc.) in relation to establishing the parameters that best describe the occurrence using qualified and calibrated equipment best suited for the determination of the designated parameters.

Mechanical energy

[biomedical, general, mechanics] *See* WORK.

Mechanical wave

[engineering, general, geophysics] Wave produced by the displacement of material. A mechanical wave can be longitudinal, as performed by the compression of AIR in ACOUSTIC WAVES, or by transverse displacement, such as the plucking of a string on a string instrument (e.g., GUITAR, harp, and PIANO). A combination wave with both transverse and longitudinal properties can for instance be an EARTHQUAKE: combination S-wave and P-WAVE. In SEISMOLOGY, SURFACE WAVES are generally shear waves or TRANSVERSE WAVES, whereas in the core shear waves are not feasible and elastic compression is the main mode (see Figure M.65).

Figure M.65 Mechanical wave in ropes.

Mechanics

[biomedical, energy, engineering, nuclear, mechanics] The study of objects in MOTION. The motion is for instance, but not limited to, VIBRATION of a chime or cymbal, rotation of a curved billiard ball, as well as a spinning top, and the trajectory of a flare.

Mechanoreception

[biomedical, mechanics] Biological sensing mechanism of action that provides the fundamental basis for touching, HEARING, changes in posture, changes in external or internal pressure, and general strain (biting with the jaw, bending a joint, etc.). The mechanoreception takes place on a cellular level. In the mammalian skin, there are four different types of mechanical sensor: Meissner corpuscles, Merkel disks, Pacinian corpuscules, and Ruffini endings. In the EAR, the ORGAN OF CORTI responds to the bending of a hair to produce an ACTION POTENTIAL that is sent to the brain to indicate the observation of a frequency in the cochlea (BASILAR MEMBRANE) in a specific location that is representative of a single wavelength of motion only. The glabrous SKIN with hair has sensors that respond to stretch. Most knowledge about mechanoreceptor ACTIVITY and function is based on the work by Roland S. Johansson (1950–) and Åke Bernhard Vallbo (1933–), both from Sweden, as recent as the late 1970s (see Figure M.66).

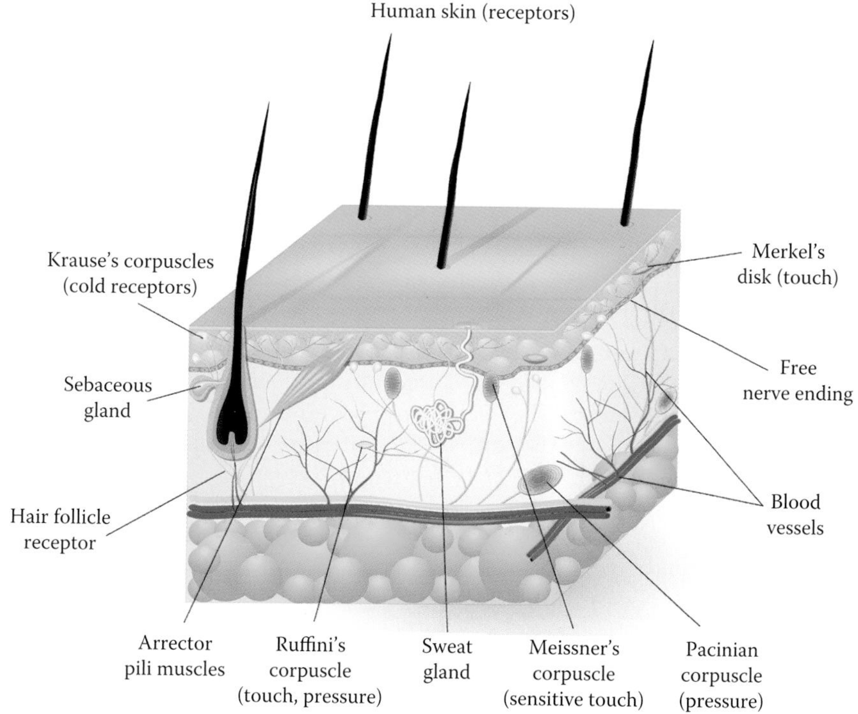

Figure M.66 Examples of mechanoreceptor in human skin.

Mechanosensitive action

[biomedical, chemical, general, thermodynamics] Operation of ION transport mediation in biological cells in response to external influences such as shear, stress, OSMOTIC PRESSURE, GRAVITY, and acoustic MECHANICS. One function in particular, next to sensing of external influences, is the protection of the CELL itself. Sensing the internal cell pressure will result in a pressure regulation mechanism that will ultimately prevent the cell from bursting. The mechanosensitive action of the cells is mediated by mechanosensitive ion channels (MSCs). These ion channels can currently be subdivided into two groups: (1) responding to fibrous protein and (2) responding to lipid bilayer stress. One measurable effect in response to applied shear and stress in the CELL MEMBRANE is the change in diameter of what is known as the bacterial large mechanosensitive channels (MscL) in the range of 5–6 nm. The Gibbs free ENERGY difference (ΔG) between the open and closed state of the channel (expressed by the cross-sectional area change ΔA) is defined by the lipid bilayer TENSION (T) as $\Delta G = T\Delta A$. Apart from the change in area, there are also changes possible in the shape of the opening, without actual changes to the area. The shape change may provide a preferred vehicle for certain proteins to be transported through the MEMBRANE to act as signaling proteins.

Medicine

[biomedical, electronics, fluid dynamics] Diagnostic and therapeutic modality that uses ENGINEERING and science to either acquire vital signs, produce anatomical and physiological images, or deliver chemical means (therapeutic design for disease treatment), and ENERGY as well as mandates exercise routines to make a best effort in returning the physical condition and vital signs of an individual to established states that are considered within the normal range for a person of a certain AGE, specific sex, and with a general dietary and exercise history, as well as geographical location while also considering potential genetic influences as well as work-place and living condition exposure to the ELEMENTS and foreign materials such as pollution (roughly defined as chemical substances that are not common occurrence or/and have been established as reagents that diminish specific or general levels of physiological, anatomical values, and vital signs). Based on the acquired information, a treatment can be designed to attempt to remove the cause or eliminate the effects of a physical condition, ranging from allergies, fractures, to cancer to the natural phenomenon of childbirth. An additional host of physiological conditions and anatomical conditions are involved in practicing medical science, some are purely chemical in nature based on an imbalance resulting from a broad range of influences, some genetically predetermined, some resulting to exposure to chemicals. Biological systems are integral systems where no single anatomical or physiological aspect stands isolated from all the other activities and conditions in the body and metabolistic activities. Medicine has a long history (dating back thousands of years) that has been influenced by prejudice, lack of diagnostic abilities, as well as generally incomplete information about the physiological integration of contributing factors to a perceived symptom. The multifaceted aspects of engineering (medical device development), drug interaction (chemical design), and psychological integration are only providing major or minor attributes of a complete description for the affliction or the general state of genetic evolution. Even though a broken LEG can be a straightforward cause-and-effect diagnosis with a well-defined treatment modality, the healing process may not be universal or straightforward (*also see* **Bayesian methodology, Bayes' theorem** [i.e., evidence-based medical informatics]) (see Figure M.67).

(a)

(b)

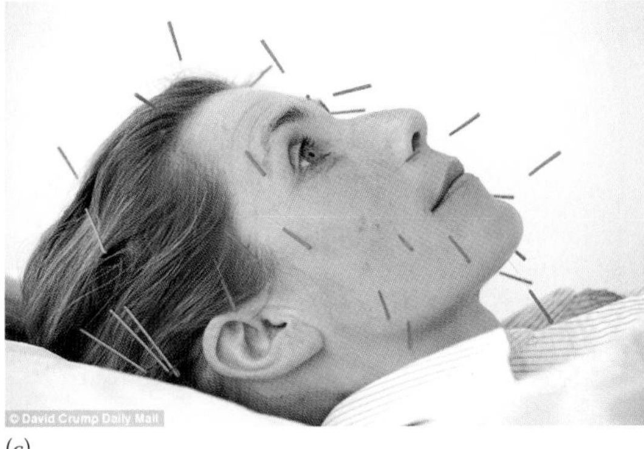

(c)

Figure M.67 (a) Paramedics acquiring basic vital signs to establish a patient's acute health status, (b) array of vital signs acquired during a medical examination (e.g., HR: hear-rate; BP: Blood-pressure; SPO2: oxygen saturation; and Resp: respiration rate), and (c) alternative medical approach based on acupuncture techniques.

Meissner (Meiβner), Walther (1882–1974)

[general] Physicist from Germany. Meissner is best known for his superconductor work, in collaboration with Robert Ochsenfeld (1901–1993) (see Figure M.68).

Figure M.68 Walther Meissner (Meiβner) (1882–1974).

Meissner effect {Meiβner effect}

[general] The obliteration of the magnetic field inside a superconductor in comparison to a regular conducting medium. Described in 1933 by the German physicists Walther Meissner (1882–1974) and Robert Ochsenfeld (1901–1993).

Meitner, Lise (1878–1968)

[atomic, nuclear] Physicist from Austria, famous for her contributions to radioactivity and the description of the concept of nuclear fission with her nephew Otto Robert Frisch (1904–1979) in 1938. Unfortunately Lise Meitner was not awarded the Nobel prize in Physics for her contributions to the work of fission, although her colleague Otto Hahn (1879–1968) was awarded in 1944 (see Figure M.69).

Figure M.69 (a) Lise Meitner (1878–1968) at the 1933 Solvay conference (Structure et propriétés des noyaux atomiques; Structure and properties of the atomic nucleus, under the leadership of Paul Langevin) on the front row, second from the right. Two other notable female physicists represented at this conference are also shown: Marie Curie (1867–1934) and Irène Joliot-Curie (1897–1956). (b) Lisa Meitner providing a lecture at the Catholic University in Washington. DC, USA in 1946.

Melting point

[general, thermodynamics] Phase transition TEMPERATURE (T) from solid to LIQUID at a fixed PRESSURE (P) for a constant VOLUME (V) of medium. Phase transition in the opposing direction is referred to as FUSION. For the melting PHASE TRANSITION, the change in Gibbs free ENERGY is zero: $\Delta G = 0$; this provides the condition during melting defined by the ENTROPY (S) as $\Delta S = \Delta H/T$ at constant temperature with H the enthalpy of the system. Under constant temperature, the melting point will be a function of pressure (volume of a solid is fixed), such as the one observed underneath the blade of an ice skater. The melting point can be lowered by the addition of a CHEMICAL COMPOUND, providing "freezing-point depression." Lowering the melting point will require a lower temperature under constant pressure to achieve melting; hence a solid can be promoted to melt by spreading for instance SALT on ice, as used on roadways during snow storms or FREEZING rain. The melting point as a function of pressure or volume can be found from the PHASE DIAGRAM plot in a pressure–volume curve (PV diagram), or pressure–temperature curve (PT diagram) (*also see* **FREEZING POINT** *and* **FREEZING**) (see Figure M.70).

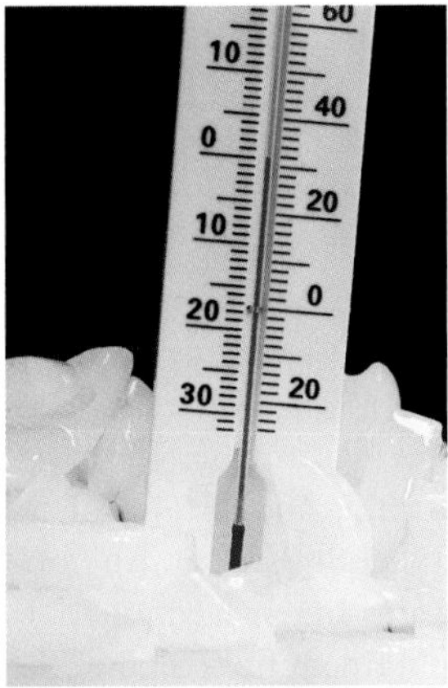

Figure M.70 Melting ice with water with a thermometer indicating 0°C, the melting point for ice.

Membrane

[biomedical, chemical, general] All cells in biological entities are sealed off by a membrane. The membrane provides various functions, ranging from protection of the cellular content, transportation of nutrients (oxygen) and waste, and communication with neighboring cells, to extending its function to acquiring information about the chemical and mechanical circumstances affecting the CELL. The content of the cell is primarily designed to sustain the cell, and supporting a renewable ENERGY source: ATP (ADENOSINE TRI-PHOSPHATE). The CELL MEMBRANE is a hydrophobic lipid bilayer, repelling the water DIPOLE. Membranes are mostly made up of phospholipids such as amino phospholipids, phosphatidylcholine, phosphatidylglycerol, phosphatidylinositol, and sphingomyelins. The phosphatidylinositol structure provides one polar head and two nonpolar lipid chains, with inherent chemical properties. The cell membrane has specific properties related to chemical BARRIERS, chemical transport, and related electric trans-membrane (electric-) potential. The cell membrane is highly permeable to a large selection of hydrophobic molecules, and in particular to lipid-soluble solutes such as ALCOHOL, next to vitamin A and vitamin E, as well as steroids. In contrast, the permeability of water-soluble or hydrophilic molecules is restricted to mainly small molecules only. The cell membrane maintains a transmembrane potential that is derived from the ION gradients, described by the NERNST EQUATION for the membrane potential. The key ions involved in the chemical potential are POTASSIUM (K^+), sodium (Na^+), and chlorine (Cl^-). In addition to the steady-state potential, the membrane can depolarize as well for an ACTION POTENTIAL that can communicate events to the central nervous system and the commands to the brain or to the muscles and the organs and glands. The DEPOLARIZATION process involves the active and passive transport of the key ions across the membrane by means of ion pumps and opening and closing of selective pores: gates. One example is the ion selectivity of the KcsA Potassium channel. This ION CHANNEL has the ability to discriminate between K^+ and Na^+ ions, providing a mechanism for K^+ ions to pass through approximately 1000 times more rapidly than Na^+ ions. This channel has an equilibrium diameter of 40 Å, including the channel protein and a small portion of the membrane. The channel has an approximate length of 89 Å, including the length of the channel protein, as well as 30 Å intracellular space and 25 Å extracellular space. The channel protein provides what is known as the sodium–potassium pump as well as mitigating the passive ion conductivity. The potassium pump provides an active mechanism-of-action to restore the intra- and extracellular ion gradients. The electronic formation of the action potential is described by the HODGKIN–HUXLEY EQUATION. Transmembrane proteins that form the ion channels span the width of the lipid bilayer and support many cellular functions. Some of the transmembrane functions include proton transport (i.e., ACTIVE TRANSPORT: proton pump), water transport, but also act as receptors. A large portion of transmembrane sensors are chemical sensors in nature and belong to the seven transmembrane helix (7TM) family. Due to its chemical response, this receptor protein is popular in medication, and better than 50% of therapeutic and recreational drugs target members of this particular family. One specific receptor example is the transmembrane protein BACTERIORHODOPSIN. Bacteriorhodopsin has a segment that is light sensitive and responds with the onset of a process that can lead to an action potential within femtoseconds of being excited by a PHOTON. Note that a full transmembrane potential is required to reach a threshold of chemical imbalance (deviation from the steady state NERNST POTENTIAL) before the action potential sequence takes full effect. The bacteriorhodopsin harvests light energy and is present in the membranes of some halobacteria as well as in the RODS of the EYE. Bacteriorhodopsin converts the light energy to electrostatic energy, which in turn provides the vehicle to transport protons out of the cell (PTR). The resulting proton gradient (H^+) leads to a large PH gradient across the cell membrane. The acidity is then used to create renewable energy in ATP when the cell allows a proton to move back into the cell, by means of another transmembrane protein, ATP synthase. The PROTON transport is linked with the empirical valence bond (EVB), which defines the breaking and forming of associated chemical bonds, in particular the covalent bonding to hydrogen or dissociation of hydrogen. An important point about the EVB model is that the reaction must be carried out both in water and in the protein. For proton transfer (PT) reactions, the change in free energy of the PT can be obtained if one knows the reaction coefficient (pK_a values) of the donor (DH^+) and the protonated acceptor (AH). The Gibbs reaction energy is described as follows in kcal/mol: $\Delta G_{PT}^{w}\left(DH^{+}+A^{-}\to D+AH\right)_{\infty}=1.38\left(\Delta pK_{a}^{w}\right)$, where ∞ represents the fact that the donor and acceptor are separated by a great DISTANCE (see Figure M.71).

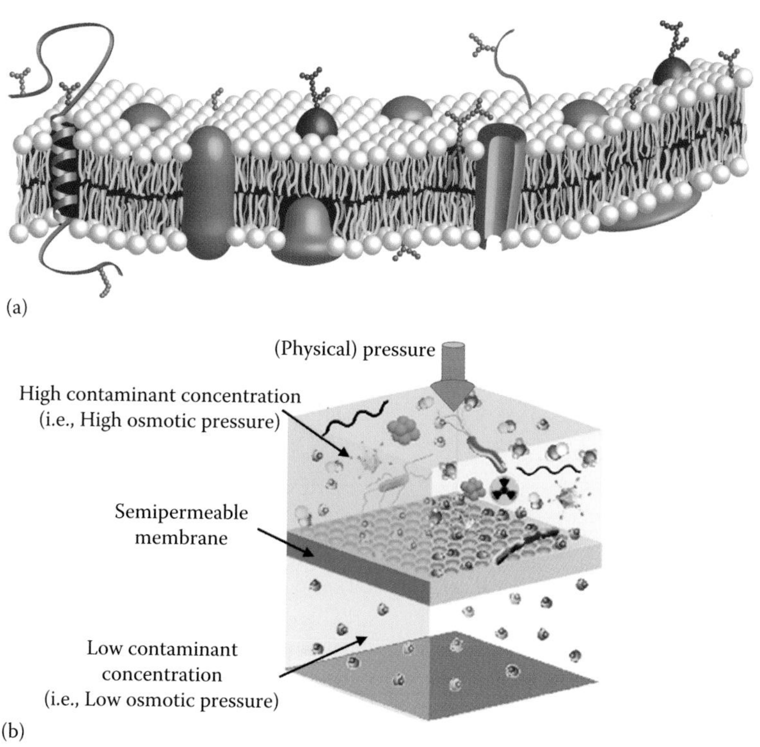

Figure M.71 (a) Illustration of the construction of the membrane of a biological cell and (b) the use of a membrane in water filtration by means of reverse osmosis.

Membrane capacitance

[biomedical, chemical, electronics] Considering a membrane equivalent electronic configuration composed of capacitance (C_m), RESISTANCE (R_i), and CURRENT (I) and voltage (V_{Nernst}, respectively, $\Delta\Phi_m$) sources, the equivalent circuit for a MEMBRANE can be represented by an electronic schematic. The storage of ionic charges on either side of the membrane presents similar concepts as a standard plate CAPACITOR does. This capacitor however is subject to ION leakage and mediated conduction, making the capacitance a time-dependent phenomenon. The cellular membrane ion pumps form the current sources, whereas the QUASI-STEADY-STATE single ion concentrations on the respective sides of the membrane generate a NERNST POTENTIAL (V_{Nernst}). The Nernst potential represents the chemical potential resulting from the ion concentration as well as the membrane ion DIFFUSION with respect to the individual ions: permeability. For additional ions, the membrane potential is described by the Goldman equation (introduced by DAVID E. GOLDMAN (1910–1998), ALAN LLOYD HODGKIN (1914–1998), and BERNARD KATZ (1911–2003); also known as the GOLDMAN–HODGKIN–KATZ VOLTAGE EQUATION): $V_{\text{Goldman}}=(RT/F)$ $\left[p^{*}_{[\text{Na}]}[\text{Na}^{+}]_{\text{out}}+p^{*}_{[\text{K}]}[\text{K}^{+}]_{\text{out}}+p^{*}_{[\text{Cl}]}[\text{Cl}^{-}]_{\text{in}}\right]/\left[p^{*}_{[\text{Na}]}[\text{Na}^{+}]_{\text{in}}+p^{*}_{[\text{K}]}[\text{K}^{+}]_{\text{in}}+p^{*}_{[\text{Cl}]}[\text{Cl}^{-}]_{\text{out}}\right]$. In this concept, the permeability constant for the ions of interest is represented by $p^{*}_{[i]}$, where the subscript signifies the ions: sodium (Na^+), POTASSIUM (K^+), and chlorine (Cl^-); square brackets denote the concentration of the respective ion ([Ion]); T is the temperature; R is the GAS constant ($R=8.314$ J/molK); and $F=96485$ C/mol is the FARADAY CONSTANT. The subscripts “in” and “out” denote the ion migration for the CELL. A typical value for the RESTING POTENTIAL is −90 mV. It is negative because cells are more negative relative to the surrounding medium. Cells that are excitable have the ability to rapidly reverse the potential, causing it to be slightly positive. The potential that is generated in this process is known as the ACTION POTENTIAL.

M

The total sum of the currents can be described using KIRCHHOFF'S LAW (named after GUSTAV ROBERT KIRCHHOFF [1824–1887]): $C_m(d\Delta\Phi_m/dt) + I_{Na} + I_K + I_{Leak} - I_{pump} = 0$, where I_{Leak} represents the current resulting from free moving charges through orifices in the membrane, $\Delta\Phi_m$ is the Nernst potential across the membrane, I_{pump} is the current composed of ions forced into the cellular system, and I_{Na} and I_K respectively indicate the current from gated ion conduction for sodium and potassium. Including the respective ion conductance (g_i) and NERNST POTENTIAL for the ions involving the membrane capacitance is tied to the ion FLOW under steady-state conditions by OHM'S LAW as $C_m(d\Delta\Phi_m/dt) = I_{pump} - (\Delta\Phi_m - \Delta\Phi_{Na})g_{Na} - (\Delta\Phi_m - \Delta\Phi_K)g_K - (\Delta\Phi_m - \Delta\Phi_{Leak})g_{Leak}$. Also considered is the equivalent membrane circuit (see Figure M.72).

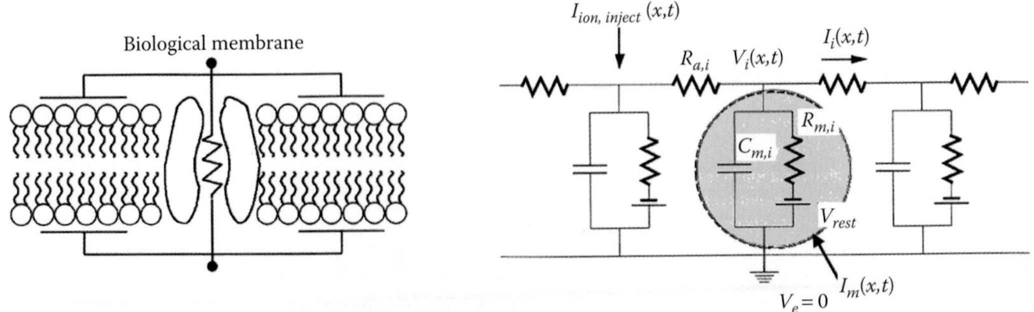

Figure M.72 Equivalent circuit for a biological cell, generally also capable of producing an action-potential.

Membrane potential

[biophysics, chemical, energy] Also called RESTING POTENTIAL of a CELL. Cells have the chemical and genetic content enclosed by membranes. The MEMBRANE controls the in and out flows of ions (e.g., nutrients and wastes) by means of voltage-gated gap junctions and ION channels. The trans-membrane potential is the result of ion composition difference between intracellular and extracellular compartments, next to the POLARIZATION of the molecules of the membrane in specific locations such as the ion channels. For every cell, two ionic solutions are separated by a membrane with similar and dissimilar ions on either side. The membrane is apparently permeable to some of the ions. This permeability results in both an electric potential and OSMOTIC PRESSURE across the membrane. This condition is known and the DONNAN EQUILIBRIUM between the two sides of the membrane. The CELL MEMBRANE is assumed to contain a one-for-one sodium/POTASSIUM ($Na^+ \Leftrightarrow K^+$) exchange pump. However, the cell membrane is 50 times more permeable to K^+ and chlorine (Cl^-) than to Na^+. The net efflux of 388 ions requires a net efflux of 69,840 H_2O molecules to maintain osmotic balance. In the intracellular compartment, potassium levels are high in comparison to the extracellular compartment. Sodium levels are high in the extracellular compartment in comparison to the intracellular compartment. In addition to the Na^+/K^+-pump there will be free DIFFUSION, which is described by Fick's law: $J_S = -D(d[S]/dx)$, with D the diffusion coefficient and $[S]$ the arbitrary ion concentration and dx the DISTANCE over which the diffusion takes place. Additionally, there is a significant concentration of negatively charged, impermeable proteins in the intracellular compartment that accounts for an appreciable portion of the NEGATIVE CHARGE in the intracellular compartment relative to the extracellular compartment. The separation of charges on either side of the cell membrane describes a CAPACITOR that has an electric potential associated with the charge distribution. A standard parallel plate capacitor consists of two conducting plates of area separated by distance *d*. A POSITIVE CHARGE (q^+) resides on one plate (i.e., extracellular liquid), while an effective negative charge (q^-) resides on the other (i.e., intracellular liquid). The electric field between the plates is $E = Q/A\varepsilon_0 = \sigma_e/\varepsilon_0$, where Q represents the total charge present on the plate with surface area A, yielding a surface charge density σ_e and ε_0 is the electric permittivity. This charge distribution provides an electric potential: $V = -d(Q/A\varepsilon_0) = Q/C_m$, where d is the separation between the two plates and C_m represents the membrane capacitance. The initial description of the membrane potential used the ion distribution. WALTHER HERMANN NERNST (1864–1941) developed an equation simply describing membrane potential as being based on differing ion concentrations on the outside (extracellular: *e*) and inside (intracellular *i*) of the membrane, which is described in equilibrium case (i.e., Donnan equilibrium,) as $V_m = V_i - V_e = (RT/nF)\ln([S]_e/[S]_i) = (KT/q)\ln([S]_e/[S]_i) = 26\ \mathrm{mV}\ \ln([S]_e/[S]_i)$, where $F = 95{,}484.56\ \mathrm{C/mol}$ is the Faraday's constant, that is, the charge on a MOLE of electrons multiplied by n the number of moles in the SOLUTION, q is the charge, $[S]_e$ is the extracellular ion concentration of one specific ion ("S"), $[S]_i$ is the intracellular ion concentration, $R = 8.314\ \mathrm{J/mol{*}K}$ is the IDEAL GAS constant, and K = the Boltzmann constant. This factors in that, in order for an ion to contribute to a membrane potential, the membrane must be permeable to that ion (*also see* **ACTION POTENTIAL**). The main ions involved in the transmembrane displacement current are POTASSIUM (K^+), sodium (Na^+), chlorine (Cl^-), and calcium (Ca^{2+}). In resting cells, the ion current from chlorine and calcium can be neglected. Each ion has a net current associated with the mobility (represented by the conductance) described as $I_S = g_S(V_m - V_S)$, where the subscript m designates the membrane potential and g_S is the ionic conductance for ion S. DAVID E. GOLDMAN (1910–1998) worked together with SIR ALAN LLOYD HODGKIN (1914–1998) and SIR BERNARD KATZ (1911–2003) to expand on the NERNST EQUATION including all PERMEANT ions describing the membrane potential as $V_m = (58\,\mathrm{mV})\log_{10}\left(p^*_K[K^+]_e + p^*_{Na}[Na^+]_e + p^*_{Cl}[Cl^-]_i / p^*_K[K^+]_i + p^*_{Na}[Na^+]_i + p^*_{Cl}[Cl^-]_e\right)$ (often referred to as the Goldman equation), where p^*_S is the RELATIVE PERMEABILITY for each specific ion. Some of the ion channels are responsive to external influences such as sound, GRAVITY, OSMOTIC PRESSURE gradients, and more, and these ion channels operate under a principle referred to as MECHANOSENSITIVE ACTION (see Figure M.73).

M

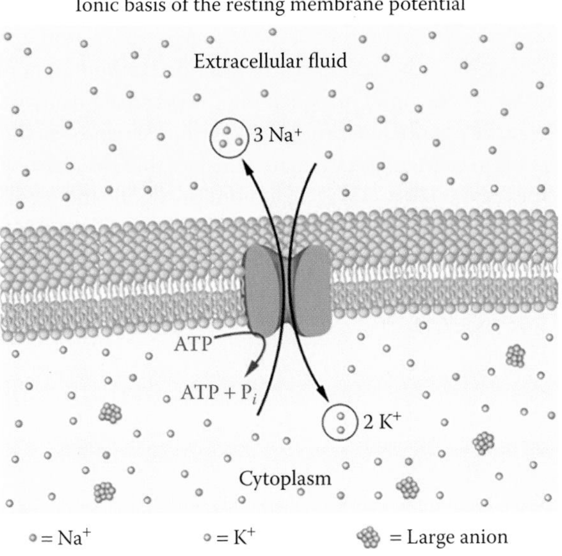

Figure M.73 Cell electrical potential mechanism based on chemical gradients.

Mendel, Gregor Johann (1822–1884)

[biomedical, computational, general] Scientist and friar in the then Austrian empire, now Czech Republic. Dr. Mendel realized the concept of chance in combination theory, in particular related to genetic transfer of recessive traits. He described in 1865 how the chance of the expression of the attributes of the recessive gene is related to the occurrence of the square root of the chance of the gene being carried forward (general concept of heredity). He is partially known as the father of modern genetic causality statistics. One of Mendel's professors in Vienna was Christian Andreas Doppler (1803–1853) (see Figure M.74).

Figure M.74 Gregor Johann Mendel (1822–1884).

Mendeleev, Dmitri Ivanovich [Дми́трий Ива́нович Менделе́ев] (1834–1907)

[atomic, chemical, mechanics, nuclear, quantum, solid-state] Russian scientist and chemist. Mendeleev's discoveries of a pattern in the structural and energetic configuration of the elements led to the composition of the periodic table of elements, based on the numerical patterns in atomic weights of known substances. He proposed the periodic law, describing the electron configuration pattern for the ranking of elements. The quantum theory was essential in explaining the perceived regularities. Mendeleev's work was pivotal in revealing the atom as the essential building block of the elements whether or not in molecular form. The periodic table is also referred to as Mendeleev's chart. The fact that the chart had several gaps led him to discover three additional elements: gallium (1871), scandium (in 1879), and germanium (1886). Additional work of Mendeleev was in THERMODYNAMICS and GAS LAW. He described the concept of critical temperature before the experimental and theoretical verification in the 1860s by Thomas Andrews (1813–1885) (see Figure M.75).

Figure M.75 Dmitri Ivanovich Mendeleev (1834–1907).

Meniscus

[biomedical, mechanics] From the Greek word "μηνισκοζ" meaning crescent. Cartilage-based disk with the shape of a "C" positioned between the tibia and the femur acting as a SHOCK ABSORBER and reducer of FRICTION in the knee joint (see Figure M.76).

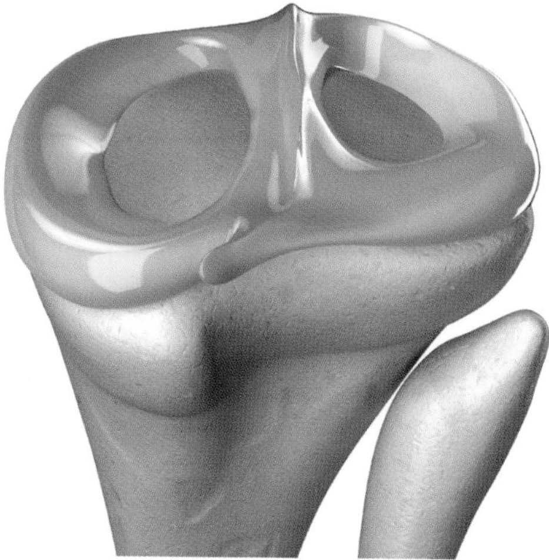

Figure M.76 Meniscus of the knee in the human leg.

Meniscus

[fluid dynamics, general] The curvature of a liquid surface in a confined space that holds the LIQUID to the surface by cohesive force, either concave (attractive force from the container, i.e., CAPILLARY [e.g., GLASS], is greater than the cohesive forces within the liquid) or convex (greater COHESION within the liquid) (see Figure M.77).

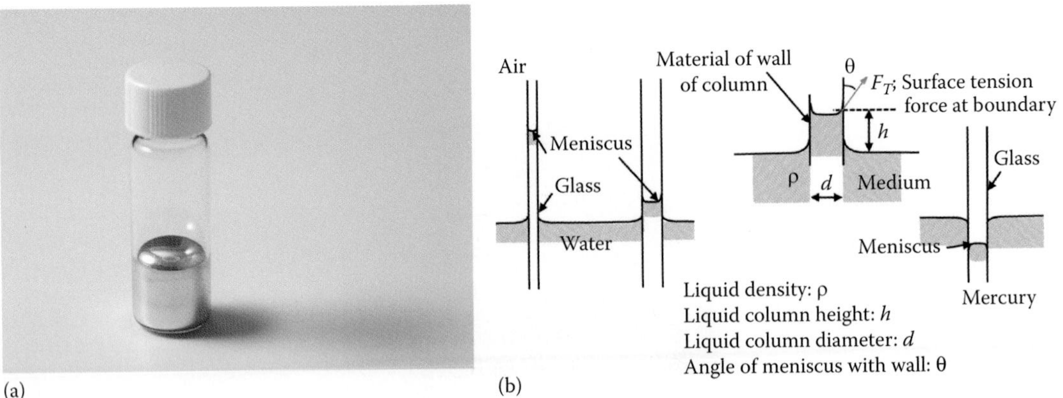

Figure M.77 (a,b) Liquid surface meniscus on mercury column in narrow flask.

Meniscus lenses

[biomedical, general, optics] Thin LENS used in spectacles (EYE glasses) for corrective VISION (see Figure M.78).

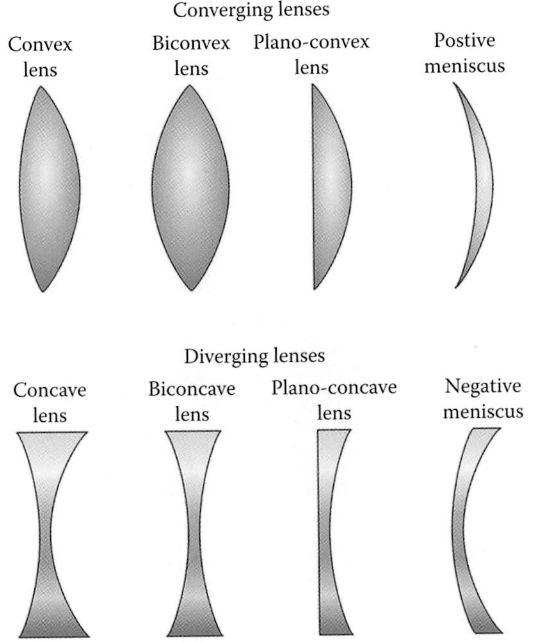

Figure M.78 Meniscus lens concept.

Menten, Maud Leonora (1879–1960)

[biomedical, computational] Canadian scientist, primarily known for her work related to MEDICINE, specifically on chemical reactions and enzyme KINEMATICS (*also see* **LEONOR MICHAELIS (1875–1949)** *and* **MICHAELIS–MENTEN EQUATION**) (see Figure M.79).

Figure M.79 Maud Leonora Menten (1879–1960). (Courtesy of Smithsonian Institution, Washington, DC.)

Menzel, Donald Howard (1901–1976)

[atomic, chemical, nuclear] Scientist from the United States. His work with RAYMOND THAYER BIRGE (1887–1980) led to the discovery of radio isotopes of hydrogen that occur under normal circumstance in a fraction of the whole with mass number 1 and 2 respectively in a 45,000:1 ratio, established in 1931. Additional contributions to the solid state and chemistry knowledge were in the description of the chemical structure of stars as well as the parameters of the physical structure of the CHROMOSPHERE of the Sun (see Figure M.80).

Figure M.80 Donald Howard Menzel (1901–1976), photograph by Babette Whipple. (Courtesy of Elizabeth Menzel Davis.)

Mercury barometer

[astrophysics, general, geophysics] Hollow device that has one LEG vacuum sealed, whereas the other leg is exposed to the outside AIR. The shape can be straight cylinder, U-shaped, or tube in a basin exposed to outside air with the top sealed. Through the law of COMMUNICATING VESSELS, the column of mercury rises and lowers when the force on the exposed mercury MENISCUS varies with the external pressure; hence, the height in the VACUUM column is an indication of the force applied by the outside air, with height (h) reaching to the edge of the ATMOSPHERE and density ρ, on the surface area in equivalence to the force applied by the height of the column of mercury. Hence the PRESSURE (P) is sometimes expressed in height (h) of millimeters mercury from $P = \rho g h$. The first MERCURY BAROMETER was introduced by EVANGELISTA TORRICELLI (1608–1647) in 1643. The term mercury barometer is attributed to ROBERT BOYLE (1627–1691) (see Figure M.81).

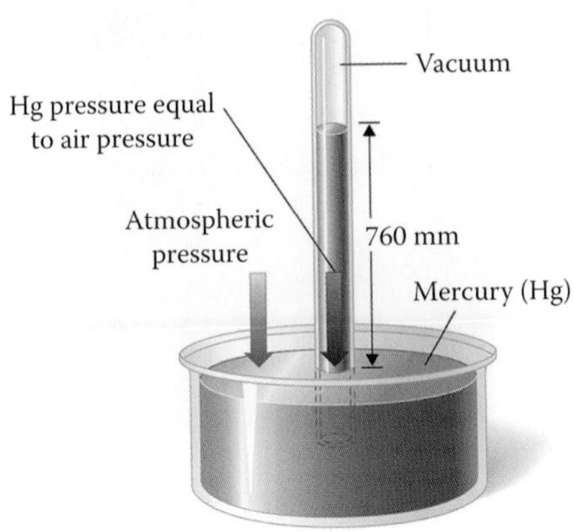

Figure M.81 Diagram of open mercury barometer. (Courtesy of Bruce A. Averill and Patricia Eldredge.)

Mercury cell

[general] Solid-state disposable BATTERY with "dry-cell" potential of $1.4V$. The advantage of the mercury cell battery is the small size (as used for instance in calculators, HEARING aids, and watches).

Mersenne, "father" Marin (1588–1648)

[acoustics, computational, general] Scientist, theologian, mathematician, and experimentalist from France. Marin Mersenne is often referred to as the father of ACOUSTICS. Father Mersenne was a contemporary of Constantijn Huygens (1596–1687), composer and poet, and the father of the physicist CHRISTIAAN HUYGENS (1629–1695) from the Netherlands, and GALILEO GALILEI (1564–1642), with both he exchanged scientific communications, as well as with numerous other international collaborators of that era. His specific interests were in restructuring the European mathematics efforts and worked with Étienne Pascal (1588–1651), as well as his son BLAISE PASCAL (1623–1662) among other people. Due to his fascination with music, he also became well versed in the acoustics phenomena and described the technical details in 1627, including the dependence of the FREQUENCY (ν) on a string as a function of the square root of the applied tension (F_T) and with respect to the length (ℓ) and mass (m), yielding the resonant frequencies of a string with linear mass density $\mu_\ell = m/\ell$

(specifically accounting for the diameter of the string), providing base frequency ($n = 1$) and higher harmonics ($n = 1, 2, 3, \ldots$): $\nu_n = n/2\ell\sqrt{(F_T/\mu_\ell)}$. His work also provided an in-depth definition and range of values for the speed of SOUND (see Figure M.82).

Figure M.82 "Father" Marin Mersenne (1588–1648).

Merton mean speed theorem

[computational, general] Lemma proposed by a group of academics from Oxford, United Kingdom (the so-called Oxford Calculators of Merton College), and French collaborators in the fourteenth century (including the mathematician NICOLE ORESME [c. 1320–1382]), stating that a body that is unvaryingly accelerated will travel an equal DISTANCE as a body with uniform speed, when the accelerated body has a speed that is half its final velocity. The theorem attempts to quantify uniformly accelerated MOTION by matching it to uniform motion.

Meson

[energy, general, nuclear, quantum] Elementary particle component of one quark and one antiquark. A short-lived particle carrying a positive, negative, or zero charge, and having a variable mass in multiples of the mass of the electron. Also called mesotron. They are the complementary particles of BARYON, another subclass of the PARTICLE group HADRON. Mesons, which obey BOSE–EINSTEIN STATISTICS and have zero or integral SPIN ($s = 0, 1, 2, \ldots$), are also known as bosons. The known mesons are π, K, ρ, ω, –; K (heavy), KAON, L (light), mu (μ) and pi (π), and PION; and most recently a four-quark hadron: Z(4430) has been introduced, consisting of two quarks and two antiquarks. In contrast, baryons obey FERMI–DIRAC STATISTICS and have half-integral spin; they are also known as fermions. Masses of the known mesons as well as baryons range from one-seventh of that of the PROTON for the pi meson, extending 10 times the proton mass. Mesons are subjected to the STRONG NUCLEAR FORCE, in contrast to the LEPTON (see Figure M.83).

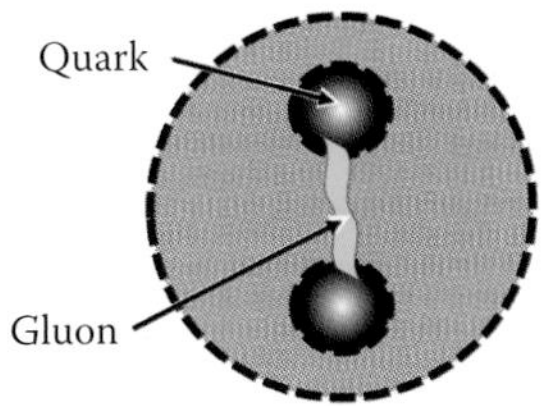

Figure M.83 Graphical representation of the Meson concept.

Meson theory of nuclear forces

[atomic, nuclear] Hypothesis basing the assumption of a nucleon–nucleon potential, a MESON field, which has similarities with electromagnetic fields however with a much greater force and much shorter range. Also known as the Yukawa theory.

Mesosphere

[energy, geophysics] Atmospheric layer between the stratopause and the mesopause, at an altitude between approximately 50 and 80 km. A type of LIGHTNING referred to as sprites can appear in the mesosphere above thunderstorms. In this layer, near the North and South POLES peculiarly, high-altitude noctilucent clouds are sometimes formed (see Figure M.84).

Figure M.84 Mesosphere of earth's atmosphere.

M

Metabolic activity

[biomedical, chemical, thermodynamics] The full complement of all chemical reactions that supports and maintains the cellular ACTIVITY (i.e., "life") in an organism. Metabolic activity involves the transformation of MATTER to ENERGY on a cellular level. Both ELEMENTS are required to sustain life. Two types of metabolic processes are available on a chemical level: anabolic and catabolic. The anabolic METABOLISM is constructive, forming large molecules from small molecules in an ENDOTHERMIC PROCESS. The catabolic mechanism is exothermic and breaks down large molecules. Every person has an individualized metabolic rate, depending on hormonal balances and past and present activity, with inherent AGE and gender related implications. Due to this individualized metabolic activity, a purely nutrition-based weight control by means of diets never yields the same outcome for everyone. A baseline metabolic rate can be used linking CALORIC consumption requirements against the weight of the biological entity.

Metabolic flux analysis (MFA)

[biomedical, chemical, computational] Methodology for the determination of the migration of metabolic chemical pathway fluxes. The intracellular fluxes are derived from a model for the major intracellular reactions based on intracellular MASS BALANCE for all respective metabolites. The stoichiometric model defines the metabolic flux-pathway map, representing the CONSERVATION OF MASS on a purely chemical level, that is, atomic constituents. The parameters used in the computational process are the physical quantities of extracellular fluxes, as measured by chemical concentrations, including the derived representative uptake rates of substrates as well as secretion rates of metabolites. The FLUX calculations provide a multiparameter diagram of the biochemical reactions with an approximation of the steady-state rate for each individual reaction in the diagram (i.e., the flux); this yields a metabolic flux map. MFA studies are executed by making cells consume a radioactively labeled substrate (e.g., ^{13}C-labeled GLUCOSE). Subsequently the incorporation of the ISOTOPE is measured to determine the reaction mechanism. The downstream metabolites are derived from mass spectrometry. The computational model of the intracellular metabolic network defines the pathway fluxes in association with physical measurements of extracellular nutrient consumption and constituent excretion rates of the respective isotope- labeled data. The detection mechanism replies on the production of microbes with imbedded ^{13}C-labeled glucose, followed by gas-CHROMATOGRAPHY mass spectrometric QUANTIFICATION of amino acids with protein-bound ^{13}C-patterns. By systematically accounting for all extracellular ^{13}C in and out fluxes as well as all other major intracellular pathways, the MFA can simulate and recreate the cellular METABOLISM based on comprehensive flux maps. The metabolic flux analysis network describes the conversion of fundamental raw material S_0 into substance S (consider for instance the intake of substrate from outside of the cell). Subsequently, substance S is converted into material A and B through the respective reactions $r1$ and $r2$. Furthermore, A is converted to chemical substance C by reaction $r3$, and reaction $r4$ converts constituent B into D. In general, the reaction in the map does not contain the specific stoichiometric information. The map is supplied with additional biochemical reactions, for which the stoichiometric relationships have been established and verified. The following examples are an indication of potential sequence of events: glucose + PEP → glucose − 6 − P + pyruvate, where PEP represents phosphoenolpyruvic ACID, which can be converted to glucose; respectively: pyruvate + NADH → lactate + NAD$^+$, or glucose − 6 − P + ATP → 2 − glyceraldehyde − 3 − P + ADP, where ATP (ADENOSINE TRIPHOSPHATE) and ADP (ADENOSINE DIPHOSPHATE) are the energized and reduced forms of the renewable intercellular ENERGY source and NADH (nicotinamide adenine dinucleotide) the coenzyme and electron donor. The potential reaction balance proceeds as follows: reaction 0 (raw material conversion): $S_0\,\overrightarrow{r0}\,S$; respectively $S\,\overrightarrow{r1}\,A$, $S\,\overrightarrow{r2}\,B$, $A\,\overrightarrow{r3}\,C$, and $B\,\overrightarrow{r4}\,D$. In these cases, the material balance turns out to be: $dS_0/dt = -r_0$; $(dS/dt) = r_0 - r_1 - r_2$; $dA/dt = r_1 - r_3$, $dB/dt = r_3 - r_4$; $dC/dt = r_3$; $dD/dt = r_4$, where r_i is the respective reaction rate for each process, which can be represented in matrix format, yielding the stoichiometric matrix $\tilde{G}$, and the reactions are captured by the reaction vector

$$\tilde{v} = \begin{pmatrix} r_0 \\ r_1 \\ r_2 \\ r_3 \\ r_4 \end{pmatrix},$$

providing

$$\begin{pmatrix} S_0 \\ S \\ A \\ B \\ C \\ D \end{pmatrix} = \tilde{G}^T\tilde{v} = \begin{bmatrix} -1 & 0 & 0 & 0 & 0 \\ 1 & -1 & -1 & 0 & 0 \\ 0 & 1 & 0 & -1 & 0 \\ 0 & 0 & 1 & 0 & -1 \\ 0 & 0 & 0 & 1 & 0 \\ 0 & 0 & 0 & 0 & 1 \end{bmatrix} \begin{pmatrix} r_0 \\ r_1 \\ r_2 \\ r_3 \\ r_4 \end{pmatrix},$$

where

$$\begin{pmatrix} S_0 \\ S \\ A \\ B \\ C \\ D \end{pmatrix}$$

represents the state vector, containing the state variables (see Figure M.85).

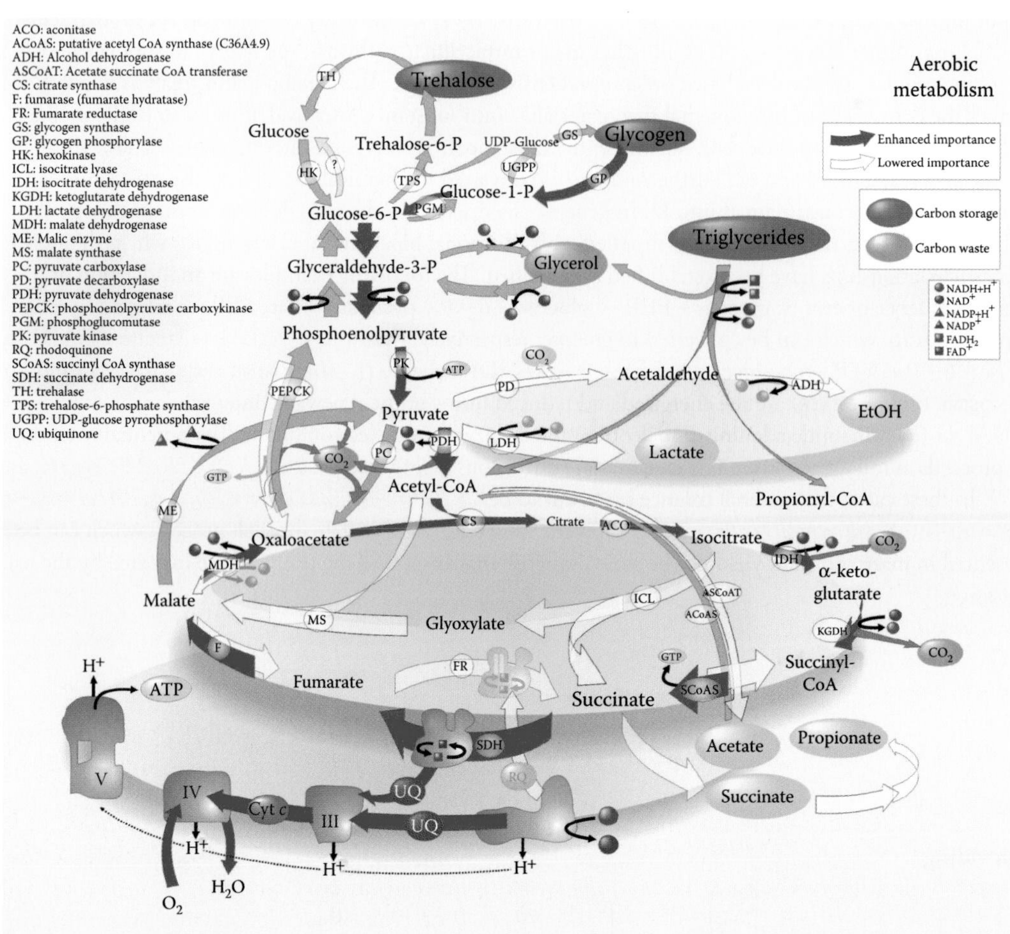

Figure M.85 Metabolic activity schematics. (Courtesy of Intermediary metabolism; Bart P. Braeckman, Koen Houthoofd, Jacques R. Vanfleteren. Wormbook; Intermediary metabolism (February 16, 2009), WormBook, ed. The C. elegans Research Community, WormBook, doi/10.1895/wormbook.1.146.1, http://www.wormbook.org: http://www.wormbook.org/chapters/www_intermetabolism/intermetabolism.pdf.)

Metabolism

[biomedical, chemical, computational] Cellular physiological process of chemical conversion (e.g., consumption; for instance, proteins and carbohydrates) and formation of the renewable ENERGY source ADENOSINE TRIPHOSPHATE (ATP) from ADENOSINE DIPHOSPHATE (ADP) and phosphor under influence of nucleic ACID catalysts and enzymes such as insulin. The process is dependent on the formation of solutes from solids (with a specific rate constant) and relies on DIFFUSION for some of the supply passive mechanisms as well as ACTIVE TRANSPORT through the cellular MEMBRANE. The metabolic pathway also involves the RESPIRATION process for oxygen supply used for OXIDATION and exothermic reactions. The metabolic process can be modeled in a first-order approximation by an EULER METHOD, linking the respective chemical constituent gradient in the chemical PHASE TRANSITION (f) by location (x_n, with neighbor x_{n+1}) as $x_{n+1} = x_n + \Delta x f\left(x_n, y_n\right)$, and in second order by the RUNGE–KUTTA approximation $k_1 = xf\left(x_n, y_n\right)$, where k_1 is the formation rate of phosphorylation of enzyme R by kinase, with R representing the concentration of enzyme R, x a location parameter;

$k_2 = xf\left(x_n + (1/2)x, y_n + (1/2)k_1\right)$, where k_2 is the loss rate of phosphorylation of enzyme R by a pH change influence, and $x_{n+1} = x_n + k_2 + \mathcal{O}(x^3)$, with $\mathcal{O}$ a chemical reaction function (with an associated reaction response).

Metacenter

[fluid dynamics] The theoretical vertical line passing through the center of BUOYANCY with respect to the vertical line passing through the CENTER OF GRAVITY when a floating body is tipped, hence crating a torque. The center of buoyancy is the effective center of the displaced fluid (e.g., the FLUID displaced by the hull of a ship), the point where the buoyant force is theoretically acting on under steady-state conditions (see Figure M.86).

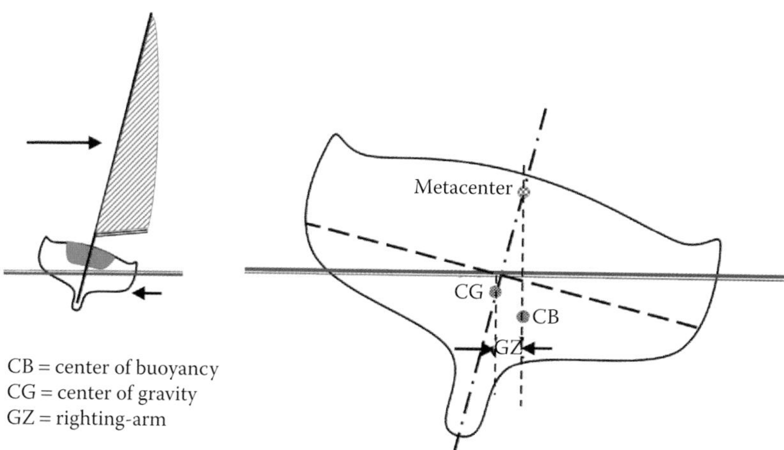

Figure M.86 Metacenter, in this case outlined for a tipping sail-boat.

Metacentric height (h_m)

[fluid dynamics] Condition for the stability of a solid floating body. A specific example is found for ships, in particular with respect to a solid load. The DISTANCE between the center of mass of the floating body and the METACENTER for the floating body (h_m), where the CENTER OF GRAVITY should exert a torque with respect to the metacenter that forces the floating object to erect itself, meaning prevent it from tipping over. Metacentric height has consequences for the natural period of rolling for the hull of a ship. A large metacentric height will result in shorter periods of roll, which will create uncomfortable sensations generally for passengers. Specifically there is an optimal range associated with the metacentric height for stability and comfort. The period of roll (T_{roll}) is expressed as $T_{\text{roll}} = 2\pi R_g / \sqrt{(gh_m)}$, where g is the GRAVITATIONAL ACCELERATION, and $R_g = \sqrt{(I/A)}$ the RADIUS OF GYRATION, also referred to as gyradius, where I is the MOMENT OF INERTIA of the object in the direction of roll, and A is the surface area of the buoyant object under the LIQUID surface. The radius of gyration is a measure of the size of an object, in this case the surface of a floating body, given by the root mean square distance for a representative number of locations on the surface of the objects and associated parts with respect to the center of gravity over the length of the object. This will place a limitation on the validity of the radius of gyration with respect to a minimum longitudinal dimension.

Metal

[general, mechanics, nuclear, quantum] ELEMENT or alloy with a shine, the metallic shine and have a high density. Metals are generally not pliable. Metals are conductive for electric current and are good thermal conductors at room temperature; however, not all metals are magnetic. Certain metals are LIQUID at room temperature, for instance mercury and gallium-based alloys, since GALLIUM is generally not found in free form. The conductivity of metals is the result of one or more loosely bound valence electrons that can easily be freed. The relative ease of releasing the outer electron results from a low IONIZATION ENERGY and low ELECTRONEGATIVITY for the respective ELEMENTS. Metals are found in the PERIODIC TABLE OF ELEMENTS as groups; group IA and group IIA (the alkali metals, which can be considered the most active metals) and the transition elements, groups IB to VIIIB. Alkali metals have their outermost (VALENCE) electron in an s-electron configuration (the BOHR ATOMIC MODEL) orbit. Metals include, but not limited to, the following elements: aluminum, caesium (cesium), calcium, copper, francium, gallium, germanium, gold, IRON, lead, LITHIUM, mercury, neodymium, platinum, potassium, rubidium, silicon, silver, sodium, TITANIUM, uranium, and additionally alloys such as brass and bronze. Most metal oxides are transparent (most well-known metal oxides: the ceramic [white] aluminum oxide [Al_2O_3], and the transparent silicon oxide [SiO_2]), specifically also forming garnet crystals. The metallic structure relies on the metallic bonds holding the atoms together. Metallic bonds are electromagnetic interactions between atoms resulting from delocalized electrons (the conduction electrons), basically allowing the valence electrons to share hosts. The quantum-mechanical aspect of the metallic bound allows the conduction electrons to distribute their density (as a "cloud") equally over all atoms, where the atoms inherently function as neutral (noncharged) entities. The metallic structure relies on close-packed fitting, with as many atoms as possible into the available atomic volume. Each ATOM in this structure has 12 touching neighbors. For the applicable metals, this is described as "12-co-ordinated." Certain metals are packed less densely (notably those in group 1 of the periodic table), having only 8 neighboring atoms touching. These configurations are called "8-co-ordinated." Generally metals are not dramatically efficient in their organization. Any piece of metal is made up of regions of regularity, consisting of grain boundaries at which the atoms have become misaligned form the ideal homogeneous LATTICE structure, forming "crystal grain." The "crystal grains" allow for the formation of localized current loops, creating localized magnetic fields as described by the BIOT–SAVART LAW. These current loops, and implied associated MAGNETIC FIELD vector, can line up to form a PERMANENT MAGNET.

Metal detector

[electronics, general] Detection device responding to the changes in DIELECTRIC properties, which result in a change in the self-inductance of a coil in an *LRC* circuit (INDUCTOR (*L*), RESISTOR (*R*), and CAPACITOR (*C*) electronic resonator), with the inherent change in resonant frequency $\omega_0 = (LC)^{-(1/2)}$ ($\nu = \omega_0/2\pi$), with the bandwidth defined by the QUALITY FACTOR: $Q = \omega_0 L/R$. The bandwidth provides a means of separation with respect to particular electronic material properties. This mechanism of action is applied to passengers on airport screening, and by treasure hunters looking for coins and jewelry (see Figure M.87).

Figure M.87 Metal detector, popular tool for treasure hunters.

Metal fatigue

[general, mechanics] Localized gradual structural damage to a structure made from alloys or metals resulting from cyclic or infrequent repetitive loading in addition to thermal stress, either gradients or broad range fluctuations (with associated EXPANSION/contraction patterns in three-dimensional configuration). The FATIGUE results from applied nominal maximum stress below the ultimate TENSILE STRESS of the material, and generally less than the yield stress limit. When a certain stress threshold is exceeded, on a MICROSCOPIC level, certain threshold, cracks will form, weakening the integrity of the structure on a MACROSCOPIC scale. The continued exposure to the forces involving the implementation of MATERIAL FATIGUE will eventually result in breakage. Forces can for instance result from geophysical origins such as wind generating a RESONANCE or earthquakes, or man-made such as traffic, and repetitive use. One specific example is the TACOMA NARROWS BRIDGE disaster (November 7, 1940) resulting from a specific wind FLOW causing the suspension cable to provide a resonance VIBRATION (aeroelastic flutter) that made the bridge collapse after an exposure over a 2-year time frame, ultimately resulting in a severe oscillatory MOTION that lasted only a few hours when exposed to a steady 65 km/h wind from the southwestern direction (perpendicular to the axis of the bridge), generating a mixed WAVE pattern consisting of transversal, longitudinal, and rotational vibration modes (see Figure M.88).

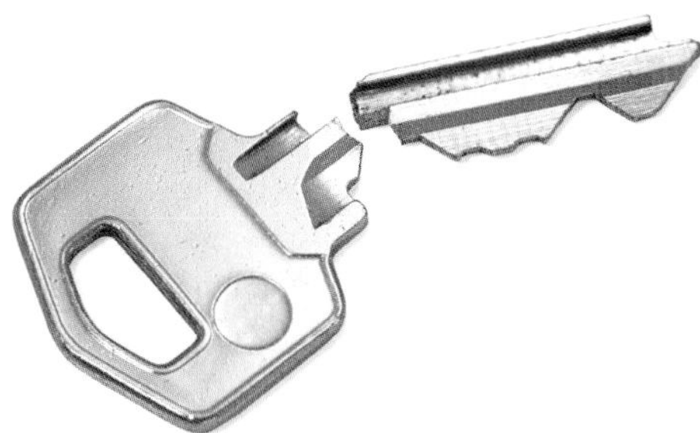

Figure M.88 Broken key that has bent beyond the failure-mode, or bent multiple times, causing thermal restructuring of the internal molecular build-up to loose cohesion.

Metastable state (equilibrium)

[atomic, nuclear, thermodynamics] An excited state of a NUCLEUS or an ATOM with a short lifetime, which returns to the GROUND STATE by the emission of a GAMMA RAY or visible or infra-red electromagnetic emission over a measurable half-life. The excited state of an atom that, in QUANTUM mechanical terms, describes the transition from "forbidden" metastable states, which are less probable than the ALLOWED TRANSITIONS from other vetted EXCITED STATES. Particularly, the lifetime of an excited state that is *longer* than the ordinary excited states and that is universally shorter than the lifetime of the ground state, which is the lowest energy state, and is predominantly stable. Nuclides with identical numbers of protons but different neutrons are referred to as isotopes, in metastable state. The nuclides with measurable ("long-lived") life-time have isomeric energy states that are identified as separate nuclei, respectively, designated as ISOMERS. On a MACROSCOPIC level, this also applies to the nonpreferential, and hence less stable, physical condition of a system that can be long-lived with respect to the system's most stable state. The latter has as example isomerization. In isomerization high-energy isomers are perpetuated by the creation of (conceivably large) BARRIERS in the potential energy, preventing degrading to the ground state. Atomic metastable conditions can be identified by for instance the ZEEMAN EFFECT, based on spectroscopic diagnostic principles. Another macroscopic example on LATTICE base for carbon at standard temperature and pressure is diamond as a metastable form. Diamond can degenerate to graphite, providing excess kinetic energy, only after overcoming the POTENTIAL BARRIER associated with the crystalline LATTICE structure, captured by dispensation of activation energy. The computational aspects of metastability can for instance describe the energies and lifetimes of ionic and molecular states, including but not limited to vibronic and rotational–vibronic states. On macroscopic scale, the metastable state can refer to a condition that may release potential energy as kinetic energy, such as an avalanche for a metastable mass of snow on the edge of a mountain cliff (*also see* LASER) (see Figure M.89).

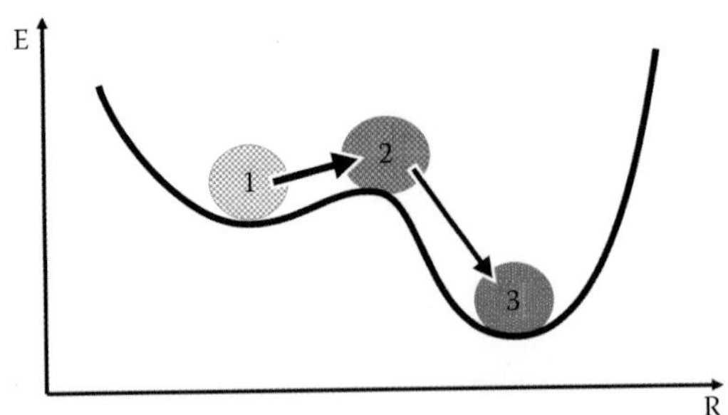

Figure M.89 Energy configuration for a metastable state: a metastable state of weaker energy configuration [potentially an atomic bond, or vibrational state, or cohesive attraction on macroscopic scale] (#1), a transitional 'saddle' configuration (#2) and a final state of stronger bond (#3).

Meteor

[astrophysics, geophysics, mechanics] Encounters of galactic projectiles with the Earth's ATMOSPHERE, were the burn up, and create a visible flash. The observed flash is referred to as a meteor. Meteors occur in the thermosphere. Meteors enter the Earth's ATMOSPHERE at velocities generally ranging from 10 km/s to 75 km/s, keeping in mind that the earth's angular velocity in an orbit around the Sun is on average 30 km/s. Also known as "shooting star," a visible streak of light across the field of view. One of the annually reoccurring meteor showers is the Perseid meteor shower in the first part of August, associated with the COMET Swift Tuttle. The Perseid meteor shower received its name from the direction at which it is seen entering the Earth's ATMOSPHERE, with the constellation Perseus in the background. This particular meteor shower has been dated back to 36 AD in Chinese astronomical records, but the annual recurrence was documented by Adolphe Quetelet (1796–1874) from Belgium in 1835 (see Figure M.90).

Figure M.90 Meteor entering the Earth's atmosphere.

Meteorite

[astrophysics, geophysics, mechanics] Solid space debris released by the break-up of comets and ASTEROIDS.

Meteoroid

[astrophysics, geophysics, mechanics] The smallest projectiles within the SOLAR SYSTEM, ranging in size from large fragments released by the breakdown of ASTEROIDS or comets, to dust expressed as extremely small micrometeoroids.

Meteorology

[energy, fluid dynamics, general, geophysics] Field of PHYSICS dealing with physical phenomena in the lower part of EARTH's ATMOSPHERE directly related to the weather and providing warnings for people in the path of inclement weather. Several devices have been developed in relation to this field such as the ANEMOMETER, BAROMETER, HYGROMETER, RAIN GAUGE, THERMOMETER, and wind vane (see Figure M.91).

Figure M.91 Aspect of meteorology. Illustrations of the duties and roles in meteorology.

Meter (m)

[general] Dimension of length in the Systèm International (SI) units system. The origins of the meter date back to the early part of the eighteenth century. The meter was defined as the length of a PENDULUM having a half-period of 1 s; later this was superseded under the rule of Napoleon Bonaparte (1769–1821) in 1791 as 10^{-7} time the length of the meridian through Paris from the pole to the equator. However, there is an inherent error in this definition due to the flattening of the EARTH due to its rotation, introducing a deviation of 0.2 mm. In 1889 the meter was defined as the DISTANCE between two marks on a bar of alloy of platinum with 10% iridium, "accurate" within 0.0001%. In 1960 the definition was replaced by the wavelength of the emission from krypton-86 (transition between $2p_{10}$ and $5d_5$, generating a wavelength of 605.7 nm), specifically 1/299,792,458 (reference speed of light) of the distance traveled in a VACUUM over 1 s interval (placing the accuracy within the definition of measurement of time).

Method of moments

[acoustics, computational, fluid dynamics, mechanics] One of the oldest NUMERICAL (i.e., discrete) computational methods for obtaining point estimators, primarily based on the LAW OF LARGE NUMBERS. The SOLUTION mechanism is based on solving linear partial differential equations that have been reformulated as integral equations. In an arbitrary experiment, there will be an observable, real-valued variable X based on PROBABILITY. The distribution of the variable X can be assigned with n unknown parameters. The set of parameters can be represented by a virtual n-dimensional parameter space, with the vector coordinate $\vec{\chi} = (\chi_1, \chi_2, \chi_3, \ldots, \chi_k)$. In order to fully define the vector, the system needs to be measured k-times, which yields a mean $(\chi = 1/k\sum_{i=1}^{k}\chi_i)$ and VARIANCE (σ^2). The method of moments estimator for the variance provides $\Sigma^2 = \Sigma_2 - \langle\chi\rangle^2 = 1/k\sum_{i=1}^{k}(\chi_i - \langle\chi\rangle)^2$. This mechanism essentially solves for boundary conditions, rather than for the analog stretch of continuous space of the media and objects. In the process of formulating the interaction of electric and magnetic fields with MATTER and the environment, the method of moments provides a tool to solve the MAXWELL EQUATIONS. The method of moments can for instance be used to calculate ANTENNA configuration, efficacy, and function, as well as compatibility with the environmental and atmospheric conditions for interaction with ELECTROMAGNETIC RADIATION, specifically the electromagnetic WAVE propagation in a medium other than in free space (i.e., VACUUM). The key component in the solution mechanism is the formulation of Maxwell's equations as a system of hyperbolic partial differential equations. Alternatively, the objects and the media themselves can be approximated as a distribution of discrete dipoles in order to approximate SCATTERING and absorption of electromagnetic radiation by targets of arbitrary geometry. The accuracy will depend on the number of defined interactions (nuclei in the media, and objects) in the system. Also referred to as the method of weighted RESIDUALS.

Metric system

[general] Units scaled in decimal proportions (yotta: 10^{24} …→ yocto: 10^{-24}) (*see* **SI-UNITS, LE SYSTÈME INTERNATIONAL D'UNITÉS**).

VALUE	VALUE: NORMAL	NOUN	PREFIX (SI)	SYMBOL
1.0E+24	1 000 000 000 000 000 000 000 000	Septillion	Yotta-	Y
1.0E+21	1 000 000 000 000 000 000 000	Sextillion	Zetta-	Z
1.0E+18	1 000 000 000 000 000 000	Quintillion	Exa-	E
1.0E+15	1 000 000 000 000 000	Quadrillion	Peta-	P
1.0E+12	1 000 000 000 000	Trillion	Tera-	T
1.0E+9	1 000 000 000	Billion	Giga-	G
1.0E+6	1 000 000	Million	Mega-	M
1.0E+3	1 000	Thousand	Kilo-	k
1.0E+2	100	Hundred	Hecto-	h
1.0E+1	10	Ten	Deca-	da
1	1	—		
1.0E–1	0.1	Tenth	Deci-	d
1.0E–2	0.01	Hundredth	Centi-	c
1.0E–3	0.001	Thousandth	Milli-	m
1.0E–6	0.000 001	Millionth	Micro-	μ
1.0E–9	0.000 000 001	Billionth	Nano-	n
1.0E–12	0.000 000 000 001	Trillionth	Pico-	p
1.0E–15	0.000 000 000 000 001	Quadrillionth	Femto-	f
1.0E–18	0.000 000 000 000 000 001	Quintillionth	Atto-	a
1.0E–21	0.000 000 000 000 000 000 001	Sextillionth	Zepto-	z
1.0E–24	0.000 000 000 000 000 000 000 001	Septillionth	Yocto-	y

Metrology

[acoustics, fluid dynamics, general, mechanics, optics] The science of all practical and theoretical aspects of taking and recording measurements.

Michaelis, Leonor (1875–1949)

[biomedical, computational] Physician from the Prussian Empire, Germany, biochemist, and physical chemist. Michaelis worked with MAUD MENTEN (1879–1960) on the mathematical description of enzymatic kinetic interaction and reaction equations (*also see* **MICHAELIS–MENTEN EQUATION**) (see Figure M.92).

Figure M.92 Leonor Michaelis (1875–1949). (Courtesy of Humboldt-Universität zu Berlin, Berlin, Germany, Universitätsbibliothek.) Porträtsammlung Berliner Hochschullehrer; Historische Sammlungen der Universitäts-Bibliothek; Berlin, Germany.

Michaelis–Menten equation

[biomedical, computational] Mathematical description of the transport of substrates (concentration: $[S]$) and drug-related events that have an enzyme (concentration: $[E]_0$) as a catalyst to drive the reaction. Mediated DIFFUSION is faster than regular diffusion described by the DIFFUSION EQUATION. The reaction will have a production rate ($v_{reaction}$) that changes with time and is dependent on the chemical concentrations of the constituents. An example of this type of reaction is the binding of oxygen to hemoglobin, which for one depends on the partial oxygen pressure next to the acidity (pH) among other factors such as a catalyst. Frequently the SOLUTION is derived by graphical interpretation with for instance the EADIE–HOFSTEE PLOT. The need for this type of computational approach is due to the often ill-defined experimental boundary conditions. The Michaelis–Menten equation is best described as $v_{reaction} = V_{max}([S]/(K_M + [S])) = k_{cat}[E]_0([S]/(K_M + [S]))$, where V_{max} is the maximum reaction velocity, K_m is the Michaelis–Menten constant, indicating the concentration at which the reaction rate for the enzyme is at half the maximum production rate or reaction velocity, and k_{cat} is the rate of conversion for the substrate molecules to the final product, also referred to as the turnover number. In this case, a small Michaelis–Menten constant (K_m) indicates a high binding affinity. Other applications are for instance DNA–DNA hybridization, and antigen to antibody binding (*also see* **LANGMUIR EQUATION** for equivalence in the description of ADSORPTION of biomolecular constituents, next to nuclear reactions).

Michelson, Albert Abraham (1852–1931)

[acoustics, atomic, biomedical, general, optics] Physicist and scientist from Germany/Poland, born in what was at the time known as the Kingdom of Prussia, later immigrated to the United States. Michelson is primarily known for his contributions in OPTICS. In 1907 Albert Michelson received the Nobel prize in Physics for his work in SPECTROSCOPY and optical instrumentation (see Figure M.93).

Figure M.93 Albert Abraham Michelson (1852–1931). (Courtesy of Smithsonian Institution.)

Michelson interferometer

[acoustics, atomic, biomedical, general, optics] Path length balanced device that generates INTERFERENCE when the path of the ENERGY traveling to and from the target or probe site is equal to the length of the path traveled by the identical energy signature (frequency, PHASE, designation [PARTICLE, electromagnetic, pressure wave, etc.] and other parameters of identification and material conditions) in a standardized reference path. The path length equivalence is determined by the coherence length of the WAVE package. The Michelson interferometer can be free space or fiber optic. The Michelson interferometer is characterized by four arms, one incoming, one arm that leads to the target (probe site), one reference arm, and the fourth provides the mechanism of detection of interference as a sensor branch. An optical balancing construction where a beam is split into two components that are branching off in perpendicular directions to interact with two media in the respective arms of the INTERFEROMETER, mainly reflective objects returning the two beams back to a 4th arm where they reunite and the wave patterns interact based on the respective phases of the two beams of electromagnetic radiation as a function of location. When the light is in phase, the interference will be constructive, alternatively when in the opposite phase the waves will cancel each other (destructive interference) (see Figure M.94).

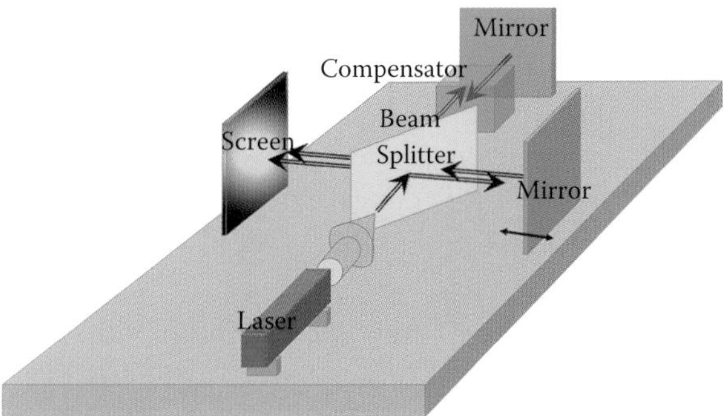

Figure M.94 Michelson interferometer.

Michelson–Morley experiment

[atomic, nuclear] Experimental design to prove/disprove the existence of ether (also known as AETHER), by ALBERT MICHELSON (1852–1931) and EDWARD MORLEY (1838–1923) in 1887. Ether is the historically assumed medium for the propagation of ELECTROMAGNETIC RADIATION, a concept dating back to BC from the philosophies of the Greek scientists. The experimental sign was attempting to determine the relative MOTION of the EARTH with respect to the perceived LUMINIFEROUS ETHER. The design of the experiment used an INTERFEROMETER to determine the path length difference traveled between arms of a split beam of light. In case the path length of two arms (each with length $L_{\mathrm{arm}}{}^{i}$) is equal, the light will be additive (constructive interference). A similarity can be found with swimming a track parallel to the FLOW of a river and perpendicular respectively, returning at the point of origin over equal distances, executed by two equally capable swimmers departing exactly at same time. The difference in path length expressed as the time traveled along the "ether" and perpendicular to the ether was expressed as $\Delta t \cong (L_{\mathrm{arm}}/c)\beta_M{}^2$, where $\beta_M = v/c$, with v the speed of the object, and $c = 2.99792458 \times 10^8$ m/s the speed of light. The movement of the Earth would account for the lengthening/shorting of the measuring arm, while the reference arm would remain constant, resulting in a shift of INTERFERENCE fringe in the sensing arm. This phenomenon however went unobserved and the ETHER concept was dismissed. The MICHELSON INTERFEROMETER will provide a respective fringe shift for influence of moving ether expressed as $n = \ell v^2/\lambda c^2$, where ℓ is the respective arm length, and λ the wavelength of the light.

Microarray

[biomedical] A lab-on-a-chip. A two-dimensional array constructed on a solid substrate, made of a GLASS or silicon thin-film CELL. The array assays a large quantity of biological material. The miniaturized microarray detection method is primarily used in DNA analysis, and through high-throughput screening, multiplexed and PARALLEL PROCESSING of the configuration of the complex molecule can be derived (see Figure M.95).

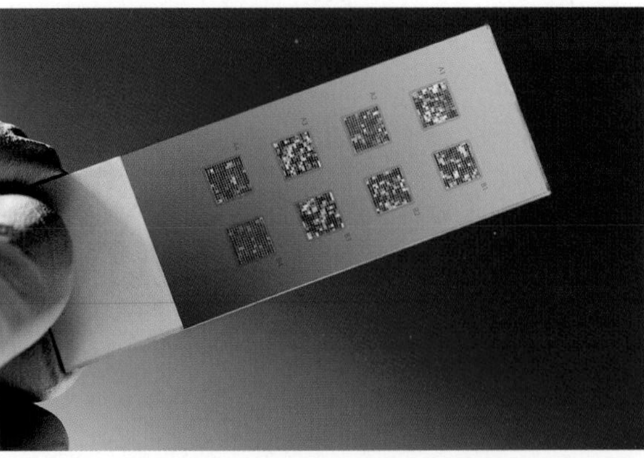

Figure M.95 DNA-Microarray.

Microelectronic-mechanical systems (MEMS)

[acoustics, electronics] Electromechanical systems of integrated electronic and mechanical interactions of components (see Figure M.96).

Figure M.96 MEMS device miniature microphone/speaker set.

Microfluidics

[biomedical] Fluid manipulation in conduits with dimensions of less than 1 mm diameter. Microfluidics is found in biological PERFUSION, inkjet printers, and "lab-on-chip" designs for chemical analysis as well as targeted delivery at a MICROSCOPIC level. The RHEOLOGY of blood in capillaries is an example of microfluidics that changes the FLUID behavior due to the size of the red blood cell, forming a flat velocity profile in the center of the tub.

Microgravity

[biomedical, general] Projectiles in free fall are generally considered to be weightless. Microgravity can be created in a plane flying in a parabolic arc lasting only several seconds (see Figure M.97).

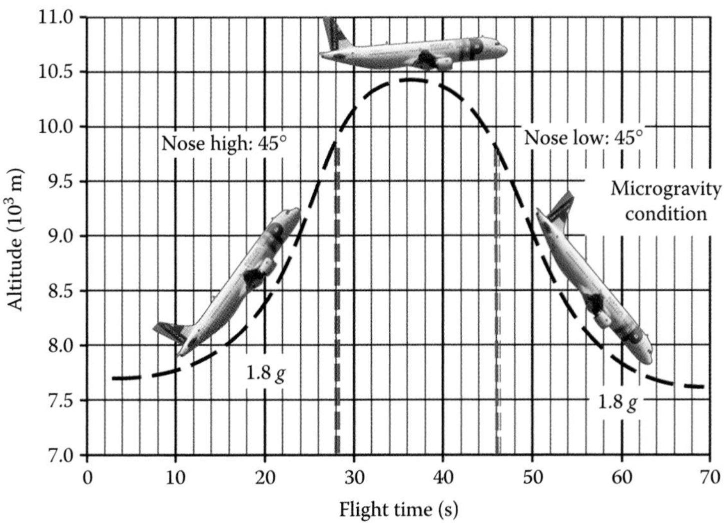

Figure M.97 The time event for microgravity during specialized flight patterns.

Microphone

[acoustics, electronics] Device designed to convert pressure fluctuations into an electronic SIGNAL from recording purposes or for real-time amplification and transmission over loud speakers or over RADIO or television channels as well as telephone systems (including mobile phone and ham-radio). A microphone can be constructed from piezoelectric material that under mechanical deformation produces an electric signal that changes in frequency and AMPLITUDE in direct correlation (cause-and-effect) with respect to the external mechanical stimulus. The mechanical stimulus can be changed in density of a GAS, or physical compression due to movement of a mass of solid or LIQUID (see Figure M.98).

Figure M.98 Microphone, classic design.

Microprocessor

[electronics, general] Integrated circuit used for performing computational algorithms. Semiconductor CHIP containing a central processing unit (CPU) electronic circuit configuration. The first microprocessor was introduced in 1974 by the Intel® Corporation (founded in 1968) with 8-bit capability, leading to the rapid reduction in the size of the computer to a portable device. The microprocessor forms the HEART of every modern day computer and control unit. Microprocessors provide the logic for most digital devices, ranging from fuel injection to nuclear power plant temperature regulation. The microprocessor is designed with a specific clock speed, well in excess of 2.4 GHz at the time of this work, indicating the number of calculations that can be performed per SECOND. Next to the processor speed, a microprocessor is classified by the bandwidth of the SIGNAL; 8-, 16-, 32-, 64-, or 128-bit (not common in personal computers [PCs]). The processor's "bit" parameter refers to the MAGNITUDE of the data types that the processor can handle next to the size of its registry. A 64-bit processor has the capability of storing 264 computational values, where the data are also temporarily stored in memory addresses. The 64-bit CPU is hence capable of accessing over 10^9 times as much physical memory in comparison to a 32-bit processor (see Figure M.99).

Figure M.99 Microprocessor.

Microsaccade

[biomedical, electronics, theoretical] μ-saccade, small random movements (plural) of the EYE across the field of view outlined by the azimuthal and the polar ANGLE in a spherical coordinate system. The movement is predominantly involuntary and is supposedly designed (biologically) to avoid retinal SATURATION. Ocular fixation on a single point in the view will eventually bleach out and will become invisible unless the eye moves away from this point. The body is generally more responsive to change than to status quo. This small amount of eye movement is disorganized with no preferential pattern. Other MOTION of the eye with respect to fixation on a view-point is classified as TREMOR and DRIFT. The movement is shorter than a regular SACCADE. The angular motion in humans and animals ranges from 2 to 120 arcmin. This phenomenon was first documented by Robert Darwin (1766–1848) a medical doctor from Great Britain, the father of the naturalist, genetic researcher, and geologist Charles Darwin (1809–1882). Microsaccades also provide the mechanism for the visual interpretation that a pattern of small markings in a dense distribution is moving when looking at it in a fixed stare (see Figure M.100).

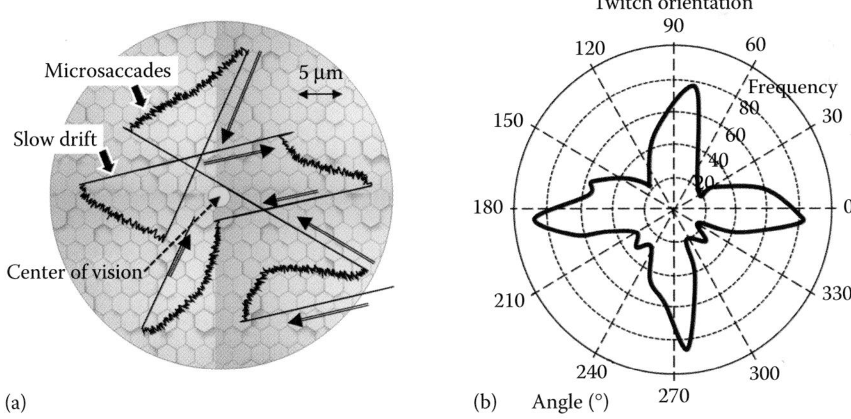

Figure M.100 (a) Illustration of how the microsaccades, high-frequency twitches, are superimposed on the normal drift motion (saccades) of the eye movement and (b) representative frequency and angular distribution of microsaccades.

Microscope

[general, imaging, optics] Device used to provide a detailed view of an object with greater RESOLUTION than what can be obtained with the naked eye, with no specific lower limit on the magnification. The standard microscope was what we now consider a magnifying GLASS. The MICROSCOPE is generally constructed of one or more optical ELEMENTS, including lenses, mirrors, and prisms. The use of more than one optical ELEMENT constitutes the compound microscope. The standard optical microscope was developed between 1590 and 1608, independently (debatably), by two teams of LENS makers (eye glasses) from the Netherlands: HANS JANSEN (sixteenth century, no exact dates), and ZACHARIAS JANSEN (1580–1640) and HANS LIPPERSHEY (1570–1619). The microscope was the result of experimentation with lenses since the first eye-glasses were introduced between 1282 and 1285 in Florence, Italy by Alessandro di Spina. The concept was the culmination of the publication of the properties of curved glass providing magnifying by ROGER BACON (1214–1294) in 1262. The compound microscope is attributed to ROBERT HOOKE (1635–1703) in Great Britain, created in 1665, while a similar device was concurrently constructed by Jan Swammerdam (1637–1680) in the Netherlands in 1675. The Hooke microscope was actually constructed by a London instrument maker named Christopher Cock (seventeenth century, no exact dates). The Hooke microscope attained a magnification of 30 times. The Swammerdam microscope reached magnification of 150 times. The microscope was improved by the lens-maker ANTONIE VAN LEEUWENHOEK (1632–1723) from the Netherlands, published in 1716. The van Leeuwenhoek microscope used pinholes and lenses made from water droplets. This device was used in the eighteenth century for the equivalent to current medical pathological investigation. Microscopes in the early 1700s were made using crown glass. In 1733, a breakthrough discovery was made by the amateur optician, Chester Moor Hall (1703–1771) from Great Britain, minimizing CHROMATIC ABERRATION through a combination of lenses made with different refractive materials to form a complex lens. This discovery can be attributed to the introduction of a new lead-containing flint glass. The microscope forms an IMAGE of an object placed in the (adjustable) FOCAL PLANE of a set of or single magnifying glass(es). The magnifying glass is a biconvex axial symmetric glass spheroid. Light reflects from the object (specimen) placed under the lenses and is refracted at the air–glass interface and again exiting at the glass–air interface. In case the formed image cannot be projected on a screen, it is defined as a virtual image. Alternatively when the image can be projected on a screen, the image is defined as real. The refracted light is hence focused by the lens providing the formation of an image, either virtual or real. When a virtual image is formed, the EYE can observe this on the RETINA, appearing on the same side of the lens, and in the approximately similar azimuth and ZENITH locations, as where the object is located. The virtual image formed by the lens and observed by the eye is most sharp when its position falls in the NEAR POINT of the eye. The near point of the eye is the closest DISTANCE between an object and the cornea of the lens of the eye that can be perceived as a well-defined image by the retina. The near point for the average human being is approximately 250 mm removed from the cornea. In order to understand the function of the microscope, first some of the basic principles of ray forming by a single lens in image formation need to be described. Two general types of lenses can be distinguished: concave and convex. A concave lens is thinner on the optical axis than farther removed from the axis of symmetry. Concave lenses are also called diverging lenses since they will never produce a real image. Convex lenses are thicker on the optical axis and will produce a real image on the opposite side of the lens when the object is at a distance greater than the focal length. When the object is at a distance shorter than the focal length, the convex lens will also form a virtual image. The distance on the optical axis of the lens with respect to the material center to the plane where the light from an object at infinity forms the smallest real image, generally undistinguishable since all rays from every point on the object converge, is known as the focal distance f. The focal length is positive for the convex lens (also known as POSITIVE LENS) and the focal length for a concave lens is negative (virtual, and this lens is also called a "negative lens"). The image of the object formed by the convex lens appears inverted in the FOCAL POINT. The power of the lens is defined as the inverse of the focal length of the lens. The image formed by any lens is a factor or fraction greater than the object. The object has a height h_o, the image has a height h_i, and the distance of the image to the lens is d_i, while the object distance from the lens is d_o. The lateral magnification for a simple lens is defined as the ratio of the image height over the object height, which can be shown by geometric analysis to be equal to the ratio of the respective distances as $M = h_i/h_o = d_i/d_o$. Modern microscopes have a minimum of two lenses or two lens sets (corrections for chromatic and spherical aberration), and objective and an ocular. The ocular lens is located in the eyepiece of the microscope. The ocular generally has a magnification of 10 times. The objective lens is placed closest to the specimen on the examination stage. The objective is selected to suit the required total magnification for the investigation of details with the appropriate resolution. The total magnification is the product of the two respective magnifications for the two lens systems. Based on the Raleigh criterion or ABBE CONDITION, the maximum magnification for a standard optical microscope operating at the wavelength with peak retinal sensitivity (570 nm) is 600 times. Different types of microscope have been developed to overcome the limitations in OPTICAL MAGNIFICATION. Additionally, the standard optical microscope has been outfitted with techniques to take advantage of the electromagnetic parameters, including phase and wavelength, and polarization ANGLE to enhance the contrast for optimization in detection of deviations from the norm. One type of microscope takes advantage of the wave properties of light and is called the INTERFERENCE microscope, taking advantage of the fact that the optical path length varies with local index of REFRACTION. The PHASE contrast microscopy also relies on interference of light waves, with deviations resulting from diffraction, with associated phase retardation. Another type of microscope uses the DISPERSION of light in tissues based on the direction of the electric field and the direction of the electric influences of the medium under investigation, known as BIREFRINGENCE of most tissues. In particular, the loss of the birefringence resulting from clinical (disease) or external damage to the tissue, artificially induced (e.g., coagulation), and is referred to as polarization microscope. Many other MICROSCOPIC devices have been developed over time, not all based on the optical principles. Some optical microscope variations are fluorescent microscopy, confocal microscopy, scanning optical microscopy, two-photon microscopy, and near-field-scanning optical microscopy. One of the latest microscope introductions is three-dimensional imaging with optical coherent tomography (OCT) imaging devices, based on the phase information of the wave property of light, relying on interference. Microscopes using other techniques are the ELECTRON MICROSCOPE based on the DE BROGLIE WAVELENGTH of an accelerated charge PROJECTILE as does the helium-ion microscope. Additional resources are the ATOMIC-FORCE MICROSCOPE (AFM) using the electronic attraction and repulsion of the medium and an extremely fine needle tip mounted on a cantilever (see Figure M.101).

Figure M.101 Microscope.

Microscope, atomic force

[general] *See* **ATOMIC FORCE MICROSCOPE.**

Microscope, compound

[general] *See* **MICROSCOPE** *or see* **COMPOUND MICROSCOPE.**

Microscope, confocal

[general] *See* **CONFOCAL MICROSCOPE.**

Microscope, electron

[general] *See* ELECTRON MICROSCOPE.

Microscope, He-ion

[general] *See* HELIUM-ION MICROSCOPE.

Microscope, nuclear

[general, nuclear] *See* NUCLEAR MICROSCOPE.

Microscope, resolving power

[atomic, nuclear] *See* RESOLVING POWER.

Microscope, scanning ion-conductance

[general] *See* SCANNING ION-CONDUCTANCE MICROSCOPE.

Microscopic

[biomedical, chemical, general, solid-state] Not visible by the naked eye, requiring visual aids to identify the characteristics; that is, the use of a magnifying GLASS or MICROSCOPE.

Microstate

[general, mechanics, thermodynamics] Thermodynamic condition that applies to a MICROSCOPIC subsegment of a system. This principle applies specifically to statistical MECHANICS. The assembly of all local microstates dictates the collective macrostate of the medium or entire system.

Microtome

[biomedical, mechanics] Precision cutting device used for preparation of histology slides. The tissue in most cases is embedded in paraffin after being fixed first in formaldehyde or equivalent chemical. Additional operational mechanism of action employs a frozen section and the device is called a cryostat microtome (see Figure M.102).

Figure M.102 Microtome cutting device used for histology slide preparation. An extremely thin slice of tissue imbedded in paraffin is cut from the large formaldehyde fixed block and curls off the blade. The wafer-thin slice of tissue is subsequently placed on a microscope glass-slide for examination of the tissue structure and potential identification of pathological deviation in cell structure (e.g., cancer cells mixed-in with the regular organ cells) under microscopic examination.

Microwave

[general] Electromagnetic WAVE in the wavelength spectrum ranging from order of millimeter to 1 m, or equivalently, with frequencies ranging from 300 to 0.3 GHz. Most well-known is microwave radiation in the 2.54 GHz range (wavelength: $\lambda = 124$ mm), used in wireless communications such as CELL phones and bluetooth, and the heating of food in the MICROWAVE OVEN. Microwave radiation is generally produced by a magnetron electronic device (see Figure M.103).

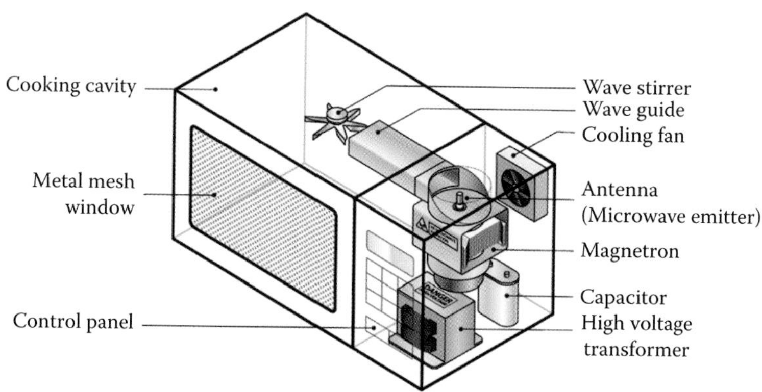

Figure M.103 Microwave with magnetron signal generator depicted.

Microwave imaging

[general] Due to the relatively high-penetration potential of microwave radiation through various media as a function of wavelength, the use of microwave ELECTROMAGNETIC RADIATION can be used as a mechanism for functional and anatomical imaging of biological media as well as for commercial imaging, such as radar. On a biological scale, the electromagnetic interaction with DEPOLARIZATION of groups of cells forms a perturbation that can be localized using line-of-sight, specifically when applying multiple rays at a relative ANGLE with each other in a synchronous detection mechanism arranged in circular symmetry. Radar (acronym for radio detection and ranging) relies on the deflection and detection for boundaries under an operating mechanism very similar to ultrasonic biological imaging and ultrasonic radar. The use of frequency modulation provides an added mechanism for enhanced RESOLUTION and spectral information about the physical properties of the object under scrutiny (see Figure M.104).

Figure M.104 (a) Microwave signal detection used by police officer for the assessment of the velocity of moving automobiles and (b) spinning RADAR antenna on a ship for reconnaissance.

Microwave oven

[general] Device that relies on the use of millimeter ELECTROMAGNETIC RADIATION for vibrational excitation of MOLECULAR MOTION (i.e., DIELECTRIC heating), resulting in localized heating of the object. The local temperature is the average kinetic ENERGY of the molecular vibrations ($T = (3/2k_b)mv^2$, where k_b is the Boltzmann coefficient, m is the average molecular mass, and v is the vibrational, rotational, and translational velocity). The use of primarily 2.54 GHz limits the use to heating of materials that contain water such as meat or just liquids. The frequency of 2.54 GHz still has relatively low absorption in water vibration, which ensures deep penetration and volumetric heating. High attenuation at higher frequency MICROWAVE will result in primarily surface heating. Large industrial ovens operate at 0.915 GHz (see Figure M.105).

Figure M.105 Microwave oven used to heat-up a cup of tea.

M

Middle ear

[biomedical, general] Anatomical segment in the HEARING mechanism for mammals conveying the longitudinal pressure WAVE incident on the eardrum (tympanic membrane) at the end of the OUTER EAR, to the over window on the cochlea of the INNER EAR. The middle ear has a mechanism of controlling the LOUDNESS of the sound propagated to the inner ear (primarily to prevent structural damage as well as increase the AMPLITUDE and frequency resolution). The pivoted bone system (OSSICLES) in the middle ear consisting of the malleus ("hammer"), incus ("anvil"), and stapes ("stirrup") that can be relaxed with respect to its interconnection, hence reducing the MAGNITUDE of translational movement; reducing the AMPLITUDE applied to the oval window. Keeping in mind that the tympanic MEMBRANE is 20 times larger in area than the oval window, this indicates the first mechanism of "amplification" available for hearing. The ossicles can respond to a displacement of the tympanic membrane in the order of nanometers, setting the lower limit of hearing at (approximately) 0 dB at approximately 3500 Hz for a healthy young human ear. With excessive loudness, the fibrous/muscular connections between the ossicles wear down, reducing the sensitivity, leading to gradual procession of deafness. Additionally age-related degeneration of the ELASTICITY of biological materials hearing will decline in both frequency response and intensity sensitivity (see Figure M.106).

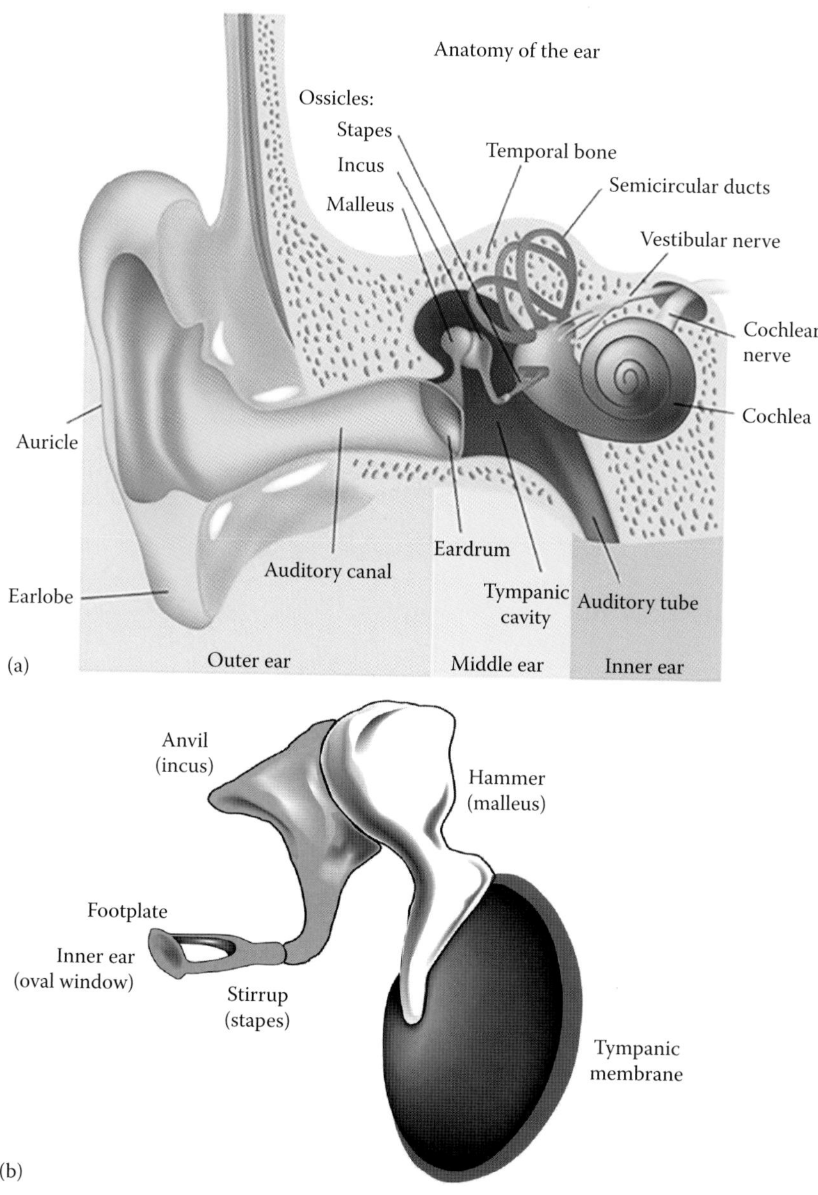

Figure M.106 (a) Full diagram of auditory subsystem (ear) and (b) outline of the Middle ear for Homo sapiens (humans); left to right: eardrum, malleus, incus, stapes. The eardrum forms the separation from the outer-ear, whereas the stapes are connected to the inner ear at the oval window.

Mie, Gustav Adolf Feodor Wilhelm Ludwig (1868–1957)

[optics] Physicist from Germany. Mie is best known for his description of the interaction of light with large particles in 1908. Mie scattering stand in comparison to Rayleigh scattering for particle size equal to or smaller than the wavelength (see Figure M.107).

Figure M.107 Gustav Adolf Feodor Wilhelm Ludwig Mie (1868–1957).

Mie absorption

[astrophysics, biomedical, optics] Numerical method used to calculate the maximum absorption coefficient of a medium constructed primarily of spherical particles in clear (i.e., transparent) suspension. In line with the spherical geometry of the particulate constituents, the model is symmetric that allows for separation of variables in the Helmholtz equation ($(\nabla^2 + k^2)\Psi(r,\theta,\phi) = 0$, in spherical coordinates, where ∇ is the Laplace operator, and $k = \omega/c = 2\pi/\lambda_0$ the wavenumber, where $\omega = 2\pi\nu$ is the angular velocity, ν the frequency, λ_0 the wavelength of a monochromatic electromagnetic source, and c the speed of light) for the interaction of the radiant energy fluence rate (Ψ) with the medium that applies to this condition. Separation of variables ($\Psi(r,\theta,\phi) = \mathrm{R}(r)\Theta(\theta)\Phi(\phi)$, with a radial component $\mathrm{R}(r)$, a cylindrical component $\Theta(\theta)$, and an azimuthal component $\Phi(\phi)$), results in three ordinary differential equations $(d^2\{r\mathrm{R}(r)\})/dr^2 + \left(k^2 - [n(n+1)]/r^2\right)r\mathrm{R}(r) = 0$, where n is a separation constant with solutions as spherical Bessel functions or spherical Hankel functions of the first kind or spherical Neumann functions, $(1/\sin\theta)(d/d\theta)\left(\sin\theta(d\Theta(\theta)/d\theta)\right) + \left(n(n+1) - m^2/(\sin\theta)^2\right)\Theta(\theta) = 0$, where m is another separation constant with a Legendre function ($\mathrm{P}_n^m(\theta)$) as solution $\Theta(\theta) = \mathrm{P}_n^m(\theta)$, and $d^2\Phi(\phi)/d\phi^2 + m^2\Phi(\phi) = 0$ with $\Phi(\phi) = \mathrm{e}^{im(\phi)}$. From these solutions, the absorption efficiency for a sphere (Q_{abs}) can be derived, which is a direct representation of the absorption coefficient (μ_a): $Q_{\mathrm{abs}} = 2/\xi\sum_{n=1}^{\infty}\left\{(2n+1)[\Re(a_n + b_n) - (|a_n|^2 + |b_n|^2)]\right\}$, where a_n and b_n are coefficients that are functions of the size parameters: $\chi = kr_1$ and $\xi = k(r_1 + e)$.

Mie scattering

[astrophysics, computational, optics, particle] Theoretical approximation of the attenuation resulting from scattering based on a spherical particle model. Mie scatter stands next to Rayleigh scattering for atomic and molecular media, such as the creation of the blue sky by means of atmospheric gasses. Both the directional pattern (profile of scattering angle) and magnitude of attenuation resulting from redirecting the electromagnetic wave while interacting with dielectric units with spherical geometry in transparent suspension (e.g., tissue model, space dust, atmospheric vapor [i.e., haze/fog/clouds] or dust, and paint). In the case where the dimension of the PARTICLE characteristics of the ELECTROMAGNETIC RADIATION interacts (i.e., WAVICLE) with is of the order of MAGNITUDE of the WAVELENGTH of the RADIATION, the interaction closely approximates GEOMETRICAL OPTICS. A more precise definition involves the SOLUTION of the MAXWELL EQUATIONS applied to the interface with an isotropic, homogeneous, dielectric sphere. The Maxwell equations solved in spherical coordinates yields the SCATTERING CROSS SECTION: σ_M, and a SCATTERING ANISOTROPY FACTOR: g (see Figure M.108).

Figure M.108 Overcast sky, potentially with dust, providing Mie scattering red glow.

The scattering anisotropy factor is also described by what is generally referred to as a SCATTERING PHASE FUNCTION. The scattering phase function is defined by the PROBABILITY of a PHOTON being scattered in the direction θ, expressed by $P(\theta)$. This yields $g = \int_0^{4\pi} P(\theta)\cos\theta \, d\omega$, where ω represents the SOLID ANGLE of space. This can also be expressed in vector format. In this case photons are approximated as rays. A photon is regarded as coming in from direction $\vec{s}$, and after scattering the photon path is redirected into direction $\vec{s}'$. This provides the following statement for the angular scattering probability distribution: $g = \int_0^{4\pi} P(\vec{s},\vec{s}')\cdot(\vec{s},\vec{s}')\,d\omega$. This accounts for events taking place over the full 4π steradian, a.k.a. spherical geometry. This process often assumes spherical symmetry, which accounts for a radially, and often axially, homogeneous medium.

Milky Way

[astrophysics, thermodynamics] GALAXY constructed of stars, planets, and dust and GAS in which the Earth's SOLAR SYSTEM is located. The generally accepted view and calculated description of the Milky Way is a flat dual "cymbal" shaped assembly of over 100 billion stars and in the order of 400 billion planets. A rough estimate of the diameter of the Milky Way is at this moment in the order of 5.22×10^4 lightyears. The "bulge" in the center of the Milky Way has a spheroidal distribution of stars and planets and potentially a "BLACK HOLE" in the center. The currently accepted value of the DISTANCE of the Sun from the galactic center is 2.77×10^3 light-years, or 8.5 kiloparsecs (a parsec is equal to 2.06×10^5 times the average distance between the Sun and the EARTH), located approximately half-way between the center and the edge of the Milky Way galaxy. A resembling shape of a spiral galaxy is shown for the Splinter Galaxy. All planets, gasses, and stars revolve around the center of the Milky Way in a uniform fashion, with relatively a constant rotational velocity in the plane of the disk; the velocity at the location of our SOLAR SYSTEM is approximately 240 km/s. The disk of the Milky Way is surrounded by a spheroidal collective of stars, described as a halo, which is seemingly devoid of gasses and dust (see Figure M.109).

Figure M.109 Reconstruction of what the Milky Way may look like observed from within the distant galaxy (so far we have not traveled outside our solar system), let alone outside our Milky Way.

M

Miller indices

[atomic, nuclear] "Vector" style notation system in crystallography to specify directions and planes in crystal lattices (namely Bravais lattices). The Miller index for a plane defines how the plane intersects with any of the main crystallographic axes of the crystal, respectively solid, and also applies to any parallel plane (*also see* LATTICE PLANES) (see Figure M.110).

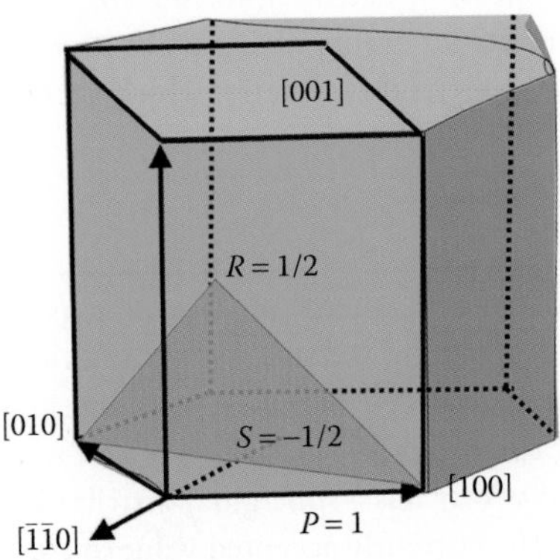

Figure M.110 Miller indices for atomic lattice structures.

Millikan, Robert Andrews (1868–1953)

[atomic, general, nuclear] American scientist and experimentalist. Millikan's contributions to the nuclear model are in his "oil-drop" experiment and the verification of the PHOTOELECTRIC EFFECT in both experimental and mathematical concepts (see Figure M.111).

Figure M.111 Robert Andrews Millikan (1868–1953), in 1917. (Courtesy of University of Chicago Science Series.)

Millikan oil-drop experiment

[atomic, general, nuclear] An atomizer provides a continuous droplet stream of OIL droplets that fall through the central hole of two plates that have an ELECTRIC FIELD (E) applied. An applied continuous beam of X-RAY radiation forms a mechanism for charging the droplets. Charged droplets will be suspended, actually lifted, while the uncharged (neutral) droplet will continue in free fall, reaching the TERMINAL VELOCITY v_g. The balance of the three forces, GRAVITATION, FLOW resistance, and electric field force, will result in a rising velocity of constant magnitude, depending on the electric filed velocity (v_E). The experimental design was implemented by Robert Millikan (1868–1953) and coworkers in 1909. The experiment provided the MAGNITUDE of the charge of an electron (q): $q = (k/e)(\overrightarrow{v_g} + \overrightarrow{v_E})$, where k_S is a proportionality factor derived by GEORGE GABRIEL STOKES (1819–1903) for the flow resistance $F_R = k_S v = 6\pi\eta r v = 18\pi\left\{\eta^3 v_g / 2g(\rho - \rho_a)\right\}$, where η is the VISCOSITY of the resisting medium, r the radius of the body in FLOW (i.e., droplet radius), g the GRAVITATIONAL ACCELERATION, ρ_d the density of the oil, ρ_m the density of the medium, and v the magnitude of PARTICLE velocity (see Figure M.112).

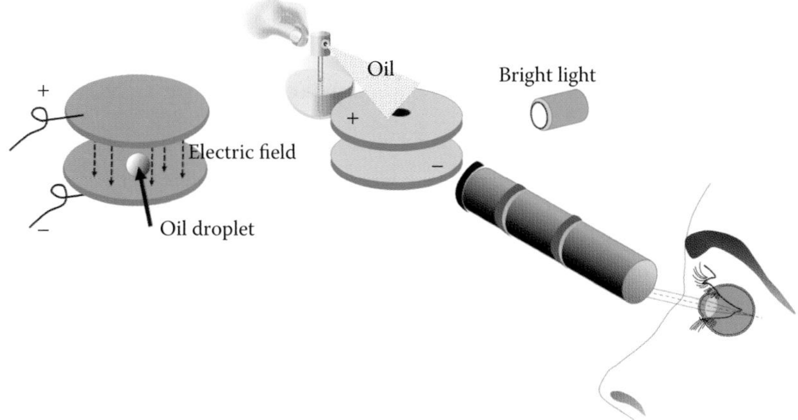

Figure M.112 Millikan's oil-drop experiment.

Minimum dissipation theorem

[fluid dynamics] Theoretical approach in nonequilibrium THERMODYNAMICS to form a prediction of likely steady state situations as well as other dynamical structures that a physical system, specifically pertaining to ENERGY flow and real flow, might exhibit. Helmholtz formulated the minimum dissipation energy principle as the energy difference of a stationary flow of INCOMPRESSIBLE FLUID with respect to FLOW with arbitrary MOTION while containing the same velocity distribution. In 1869, HERMANN VON HELMHOLTZ (1821–1894) stated his principle of least viscous dissipation of kinetic energy. This principle entails that for a steady flow in a viscous fluid, with the small flow velocities on the boundaries of an incompressible fluid, under steady-state conditions, will evolve in currents with turbulent tendencies. This perturbation of the LIQUID flow will evolve in a distribution within which the dissipation of kinetic energy by FRICTION is minimal. The bases for the minimal dissipation of energy is that these fluid motions will be below the threshold for TURBULENCE due to viscous forces. In 1878, Helmholtz applied similar principles to electric currents in a SOLUTION of electrolytes that exhibits a concentration gradient. This balance of forces shows nonequilibrium coupling between forces resulting from electric effects and based on DIFFUSION resulting from the concentration gradient. The reciprocal relation discovered by Helmholtz was later redefined by the Norwegian scientist, chemist, and mathematician Lars Onsager (1903–1976). The original expression of Hermann von Helmholtz in 1868 was later redefined by Onsager in 1931 in terms of a force (F, a hypothetical thermal "force," which proved the mechanism-of-action for the conduction of heat) as $F = \int_V \Phi dV \overset{\delta F=0}{\rightarrow}$ minimum, where $\Phi = 1/2\sum_{i,j=1}^{n} R_{ij} J_i J_j$, and J_i and J_j are SCALAR forms of thermodynamic flows and R_{ij} the flow corresponding to the RESISTANCE for a VOLUME (V) outlined by a surface (S). This indicates the viscous dissipation that can be minimized. For the Stokes flow, this relates to the rate of strain within the fluid e_{ij}^{v} (TENSOR), while the flow velocity is bound by $\nabla \cdot \vec{v} = 0$, where the velocity can be disbanded in two components as $\vec{v} = \vec{u} + \vec{w}$, providing two respective rates of strain components e_{ij}^{u} and e_{ij}^{w} as $\int_V e_{ij}^{v} e_{ij}^{v} dV = 2\int_{\delta V} w_i n_j e_{ij}^{u} dS - 2\int_v \vec{w} \cdot \nabla P dV$, where P is the local pressure. The second term is negligible by definition under the assumed flow conditions, while the first term reaches zero as the components $w_i = 0$ on the surface. The Dutch mathematician Diederik Korteweg (1848–1941) in 1883 verified Helmholtz's hypothesis, stating that in any basically connected region, with known boundary velocities, meaning that the squares and products of the velocities of an incompressible viscous fluid may be neglected when small and uniformly distributed, there will be only one solution to the equations for the steady motion, and this solution is always nondiverging and stable.

Minimum energy

[fluid dynamics] Statement by LORD KELVIN (1824–1907) in 1910 pertaining to the fact that an irrotational motion of a LIQUID occupying a simply connected region contains less kinetic ENERGY than any other (rotational or otherwise turbulent) motion corresponding to a mechanism of MOTION that has equivalent normal velocity conditions on the outlying boundary of the system's domain (e.g., surface of a volume of FLUID in FLOW). A theorem in FLUID DYNAMICS relates the steady state condition to minimum kinetic energy of an ideal fluid. The ideal fluid will be inviscid, incompressible, and irrotational. The SOLUTION provides statements concerning the POTENTIAL FLOW uniqueness. Also known as Kelvin's minimum energy theorem (*also see* **MINIMUM DISSIPATION THEOREM FOR COMPARISON**).

Minimum mean square error

[acoustics, computational] In the process of making systematic estimates on behalf of predictions with respect to quantities or making predictions, the use of data obtained from similar systems can be useful but error prone. Certain assumptions or established connects must be made between the unknown and the known systems of values. Choosing the estimate wisely will rely on establishing a minimum mean square error. Combining multiple values that are somehow correlated to another ultimate parameter relies on a process referred to as linear minimum mean square error estimation, applying recursive values to provide the additive error. The estimate can be based on a PROBABILITY distribution ($f_Y(y)$), which is either known on inferred, providing the estimate ($\hat{y}$) for a random variable (Y). For this the minimization process follows, minimize: $\text{ERROR}\left[(Y - \hat{y})^2\right] = \int (y - \hat{y})^2 f_Y(y) dy$, which yields the variance $\sigma_Y^{\ 2}$.

Minimum phase filter

[acoustics, computational, theoretical] Electronic or mechanical (ACOUSTICS) filter based on the fact that the linearity of response to the PHASE of a WAVE is not critical in preserving the waveshape. In this case, we may allow the phase to be arbitrary, or alternatively to define the phase in such a way that the AMPLITUDE response to the process (and inherently the processing algorithm) is easier to match. In SIGNAL processing, the minimum phase filters are by definition stable due to the fact that the POLES must be inside the unit circle of the defined region of validity. In addition, the inverse filter is also stable when the operator is minimum phase since the function zeros must also be inside the unit circle. Mathematically, minimum phase filters form an algebraic operator group in which the ELEMENTS are formed by respective IMPULSE RESPONSE contributions and the group operation is formed by convolution.

Minimum velocity of water waves

[fluid dynamics] Wavelength- dependent formulation defining the validity of applying the WAVE EQUATION to a problem in the transition from CAPILLARY WAVES to GRAVITATIONAL WAVES. This velocity limit places a threshold on the application of the wave model to be used. Under capillary WAVE MOTION, the SURFACE TENSION has an over powering force influence on the wave description. Generally, water waves with a wavelength less than $\lambda = 0.0173$ m can be considered capillary waves. At this point, the PHASE VELOCITY has a minimum value 0.231 m/s. Note that the velocity of water waves (v) beyond this point is a function of depth (h), as $v = \sqrt{((g\lambda/2\pi)\tanh[2\pi(h/\lambda)])}$, which goes asymptotically to $v = \sqrt{(g\lambda/2\pi)}$ for deep water (see Figure M.113).

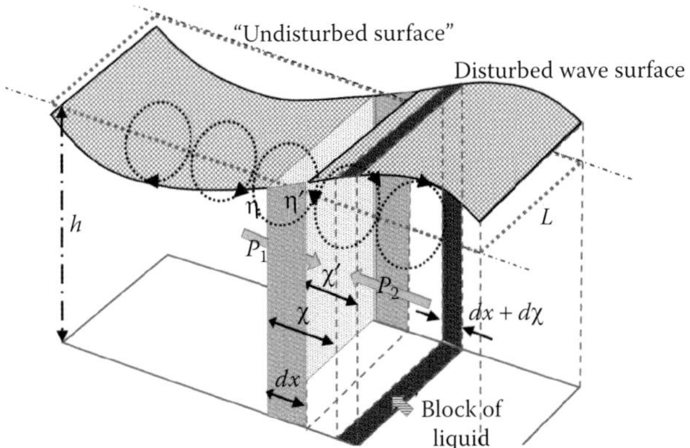

Figure M.113 The velocity of waves on water (liquid in general) is a function of the depth h to $h+\eta$ with respect to wavelength (i.e., prone to dispersion) while the water surface moves down the "slice" of water to the bottom of the ocean or river will change in "thickness" dx tro $dx+d\chi$ with respect to the raised water surface, providing for the slice of width L in continuity: $Lhdx = L(h+\eta)(dx+d\chi)$, which yields $\eta = -h(\partial\chi/\partial x)$, converted into the wave-equation: $\partial^2\chi/\partial t^2 = gh(\partial^2\chi/\partial x^2)$, which provides the wave velocity $v = \sqrt{(gh)}$, g the gravitational acceleration.

Mini-sparker

[acoustics, computational, geophysics] Agitation source in a geophysical seismic model, primarily based on mechanical pulse response. The concept also applies to computational modeling of the response of hydrophones in deriving the WAVE diffraction response function and in calibration. The mini-sparker will have a frequency response (i.e., spectral profile) and pulse shape. On a smaller scale, the process applies to sonic imaging in marine applications, such as submarine echo ranging.

Mirror

[general, mechanics, optics] Device that forms an image of an object be means of reflection. Optical and acoustical mirrors can be concave with a focal point on the side of the source, or convex, where the focal point is on the opposite side of the device surface with respect to the source. Generally concave will form either a virtual (when the object is placed at a distance closer than the focal point) or a real image, whereas convex mirrors and flat mirrors always form a virtual image. The focal point (f) of a curved mirror is half the radius of curvature (R): $f = R/2$. The image magnification (M) is the ratio of the image size (i) to the object size (o): $M = i/o$. Parabolic mirrors provide a mechanism to generate a parallel beam from a source with finite dimensions placed in the focal point. The headlights of an automobile are most known for their parabolic mirror shape. Alternatively, the collection of waves from a not perfectly parallel on-axis source to form an image in the focal point of a parabolic mirror will be more likely to form a small spot size than a spherical mirror, providing corrections to spherical aberrations. Radio antennas provide the best example of parabolic collection devices, specifically requiring a less than perfect on-axis alignment. Only an infinitely small source will produce a parallel outgoing beam when placed in the focal point of a spherical mirror. Mirrors are used to direct the path of sound waves, radio and television waves and optical rays. The exercise of outlining the formation of an image resulting from a source configuration and a mirror design is referred to as ray tracing, and can be performed with pen and paper or by computer simulations. In a complex system, both lenses and mirrors can be applied. An aspherical mirror is not symmetric as compared to a standard parabolic mirror. One specific example of an aspherical mirror is found on the passenger side of the car (objects are closer than they appear).

Mirror formula

[general] Formula describing how the size of the object (o) and the image size (i) are linked by the radius of curvature of the reflecting object ($R_{reflect}$) used to generate the image: $1/o + 1/i = 2/R_{reflect}$, note that a converging mirror (concave) has positive radius, and a convex mirror has negative radius, where a positive image reflects a real image and a negative image means virtual.

Mirror nuclei

[atomic, nuclear] Atomic nucleus that is constructed of a respective number of neutrons and protons that, in comparison with another nucleus, are mutually interchanged; the number of protons may match the number of neutrons of the mirror and vice versa. The mirror nuclei are generally isotopes, such as ^{14}O and ^{14}C, and may be short-lived. Mirror nuclei will have a mass difference that is the result from the difference in energy (E) configuration between the two nuclei, expressed by the respective energy states (s_i, with respect to ground state s_0), and specifically the difference in the total population assembly (n, representing the Green's function of occupation for the new with respect to the old nucleus for an isotope; the energy content of the changed state of the isotope [the "mirror"] is compared to the indigenous state of the original stable nucleus) of energy states: $\Delta E = a^2 \Sigma \Gamma^{s0\,s0}_{s_i\,s_i}(n'_{s_i} - n_{s_i})$, where $\Gamma^{s0\,s0}_{s_i\,s_i}$ represents the Coulomb interaction on an elementary particle level for the constituents of the nucleus.

Mitochondria

[biomedical, energy] Specialized cellular component (organelles) in living cells that use oxygen. The living cell (eukaryotic) has a nucleus. The mitochondria have the sole responsibility for the production and storage of energy to make the cell operate, specifically the formation of adenosine triphosphate (ATP) synthesis. In the process executed by the mitochondria, oxidation of simple organic compounds produces electrons generated during a chain of four membrane-bound enzymes, housed in the membrane. The reduction process is referred to as the electron transport or respiratory chain. The final stage involves the reduction of oxygen to produce water, generating an electron movement that builds a proton gradient across the membrane. The proton gradient drives the ATP generation as a turbine. The mitochondria additionally house several metabolic enzymes that support the survival of the cell. The inner structure of the mitochondrial membrane uses surface enlargement for optimal performance, since all energy processes take place in the membrane itself, next to the storage in the LIQUID of the organelle. The outer membrane consists of a lipid bilayer that is freely permeable to a broad range of molecules. The permeability to the molecules, specifically smaller than about 5000 daltons, results from the abundance of a channel-forming protein called porin. Some of the enzymes in the mitochondrial FLUID also assist in the production of phosphates that can be converted to ATP, by phosphorylating other nucleotides. Mitochondria have a diameter ranging from 0.5 to 1.0 μm and length ranging from 1 to 10 μm, depending on the type of cell in the biological system (see Figure M.114).

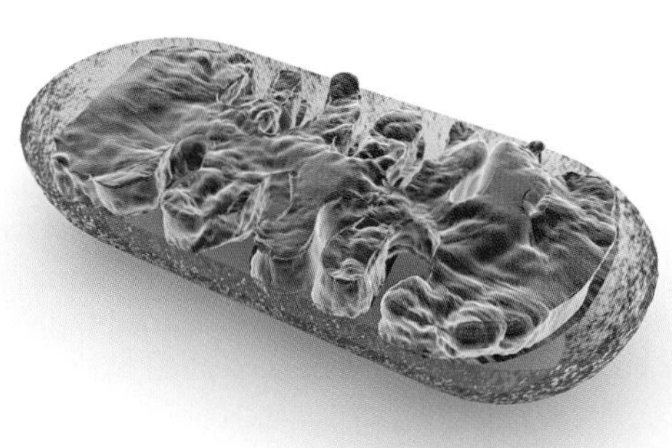

Figure M.114 Microscopic view of a mitochondria in a biological cell.

Mixing

[biomedical, chemical, thermodynamics] Combining fluids and solids. When solids, liquids, and gases are mixed their respective thermodynamic properties as well as that of the combined system will be altered. Mixing a SOLVENT with one of more solutes, or blending constituents in different phases, to form a single PHASE is mixing. Dissolved oxygen in BLOOD forms a mixture as does coffee with milk and sugar. Atmospheric AIR is a mixture of nitrogen, oxygen, argon, and TRACE elements as well as water VAPOR, all acting as ideal gases. The Gibbs ENERGY of a mixture forms the sum of the fractional components, expressed by means of the number of moles (n) and the respective partial molar Gibbs energy ($G^* = \mu_{\text{chem}}$; which is equal to the chemical potential): $G = \sum n_i G^*_i$. Based on the fractional contribution (n_i/n) the change in Gibbs free energy due to mixing is $\Delta G|_{\text{mix}} = nRT\Sigma_i(n_i/n)\ln(n_i/n)$, with GAS constant: $R = 8.3144621(75)$ J/Kmol and the process at temperature T. In case the mixture is for gases at pressure P_i, the Gibbs energy for the mixture can be written as $\Delta G|_{\text{mix}} = \Sigma_i n_i\left(\mu_{\text{chem},i} + RTl\,nP_i\right)$. Similarly, the entropy change as a result of mixing is $\Delta S|_{\text{mix}} = nR\Sigma_i(n_i/n)\ln(n_i/n)$. The enthalpy change is provided by $\Delta H|_{\text{mix}} = \Delta G|_{\text{mix}} + T\Delta S|_{\text{mix}}$. In all cases, the entropy of the mixture will be greater than that of the components separately. The first-order derivative of the Gibbs free energy provides a negative, implicating that mixing is generally spontaneous. The second-order derivative of the entropy will also always be negative, indicating that the mixture will be adverse to phase separation and supports miscibility (i.e., no preferential mixing ratio) (*also see* **RAOULT'S LAW, HENRY'S LAW, FUGACITY,** *and* **GIBBS–DALTON MIXTURE**).

Mixing length (ℓ_m)

[fluid dynamics] In FLUID flow the mixing length describes the DISTANCE (ℓ_m) over which the momentum transfer takes place within a NEWTONIAN FLUID thin shear BOUNDARY LAYER by means of TURBULENCE Reynolds stresses under the influence of Boussineq eddy viscosity (mathematician from France, Joseph Valentin Boussineq [1842–1929]), and is proportional to the half-width of the shear layer (ℓ_s) for free SHEAR FLOW. The ratio of shear layer to mixing length for specific objects is, for instance, $\ell_m = 0.09\ell_s$ for plane JET flow, and $\ell_m = 0.075\ell_s$ for circular jet flow. The concept was introduced by LUDWIG PRANDTL (1875–1953) in. The eddy VISCOSITY MODEL is described as $-u_i'u_j' = \eta_T\left((\partial U_i/\partial x_j) + (\partial U_j/\partial x_i)\right) - 2/3\,\delta_{ij}k_{\text{Boussineq}}$, where $u_i' u_j'$ is the average of the product of the horizontal and vertical components, known as REYNOLDS STRESS, $\eta_T = \ell_m'^2 \left|\partial U_k / \partial x_k\right|$ is the eddy viscosity, measured in the direction of FLOW, u_n' the FLOW velocity components in the respective dimensional reference frame with components $(n = (i, j, k))$, U_n is the, δ_{ij} the Kronicker delta function, and $k_{\text{Boussineq}} = \left|u_m' u_m'\right|/2$. Ludwig Prandtl (1875–1953) proposed that the mixing length is linked to the eddy viscosity and the turbulent velocity as $\eta_T \sim u\ell_m$; furthermore, Prandtl postulated a link between the flow velocity component and the turbulent velocity component as $u \sim \ell_m \left|\partial U_j / \partial x_j\right|$. (*Note*: For incompressible flow of a homogeneous fluid the flow velocities can be split into a mean part $[u_i]$ and a fluctuating part $[u_i']$ using Reynolds decomposition, defined as $u_i = u_i + u_i'$.)

Mixing time ($\theta_m = t_m/t_C$)

[chemical, computational, mechanical, thermodynamics] Dimensionless number yielding the ration between the time to phenomenological time frame: t_m, and the time to pass through one CIRCULATION loop, cycling time: t_C. In computational PHYSICS this refers to the relative time that RANDOM WALK phenomena will intersect. In MECHANICS it relates to the time frame needed to achieve a set level of homogeneity during physical joining of two or more constituents. In THERMODYNAMICS the mixing time describes the time span in which a phenomenon will evolve into an irreversible process and the ENERGY transitions involved in the time lapse. In computational physics the MARKOV PROCESS will reach a predefined form of homogeneity in PROBABILITY of the distribution of states at the end of the mixing time, also called MARKOV CHAIN MIXING TIME.

MKSA system

[general] System of units based on the elementary parameters: length, meter (m); mass, kilogram (kg); time, second (s); and current (charge flow), AMPERE (A). This makes the Coulomb unit (C), for charge $C = As$. The unit volt (V) for electric potential becomes $V = kg/m^2 s^2 C = kg/m^2 s^3 A$.

PHYSICAL PARAMETER	UNIT	SYMBOL	DIMENSION	LOGISTIC PARAMETER	FUNCTION
Angular momentum	*kgm²/s*	*L*	ML^2T^{-1}		$\vec{L} = \vec{r} \times \vec{p}$
Angular velocity	*rad /s*	ω	T^{-1}		$\omega = \frac{d\theta}{dt}$
Capacitance	Farad: *F*	C	$M^{-1}L^{-2}T^{-2}Q^2$		$Q = CU$
Charge	Coulomb: *Coul*		Q	q	elementary
Current	Ampere: *A*	I	$T^{-1}Q$		
Energy, work	Joule: *J*	E,U,W	ML^2T^{-2}		
Force	Newton [*N*]	F	MLT^{-2}		
Inductance	Henry [*H*]	L	ML^2Q^{-2}		$V = L\left(\frac{dI}{dt}\right)$
Length	Meter [*m*]	ℓ	M		elementary
Magnetic flux	Weber [*Wb*]	Φ	$ML^2T^{-1}Q^{-1}$		$\Phi = \int \vec{B} \cdot d\vec{S}$
Magnetic induction	Tesla	*B*	Wb/m^2		
mass		m			
Momentum	kgm/s				$p = mv$

(*Continued*)

PHYSICAL PARAMETER	UNIT	SYMBOL	DIMENSION	LOGISTIC PARAMETER	FUNCTION
Potential, voltage, emf	Volt [*V*]	U, ε_{emf}; emf			$U = \frac{\Delta E}{q}$
Resistance	Ohm [Ω]	R	$ML^2T^{-1}Q^{-2}$		
Time	Second [*s*]	t	T		
Velocity	*m*/*s*	*v*	LT^{-1}		$v = \frac{ds}{dt}$

Möbius, August Ferdinand (1790–1868)

[astrophysics/astronomy, computational, mechanics] Mathematician and astronomer from Germany, the Prussian Empire. Möbius is best known for his contributions to analytic geometry and his work in topology. Möbius designed the belt that has only "one surface," the Möbius band, or Möbius strip (see Figure M.115).

Figure M.115 August Ferdinand Möbius (1790–1868).

Möbius band

[computational] Strip of material that has a twist in it so that one can follow the surface around 720° and return to the same point, while a 360° passage will not cross with any points that were passed on the track. This is referred to as an infinite band, or strip, described by August Ferdinand Möbius (1790–1868) (see Figure M.116).

Figure M.116 Illustration of the Möbius band concept.

Mode conversion

[acoustics] Sound traveling in a solid material can convert its ENERGY into a different format. One example is a longitudinal (e.g., acoustic) compression wave (P-WAVE, i.e., pressure wave) incident on an interface at an ANGLE. Due to the MICROSCOPIC interaction the longitudinal displacement can cause PARTICLE movement in the transverse direction, which initiates a shear wave (S-wave), or transverse wave (*also see* **LAMB WAVE, EVANESCENT WAVE,** *or* **RALEIGH WAVE**). Nonperpendicular wave incidence on an interface between two media with different acoustic impedances will also generate mode conversion. S-waves and P-waves can be transformed into each other at discontinuities, such as rock-faces in soft crust during an EARTHQUAKE. S-waves can be transmitted in polarized form. Acoustic S-waves were described in the 1800s based on the stress–strain relationship for an isotropic solid, providing the stress relation: $\tau_{ij} = \lambda_L \delta_{ij}\epsilon_{ii} + 2\mu_L\epsilon_{ij}$, where μ_L and λ_L are the Lamé coefficients, introduced by GABRIEL LAMÉ (1795–1870), $\epsilon_{ij} = (1/2)(\partial_j v_i + \partial_i v_j)$ and respectively $\epsilon_{ii} = \partial v_i/\partial x_i$ strain, v_i the velocity in the direction i, ∂_i the gradient change normal to the MOTION, and δ_{ij} the Kronecker delta function. This transforms into the SEISMIC WAVE equation: $\rho(\partial^2\vec{v}/\partial t^2) = (\lambda_L + 2\mu_L)\nabla(\nabla\cdot\vec{v}) - \mu_L\nabla\times(\nabla\times\vec{v})$, where ρ represents the density of the medium.

Mode-locked laser

[energy, optics, quantum] Laser operating under pulsed conditions that use either an active ELEMENT (an optical modulator: e.g., crystal such as KTP) or a nonlinear passive element (a absorber that can saturate, holding the excitation process and subsequent release followed by a very high ENERGY burst of photons at the wavelength of the medium) in the laser cavity, and are capable of producing extremely short pulses, in the order of femto- and picosecond duration. The spectral width of mode-locked lasers is broad due to the condition linking frequency bandwidth ($\Delta\nu$) to time of light pulse (Δt) as $\Delta\nu\Delta t \geq 1/4\pi$. Active mode-locking can be achieved by integration of either an electro-optic or an acousto-optic modulator in the laser cavity. Examples of active modulators are a Mach–Zehnder integrated optic modulator, or a semiconductor electro-absorption modulator. If the modulation frequency is synchronized with the resonator path of the laser cavity the laser will produce light only at the resonant convergence maxima. Technically, the operational mode of the modulator needs to lock-in with the preferred laser mode (see Figure M.117).

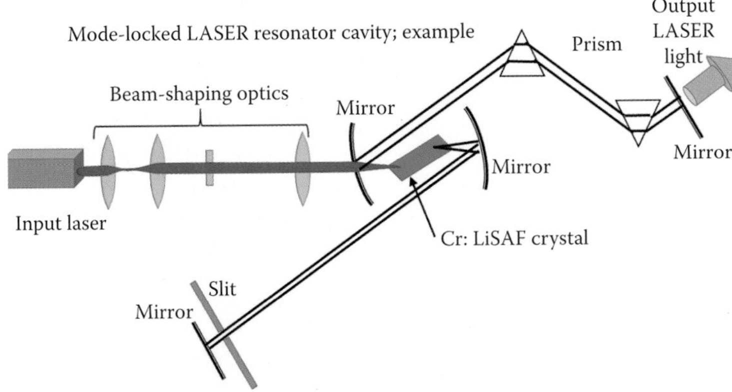

Figure M.117 Graphical representation of the Mode-Locked LASER concept.

Moderator

[nuclear] Rod in a nuclear power reactor that moderates the rate of degradation of URANIUM (^{235}U), by means of slowing down the released fast neutrons, created during the disintegration that can initiate the expedited fission DECAY of the unstable uranium to ^{236}U, under $^{235}\mathrm{U} + n_{\mathrm{slow}} \rightarrow {}^{236}\mathrm{U} \rightarrow X + Y + \nu n_{\mathrm{fast}}$, where the reaction is sustained when the constant $\nu_{\mathrm{neutron}} > 1$, the MULTIPLICATION FACTOR, and X and Y are short-lived reaction products. The reaction is regulated by absorbing neutron in carbon rods, known as control rods, regulating the quantity ν_{neutron}. Keeping in mind that naturally occurring uranium (as used in the fuel

rods) only consists of 0.72% ^{235}U, with the balance ^{238}U; which converts to ^{239}U under absorption of a NEUTRON, thus depleting the FISSION process, however the reaction CROSS SECTION is less than 1 barn $\cong 10^{-28}$ m^2, while the cross section for ^{235}U is 582 barn. Generally for uranium the process is well controlled for $\nu_{neutron} = 2.47$, while for PLUTONIUM (^{239}Pu) $\nu = 2.91$ (see Figure M.118).

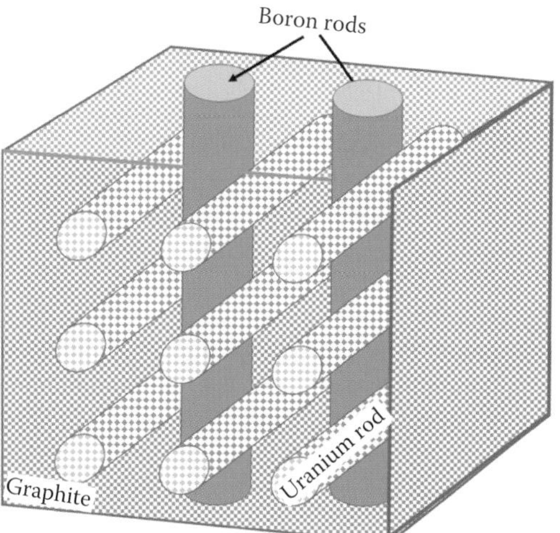

Figure M.118 Boron moderator rods in uranium nuclear power reactor.

Modes of vibration

[general, mechanics] The geometrical deformation patterns in a vibrating MEMBRANE or disk, such as percussion instruments (drums and timpani), as well as in the working of the eardrum. The WAVE EQUATION in two dimension will provide the superposition of multiple waves with different or equal wavelengths traveling or standing in various directions within the vibrating surface: $\partial^2 u/\partial t^2 = v^2\left((\partial^2 u/\partial x^2)+(\partial^2 u/\partial y^2)\right) = v^2\left((\partial^2 u/\partial r^2)+(1/r)(\partial u/\partial r)+(1/r^2)(\partial^2 u/\partial \theta^2)\right)$, where u signifies a field MAGNITUDE or a displacement in a Cartesian coordinate system or in a cylindrical coordinate system, and v is the velocity of propagation of the transverse or LONGITUDINAL WAVE in the medium, since the wave may also be confined to a thin layer of gaseous medium. The classification of the EIGENFUNCTION solutions for each geometry provides an indication of the wave form on the surface. The number of modes are a function of the SURFACE TENSION, the diameter (characteristic lengths; the larger the characteristic length the greater the number of modes), elastic modulus, and thickness. These all provide the boundary conditions to the acoustic problem. The AMPLITUDE for higher modes for a small diameter drum will be proportionally less and become negligible (i.e., higher modes become critically damped) (see Figure M.119).

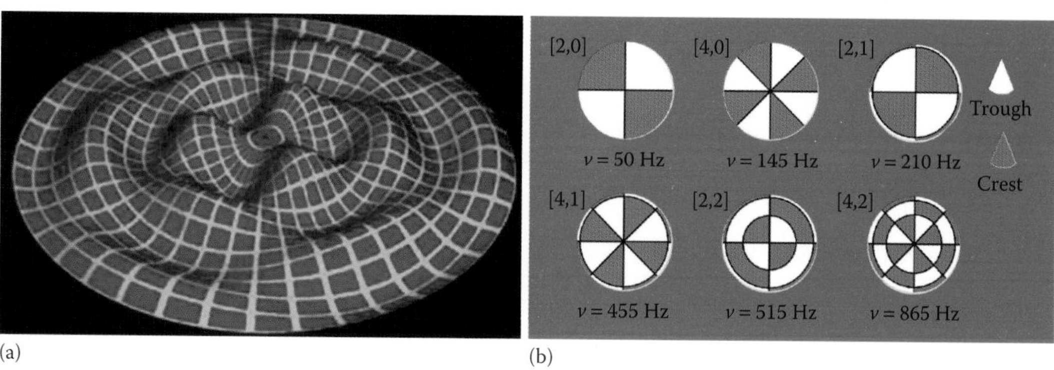

Figure M.119 (a) Outline of some of the simpler modes of vibration for a circular plate. (b) Various, selected (not all) vibrational modes for a circular skin under tension (i.e., drum surface) or metal (steel drum).

Modulus decay

[energy, fluid dynamics, quantum] Generic cosmic SCALAR fields in the GRAND UNIFIED THEORY have consequences which can be analyzed in the form of moduli which will primarily DECAY through gravitationally suppressed interactions only. This generates a production mechanism of gravitinos (the hypothetical GRAVITATION particles) resulting from moduli decay.

Modulus of elasticity (*Y*)

[general, mechanics] The ratio of the stress to the strain. Description of the elastic properties of linear objects such as cables, shafts, or structural columns subjected to stretch or compression. ELASTICITY is a material property that will result in the restoration to the original shape of the object after distortion (*see* **HOOKE'S LAW**). Also referred to as the "Young's modulus" of the material.

Modulus of rigidity

[mechanics] Coefficient of ELASTICITY with respect to an applied shearing force, used in materials science $G_{rig} \equiv \tau_{xy}/\gamma_{xy} = (F/A)/(\Delta x/l) = Fl/A\Delta x$. Defined as the ratio of SHEAR STRESS (the force $[F]$ per unit area (A): τ_{xy}) to the displacement (Δx) per unit length (l) of the object (i.e., the shear strain: γ_{xy}), derived from the slope of a stress–strain curve. It is also known as shear modulus.

Moens, Adriaan Isebree (1846–1891)

[fluid dynamics] Scientist and physician from the Netherlands. When focusing his research on the principles of arteriosclerosis and vascular stiffness his work produced the foundations for the mathematical description of pulse propagation in flexible tubes in 1878. His collaborator was the mathematician from the Netherlands, Diederik Korteweg (1848–1941). Moens was a close friend of WILLEM EINTHOVEN (1860–1927), the scientist from the Netherlands who introduced the acquisition of the electrocardiogram (see Figure M.120).

Figure M.120 Adriaan Isebree Moens (1846–1891). (Courtesy of Museum Boerhaave.)

Moens–Korteweg equation

[fluid dynamics] *See* **MOENS–KORTEWEG VELOCITY.**

Moens–Korteweg velocity

[computational, fluid dynamics] Mathematical description of a FLOW process in a flexible tube, such as a BLOOD vessel or rubber tube (e.g., oil filling, gasoline pumping, etc.), allowing for local expansion in the cross-sectional flow area. The principle was introduced by the Dutch team ADRIAAN ISEBREE MOENS (1846–1891) and Diederik Korteweg (1848–1941). The elastic WALL expansion process produces a WAVE propagation that travels with a propagation velocity: $v_{MK} = \sqrt{(E_Y \tau_{wall}/2R\rho)}$, where E_Y represents the elastic modulus of the tube, τ_{wall}

the local wall thickness, R the radius of the tube, and ρ the LIQUID medium density; under the assumption that EXPANSION is isotropic and responds in isovolumetric change with respect to pulse pressure. It is also known as the MOENS–KORTEWEG EQUATION. This approach is an extension to the NAVIER–STOKES EQUATION.

Moiré pattern

[acoustics, fluid dynamics, optics] The term Moire has its origin in a woven fabric pattern that creates an impression of three-dimensional depth and speaks to the imagination. The original silk textile weave resembles water waves, dating back to a process found in the fourteenth or fifteenth century called "marmoreus," later (mid-sixteenth century) interpreted as "mohair." In the mid-seventeenth century his was interpreted in French as "mouaire." In the early nineteenth century the term made it back to English as "moire." Form of ALIASING, where two identical patterns are overlaid at a slight ANGLE to each other whereby false patterns can be observed in an IMAGE. The patterns can be produced by optical aberrations, defects in instrumentation, inferior quality of optical ELEMENTS (lenses, windows), or intentionally resulting from illumination of an uneven surface through a grid pattern where the LIGHT SOURCE is placed at an angle from the observer. The latter will create irregularities in the cross pattern based on the elevation of the uneven surface observed behind the multislit screen. A picket fence can provide the conditions to observe the topography of a flowerbed and grass field while the Sun illuminates through the fence at great ZENITH ANGLE (with respect to the normal). For SOUND, the overlap of two waves can result in a "beat" that is the consequence of the differences between two patterns. In moving patterns, the beat of light and dark also has a beat that is associated with the velocity at which the two patterns move with respect to each other. An optical Moiré pattern can also result from the limitations in RESOLUTION of the recording device with respect to the spatial frequency of a pattern under observation, which can be the EYE looking at a fine line pattern (see Figure M.121).

Figure M.121 Moiré pattern. The fringe interference pattern spatial density can be used to identify elevation when a line pattern is projected on an uneven surface and viewed through a screen with the same spatial frequency as the pattern emerging from the projector, without the requirement of stereoscopic vision.

Moist air

[thermodynamics] Quantification of the amount of water vapor in the AIR (*see* **RELATIVE HUMIDITY, ABSOLUTE HUMIDITY,** *and* **SPECIFIC HUMIDITY**).

Molar heat capacity (c_m)

[atomic, thermodynamics] Quantity of HEAT (Q) required to produce a temperature (T) rise in a quantity of substance, measured in moles (n) of chemical constituents: $c_m = (1/n)(dQ/dT)$, expressed in J/mol°C, which is, for instance, $c_m^{H_2O} = 75.3$ J/mol°C and $c_m^{Gold} = 25.4$ J/mol°C. This is very similar to the SPECIFIC HEAT of a medium, quantified by mass, which has the following values, at constant pressure $c_p^{H_2O} = 4180$ J/kg°C and $c_p^{Gold} = 130$ J/kg°C.

Molar mass

[thermodynamics] Mass associated with a MOLE of atoms, ions, or molecules quantified by the number of components expressed by AVOGADRO'S NUMBER.

Molding stresses

[acoustics] Residual stress resulting from shape formation in a mold. Residual, or molding stress, is a process-induced stress, encapsulated in a molded part. The stress can result from either FLOW during injection molding or thermal effects (cooling [thermal gradients] or curing related). When the molding stress is greater than the internal COHESION forces the part will warp upon ejection from the mold.

Mole

[atomic, biomedical, chemical, general, thermodynamics] Unit to express the number of atoms, electrons as well as ions and specifically molecules in a volume of medium, either dissolved or as dry mass. The carbon ATOM was initially used to quantify the number of atoms in a mass yielding that 12 g of carbon consists exactly of one mole of carbon [^{12}C] atoms. The number of specific items in 1 mole is defined by the AVOGADRO NUMBER ($N_A = 6.02214078 \times 10^{23} \pm 1.8 \times 10^{16}$[atoms/gram] or [molecules/gram][2011 definition]), representing $6.02214078 \times 10^{23} \pm 1.8 \times 10^{16}$ atoms of carbon-12 in 12 g of carbon substance. The definition of molecular mass and quantity of substance dates back to 1805, when JOHN DALTON (1766–1844) published the first table of atomic weights.

Molecular band

[atomic, chemical, nuclear, optics, thermodynamics] Absorption lines observed when a pure substance of molecular emulsion is illuminated by broadband ELECTROMAGNETIC RADIATION. Similarly, during excitation (heating or electric current as well as other means of ENERGY delivery), the spectral emission lines comprise a pure substance of single molecular composition. The "empty" orbital electron bands are separated from the "occupied" electron orbital bands in atomic and molecular structure by the FERMI ENERGY (see Figure M.122).

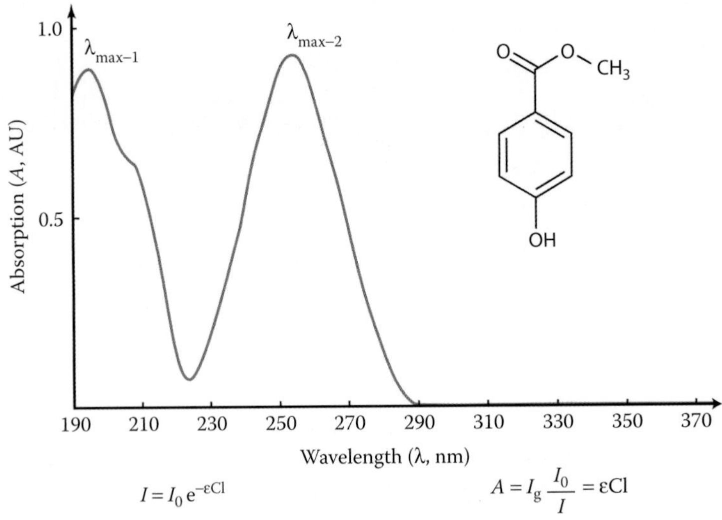

Figure M.122 Molecular absorption spectrum for the chemical compound Paraben.

Molecular beam

[atomic, nuclear] Stream of molecules ejected within a small SOLID ANGLE, moving in the same general direction. The emission of molecules can be through an evacuated chamber or from a pressure NOZZLE. Due to the essentially one-directional MOTION of the atoms, ions, or molecules, specific properties can be studied under deflection by electric and/or MAGNETIC fields. The molecular beam may be directed onto a target, consisting of GAS, a solid, or intercept an alternative beam of atoms, ions, or molecules. Molecular beams are inherently of low density to avoid collisions.

Molecular beam epitaxy

[computational, fluid dynamics, mechanics, solid-state, thermodynamics] A specific process used in the formation of crystal structure invented at the Bell Laboratories in the late 1960s and is used in the formation of transistors and other electronic components. The EPITAXIAL GROWTH process requires high or ultrahigh VACUUM conditions and slow deposit rate, significantly less than 1 nm/s, forming a single crystalline layer on a formed or existing crystalline substrate.

Molecular diameters (σ_{molec})

[nuclear] Based on the van der Waals equation, the "covolume" component, $b = 4N_aV$, with N_a AVOGADRO'S NUMBER and V the volume of the MOLECULE, can be used to derive the size of the molecule in a GAS, when taking the volume of one molecule ($V_{\text{molec}} = (4/3)\pi\sigma_{\text{molec}}^{3}$) when dividing by the Avogadro's number based on the value of b. In the KINETIC THEORY of gases the molecular diameter can be used to define the VISCOSITY: $\eta = 5/(16\sigma_{\text{molec}}^{2})(mkT/\pi)^{1/2}$, where k is Boltzmann's constant, T the temperature of the gas, and m the mass of the molecule of the gas, assuming that the molecules behave as hard spheres.

Molecular dynamics

[computational] Theoretical study of the physical movement of atoms and molecules by means of simulation of an N-body interaction. The particulate (atoms and molecules) trajectories are derived from NUMERICAL solutions to Newton's EQUATIONS OF MOTION for a system of interacting units. The forces between the particulates and the acting potential ENERGY result from molecular mechanic force field definitions.

Molecular heat

[atomic, nuclear] Heat capacity per MOLE for a pure ELEMENT of material: amount of heat required to raise the temperature of 1 mole of a substance 1 K (*also see* **MOLAR HEAT** *and* **HEAT CAPACITY**).

Molecular motion

[nuclear] *See* **BROWNIAN MOTION.**

Molecular spectra

[atomic, nuclear] *See* **MOLECULAR SPECTROSCOPY.**

Molecular spectroscopy

[atomic, quantum, solid-state] Under atomic SPECTROSCOPY the examination can be based on a gaseous state under electric discharge that separates the atoms into neutral or charged atoms. Alternatively, the GAS may be molecular in composition and irradiated by an external excitation source of ELECTROMAGNETIC RADIATION. The molecules undergo ENERGY transitions based on GROUND STATE excitation or return. In general three excitation processes can be distinguished: electronic excitation, vibrational excitation, and rotational excitation, specifically due to the fact that the MOLECULE may be asymmetric. For a diatomic molecule the Hamiltonian (H) for the MOTION wavefunction approach can be written as (assuming that the rotational excitation is relatively small compared to the first two): $H = -(\hbar/2m_1)\nabla_1^2 - (\hbar/2m_2)\nabla_2^2 + V(r_{12})$, where ∇_i^2 is the second-order derivative with respect to the coordinates of nucleus 1 or 2 respectively, m_i the respective atomic/nuclear masses of the molecular constituents, $V(r_{12})$ the electric potential between the two components (both atomic and nuclear), and $\hbar = h/2\pi$, with $h = 6.62606957 \times 10^{-34}\,\mathrm{m^2kg/s}$ Planck's constant. This will yield the following SOLUTION for the energy levels that can be identified by spectroscopic analysis: $E = (\nu_{vib} + (1/2))\hbar\omega + (J(J+1)\hbar^2)/2\mu_m r_0^2$, where $\nu_{vib} = 0,1,2,\ldots$ the vibrational QUANTUM number, ω the vibrational frequency (the VIBRATION frequency can be associated with a "spring" phenomenon in molecular attraction), $J = 0,1,2,\ldots$ the rotational QUANTUM number (with transition selection rule: $\Delta J = \pm 1$), $\mu_m = m_1 m_2/(m_1 + m_2)$ the REDUCED MASS, and r_0 the average nuclear separation. A diatomic molecule can for instance be hydrogen chloride (see Figure M.123).

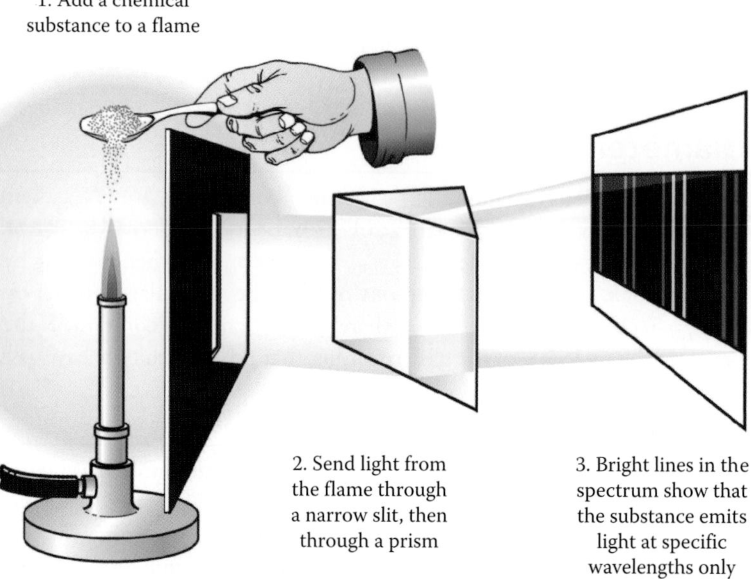

Figure M.123 Illustration of early design flame-spectroscopy device for use on molecular gasses, salts, and other chemicals.

Molecular weight

[thermodynamics] The sum of all atomic weights of the constituent atoms forming a MOLECULE.

Molecule

[atomic, biomedical, chemical, general, thermodynamics] The smallest chemical unit of material that has all the characteristics of the substance or ELEMENT in mass quantity (i.e., it can exist by itself while retaining all the properties of the original homogeneous substance; see Figure M.124). The molecule consists of two or more atoms that are held together by covalent attractive forces to form a stable unit with no externally observable charges, the molecule is electrically and electronically neutral. The most well know molecules are oxygen (O_2) and WATER (H_2O).

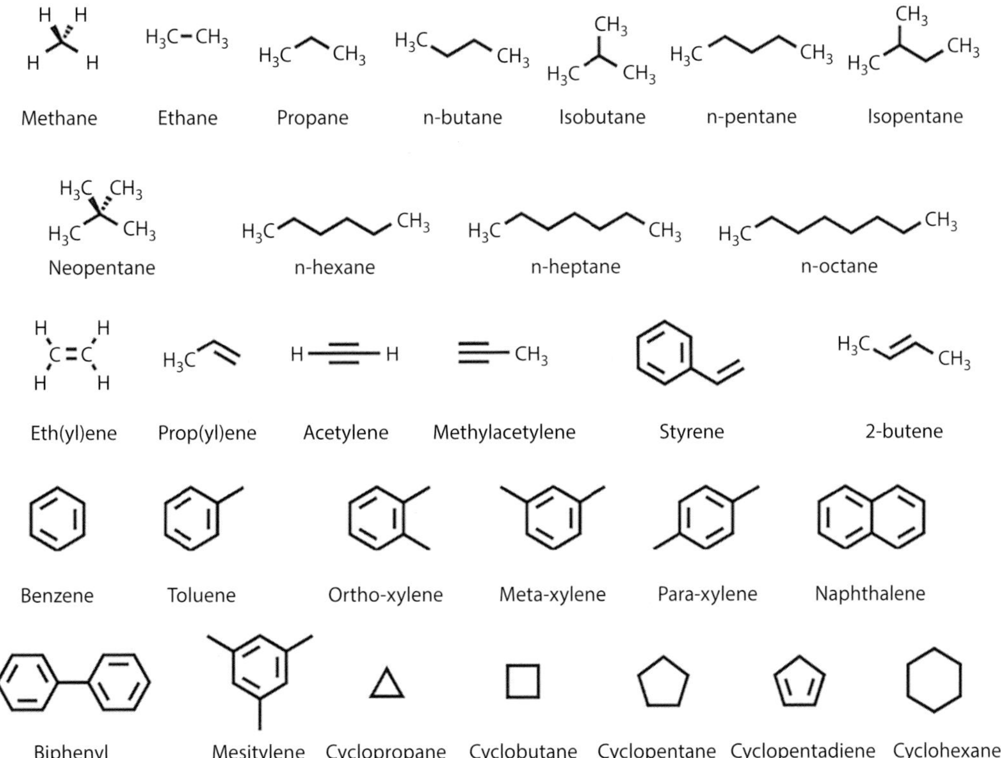

Figure M.124 Graphical representation of the molecular structure of various hydro-carbon molecules.

Mollier chart

[thermodynamics] Graphical representation of the interconnecting relationships between temperature, moisture content, and respective entropy and enthalpy of composite gases, such as the ATMOSPHERE (composed of nitrogen, water vapor, oxygen and ozone, argon, neon, helium, methane, krypton, hydrogen, nitrous oxide, and xenon). The basic Mollier chart is used to plot the total heat against entropy. The chart was designed by the German physicist Richard Mollier (1863–1935) in 1904. The Mollier chart forms an elementary design tool to account for air–grain–moisture system in a malting process, refrigeration (performance analysis of VAPOR compression systems), and is also used by power station engineers in, for instance, the steam cycle. The chart shows ENTHALPY (H) with respect to internal ENERGY U, as well as pressure P and volume V. The Mollier chart also applies to the Rankin cycle (*also see* **PSYCHROMETRIC CHART**, of which the Mollier diagram is a variant) (see Figure M.125).

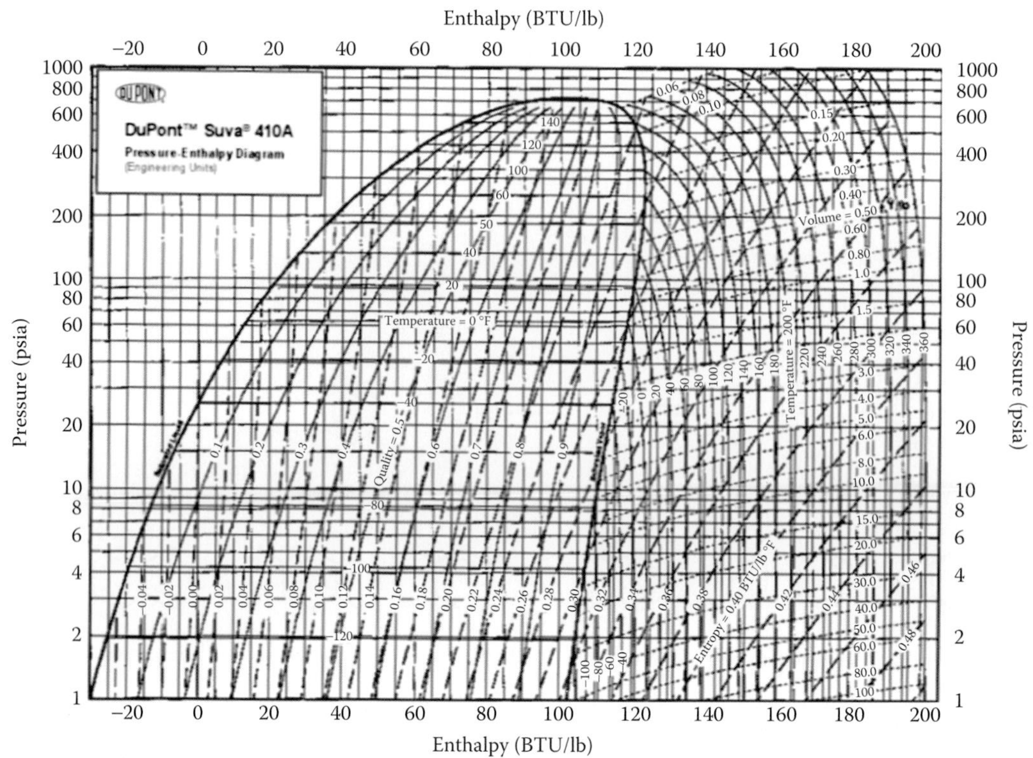

Figure M.125 Mollier entropy chart for 410 refrigerant. (Courtesy of DuPont®.)

Molniya orbit

[astrophysics, general, mechanics] Highly eccentric orbit of Russian (USSR—Union of Soviet Socialist Republics) (in Russian: Сою́з Сове́тских Социалисти́ческих Респу́блик: "CPCC") satellites at an azimuth inclination of 63.4° with orbital period of one-half of a sidereal day (sidereal time is based on the earth's rate of rotation with respect to the fixed observable stars, used by astronomers to track the position of their TELESCOPE). These satellites have been in orbit since the 1960s. In Russian the word Molniya stands for "LIGHTNING." In this configuration the SATELLITE spends the majority of time over the northern hemisphere, reaching its highest orbital DISTANCE (apogee) of 40,000 km. For continuous coverage of the northern hemisphere a minimum of three Molniya satellites will be required. Satellites of this type can be used for communication as well as espionage (see Figure M.126).

Figure M.126 Representation of the Molniya orbit on postage stamp.

Moment arm

[biomedical] The perpendicular DISTANCE from line of force application with respect to the axis of rotation. This applies to the rotational MOTION of a joint in a biological vertebrate animal produced by the torque applied by musculoskeletal attachment, such as the elbow and the knee (see Figure M.127).

Figure M.127 The moment arm of the chimpanzee, proving a powerful lever, much stronger than the human elbow (a chimpanzee will easily overpower a human).

Moment coefficient

[fluid dynamics] Heuristic method used to quantify the aerodynamic forces on an object under FLUID flow conditions. The general form for a regular object (e.g., rod, WING, plate, or a bullet) is $C_m = \alpha_1/(\mathrm{Re}^{\alpha_2}[1-\{\alpha_3\,\mathrm{Re}^{\alpha_4}\,\mathrm{arcsinh}(\alpha_5\,\mathrm{Re}^{\alpha_6})\}])$, with α_i constants that are dependent on the conditions and shape and size, and Re is the REYNOLDS NUMBER of the object subjected to FLOW. For a sphere this yields $C_{m_{\mathrm{sphere}}} = 8g/\mathrm{Re}_{\mathrm{sphere}}$, where $\mathrm{Re}_{\mathrm{sphere}}$ is the Reynolds number of the sphere in the flow, and g the GRAVITATIONAL ACCELERATION. The method is of particular relevance under transverse Blasius BOUNDARY LAYER flow. One specific example of interest refers to the aerodynamic aspect of a bullet in flight. There are several moments involved that describe the role, yaw and trajectory of a bullet, defined as follows: rolling moment coefficient—$C_\ell = \mathcal{L}/_q Sd$, where $\mathcal{L}$ is the rolling moment, S the cross-sectional surface area, q the kinetic pressure, and d the PROJECTILE diameter; SPIN dampening moment coefficient—$C_{\ell_\wp} = \partial C_\ell/[\partial(\wp\, d/2v)]$, where $\wp$ is the projectile spin rate, v the projectile velocity; overturning PITCH moment coefficient—$C_{m_o} = \mathcal{M}/qSd$, where $\mathcal{M}$ is the overtuning moment; Magnus moment coefficient slope—$C_{m_{\wp\beta}} = \partial^2 C_{m_o}/[\partial(\wp\, d/2v)\partial\beta]$, where β is the ANGLE of sideslip; pitch DAMPING moment coefficient—$C_{m_q} = \partial C_{m_o}/[\partial(\mathbb{Q}d/2v)]$, where $\mathbb{Q}$ represents the overturning moment/pitch moment. In all cases the moment aspect refers to aspects of the MOMENT OF INERTIA and the MOMENT ARM (see Figure M.128).

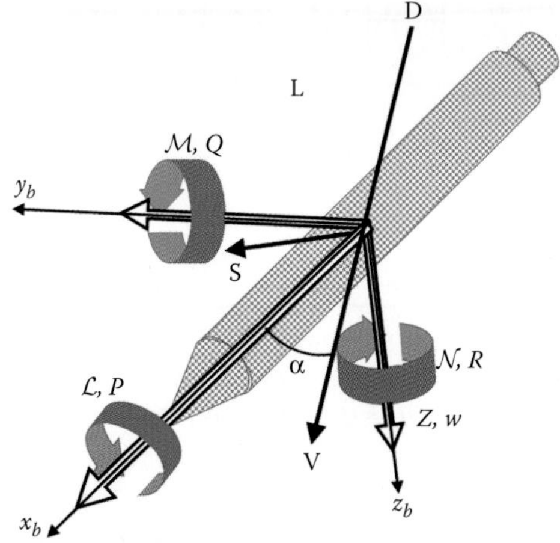

Figure M.128 The concept of moment coefficient illustrated.

Moment of a force

[general] *See* TORQUE.

Moment of inertia (I_m)

[general, mechanics] Scalar quantity that provides a mechanism to describe the rotational MOTION response of a system of particles with nonuniform or uniform distribution in a geometric shape as the consequence of an external force with respect to a particular axis of rotation. The moment of inertia is defined as $I_m = \sum_i r_i^2 m_i$, in a reference frame of choice as summarized over all the masses ($\sum_i m_i = M$) (each respective mass (m_i) or finite mass ELEMENT dm) constituent identified by (m_i) as a function of each respective location

(r_i) contributed from a system of particles (regardless of size and structure; including atoms and molecules). In integral form $I_m = \int r^2 dm = \int \rho r^2 dV$, with ρ the local density and V the volume of the constituent at a respective location. In rotational KINEMATICS, the net TORQUE (τ) of all constituents of a revolving object around the axis of rotation is defined with respect to the moment of inertia and the angular acceleration (α) as $\sum \tau = I_m \alpha$ as the rotational counterpart to NEWTON'S SECOND LAW (see Figure M.129).

Specific examples of the moment of inertia of certain shapes with uniform density are as follows:

SHAPE	MOMENT-OF-INERTIA	SHAPE DRAWING
Circular annulus with inner radius R_1 and outer radius R_2 revolving around the central axis. With M the mass of the unit.	$I_m = M\dfrac{R_1^2 + R_2^2}{2}$	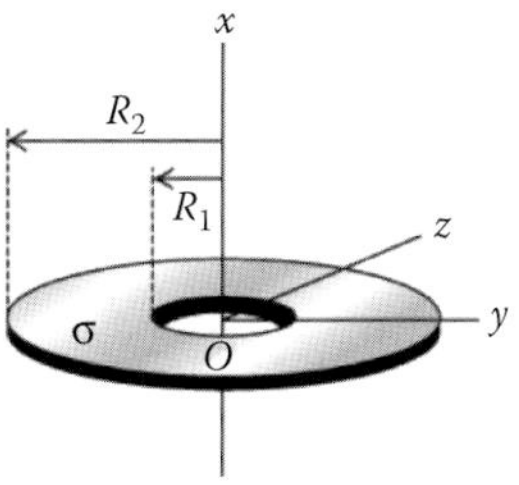 x, R_2, R_1, z, σ, y, O
Uniform right cone with maximum radius R_1 and length l revolving around the central axis. With M the mass of the shape.	$I_m = \dfrac{3}{10} MR^2$	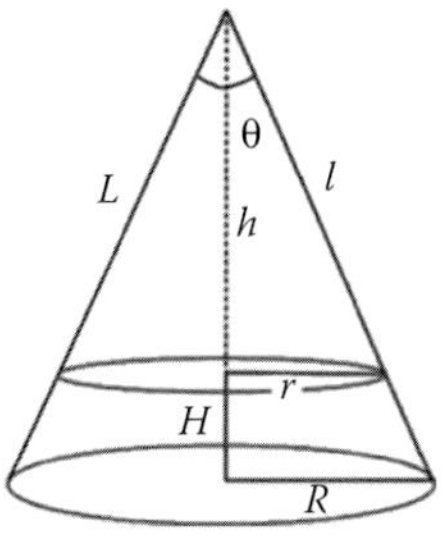 θ, L, l, h, r, H, R
Uniform thin rod length l revolving around the axis through the center of mass, perpendicular to the central axis of the geometry.	$I_m = \dfrac{1}{12} M\ell^2$	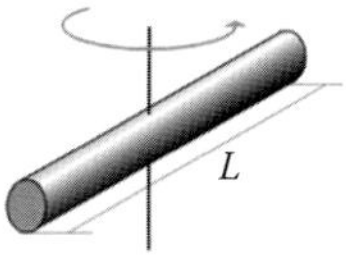 L
Uniform solid cylinder with radius R revolving around the central axis of the geometry.	$I_m = \dfrac{1}{2} MR^2$	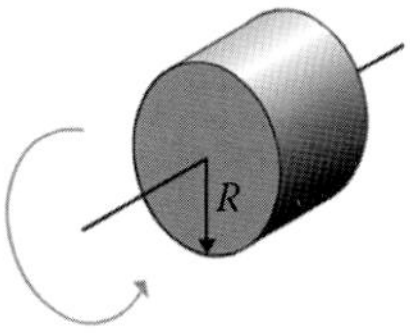 R
Uniform solid cylinder with length l and radius R revolving around the axis through the center of mass, perpendicular to the central axis of geometry.	$I_m = \dfrac{1}{4} MR^2 + \dfrac{1}{12} M\ell^2$	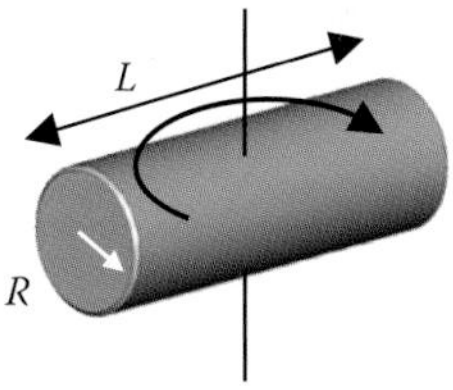 L, R

Figure M.129 Moment of Inertia.

Moment of inertia (*L*), spin rate

[general, mechanics] In figure skating, the skater can retract the arms and/or an extended LEG, resulting in an increase in rotational velocity based on CONSERVATION OF ANGULAR MOMENTUM, since I_m is reduced with the diminished lengths of the components. The same principles apply to a merry-go-round, moving to and fro the edge changes the rotational angular velocity (see Figure M.130).

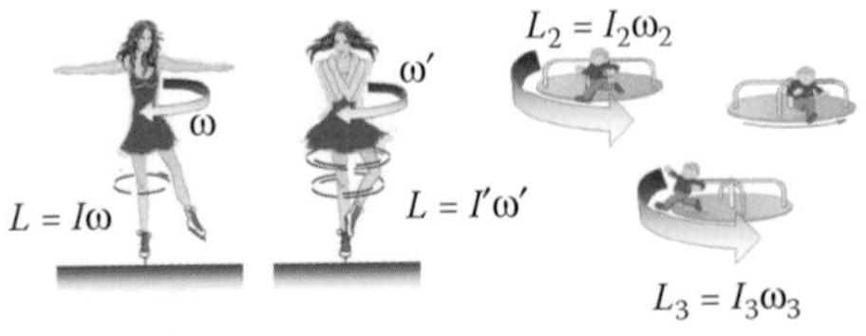

Figure M.130 Spin rate Moment of Inertia.

Momentum ($\vec{p}$)

[mechanics, nuclear] The fact that a body in MOTION tends to stay in motion is captured by the momentum of the body as the MASS (m) multiplied by the velocity (v) expressed as $\vec{p} = m\vec{v}$. More generally, the momentum of a massless entity can be captured as the rate of change (over time: t) in net ENERGY ($E = KE + PE$, where KE is the kinetic energy and PE the potential energy, respectively) as a function of velocity (v), expressed as $\vec{p} = dE/dv$. Under the conditions of NEWTON'S SECOND LAW a body will increase or decrease in momentum directly proportional to the applied net force (F), expressed as $\Sigma\vec{F} = d\vec{F}/dt$. Analogously, an ISOLATED SYSTEM will have conservation of momentum since no external forces are applied. There is a close relation with impulse, however, momentum generally provides a more useful concept. In PROPULSION with a gas-burning jet ENGINE, the mass of the object will vary (i.e., diminish: Δm), ejecting the propulsion waste with a velocity: $\vec{u}$ yielding the following condition involving the (conservation of) momentum: $d\vec{p}/dt = m(d\vec{v}/dt) - \Delta m(d\vec{v}/dt) + \vec{u}(dm/dt)$; note, there is no external force. (*also see* **ANGULAR MOMENTUM**). The product of the mass of a body and its velocity. CGS unit: gm-cm/s (see Figure M.131).

Figure M.131 The game of croquet illustrating the concept of Momentum, in specific the transfer of momentum.

M

Momentum change (Δp)

[general] In classical MECHANICS the change of momentum is the impulse: $J = \Delta p$ of a system. The change of momentum with respect to time is force ($F = dp/dt$) resulting from the change in momentum, applied to the phenomenon that made the momentum change; for instance, hitting a nail with a hammer over a short period of contact makes the hammer drive the nail into the wood, or a baseball fly into the outfield (see Figure M.132).

Figure M.132 How the change in momentum provides the force to drive a nail into a piece of wood.

Momentum eigenfunction

[atomic, fluid dynamics] In particle FLUX theory a free particle can be considered to be suspended by a constant potential V, that can be assumed $V = 0V$, which provides the one-dimensional SCHRÖDINGER EQUATION: $-(\hbar/2m)(d^2\Psi/dx^2) = E\Psi$, which yields a WAVE EQUATION solution $\Psi = Ce^{ikx} + De^{-ikx}$, and $\hbar = h/2\pi$, with $h = 6.62606957 \times 10^{-34}$ m^{2}kg/s Planck's constant, and E the particle ENERGY. In order for the PARTICLE to behave with constant momentum this solution is an EIGENVALUE function (i.e., EIGENFUNCTION) of the momentum operator: $p_{x_i} \rightarrow (\hbar/i)(\partial/\partial x_i)$, this will place as boundary conditions: $(\hbar/i)(\partial/\partial x)(Ce^{ikx}) = \hbar k Ce^{ikx}$ and $(\hbar/i)(\partial/\partial x)(De^{-ikx}) = -\hbar k De^{ikx}$, which represents a particle with momentum $p_x = \hbar k$, with $k = 2\pi/\lambda$ the wavenumber of the eigenfunction with wavelength λ.

Monatomic gases

[general] Gases that consist of single atoms only, examples are all of the noble gases: argon (Ar), helium (He), krypton (Kr), neon (Ne), RADON (Rn), and xenon (Xe).

Mondeville, Henry de (1260–1320)

[biomedical, chemical, optics] (*See* DE MONDEVILLE, HENRY.) French physician. The work of De Mondeville is one of the first known documented descriptions of therapeutic applications of light, now known as photodynamic therapy, in the treatment of smallpox.

Monochromatic light

[general, optics] ELECTROMAGNETIC RADIATION of a single wavelength, such as produced by a laser. The mechanism of action of the light amplification process in LASER produces truly identical photons that are all traveling in PHASE (coherent) at one fixed wavelength. Due to ENERGY requirements, the production of monochromatic light is complex and cannot be achieved by filtration. Filtering light by spectral means such as a PRISM or a colored filter will provide light with a finite bandwidth that relies on the definition of the device used to select a specific wavelength range. Generally, filtering by any means will result in an exponential increase in device cost with decreasing waveband, reaching infinity for a single wavelength.

Monod, Jacques Lucien (1910–1976)

[biomedical, chemical] Biologist from France. Nobel Prize winner in 1965, Physiology or Medicine, with respect to the work on control of enzyme and virus synthesis in collaboration with François Jacob (1920–2013) and André Michel Lwoff (1902–1994), based on the discovery that the adjustment of enzyme concentrations in all biological cells occurs through regulation of transcription; the first step of gene expression, transcribing DNA onto RNA by means of RNA polymerase enzyme (see Figure M.133).

Figure M.133 Jacques Lucien Monod (1910–1976). (Courtesy of Memorial University of Newfoundland.)

Monod equation

[biomedical, chemical] Mathematical description of microorganism growth rate, described by JACQUES LUCIEN MONOD (1910–1976) in 1949. The equation describes the growth of microorganisms based on the maximum specific growth rate (μ_{Growth}^{Max}), the concentration of the enzyme substrate that initiates the growth process ($[S_{substrate}]$), and an empirical "half-velocity" constant defining the conversion process ($K_{conversion}$, the Monod constant; the concentration of $[S_{substrate}]$ at "half growth": $\mu_{Monod}/\mu_{Growth}^{Max}$) as $\mu_{Monod} = \mu_{Growth}^{Max}([S_{substrate}]/([S_{substrate}] + K_{conversion}))$.

Monolayer

[fluid dynamics, general, solid-state] Steady-state or FLUID dynamic single uniform one MOLECULE thick film, or layer of closely packed atoms, molecules, or cells at an interface. In FLUID DYNAMICS the monolayer forms a BARRIER between the free FLOW and the rigid or semirigid wall. The WALL may be the surface on the wing of an airplane, or the inner perimeter of a tube or BLOOD vessel. Monolayers can consist of, for instance, but not limited to lipids, nanoparticles, polymers, and proteins. Surfactants will also form a monolayer (e.g., soap). Also known as Langmuir film (see Figure M.134).

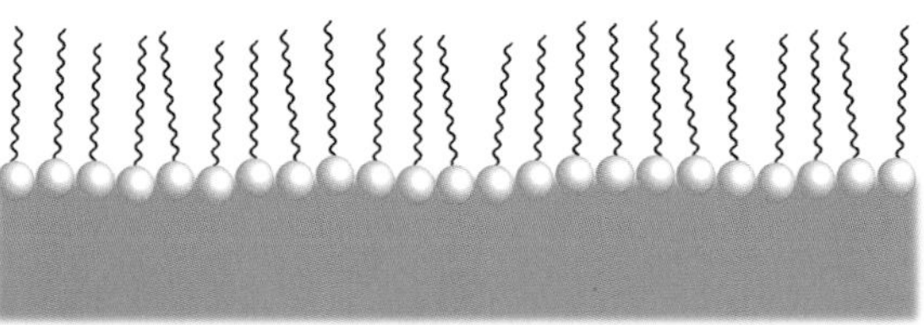

Figure M.134 Illustration of the monolayer concept with regard to soap (detergent/surfactant).

Monolithic

[electronics, general, geophysics] Geological single feature consisting of a stone or rock formation, for instance, a mountain. In semiconductor manufacturing, the monolithic layer is composed of a homogeneous ceramic or composite structure of several nanometer to micrometer thickness, with specific electronic and electromagnetic properties, potentially used to produce light through an excitation process, for instance, in customized LED development.

Monolythic

[electronics, general, geophysics] *See* MONOLITHIC.

Monomer

[biomedical, chemical] Single molecule. This MOLECULE may bind to other molecules to form a POLYMER, often used in the description of protein structures; e.g., monomeric protein. One example of a common monomer is glucose, found as a building block in plant MATTER (77%) and related as essential food constituent for human consumption. Glucose form a polymer when bond by glycosidic bonds to form CELLULOSE and starch. Another example is vinyl chloride, which is the monomer that form the synthetic POLYMER POLYVINYL CHLORIDE (PVC) (see Figure M.135).

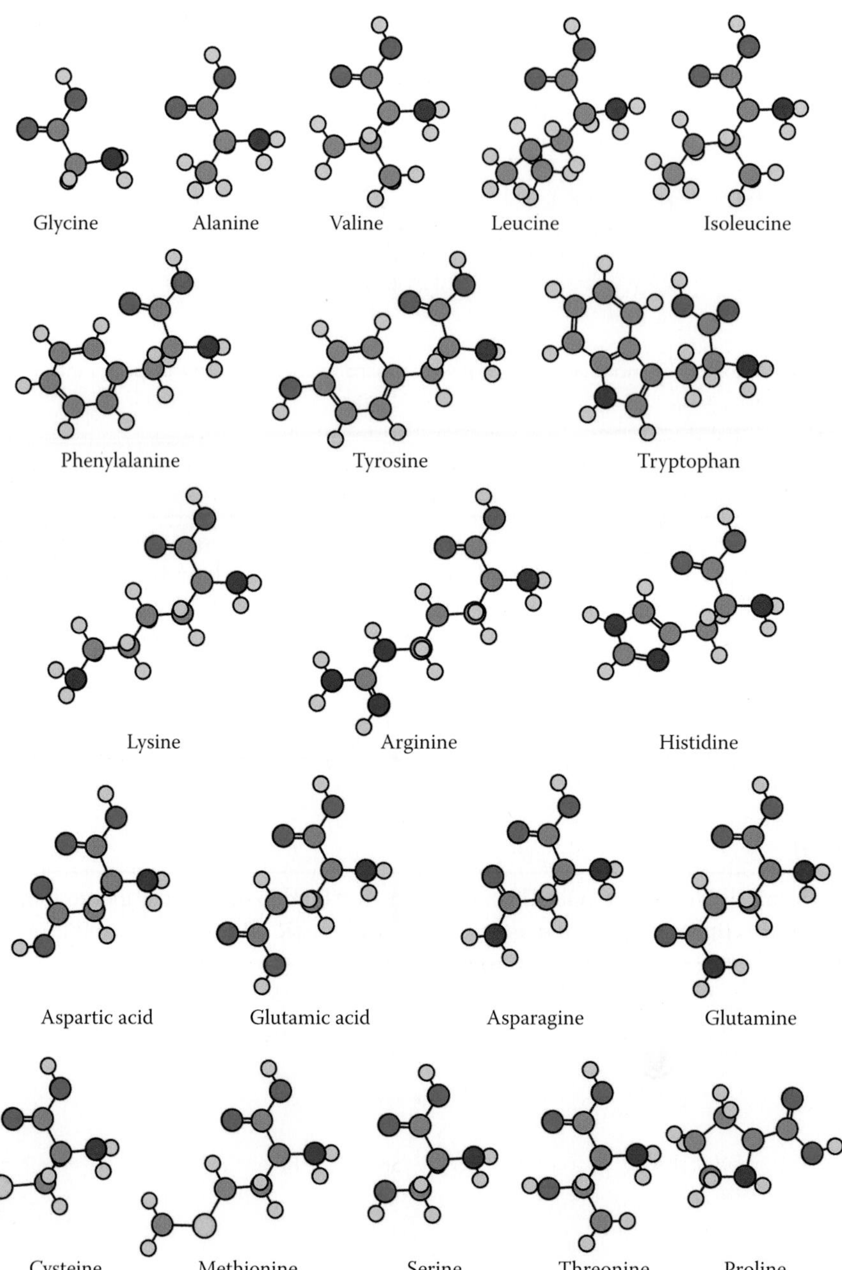

Figure M.135 Structural chemical formulas of 20 basic monomer amino acids.

Monopole, magnetic

[general] Hypothetical particle or magnetic segment within a medium, that consists of only a NORTH or south pole, as such assigned with a "magnetic charge." In practice this is inconceivable since MAGNETIC FIELD lines are by definition forming a closed loop. The theoretical concept originates from hypothetical concepts such as the GRAND UNIFIED THEORY.

Monopole antenna

[general] Mast ANTENNA that uses GROUND as a MIRROR to produce a virtual bipolar source. The monopole antenna requires half the voltage to produce the same field intensities as a free-space bipolar antenna.

Monte Carlo integration

[computational] Special technique in Monte Carlo methods used for NUMERICAL integration using random numbers based on PROBABILITY of events and associated magnitudes.

Monte Carlo method

[computational] Numerical technique for simulating analog processes based on PROBABILITY distribution of phenomena with certain distributions in MAGNITUDE with the assistance of random number generation to select specific events in the probability distribution on the fly. Monte Carlo simulation allows to account for risks process analysis in quantitative analysis and decision making, providing a range of possible effects and results with the associated probabilities that this will occur as the result of a particular choice of action. The Monte Carlo technique is used in ENERGY estimates and predictions, ENGINEERING, environmental predictions, finance, insurance, manufacturing, project management, research and development, transportation, and the utilities (e.g., oils, GAS) (see Figure M.136).

Figure M.136 Illustration of the random number distribution used in Monte Carlo modeling, roulette game-of-chance.

M

Montgolfier, Jacques-Étienne (1745–1799)

[engineering, general] Scientist and inventor from France. Together with his brother Joseph-Michel Montgolfier (1740–1810) they started the design of the Montgolfier-style hot-air balloon, approximately in 1777 (see Figure M.137).

Figure M.137 Montgolfier brothers, Jacques-Étienne Montgolfier (1745–1799) and Joseph-Michel Montgolfier (1740–1810).

Montgolfier, Joseph-Michel (1740–1810)

[engineering, general] Scientist and inventor from France. Together with his brother Jacques-Étienne Montgolfier (1745–1799) they launched the Montgolfier-style hot-air balloon, approximately in 1782.

Montgolfier-style hot-air balloon

[engineering, general] Hot-air balloon that served as the basis for the moderns hot-air balloon introduced by the two brothers Joseph-Michel Montgolfier (1740–1810) and Jacques-Étienne Montgolfier (1745–1799) from France at first ascent in 1782. The first manned balloon ride was performed in 1783 and subsequently a presentation was made to King Louis XVI of France (1754–1993) and Queen Marie Antoinette Josephina (1755–1793) from Austria (see Figure M.138).

Figure M.138 Montgolfier hot-air balloon.

Moody diagram

[fluid dynamics] Graphical tool to estimate the FLUID dynamic friction coefficients in FLOW. The derived FRICTION coefficients are also known as MOODY FRICTION FACTOR. The Moody friction factor (found as either λ_{Moody} or f_{Moody}) is a major component in the Darcy–Weisbach major loss equation (see Figure M.139).

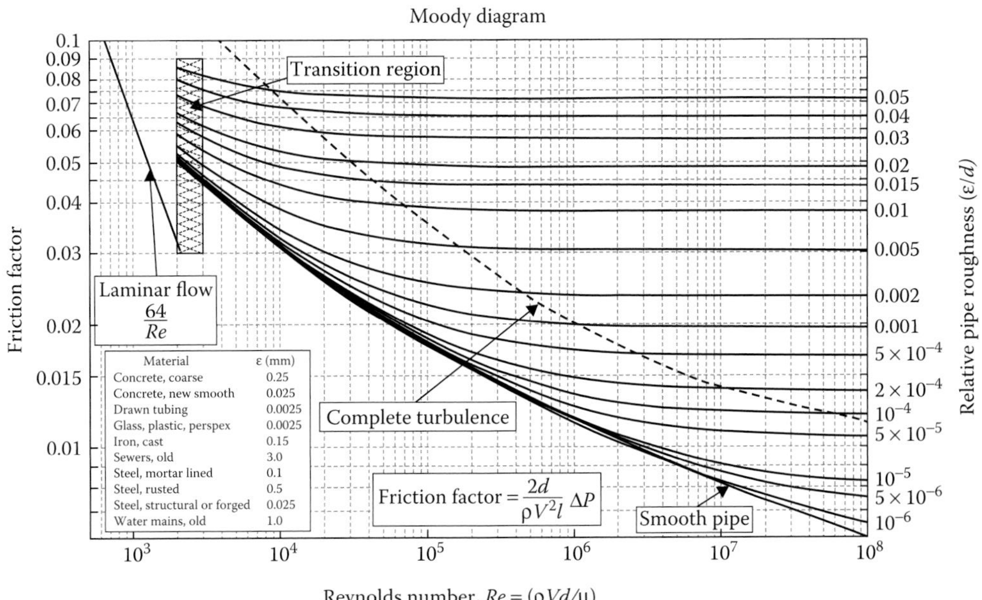

Figure M.139 Moody diagram providing a plot of the Darcy–Weisbach friction factor against Reynolds number for a range of roughness conditions. (Courtesy of S. Beck and R. Collins, University of Sheffield.)

Moody friction factor

[fluid dynamics] Coefficient of FRICTION for FLUID flow, with respect to conduit conditions. The Moody friction coefficient is a complex function of the REYNOLDS NUMBER and relative roughness. Also found as Darcy–Weisbach friction factor.

Moon

[astrophysics, general] Celestial body in stable orbit around a larger planetary object. The EARTH has one Moon at an average DISTANCE of 384,400 km (apogee: 405,503 km), with distinct crust, mantle, and core, all with geochemically well-defined compositions and total mass of 7.3477×10^{22} kg. The earth's Moon influence the tidal rise and fall due to gravitational interaction. Certain planets have more than one Moon; for instance, MARS has two moons and JUPITER, Neptune, SATURN, and Uranus each have several moons. Generally moons can also be referred to as (natural) satellites. The earth's Moon has been described in the greatest detail due to its proximity and centuries of observation. Our Moon has several phases of observation; ranging from new Moon to full Moon, with waxing from new to first quarter to full and waning to new, passing the last quarter. The observation of the Moon and its size relative to its position in the sky was described as far back as documented history reveals to the seventh century BC, providing an optical focusing and magnification by the Earth's ATMOSPHERE when close to the horizon. The Moon ORBITS the Earth in an elliptic plane, approximately in 27.3 days, with respect to the fixed stars, or about Earth 29.5 days, as described by CASSINI'S LAWS. The Moon itself has an equatorial rotation velocity of 4.627 m/s, synchronous with the PLANET Earth. Generally, same side of the Moon always faces Earth (the "near side of the Moon"), with the consequent preverbal "dark side of the Moon"; however, this "far side of the Moon" does receive equal proportions of solar exposure (*also see* **PHASE OF THE MOON**) (see Figure M.140).

(a)

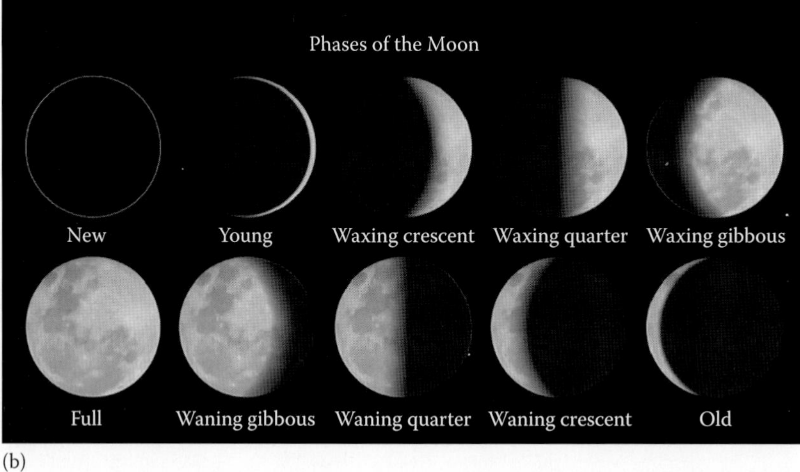

(b)

Figure M.140 (a) Moon as seen from the northern hemisphere (Courtesy of NASA) and (b) Moon phases in reference to the illumination by the Sun with respect to the position of the Moon to the Sun in the orbit around Earth as well as around the Sun while Earth revolves around the Sun.

Moore, Earle Gordon (1929–)

[computational, general, quantum] An American scientist and the founder and chairman emeritus of the Intel Corporation (a leading manufacturer of MICROPROCESSOR chips for computers, founded in 1968). His work in CHIP design prompted him to coin the statement about the technological increase in computing power, known as MOORE'S LAW, introduced in 1965 (see Figure M.141).

Figure M.141 Earle Gordon Moore (1929–). (Courtesy of Intel Corporation, Santa Clara, CA.)

Moore's law

[computational, general, quantum] Statement by EARLE GORDON MOORE (1929–) (Intel Corp.) in 1970 relating the technological advancement in MICROPROCESSOR design with respect to the perceived processing speed with 18 month increments of 200%. The alternate interpretation relates the increase of the number of TRANSISTOR components integrated on a processor CHIP in the same manner, double every 18 months to 2 years, which has been reliably appropriate for more than two decades since the first proclamation in 1965. The incremental increase of transistors is directly related to the ever reducing size of electronic hardware. In practicality, the processor power of the computer board is close to double every year at this point.

Morgan–Keenan luminosity classes

[astronomy] Classification of stars by order of luminous radiance: Ib: Supergiants; II: Bright Giants; III: Giants; IV: Subgiants; V: Main-Sequence Stars (*also see* LUMINOSITY FUNCTION *and* HERTZSPRUNG–RUSSELL DIAGRAM) (see Figure M.142).

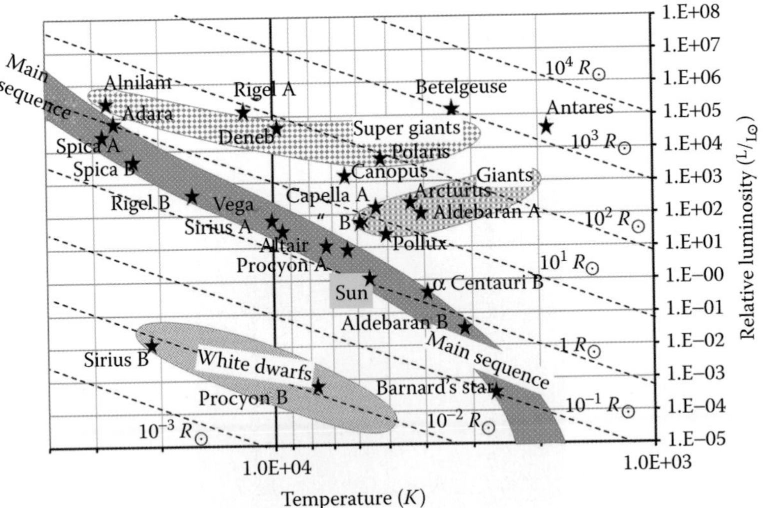

Figure M.142 Diagram of Morgan–Keenan luminosity classes, with the guiding reference: $R_\odot$, the radius of our Sun.

Morley, Edward Williams (1838–1923)

[general, optics] Scientist, physicist, and chemist as well as theologist, born in the United States. Morley is most known for his work in OPTICS and general PHYSICS as well (*see* MICHELSON–MORLEY EXPERIMENT) (see Figure M.143).

Figure M.143 Edward Williams Morley (1838–1923).

Morse, Harmon Northrop (1848–1920)

[chemical, thermodynamics] Chemist from the United States. Morse introduced refinements to the VAN'T HOFF EQUATION for OSMOTIC PRESSURE under the MORSE EQUATION. Additional work on the pressure effects of solutes was presented by ERNEST STARLING (1866–1927).

Morse, Philip McCord (1903–1985)

[chemical, computational, solid-state] Physicist born in the United States. Philip Morse derived the MORSE POTENTIAL for a harmonic oscillator, specifically applied to the nuclear forces in a diatomic MOLECULE (see Figure M.144).

Figure M.144 Philip McCord Morse (1903–1985), in 1972. (Courtesy of Massachusetts Institute of Technology [MIT] Web-Museum.)

Morse, Samuel Finley Breese (1791–1872)

[theoretical] Artist and painter from the United States who was also an inventor. In collaboration with the American physicist known for the discovery of self-induction, Joseph Henry (1797–1878), and American mechanical engineer Alfred Vail (1807–1859), the telegraph system was developed as well as the communication mechanism, referred to as Morse code (see Figure M.145).

Figure M.145 Samuel Finley Breese Morse (1791–1872) in 1840, photographer potentially Louis Jacques Mandé Daguerre (1787–1851).

Morse code

[theoretical] Pulse pattern of long and short duration pulses that represent letters in the alphabet as well as numbers. Morse code was (and still is) easily transmitted by optical, mechanical, and electronic means over great distances. The coding mechanisms is constructed of combinations of pulses with different duration, referred to as dashes and dots. The duration of a dash is three times the duration of a dot. The principle dates back to approximately 1836, where the collaborative effort of an artist Samuel F. B. Morse, physicist Joseph Henry (1797–1878), and mechanical engineer Alfred Vail (1807–1859) developed an electric telegraph system. The telegraph system was designed to send electric pulses along wires leading to an electromagnet that generated a tapping sound under the influence of the electric pulses. Samuel Morse developed a code based the duration and the silence between pulses, to convey messages. The Morse code is resilient against many noise factors and can be recognized even under low signal strength. Morse code only requires a single wire for transmittance of information. The most well-known Morse code sequence is for S-O-S (save our souls; distress call) (see Figure M.146).

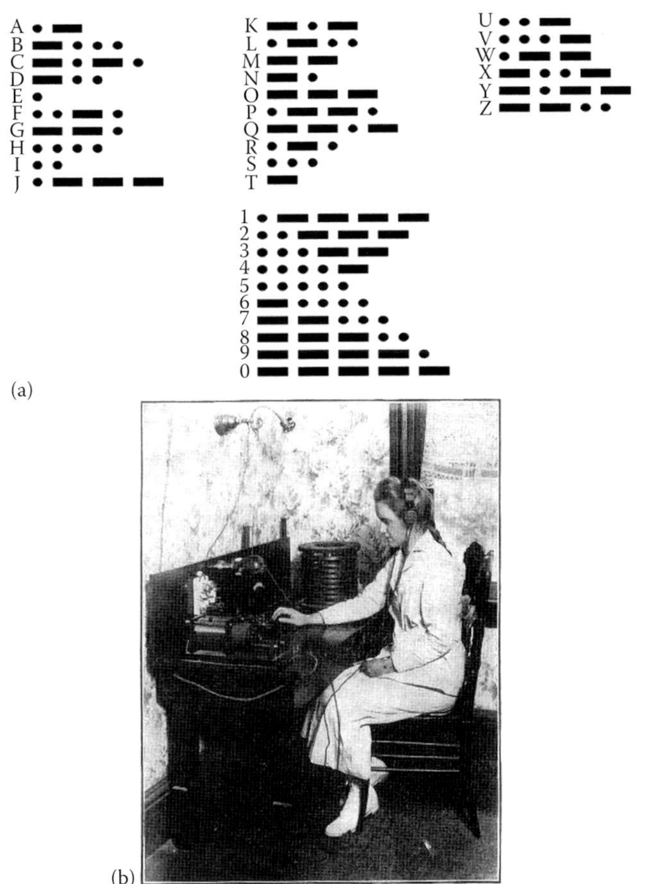

Figure M.146 (a) Morse code encryption scheme and (b) picture of person operating Morse-code apparatus with finger tapping, transmitted via telegraph system and wiring.

Morse equation

[chemical, thermodynamics] COLLOID OSMOTIC PRESSURE (Π) description formulated by HARMON NORTHROP MORSE (1848–1920), expressed as a function of the molarity of the SOLVENT ($[M]$), defined at a specific temperature (T) as $\Pi = i_{vH}\left[M\right]RT$, where i_{vH} is the VAN'T HOFF FACTOR (i.e., degree of dissociation: $i_{vH} = 1 + \alpha_{\text{dis}}\left(n-1\right)$, where α_{dis} is the fraction of the original molecules of the SOLUTE that have dissociated and n the number of ions/atoms/molecules in the dissociation product), and $R = 8.3144621\left(75\right)$ J/Kmol the universal GAS constant.

Morse potential

[atomic, chemical, computational, nuclear solid-state, thermodynamics] A simplified diatomic potential expression, constructed from the Rydberg–Klein–Rees (RKR) curves, derived by PHILIP MCCORD MORSE (1903–1985). The Morse potential ($U(r-r_e)$) is expressed as $U\left(r-r_e\right) = D_e\left(1-e^{-\beta\left(r-r_e\right)}\right)^2$, where D_e is the dissociation ENERGY (which is the nuclear potential minimum), r_e is the equilibrium DISTANCE between the respective nuclei of the diatomic molecule, and β is a correction factor for the dissociation energy and is related to the REDUCED MASS of the MOLECULE in addition to the resonance frequency harmonics ω_e. The

RESONANCE FREQUENCY of the atomic bond is ruled by a Hook's law type force as $E_\psi = (1/2\pi c)\sqrt{(k/\mu_m)}(\psi + (1/2)) = \omega_e(\psi + (1/2))$, where E is the energy of VIBRATION, ψ is the vibrational quantum number (integers), k the molecular spring constant, c the speed of light, and μ_m the reduced mass of the molecule with ATOM constituents A and B: $(1/\mu_m = (1/m_A) + (1/m_B))$. The modes of OSCILLATION are as follows: rotation, scissor, translation, and vibration (EXPANSION/contraction). Also known as the potential energy of a diatomic molecule. Equation derived by Philip Morse as a function of the separation between the atoms (r) as $(V(r) = D_{\text{well}}(1 - e^{-a_{\text{well}}(r - r_{\text{eq}})})^2)$, where D_{well} is the well depth, r_{eq} the diatomic equilibrium distance, and $a_{\text{well}} = \sqrt{(k_{\text{well}}/2D_{\text{well}})}$ is the parameter that defines the width of the POTENTIAL WELL, with k_{well} the "spring constant" at the minimum of the well (smaller value of a_{well} corresponds to a larger well) (see Figure M.147).

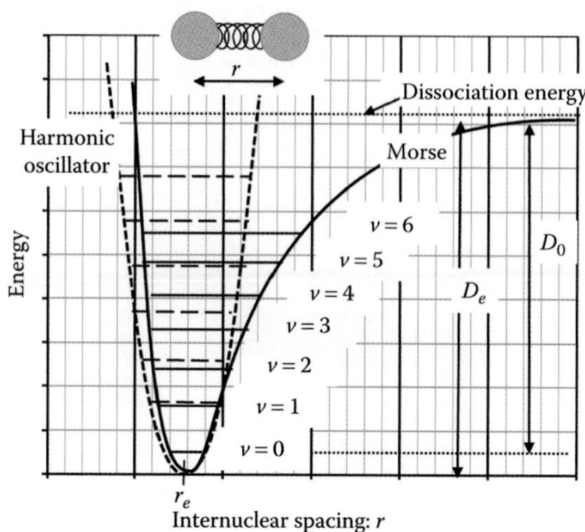

Figure M.147 Graphical representation of the Morse Potential.

Morton number ($Mo_{\text{Liquid}} = g\eta_f^4\Delta\rho/\rho_f^2\sigma^3 = We^3/FrRe^4$)

[computational, fluid dynamics] Dimensionless number that characterizes the size and shape of a droplet or BUBBLE, specifically when used together with the Eötvös number. In this definition we have the following parameters: g the GRAVITATIONAL ACCELERATION, η_f is the FLUID viscosity of the ambient medium, ρ_f the density of the ambient medium, $\Delta\rho$ the difference in DENSITY (ρ) between the LIQUID and GAS PHASE, and σ the SURFACE TENSION coefficient. Additionally, the following DIMENSIONLESS NUMBERS have been inserted: We the Weber number, Fr the Froude number, and Re the REYNOLDS NUMBER.

Moseley, Henry (Harry) Gwyn Jeffreys (1887–1915)

[atomic, nuclear] Physicist from Great Britain. Introducer of the concept of the atomic number in 1915, identifying the quantity of protons in the NUCLEUS of an ATOM, hence indicating the total positive ELECTRIC CHARGE of the nucleus. Mosley performed additional groundbreaking experimental work on X-ray SPECTROSCOPY and implementing BRAGG'S DIFFRACTION law to describe the atomic and crystalline structure of ELEMENTS and their natural occurrence. Bragg's diffraction law was developed by the British father-and-son team SIR WILLIAM HENRY BRAGG (1862–1942) and WILLIAM LAWRENCE BRAGG (1890–1971), for which they received the Nobel Prize in Physics in 1915. Moseley described the relationship between the ATOMIC NUMBER (Z) and the emission wavelength in X-RAY under CATHODE ray exposure, known as MOSELEY'S LAW (see Figure M.148).

Figure M.148 Henry (Harry) Gwyn Jeffreys Moseley (1887–1915).

Moseley diagram

[atomic, nuclear] Plot of the square root of the emission frequency of the K and L lines against the atomic number (initially a chosen integer, later connect to the atomic number by Moseley) produces a set of (almost) straight lines resulted. HENRY (HARRY) GWYN JEFFREYS MOSELEY (1887–1915) devised an apparatus for bombarding samples with electrons, of all the ELEMENTS available at the time (early 1900s) ranging from aluminum to gold and measuring the emission wavelengths (in the X-RAY), and hence the frequencies, in the spectra for the respective elements. The diagram allowed for X-ray-based identification of elements. Moseley also "discovered" certain elements that should be in the graph, since there were voids indicating new elements. The square root dependency could be explained by the Bohr theory (see Figure M.149).

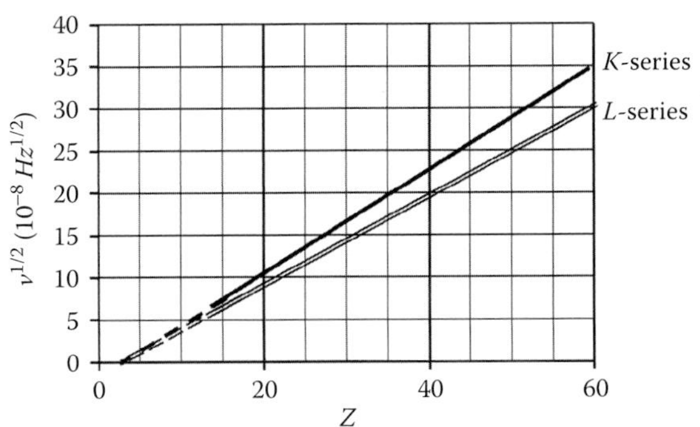

Figure M.149 Moseley diagram with frequency versus proton number (Z; atomic number). Electrons falling from the K-shell (lowest shell, highest binding energy) produce X-ray radiation known as *K*-series radiation: K_α, K_β, K_γ respectively, while the second level: L produces an *L*-series spectrum.

Moseley's law

[atomic, electromagnetism, general, nuclear] Frequency (ν) of the α-line or main K-line (K-ALPHA LINES) in X-RAY emission following the ENERGY pattern described in the BOHR ATOMIC MODEL based on the atomic number Z, designating the number of protons in the NUCLEUS, as developed by HENRY (HARRY) GWYN JEFFREYS MOSELEY (1887–1915) expressed as $\nu = [k_1(Z - k_2)]^2 = 2.476 \times 10^{15}(Z-1)^2\ Hz$, where k_1 and k_2 are emission line-dependent constant, which are equal for any Kα-line. The value of k_1 changes for the transitions from the L-shell or the M-shell (smaller value for orbits farther out, by order of MAGNITUDE each time). For the K-line $k_1 = (3cR_y/4)^{1/2}$, c the speed of light, $R_y = 1.097 \times 10^7\ \mathrm{m}^{-1}$. The RYDBERG CONSTANT is also known as Moseley's rule.

Mössbauer effect

[nuclear] Special phenomenon in nuclear resonance FLUORESCENCE under conditions of recoil-free GAMMA RAY absorption and emission. The phenomenon was recognized by Rudolf Ludwig Mössbauer (1929–2011) and described in 1958. The collision-free RESONANCE is established by initiating nuclear excitation by means of beta-decay, while simultaneously re-exciting another NUCLEUS of the same species in a resonance scheme, specifically using a collimated beam. Hypothetically, the emitter nucleus and the resonant target nucleus are refrained from movement. This approach relies on the fact that the ENERGY configuration of the process has a line width of $\Gamma^* = \lambda/2\pi\tau_{\mathrm{life}}$, where τ_{life} is the average lifetime of the excited nuclear state and λ the wavelength of the gamma DECAY, with associated (relatively large) interaction CROSS SECTION $\sim(\lambda/2\pi)^2$, and note that the PHOTON carries a momentum: $p = E/c$, where $E = h\nu$ is the photon energy for frequency ν and $c = 2.99792458 \times 10^8$ m/s, the speed of light. The realistic manifestation of this principle is emission as a mixture of resonant idealized and unconstrained spectrum. The idealized case has no nuclear motion, which is not easily (not realistic) achieved, while the unconstrained case where there is recoil resulting from the absorption of the QUANTUM momentum (see Figure M.150).

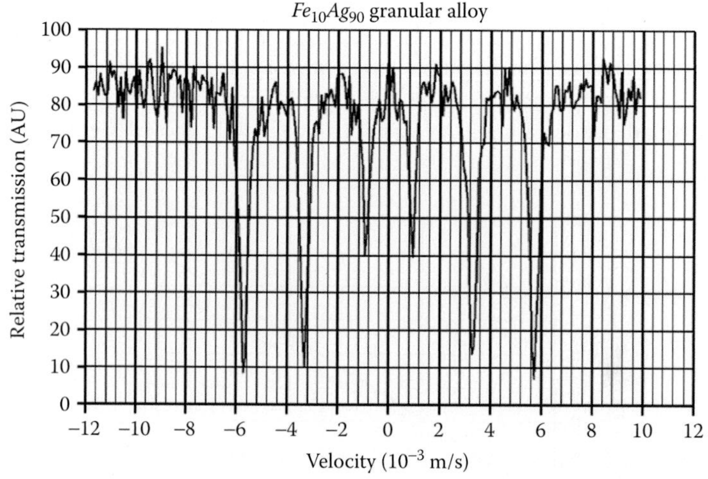

Figure M.150 Mössbauer effect.

Motility

[biomedical, computational, energy, general, mechanics] Capability of moving under the consumption of ENERGY, or having the power to move spontaneously (under a biological fuel system), in particular for unicellular biological life forms, such as spores or sperm. Even though the principle applies to all forms of life, the specific interests are in the unicellular and simple multicellular organisms. Additionally, motility also refers to the ability of an organism to transport food through the digestive tract. Examples of the food transportation are the PERISTALTIC MOTION of the intestines and esophagus (see Figure M.151).

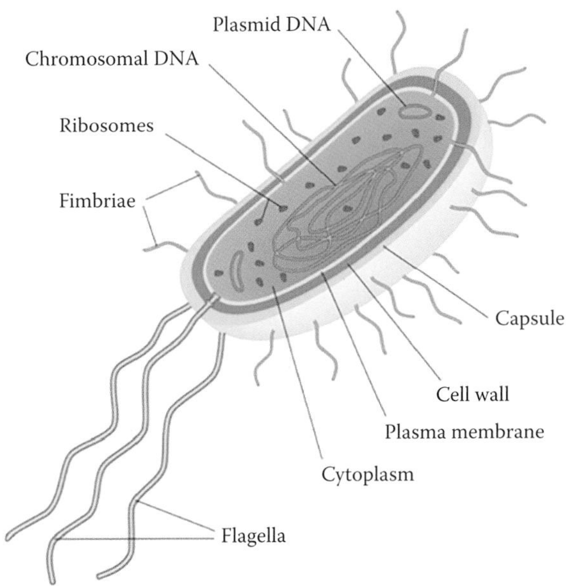

Figure M.151 The motility of a bacterial cell by means of flagella.

M

Motion

[astrophysics, atomic, biomedical, computational, energy, general, geophysics, mechanics, thermodynamics] Movement of objects in linear displacement, revolution or rotation, or VIBRATION and combinations of these such as PRECESSION. Motion can be split into two topic headings: KINEMATICS and DYNAMICS. Motion around the center of mass becomes rotation, whereas linear free-space MOTION falls under ballistics. Harmonic (vibrational) motion is widely found in many applications (mass-spring concept) as well as in atomic and molecular ENERGY configuration. Motion requires an initial force, or a sustaining force (see Figure M.152).

Figure M.152 Motion, skateboarded using the muscles in the leg to apply force to the ground to advance the bard occupied by the mechanism of motion.

Motional feedback loudspeaker

[acoustics, electronics, fluid dynamics, mechanics] Acoustic emission device with feedback mechanism to modulate the frequency profile and enhance durability. Process developed and implemented in LOUDSPEAKER devices by Philips Electronics, Best, the Netherlands (see Figure M.153).

(a)

(b) (c)

Figure M.153 Design and mechanism of operation for the motional feedback loudspeaker. (a) Inside view of feedback electronics within speaker box. (b,c) Piezoelectric pick-up on loudspeaker for feedback mechanism.

M

Motor

[general] Mechanical device that can perform work and is powered by an ENERGY source. Examples are combustion ENGINE, direct- (DC) and ALTERNATING CURRENT (AC) (electro-) motor, and wind-powered engines. Frequently the class of electromotors is the only group and energy source used to describe motor function. *Electric motors* operate based on any of the following three principles: magnetic, electrostatic, and piezoelectric; which are all physically different in providing the MOTION. The most common mechanism of action is MAGNETIC (see Figure M.154).

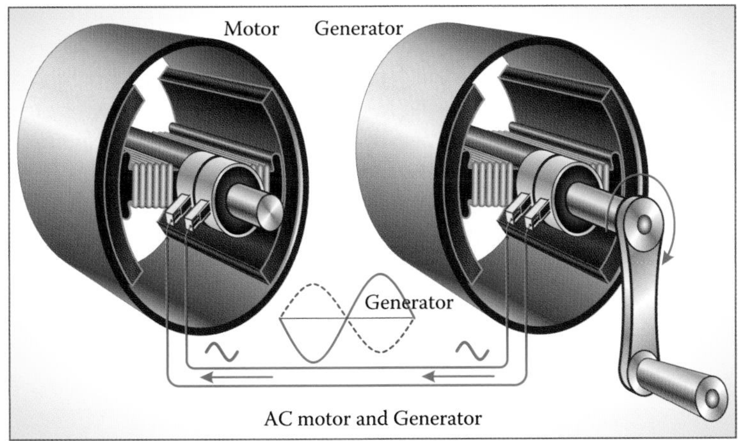

Figure M.154 Electromotor design, in comparison to an electrical generator.

Mott, Nevill Francis, Sir (1905–1996)

[nuclear] Scientist from Great Britain. In 1977, Mott won the Nobel Prize for Physics. Mott investigated the electronic structure of MAGNETIC systems. The special focus of Mott's work was on disordered systems, in particular amorphous SEMICONDUCTORS. Mott shared the Nobel Prize with PHILIP WARREN ANDERSON (1923–) and John Hasbrouck Van Vleck (1899–1980), who worked on similar projects and sometimes collaborated as well (see Figure M.155).

Figure M.155 Sir Nevill Francis Mott (1905–1996).

Moving coil galvanometer

[general] CURRENT (I) measuring device that uses a coil with N windings placed between two permanent magnets with MAGNETIC FIELD B. The torque on the coil as a function of the current passing through the coils will change the direction of a dial as an ANGULAR DISPLACEMENT (θ) attached to the coil as $I = (k/NAB)\theta$, where k is the spring constant that prevents the coil from rotating under the force, applied by a rotating spring with force $F = k\theta r$, where r is the LEVER arm of the attachment of the spring to the coil.

M-phase

[biomedical, energy] The mitotic biological CELL division process which is composed of mitosis and cytokinesis, before the G_1-phase and after G_2- and S-phases. M-phase consists of producing two identical cells in a process starting out from one cell starting in the G_1-phase; also known as the telophase. During mitosis, the organization of the cell becomes physically representative of the final mature cell (G_1-phase), the chromosomes are recoiling after they have split and reproduced in S-phase. The cell division process is preceded by a nutrient intake episode called the interphase. Cells not in cell division are in a dormant or quiescent stage, also referenced as G_0-phase. The entropy and internal ENERGY (i.e., Gibbs energy) of the cell changes with the changes in cell division (see Figure M.156).

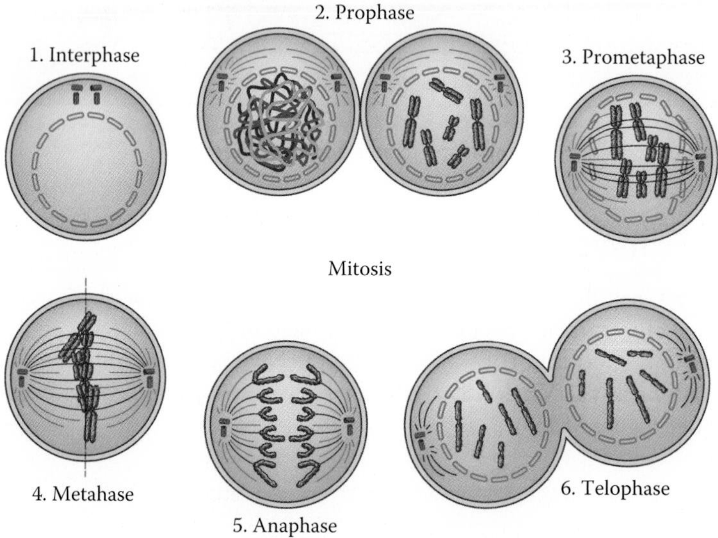

Figure M.156 M-phase in cell mitosis (cell-division), telophase; in the process starting from Prometaphase, into prophase, followed by interphase and metaphase with the anaphase culminating in the telophase.

MRI

[imaging] *See* MAGNETIC RESONANCE IMAGING.

Mu meson

[nuclear] *See* MUON.

Multiparameter inversion

[acoustics, computational, geophysics, solid-state] Wave propagation in anisotropic elastic media can be modeled by assuming perturbations to a homogeneous, single format medium, the background model.

Mathematically, the SCATTERING of the propagating waves can be approximated by implementation of a location specific pseudodifferential operator that mimics the discontinuities in the background model. The field perturbations are described by the model vector $\vec{m}=(m_1,\ldots,m_n)$, consisting of n material component parameter perturbation fields m_i. The applied field of operators, expressed as a matrix.

$$[N_{\text{opp}}]=\begin{bmatrix} N_{\text{opp}}{}^{11} & \cdots & N_{\text{opp}}{}^{1n} \\ \vdots & N_{\text{opp}}{}^{ij} & \vdots \\ N_{\text{opp}}{}^{n1} & \cdots & N_{\text{opp}}{}^{nn} \end{bmatrix}$$

yields: $[N_{\text{opp}}]\vec{m} = \overrightarrow{m_{\text{mig}}}$. The resulting migration output vector: $\overrightarrow{m_{\text{mig}}}$ contains "images" of the WAVE due to perturbations. The observed data (d_{obs}) are linked to a migration operator ($[F_{\text{opp}}]$) as $[F_{\text{opp}}]\vec{m} \approx \overrightarrow{d_{\text{obs}}}$, where $[F_{\text{opp}}][F_{\text{opp}}]^* \vec{m} = [F_{\text{opp}}]^* \overrightarrow{d_{\text{obs}}}$, with $[F_{\text{opp}}]^*$ the transposed (adjoint) matrix of $[F_{\text{opp}}]$.

Multiple linear regression

[computational] The multiple regression forms an EXPANSION to modeling the relationship between a single or functional variable: x (i.e., explanatory variable) to a SCALAR dependent variable y to include two or more explanatory variables, yielding a three-dimensional relationship.

Multiple photon photoelectric effect

[general] Multiphoton interaction can yield the sum of the ENERGY of the interacting photons, thus acting as if a shorter wavelength single PHOTON created the interaction. The PHOTOELECTRIC EFFECT is generally more effective with higher efficiency at shorter wavelength ELECTROMAGNETIC RADIATION. The multiphoton effect can be achieved under high-power density irradiation, increasing the PROBABILITY of simultaneous photon interaction on an atomic or molecular level.

Multiplication factor

[atomic, nuclear] In the general operations of a nuclear reaction, the reaction will need to be self-sustaining, which involves causing on an average more than one nuclear reactions. The multiplication factor, ν_{neutron}, is the average number of neutrons generated by one FISSION that will initiate another fission, the effective NEUTRON multiplication factor. It is also known as neutron multiplication factor. For $\nu_{\text{neutron}} < 1$, the REACTOR will not sustain a CHAIN REACTION, and is considered subcritical; whereas for $\nu_{\text{neutron}} > 1$ the reactor can go beyond the point of control by the controller bars and moderator bars and is generally considered supercritical (*also see* **MODERATOR BAR**).

Multiplicity of spectra

[atomic, nuclear, quantum] The multiplicity of spectral lines ($\mathcal{M}_{\text{spectral}}$) for atomic spectral analysis is based on quantum PHYSICS principles on atomic or molecular level. The phenomena of multiplicity of spectral lines applies both to OPTICS and magnetic resonance imaging (MRI). Optically, the principles rely on atomic excitation, specifically the SPIN orientation of the transitions: $\mathcal{M}_{\text{spectral}} = 2\Sigma + 1$, where Σ is the sum of all the spins s and is consistently the number of VALENCE electrons for specific ELEMENTS plus 1, such as POTASSIUM (K), calcium (Ca), scandium (Sc), and vanadium (V). For calcium, this provides an EMISSION SPECTRUM of singles and triplets due to the valence of 2. In NUCLEAR MAGNETIC RESONANCE (NMR) imaging, the same multiplicity applies to the PROTON resonance spectral lines, providing singlet, DOUBLET, triplet, quartet, and so on RESONANCE frequencies. In this case the spectra of a given NUCLEUS follows from spin coupling, specifically coupling to Σ number of equivalent nuclei. In the latter case, the coupling to equivalent nuclei raises the concept of equivalent ligands and uses Pascal's triangle to form the splitting pattern. For instance, 1,1,2-tribromoethane

($C_2H_3Br_3$) has two identical hydrogen nuclei, with concomitant two NMR peaks, one with multiplicity three ($\Sigma = 2 + 1 = 3$, i.e., three resonant lines—H_3—the peak has three lines; from the Pascal's triangle, it is a triplet), and one with multiplicity two (2; since H_1 and H_2 act equivalently) (see Figure M.157).

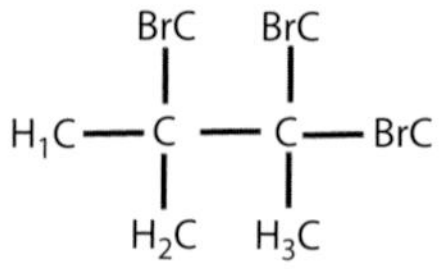

Figure M.157 Molecular bond configuration in 1,1,2-tribromoethane ($C_2H_3Br_3$) that can provide the mechanism to support Multiplicity of Spectra due to the ambivalence of the energy structure.

Multiplier tube

[atomic, nuclear, optics] *See* **PHOTON MULTIPLIER TUBE.**

Multipole

[computational, electromagnetism, solid-state, thermodynamics] Model of a symmetric periodic system by the sum of sines and cosines in the form of a FOURIER SERIES with the necessary parameters (the multipole moments) or as a set of Legendre polynomials in a spherical coordinate system. One example of the use of multipoles in approximations is applied to predicting the electric potential field due to a complex molecule by eliminating the contributions of all the respective atoms (which can become an elaborate task, specifically including the interatomic fields) and decomposing the molecule in a few multipole moments as a reasonable approximation. Examples are monopole, DIPOLE, quadrupole, octupole, and so on. Multipoles can provide an acceptable impression of how the field behaves, without the need to know the exact fundamental field.

Multipole moment

[nuclear] The collection of necessary parameters to define the coefficients in the FOURIER SERIES and the Legendre polynomials for the description of multipoles.

Multipole radiation

[computational, nuclear] Description of electromagnetic or gravitational radiation resulting from perturbations in the distribution of sources in a time-dependent system. This theoretical mechanisms can describe phenomena ranging from GRAVITATIONAL WAVES to gamma radiation due to nuclear DECAY.

Muon

[astronomy/astrophysics, atomic, general, nuclear, quantum, thermodynamics] Elementary MESON particle in the category of LEPTON, unstable but behave very similar to electrons, although with much greater mass. The muon, discovered in 1938, has a mass-equivalent ENERGY of $E = mc^2 = 106$ MeV. The discovery of the muon resulted from studying COSMIC RAYS. Generally, two types of muons can be recognized, with opposite charge, each decaying according to a specific path, into ELECTRON (e^-) or POSITRON (e^+) according to their nature, and two neutrinos according to the following rules: $\mu^+ \rightarrow e^+ + \nu_e + \overline{\nu}_\mu$ or $\mu^- \rightarrow e^- + \overline{\nu}_e + \nu_\mu$, where ν_e and ν_μ are neutrinos and anti-neutrinos ($\overline{\nu}_\mu$; $\overline{\nu}_e$), respectively, the lifetime of a muon is approximately 2 μs (see Figure M.158).

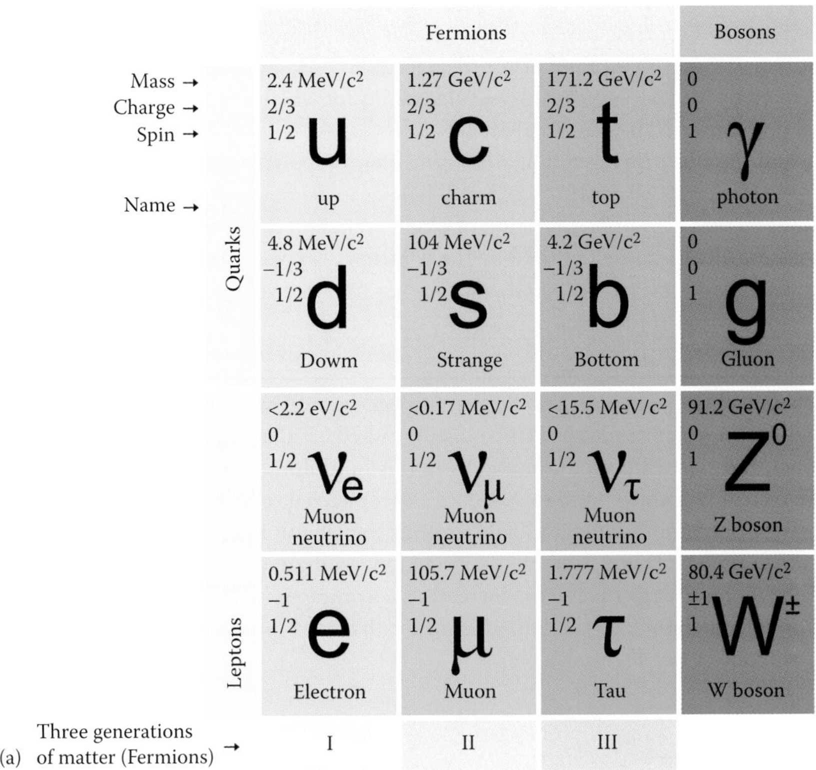

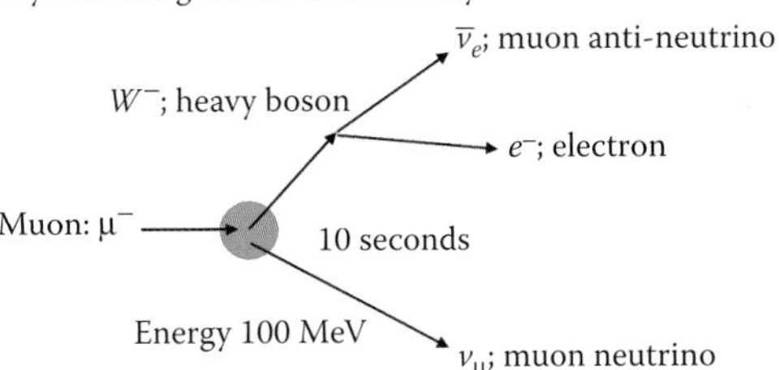

(b) The mean lifetime of the (positive) muon, $\tau = 1/\Gamma$, is approximately 2.1969811 μs.

Figure M.158 (a) Placing the muon in the scheme of elementary particles and (b) muon decay mechanism.

Murray's law

[biomedical, fluid dynamics] In hemodynamic flow there should be certain design constraints that provide conditions to ensure minimization of ENERGY requirements to maintain fluid transport. In BLOOD CIRCULATION the work performed is dependent on, but not limited to, the HEART muscle contraction, vascular COMPLIANCE as well as Bernoulli pressure gradients. Specifically with respect to vascular radius, there is an optimum in the work performed (minimal), balancing work, and momentum (p). The momentum is linked to the FLOW with (average) velocity (v or rather v_{avg} across the vessel diameter) as $p = mv \sim [d(mx)/dt]$, where the MASS (m) of liquid in a segment of vessel with radius (r) and cross-sectional area (A_{cross}) is changing over time based on the vascular compliance: $\dot{m} = dm/dt = \rho_{fluid} v_{avg} A_{cross}$, where blood is an INCOMPRESSIBLE FLUID and hence the density: $\rho_{fluid} = \text{const}$. The minimum work associated with flow is defined by Murray's law as the vascular radius for which the following hold true: $dW_{tot}/dr = 0$, where the total power exerted by the circulation $W_{tot} = W_{flow} + W_{blood}$ is the sum of the power to maintain flow W_{flow} and the effort involved in maintaining blood supply: W_{blood}. The blood flow obeys the POISEUILLE'S LAW: $W_{flow} = Q\Delta P = 8\ell Q^2 \eta_{visc}/\pi r^2$, where Q is the flow, ΔP the pressure gradient of length ℓ for a FLUID with VISCOSITY η_{visc}. The "creation of blood" relies on the synthesis of proteins and additional biological processes, which can be captured by the ARRHENIUS EQUATION: $W_{blood} = \alpha_{blood} \mathbb{V}_{blood}$, with α_{blood} the production energy for one unit of blood, and $\mathbb{V}_{blood} = \pi r^2 \ell$ the volume of blood.

Muscle

[biomedical, chemical, electromagnetism, mechanics] Mechanical MOTOR function of biological units. In humans three different kinds of muscle can be distinguished: cardiac (in the HEART), skeletal (attached to JOINTS and bone), and smooth (e.g., in the WALL of veins [multiunit] and in the reproductive system as well as the digestive system [visceral]). SKELETAL MUSCLE is connected to bone through cartilage, with seamless integration between the various biological components; the tendon integration with muscle is achieved by aponeuroses (broad fibrous sheets). Muscular contraction is a digital phenomenon. Higher frequency of pulses sent by the motor unit to the muscle increases the contraction. The motor unit itself is stimulated by the brain or through autonomic regulation. This means that the motor unit may act independently, irrespective of will power (see Figure M.159).

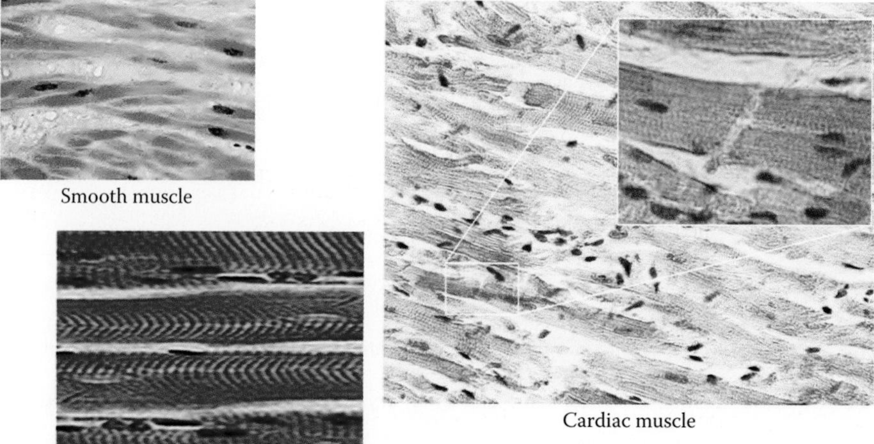

Figure M.159 (a). Types of muscles: from left to right represented by histological view: smooth, skeletal, and cardiac (Courtesy Dr. S. Girod, Anton Becker.) and (b) diagram of a motor unit.

Muscle, anatomy

[biomedical, chemical, electromagnetism, mechanics] A SKELETAL MUSCLE fiber is a thin elongated cylinder with rounded ends and may extend the full length of the muscle. Beneath its sarcolemma (CELL MEMBRANE), the cytoplasm or sarcoplasm of the fiber contains many small, oval nuclei and mitochondria. Within the sarcoplasm are numerous threadlike myofibrils that lie parallel to one another. They play an important role in muscle contractions. The myofibrils contain two kinds of protein filaments: (1) thick ones composed of the protein MYOSIN and (2) thin ones composed of the protein ACTIN. The arrangement of these filaments in repeated units are called sarcomeres, which produce the characteristic alternating light and dark striations of muscles. Light areas are the I-bands and the darker areas are A-bands. Z-lines are where adjacent sarcomeres come together and thin myofilaments of adjacent sarcomeres overlap slightly. Thus, a SARCOMERE can be defined as the area between Z-lines. Myosin filaments are located primarily within the dark portions of the sarcomeres, while actin filaments occur in the light areas. Within the cytoplasm of a muscle fiber is a network of membranous channels that surround each myofibril and runs parallel to it, which is the sarcoplasmic reticulum. Transverse tubules (t-tubules) extend inward from the fiber's membrane. They contain extracellular FLUID and have closed ends that terminate within the light areas. Each t-tubule contacts specialized enlarged portions (cisternae) of the sarcoplasmic reticulum near the region where the actin and myosin filaments overlap. These parts function in activating the muscle contraction mechanism when the fiber is stimulated. Each skeletal muscle fiber is connected to a fiber from a nerve cell. Such a nerve fiber is a branch of a MOTOR neuron that extends outward from the brain or spinal cord. The site where the nerve fiber and muscle fiber meet is called a neuromuscular junction (myoneural junction). At this junction the muscle fiber membrane is specialized to form a motor end plate. The end of the motor nerve fiber is branched, and the ends of these branches project into recesses (synaptic clefts) of the muscle fiber membrane. The cytoplasm at the ends of the nerve fibers is rich in MITOCHONDRIA and contains many tiny (synaptic) vesicles that store chemicals called NEUROTRANSMITTERS. When a nerve impulse traveling from the brain or spinal cord reaches the end of a motor nerve fiber, some of the vesicles release neurotransmitter into the gap between the nerve and the motor end plate. This action stimulates the muscle fiber to contract. A muscle fiber contraction is a complex action involving a number or cell parts and chemical substances. The final result is a sliding movement within the myofibrils in which the filaments of actin and myosin merge. When this happens, the muscle fiber is shortened, and it pulls on its attachments. The length and tension of muscles vary indirectly. In the contraction mechanism, the chemical mechanism of action involves kinesins and dyneins, which are microtubule-dependent motor proteins that advance in incremental steps toward opposite ends of the microtubule cables. Both mechanochemical enzymes make use of a pair of motor domains that take intersecting hand-over-hand advances along the surface of the microtubule. In vitro measurements have provided proof that these head domains make steps of 8 nm and generate in the order of 6 pN of peak force during a single ATP hydrolysis cycle. Chemical advancement velocities are ATP dependent of single kinesin molecules obey the Michaelis–Menten relationship. Myosins are one- and two-headed actin-dependent chemical motors with step sizes ranging from 5 nm to greater than 40 nm. In particular, the two-headed isoform of Myosin II contribute in the contractile assemblies that manipulate the sarcomere length in muscle cells as well as influence the actomyosin ring constriction as part of the cytokinesis during cell division. Because the orientation of these actin filaments have inherently different polarity, myosins reverse polarity along the myosin filaments, and ATP hydrolysis cause the actin filaments to advance toward each other as an integral part of the motor domains. One-headed myosins do not have tails that form coiled coils, in contrast to Myosin I. One-headed myosins as a result do not actively participate in contractile mechanisms. Alternatively, the tails of these myosins facilitate the binding of vesicles and organelles and in this manner to transport them in lengthwise direction along actin filaments (see Figure M.160).

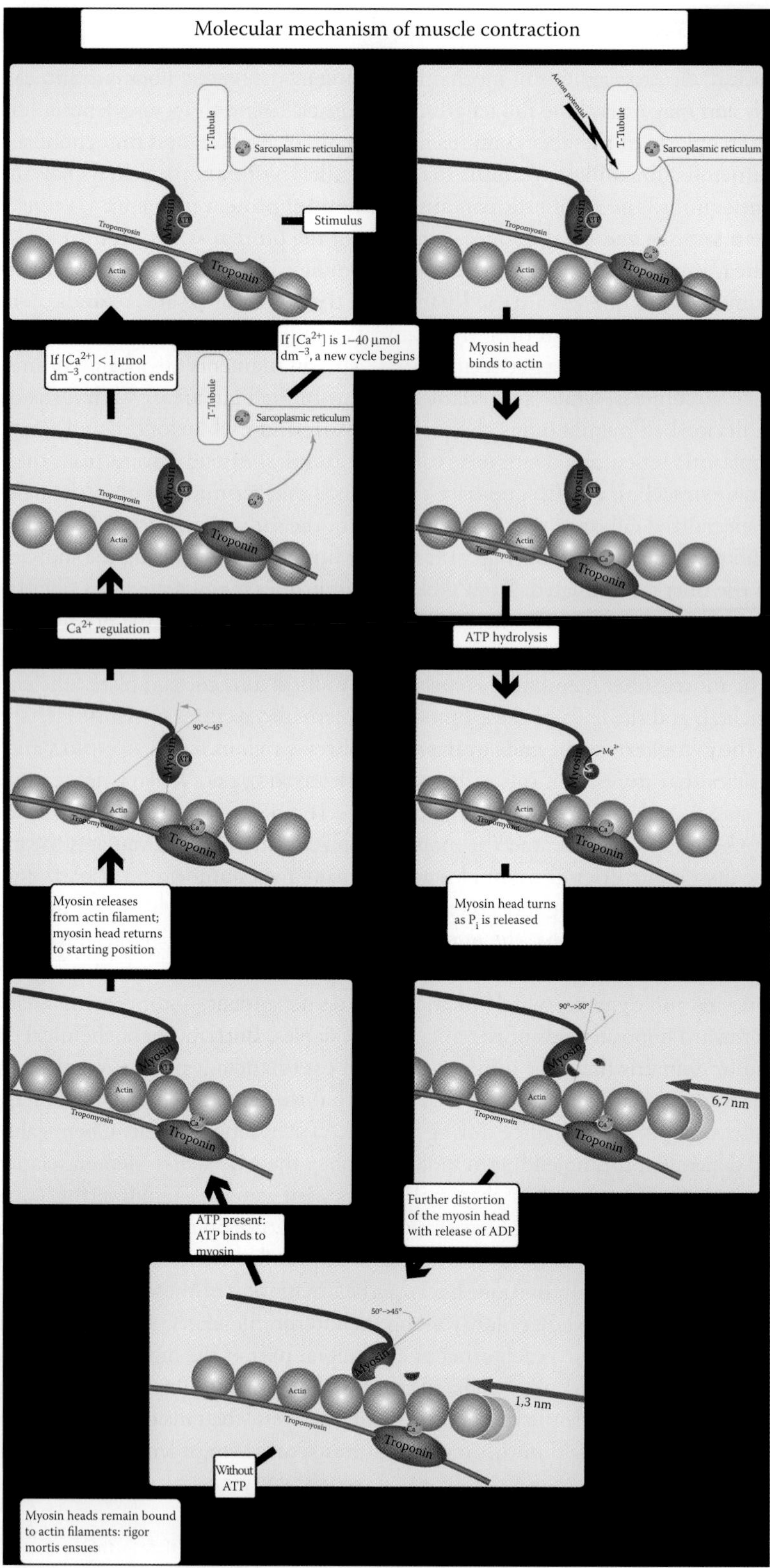

Figure M.160 Muscle fiber anatomical diagram. Muscle contraction based on the chemical attraction between actin and myosin fibers. (Courtesy Hank van Helvete.)

Muscle, major skeletal groups

[biomedical, chemical, electromagnetism, mechanics] The major SKELETAL MUSCLE groups are facial, mastication, head, pectoral girdle, arms, abdominal, pelvic, and legs. The anterior view of skeletal muscles within the HUMAN BODY shows the frontal muscle structure. The facial muscles are epicranius, orbicularis oculi, orbicularis oris, buccanitor, zygomaticus, and platysma. The epicranius covers the upper part of the cranium and has two parts, one that lies over the frontal bone and another that lies over the occipital bone. Lifting the eyebrows and making the forehead wrinkle are its main functions. Multiple stimulations of these muscles can lead to headaches. The orbicularis oculi is a ring of muscle that surrounds the EYE and is used for closing or blinking of the EYE. It also aids in the FLOW of tears. The orbicularis oris orbits the mouth and is also known as the kissing muscle since it allows the mouth to pucker and help keeping food in place is done by the baccanitor muscles. They also aid in blowing AIR out of the mouth. Zygomaticus' main function is allowing the corner of the mouth to smile or laugh. The platysma extends from the chest to the neck and its function can be seen by the expression of pouting. Chewing movements are accomplished by four pairs of muscles that are part of mastication. These muscle pairs are masseter, temporalis, medial pterygoid, and lateral pterygoid. Two of these pairs close the mouth while the others allow for side-to-side movements. The masseter is primarily for raising the jaw. A fan-shaped muscle used also for raising the jaw is known as the temporalis. The medial pterygoid is used for closing the jaw and allowing for the sliding movements. The lateral pterygoid allows the jaw to close and move forward. There are four pairs of muscles that move the head, allowing for rotation. The sternocleidomastoid is located in the side of the neck and when one side contracts, the head is turned to the opposite side. When both are contracted, the head is bent toward the chest. In the back of the neck, the splenius capitis allows the head to rotate and bend toward one side. For rotating, extending, and bending the head, the semispinalis capitis and longissimus capitis both help with these functions. Muscles that move the pectoral girdle or chest area include the trapezius, rhomboideus major, levator scapulae, serratus anterior, and pectoralis minor. The trapezius muscle raises the shoulders allowing for the "shrugging" expression. The rhomboideus major connects the upper thoracic vertebrae to the scapula and helps to raise the scapula. The levator scapulae runs almost vertical along the neck also helping to raise the scapula. Moving the scapula downward is accomplished with the serratus anterior. It also moves the shoulders forward when pushing something. The pectoralis minor lies beneath the pectoralis major and can move the ribs. For the upper arm, the muscles can be grouped by their primary actions of flexors, extensors, abductors, and rotators. The flexors are the coracobrachialis and pectoralis major, which flex the arm and move the arm across the chest. The extensors are the teres major and the latissimus dorsi that allow for rotation and moving the shoulder down and back. The supraspinatus and deltoid both help in abduction in the upper arm. The subscapularis, intraspinatus, and teres minor allow for rotation medially and laterally. In the forearm there are seven major muscles and can be categorized by their action. The flexor muscles are the biceps brachii, brachialis, and the brachioradialis all of which help in the rotation and lateral movements about the elbow. The primary extensor of the elbow is the triceps brachii. To rotate the arm, the supinator, pronator teres, and pronator quadratus allow for movements. In the wrist, hand, and fingers, the two major groups are flexors and extensors. Flexing of the wrist is accomplished with the assistance of the flexor carpi radialis and the flexor carpi ulnaris. The palmaris longus connects the humerus to the palm and functions to flex the wrist. To make a fist the flexor digitorum profundus flexes the distal JOINTS of the fingers. All four of these are flexors. The extensors of the wrist and hand are the extensor carpi radialis longus, extensor carpi radialis brevis, extensor carpi ulnaris, and the extensor digitorum. The first three aid in extending the wrist while the last one deals with the functions of the fingers. Four muscles located in the abdominal WALL region help with breathing, defecation, urination, and childbirth. These muscles are the external oblique, internal oblique, transversus abdominis, and the rectus abdonimis. All of these muscles function in a similar manner and compress the abdominal cavity. The pelvis region consists of two major muscle sheets that are the pelvic diaphragm and the urogenital diaphragm. The pelvic diaphragm has two major muscles that are the levator ani and the coccygeus that provide a sphincter-like action in the anal canal and the vagina in women. The three major muscles within the urogenital diaphragm are the superficial transversus perinei, bulbospongiosus, and the ischiocavernosus muscles. The superficial transversus perinei supports the pelvis. The other two help in urination within men and constriction of the vagina from opening in women. In the thigh, there are two groups: the anterior and posterior groups. The anterior groups' main job is for flexing while the posterior groups are for extending or rotation. The psoas major and the iliacus make up the anterior group and their function is to flex the thighs. The posterior group consists of the gluteus maximus, gluteus medius, gluteus minimus, and the TENSOR fasciae latae. These muscles help in flexing and rotating the thigh. A third group of muscles, the adductor longus, adductor magnus, and gracilis, adduct, flexes and/or rotates the thigh. The muscles of the LEG can be separated into two categories that are the flexors and extensors about the knee. The flexors are the biceps femoris, semitendinosus, semimembranosus, and sartorius and all help to flex and rotate the leg. The extensors of the lower legs are the quadriceps femoris, which extends the leg at the knee. In the ankles, feet, and toes, there are four categories of muscles based on their function. The dorsal flexors, which include the tibialis anterior, peroneus tertius, and extensor digitorum longus aid in the moving the foot upward. The plantar flexors move the foot downward and contain the GASTROCNEMIUS, soleus, and flexor digitorum longus muscles. Turning the sole of the foot outward or inward is accomplished by the two groups: the invertor and evertor. The tibialis posterior is within the invertor group and allows for the INVERSION of the foot. The eversion of the foot is done by the peroneus longus that is within the evertor group. Although each muscle is specialized within a certain area, all of these muscles help in maintaining posture and movement (see Figure M.161).

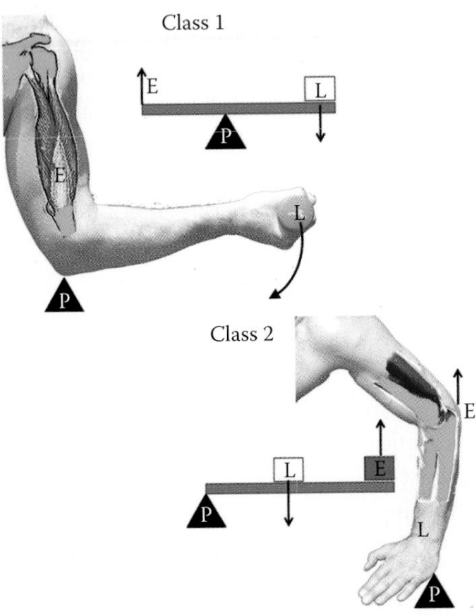

Figure M.161 Diagram of lever classes, with respective locations of movement force, resistance, and axis of rotation defining the individual classes. (Continued)

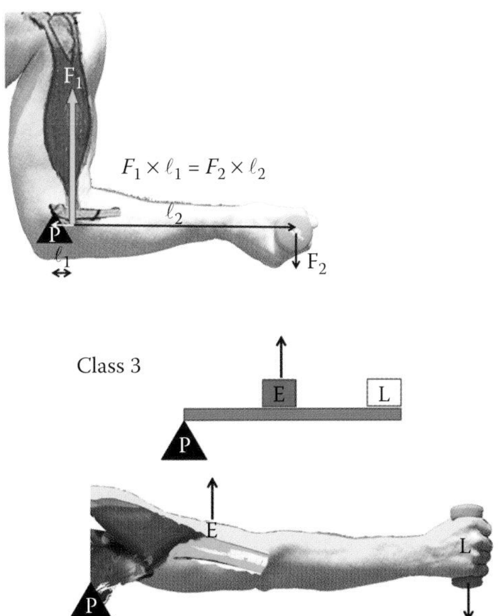

Figure M.161 (Continued) Diagram of lever classes, with respective locations of movement force, resistance, and axis of rotation defining the individual classes.

Muscle, performance

[biomedical, chemical, electromagnetism, mechanics] The following factors affecting SKELETAL MUSCLE strength and performance can be identified. Gender, AGE, training experience, muscle strength, and fatigue all affect strength performance. Muscles in humans makes up 40%–43% of the total body weight in men on world-wide average; and respectively, 23%–25% statistically averaged in women. For a healthy, average height woman who weighs 62 kg, 7 kg is composed of bones, 16 kg of organs and SKIN, 16 kg of fat, and 23 kg of muscles. Both male and female can develop muscular strength at the same rate, although due to hormones, namely testosterone, male muscles have a greater potential for strength. As humans mature, strength increases. However, roughly by age 30 (depending on a broad range of boundary conditions, including training and consumption of food, as well as natural and artificial chemicals), muscles start to degenerate. The degeneration is a reversible process but continuous training is required. The length of time devoted to training and the type of training regiment influence muscle strength. The initial length of the muscle fibers and the insertion length affect the amount that muscles can LIFT and support. Fatigue relates to the condition that the muscle does not allow for the same amount of power output. FATIGUE is highly variable and is influenced by the intensity and duration of the contractile ACTIVITY, by whether the muscle fiber is using aerobic or anaerobic METABOLISM, by the composition of the muscle, and by the fitness level of the individual. Most experimental evidence suggests that muscle fatigue arises from excitation–contraction failure of control neurons and neuromuscular transmission. The ability for muscle to change its length or lengthwise tension has been shown by the process of contraction. The underlying factor is the exchange of energy from the BLOOD stream with the muscle cells (see Figure M.162).

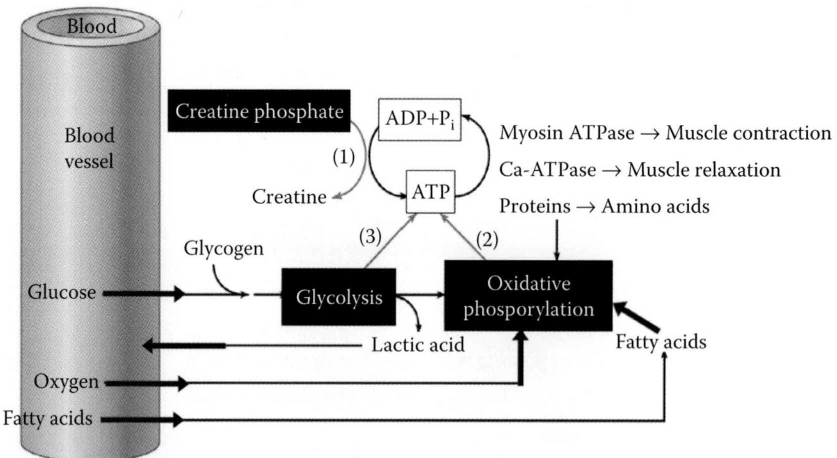

Figure M.162 Diagram of energy exchange with muscle cells to support function. In addition, the production of waste during muscle action is illustrated, eluding the potential build-up of lactic acid, generating muscle fatigue and cramp. The build-up of lactic acid degrades the natural metabolic activities.

Muscle physics, skeletal muscles

[biomedical, chemical, electromagnetism, mechanics] A LEVER is a simple mechanical machine consisting of a bar on a fixed point that transmits a force. Lever types are defined by three classes according to the axis of rotation, resistive force, and movement force. In a third-class lever, the movement force is applied between the axis of rotation and the resistive force. This lever favors movement speed over movement force. Most muscles in the HUMAN BODY use this type of lever. A second-class lever is one in which the RESISTANCE is between the movement of force and the axis of rotation. This type allows for great movement force. When the axis of rotation is between the movement force and the resistance this lever is known as a first-class lever. They are like third-class levers since they are big on movement speed and lack in movement force. The bicep MUSCLE works as a third-class lever where the movement of force is between the axis of rotation and the resistance. The mathematical relationship of the force can be calculated upon knowing some muscle measurements. People are built differently and depending on their muscle force, force lever, or resistance lever to maintain balance and perform functions. Torque is the force that tends to rotate and turn things. Mathematically, it is equal to the force multiplied by the DISTANCE. This distance is usually radial from a central point. Power is the measure of how fast work can be done. It equals the amount of torque on an object multiplied by the rotational speed. To solve power as a function of human output, the following question can be proposed: How much power can a human output? One way to solve this problem is to see how fast one can run up a flight of stairs. First, measure the height of a set of stairs that reaches three stories. Second, record the time to run up the stairs. Finally, divide the height of the stairs by the time, where this equals the instantaneous speed. The weight of the individual must also be known. For instance, if it took 15 s to run up 10 m, then the speed equals 0.66 m/s (only speed in vertical direction is important). Then one needs to figure out how much force was exerted over 10 m, this force is equal to your weight. The amount of power output = weight multiplied by speed. Power(W) = [height of stairs(m)/Time to climb(s)] * weight (Units: Newton [N]). The contractile strength of a muscle is most closely related to its cross-sectional size. The electrical ACTIVITY in muscle is due to the effect of the concentration gradients, the difference in potential across the membrane, and the ACTIVE TRANSPORT system. Positive and negative charged ions within the muscle fiber have the ability to move between intercellular fluids. These charges create a differential in potential. The net effect of these charges is a POSITIVE CHARGE on the exterior of the MEMBRANE and a negative charge on the interior. In a healthy neuromuscular system, this polarized muscle fiber remains in equilibrium until upset by an external or internal stimulus. There are different measurement techniques to measure the mechanical and electrical properties of muscle. A dynamometer measures the mechanical force or power a muscle can exert and electromyography measures the electrical activity related to muscle contractions. Dynamometers measure mechanical power and come in a variety of different configurations. One such configuration allows measurement of the clench action of hands. The basis of surface myoelectric activity is the relationship between the ACTION POTENTIAL of muscle fibers and the extracellular recording of those action potentials at the SKIN surface. Electrodes, external to the muscle fiber can be used to detect action potentials. The most common electrodes are surface and fine wire electrodes. For general muscle groups surface electrodes are suitable, however, they are limited in detecting small muscles or muscles deep within the body, where fine wire electrodes are recommended. Detection electrodes are usually used in a bipolar manner. Two electrodes are positioned on the muscles while a third is a reference (GROUND) to the body. A difference preamplifier increases the AMPLITUDE of the signals between each of the detecting electrodes and the common mode reference. Signals nearly zero are deemed common mode signals. The difference preamplifier improves the signal-to-noise ratio allowing the SIGNAL of small twitch to be detected. The most common NOISE problem is 60 Hz interference. This signal distortion occurs when the reference ELECTRODE is not applied properly, a loose wire, or when electrical fields persist (see Figure M.163).

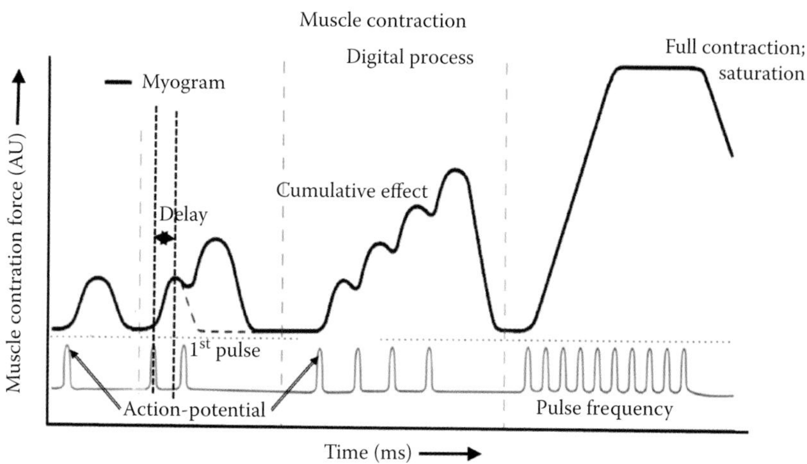

Figure M.163 Binary response of muscle contraction to electrical stimulus pulse trains.

Muscle relaxation

[biomedical] After DEPOLARIZATION the MEMBRANE of the muscle CELL repolarized, at which time the chemical "heads" on both the ACTIN and the MYOSIN of the sarcomeres are losing their attraction, allowing recoil to extend the muscle cell to expand.

Muscles, functioning

[biomedical, chemical, electromagnetism, mechanics] The length and tension of muscles vary indirectly. When a muscle contracts because of a LOAD applying a force, the MUSCLE produces one of two types of contraction: ISOTONIC or ISOMETRIC. Skeletal muscle contracts either by increasing or decreasing force while maintaining the same length (isometric) or shorten through constant force (isotonic). *Note*: Muscles generally have an ANTAGONIST or external phenomenon that increases the length of the muscle. Antagonists are for instance biceps and triceps in the human upper arm, whereas in BLOOD vessels the stretch is achieved by the pressure associated with the blood flow. A SKELETAL MUSCLE fiber is a thin elongated cylinder with rounded ends and may extend the full length of the muscle. Beneath its sarcolemma (CELL MEMBRANE), the cytoplasm or sarcoplasm of the fiber contains many small, oval nuclei and MITOCHONDRIA. Within the sarcoplasm are numerous threadlike myofibrils that lie parallel to one another. They play an important role in muscle contractions. The response to a single stimulation or ACTION POTENTIAL is called a twitch. A twitch contains three parts: a latent period, a contraction period, and a relaxation period. During the latent period, there is no change in length but the impulse travels along the sarcolemma and down the t-tubules to the sarcoplasmic reticulum. Calcium is released during this period, triggering the muscle to contract. The contraction period is when the tension in the muscle increases causing a swiveling action of the SARCOMERE components. The contraction following from the chemical attraction resulting from the electrical POLARIZATION of both the ACTIN and the MYOSIN can be described as a rate of bond-forming (number of bonds: n_b) process expressed as $dn_b/dt = k_f n_L n_R - k_r n_b$, where k_f is the forward rate constant, n_L the number of ligands involved, and k_r the reverse rate constant. GEORGE IRVINE BELL (1926–2000) defined the rate constant as $k_r = k_{r0}\exp\left[\gamma_b F/N_c k_B T\right]$, with F the applied contraction force, N_c the number of LIGAND complexes in the actin–myosin volume, $k_B = 1.3806488\times 10^{-23}$ kgm^2/s^{2}K the Boltzmann constant, γ_b the extension of the muscle defined as the DISTANCE between adjacent attractive molecules (the actin molecules grab sequential molecules on the myosin in each stage of the contraction), k_{r0} the unloaded reverse rate constant in the absence of applied forces, and T the muscle temperature (giving additional meaning to "warming-up"). The molecular ADHESION was defined by Bell as the force per unit chemical bond: $f_b = F/n_b = 0.7(k_B T/\gamma_b)\ln([L]/K_D{}^0)$, where $K_D{}^0$ is the dissociation rate for the unstressed bonds and $[L]$ the free ligand concentration. This ADHESION applied generally to all cellular molecular attractions. The muscle tension decreases during the relaxation period and returns to its original shape. The three components of the twitch and the different types of contraction are well defined. When an increase in frequency with which a muscle is stimulated increases, the strength of contraction also increases known as WAVE summation. This occurs by re-stimulation of muscle fibers while there is still muscle contraction ACTIVITY. With several stimulations in rapid succession, calcium levels in the sarcoplasm increase and produces more activity and a stronger contraction. When rapid stimulation occurs and there is not enough time between successive stimulations a buildup of calcium can occur and there will be no relaxation between stimulations. This leads to a smooth sustained contraction known as tetanus. There are three types of muscle in the HUMAN BODY: skeletal, smooth, and cardiac. Smooth muscles can be found lining organs in the body, and cardiac muscle pertains to the HEART. The movements of the bones at JOINTS and posture maintenance are the main job of skeletal muscle. Skeletal muscles mode of control is voluntary, meaning the user has control of its actions, while smooth and cardiac muscles are involuntary. Smooth muscle is controlled by the autonomic nervous system and is found primarily in the walls of organs and tubes. The spindle-shaped cells that make up the composition of this type of muscle are arranged in sheets. These cells contain small amounts of sarcoplasmic reticulum but lack transverse tubules. The cells are made up of thick and thin myofilaments but do not contain sarcomeres and therefore are not striated like skeletal muscles. Chemically, calcium binds to a protein and induces contraction. There are two types of smooth muscles: visceral and multiunit. Visceral is found in the digestive, urinary, and reproductive systems. For this type of smooth muscle, a unit is composed of multiple fibers that contract and in some cases are self-excitable. In multiunit smooth muscle, nervous stimulation activates motor units. This type is found lining the walls of large blood vessels and in the EYE. They also are located at the base of follicles and can produce a "goose-bump" effect. Cardiac muscles have a distinctly different configuration. Heart walls have three distinct layers, which are the endocardium, myocardium, and epicardium. The endocardium lines the CIRCULATORY SYSTEM, is the innermost layer, and is composed of epithelial tissue. The myocardium is the thickest layer and consists of cardiac muscles. The epicardium is a thin layer and is the external MEMBRANE around the heart. Cardiac muscle is striated and contains sarcomeres, which makes this muscle similar to skeletal. Adjacent cells are joined end-to-end at structures known as intercalated discs. These discs contain two types of junctions: desmosomes and gap junctions. Desmosomes act like rivets and hold cells tightly together while gap junctions allow action potentials to spread from one cell to another. The specific characteristic for the heart muscle is the intercalated discs with desmosomes and gap junctions. Cardiac muscle forms two functional units called the atria and ventricles. There are two of each where by the atrias both act together, followed by the ventricles. For contraction, there are two types of cells: contractile cells and autorhythmic cells. The contractile cells contract when stimulated while the autorhythmic cells are automatic. For focus of discussion of this topic, only skeletal muscle will be explored. Skeletal muscles have

the ability to shorten quickly and recover, where this action is defined as contraction. One end of the muscle, origin, is stationary while it's other end, insertion, shifts. A contraction always moves from the insertion to the origin. When a contraction occurs, both the AGONIST muscle and ANTAGONIST muscle work against each other. The agonist muscle or flexion is the muscle that is being acted upon while the antagonist or extension muscle contracts in opposition to the flexion. A contraction is only the shortening of the muscle and does not describe the actual generation of a force. A force only occurs when there is a RESISTANCE to the muscle contraction. To understand the nature of contractions, the ANATOMY of skeletal muscle must be studied. Second, the PHYSIOLOGY of muscular contraction, meaning the excitation and relaxation will be investigated. The PHYSICS of the muscle acting as a lever for skeletal muscle is one ENGINEERING point that shows the impact of the attachment to the bone to provide the level, comparing human arms to that of apes and monkeys. Muscle is composed of several kinds of tissue including striated cells, nerve, blood, and various connective tissues. The basic unit of contraction in an intact skeletal muscle is a motor unit, composed of a group of muscle fibers and a motor neuron that controls them. When the motor neuron fires an action potential, all muscle fibers in the motor unit contract. The number of muscle fibers in a motor unit varies, although all muscle fibers in a single motor unit are the same fiber type. Thus, there are fast-twitch motor units and slow-twitch motor units. The determination of which kind of fibers associated with a particular neuron appears to lie with the NEURON itself. Force of contraction within a skeletal muscle can increase by recruiting additional motor units where by this process is called motor unit recruitment. An individual muscle is separated from adjacent muscles and held into position by layers of fibrous connective tissue called fascia (a bundle). This fascia is part of a network of connective tissues that extends throughout the skeletal muscle system and its attachment with other parts. These connective tissues become either tendons or aponeuroses. The fibers in the tendon become intertwined with bone, which allows muscle to be connected with bone. Aponeuroses are broad fibrous sheets that may be attached to adjacent muscles.
The layer that closely surrounds a skeletal muscle is called the epimysium. Other layers of connective tissue called the perimysium extend inward from the epimysium and separate the muscle tissue into small compartments. These compartments contain bundles of skeletal muscle fibers called fascicles. Each muscle fiber within a fascicle is surrounded by a layer of connective tissue in the form of a thin, delicate covering called endomysium. These layers allow for some independent movement as well as allowing blood vessels and nerves to pass through (see Figure M.164).

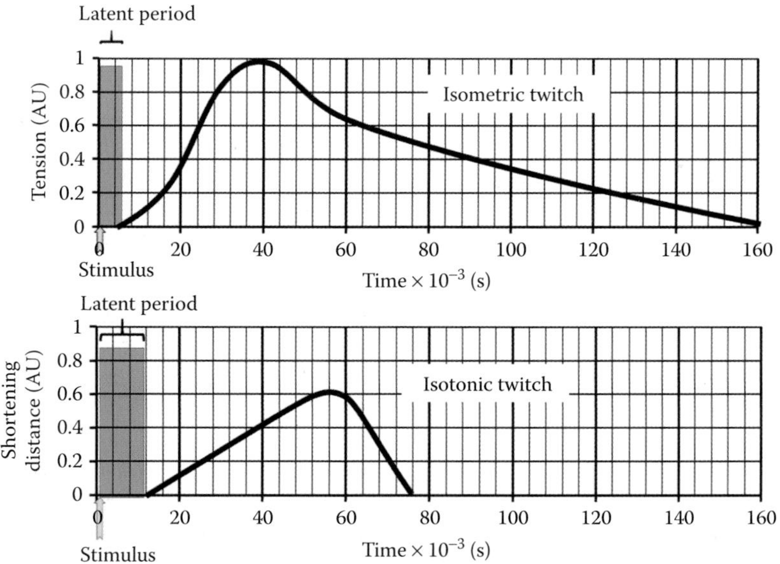

Figure M.164 Force displacement diagram of isometric (constant length) versus isotonic (constant force) muscle contraction, respectively, in response to stimulus from the motor neuron.

M

Musculoskeletal system

[biomedical, general, mechanics] Biological structure of MUSCLE attachment to bones of the skeleton in animals by means of connective tissues including cartilage, tendons, and ligaments. The muscle attachments provides the mechanism to apply a force, or more specifically, a torque which provides stability and the capacity to perform MOTION.

Musschenbroek, Pieter van (1692–1761)

[electrical, mathematics, mechanics] *See* **VAN MUSSCHENBROEK, PIETER**.

Mutual stable equilibrium

[thermodynamics] Subsystems of a composite system that is in a stable EQUILIBRIUM STATE, are in mutual stable equilibrium as well. Subsequently, when a composite system is in partial equilibrium the subsystems will be in partial mutual stable equilibrium.

mv (Product of mass and speed)

[general] The momentum (p_{motion}) of an object in MOTION: $p_{\text{motion}} = mv$, the momentum changes in response to an impulse (J). The impulse is defined as the summation of all forces (ΣF) applied over a period of time preceding the change in momentum, usually expressed as the integral over TIME (t) for the forces $J = \int_{t_1}^{t_2} F dt$.

Myelinated nerve

[biomedical, electronics] Nerve CELL with myelin envelop over a short DISTANCE at consecutive segments over the entire length of the nerve cell. Certain specialized nerve cells have formed a coalition with a separate cell to create a unique conduction system. Over time the axon is wrapped in patches of fatty, white myelin sheath at regular intervals along the length of the axon. The myelin is a secretion resulting from the ACTIVITY of specific cell type called glial cells. Oligodendrocytes produce myelin sheaths that insulate certain vertebrate axons in the central nervous system. Schwann cells have a similar function in the peripheral nervous system. Myelin builds up over time and is not fully formed at birth. The propagation speed for action potentials (conduction rate) of myelinated nerve cells is two orders of MAGNITUDE greater than that for unmyelinated nerve cells, switching from 2 m/s to 120 m/s (*also see* **NERVE**) (see Figure M.165).

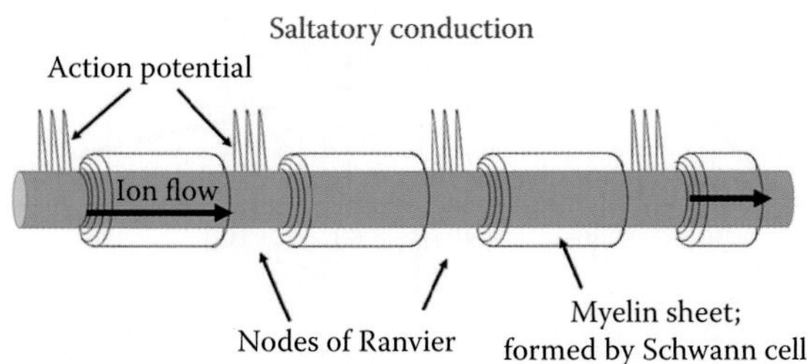

Figure M.165 Outline of the myelinated nerve principles. Description of the action-potential propagation for a myelinated nerve axon.

Myopia

[biomedical, general, optics] Optical property of the EYE where far away objects cannot be displayed sharp or in focus on the RETINA due to anatomical disorder of the eyeball that place the LENS of the eye at a too great-a-distance to the retina so that the accommodation process will no longer allow for adjustments to fully focus. The far-point of the myopic eye is relatively close, sometimes within meters, or CENTIMETERS instead of infinity. This condition can be corrected by a corrective, DIVERGING LENS, that places the object as a virtual image at a reduced DISTANCE (see Figure M.166).

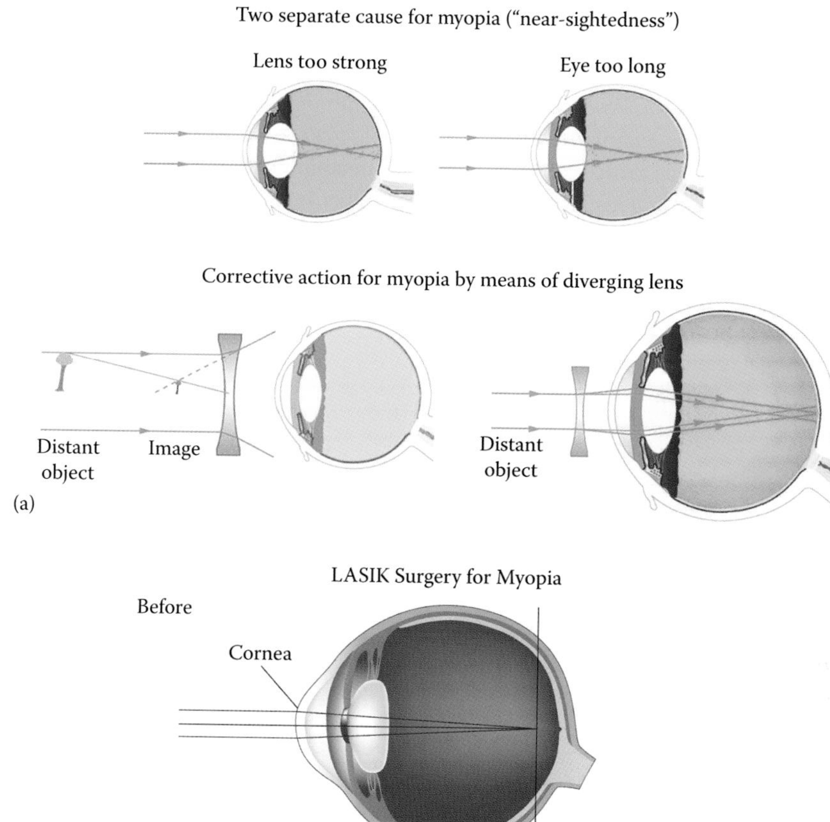

Figure M.166 (a) Myopia and vision correction by means of a lens in front of the eye and (b) the effects of LASIK surgery to correct myopia on a more permanent basis.

Myosin

[biomedical, chemical] Chemical structure working with ACTIN to perform contraction in MUSCLE tissue (*see* MUSCLE).

Myotis pulse

[acoustics, biomedical, theoretical] Frequency sweep in acoustic scanning for the *Myotis* family of bats during hunting. This specific sweep spans one OCTAVE, for instance, from approximately 40–80 kHz over a specific time span. The time span between pulses generally ranges from 50 to 100 ms is cruising mode (scanning), whereas the pulse interval can decreases to 10–50 ms sweeps during attack for hunting mode. In comparison, the acoustic pulse of the *Eptesicus* BAT is quite different. For the *Eptesicus* bat, both the sweep speed and the frequency range changes between surveillance mode and hunting mode. In hunting mode the FREQUENCY SPECTRUM is lower (i.e., shorter wavelength range with increased associated RESOLUTION) while simultaneously the pulse length is shorter. This type of SIGNAL processing is applied in other forms by several other animals. The same principles are applied both in communication as well as in diagnostic scanning applications in both biological and device imaging. For instance, the hawk applies a similar concept in VISION, switching from low resolution scanning to high-resolution hunting, using specifically different anatomic and functional regions of the RETINA, with respective signal processing on different sections of the brain. The device applications vary from mechanism of action to user interface with the operator (*see* BAT *and* ECHO-LOCATION) (see Figure M.167).

(a)

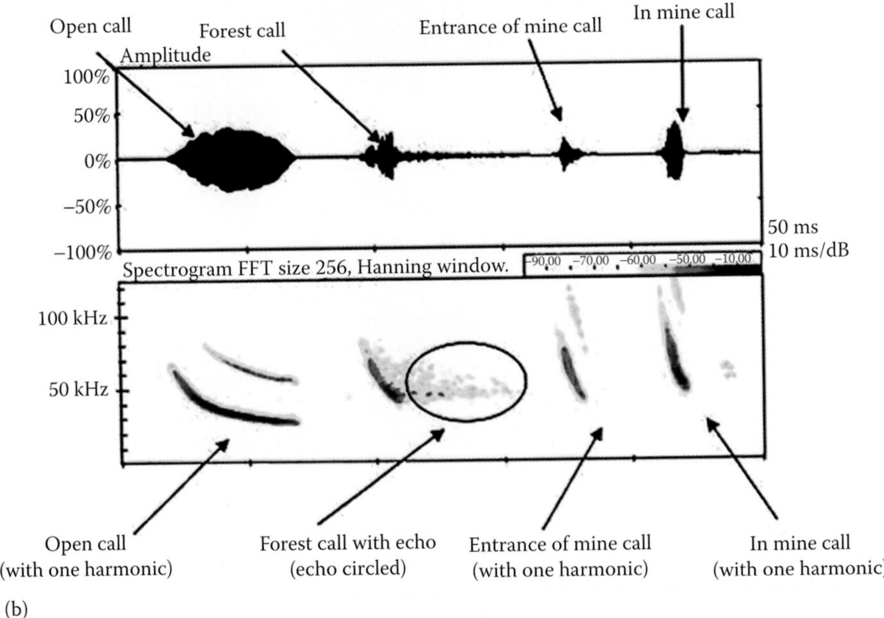

(b)

Figure M.167 (a) A bat and (b) the principle and application of the myotis pulse in bats for guidance and recognition of prey during hunting. (Courtesy of "Sarah" acquired during an award winning project with American Museum of Natural History: "The World Through a Bat's Ears"; http://www.amnh.org/learn-teach/young-naturalist-awards/winning-essays2/2005-winning-essays/the-world-through-a-bat-s-ears.)

η

[fluid dynamics] (Greek: "eta"), [coefficient of] Viscosity of a FLUID in motion, often confined to an incompressible, irrotational fluid. The ratio of shear stress to velocity gradient: $\eta = (F/A)/(dv_x/dz)$, where F is the force parallel to the surface (A) at which the VISCOSITY is determined, v_x the FLOW velocity and z the DISTANCE perpendicular to the flow. The generally accepted unit for viscosity is *poise* [P], named after the French physiologist JEAN LÉONARD MARIE POISEUILLE (1799–1869). Ten poise equal one Pascal second [Pa s]. The KINEMATIC VISCOSITY (ν_{kin}) is the viscosity per unit DENSITY (ρ): $\nu_{kin} = \eta/\rho$. The unit for kinematic viscosity is cm^2/s, which equals the unit *stokes*: $1St = 1\ cm^2/s$, after the Irish physicist and mathematician GEORGE GABRIEL STOKES (1819–1903) (see Figure N.1).

Figure N.1 Viscous flow of water from a roof after a rain storm.

N^{13}, ^{13}nitrogen

[atomic, biomedical] Radioactive isotope of ^{14}nitrogen ($^{13}_{7}N$), which decays to carbon-13 ($^{13}_{6}C$) by beta + DECAY (e^+) with a half-life of 9.965 min: $^{13}_{7}N \rightarrow {}^{13}_{6}C + e^+ + \nu_e + 1.20\ MeV$, where e^+ is a positron and ν_e and electron NEUTRINO. N^{13} is used in positron emission TOMOGRAPHY imaging. N^{13} is produced by bombarding oxygen by hydrogen (i.e., PROTON) with kinetic ENERGY of slightly more than 5.55 MeV: $O^{16} + H^1 \rightarrow N^{13} + He^4$.

N^{14}, ^{14}nitrogen

[atomic, biomedical] Standard nitrogen: $^{14}_{7}N$, discovered by the Scottish physician, chemist, and botanist Daniel Rutherford (1749–1819) in 1772. The Earth's ATMOSPHERE consists of approximately 78% nitrogen as a GAS under standard conditions. Nitrogen has a EVAPORATION temperature (boiling point) at 77.355 K = −195.795°C and a SOLIDIFICATION temperature (MELTING POINT) of 63.15 K = −210.00°C; the TRIPLE POINT is at 63.151 K under pressure of 12.52 kPa, and the critical point is at 126.192 K at

3.3958 MPa. The heat of FUSION for nitrogen is 0.72 kJ/mol and the heat of vaporization for nitrogen is 5.56 kJ/mol. Nitrogen is a popular and effective component of fertilizer. ANTOINE-LAURENT DE LAVOISIER (1743–1794) named nitrogen "mephitic air" referring to the fact that animals would not survive and flames were extinguished when under the inert 100% concentration, a name that is found to carry through in several languages. Evaporating LIQUID nitrogen provides low-rolling clouds of nitrogen and condensate water vapor (see Figure N.2).

(a)

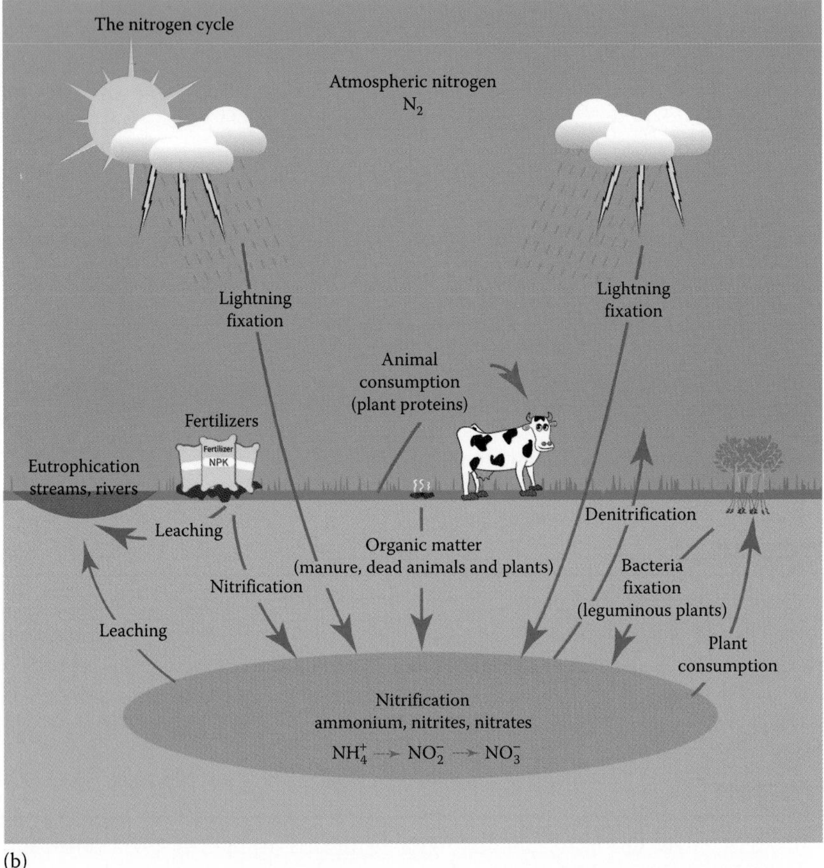

(b)

Figure N.2 (a) Nitrogen in dewar used for refrigeration of samples in test-tubes. (b) Illustration of the atmospheric nitrogen cycle.

Nabla (∇)

[computational, fluid dynamics, mechanics] Differential operator describing the mathematical operator for expressing gradient, DIVERGENCE, or curl. In mathematical expression, the application to a function (f) is ∇f, pronounced as "del f," where $\nabla f(\mathrm{x,y,z}) = (df/dx, df/dy, df/dz)$; as a Cartesian gradient, this yields $\nabla f(\mathrm{x,y,z}) = (df/dx) + (df/dy) + (df/dz)$. As an expression for divergence, the formulation is in "dot" product: $\nabla \cdot f(\mathrm{x,y,z}) = \mathrm{div}\, \boldsymbol{f}(\mathbf{x,y,z}) = (du/dx) + (dv/dy) + (dw/dy)$, where the matrix function $\boldsymbol{f}(\mathbf{x,y,z}) = u\vec{i} + v\vec{j} + w\vec{k}$ with $\vec{i}, \vec{j}, \vec{k}$ the unity directional vectors for the x, y, and z directions, respectively. The curl is a vector operator describing the rotation in infinitesimal steps of a three-dimensional vector field: $(\nabla \times f) \cdot \vec{n}$, where $\vec{n}$ is the normal vector.

National Advisory Committee for Aeronautics (NACA)

[general] A US federal agency erected in 1915 with the goal to institutionalize aeronautical research as well as to promote and undertake aeronautical activities and exploration. The agency was dissolved in 1958. The assets and its personnel were transferred to the newly created NATIONAL AERONAUTICS AND SPACE ADMINISTRATION (NASA).

National Aeronautics and Space Administration (NASA)

[general] A US agency founded in 1958 under President Dwight David "Ike" Eisenhower (1890–1969; 34th president); it is responsible for aeronautics and aerospace research and the US national civilian space program. Many exploratory rockets and manned space flights have been planned and executed by NASA, following the work initiated by the NACA in 1946 with the launch of the Bell X-1 for exploration of supersonic flight and the early 1950s launch of an artificial SATELLITE following the space journey by Sputnik-1 in 1957 launched by the Union of Soviet Socialist Republics (USSR [Russian: Сою́з Сове́тских Социалисти́ческих Респу́блик: СССР]) (see Figure N.3).

(a)

Figure N.3 (a) Representation of space flight managed by NASA; Boeing Space Launch System (SLS). (Courtesy of Boeing Corporation.) *(Continued)*

(b)

Figure N.3 (Continued) (b) NASA space flight emblem.

National Center for Biotechnology Information (NCBI)

[biomedical] A US government-funded national resource for molecular biology information founded in 1988. The NCBI is a subdivision of the US National Library of Medicine (NLM). The NLM is a branch of the US National Institutes of Health.

National Institute of Standards and Technology (NIST)

[general] NIST is the US federal technology agency instituted in 1988; its intention is to work with the industry to develop and apply technology, measurements, and standards. NIST has, for instance, advanced the development of prototype tools for experimental medical imaging techniques for diagnostics of medical conditions. Between 1901 and 1988, it was known as the National Bureau of Standards.

National Institutes of Health (NIH)

[biomedical] An agency of the US Department of Health and Human Services. The primary agency of the US government responsible for all health-related and biomedical research (see Figure N.4).

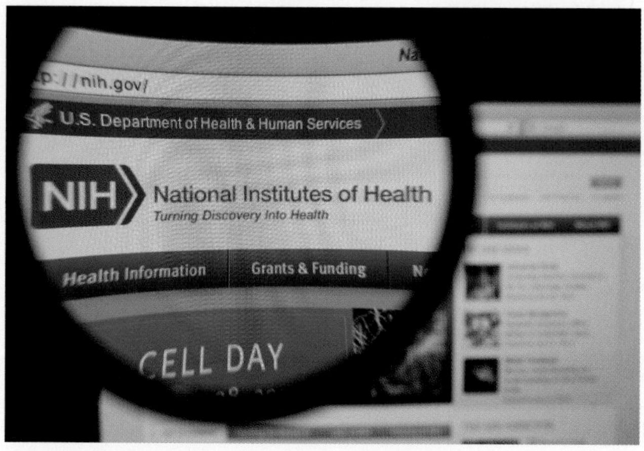

Figure N.4 Illustration of the NIH emblem.

National Library of Medicine (NLM)

[biomedical] The US medical library founded in 1836 and is the largest medical library in the world. The NLM also supports and conducts research. Additionally, the NLM support the development and training in biomedical informatics and health information technology.

Natural angular frequency

[acoustics, general] Resonant frequency of an undamped, unforced OSCILLATOR: $\omega_0 = \sqrt{(k_{spring}/m)}$, where k_{spring} is the spring-constant for the flexible medium and m the mass of the resonator in MOTION with respect to the flexible medium (i.e., spring). In case the RESONANCE is dampened by a "pod" with dampening coefficient b_{damp}, the frequency for the DRIVEN DAMPED HARMONIC OSCILLATOR becomes the resonant angular frequency: $\omega_{Res} = \sqrt{(\omega_0{}^2 - (b_{damp}{}^2/2m^2))}$. The NATURAL FREQUENCY (ν_0) associated with the angular frequency ($\nu_0 = \omega_0/2\pi$) is also referred to as the "resonant frequency" (see Figure N.5).

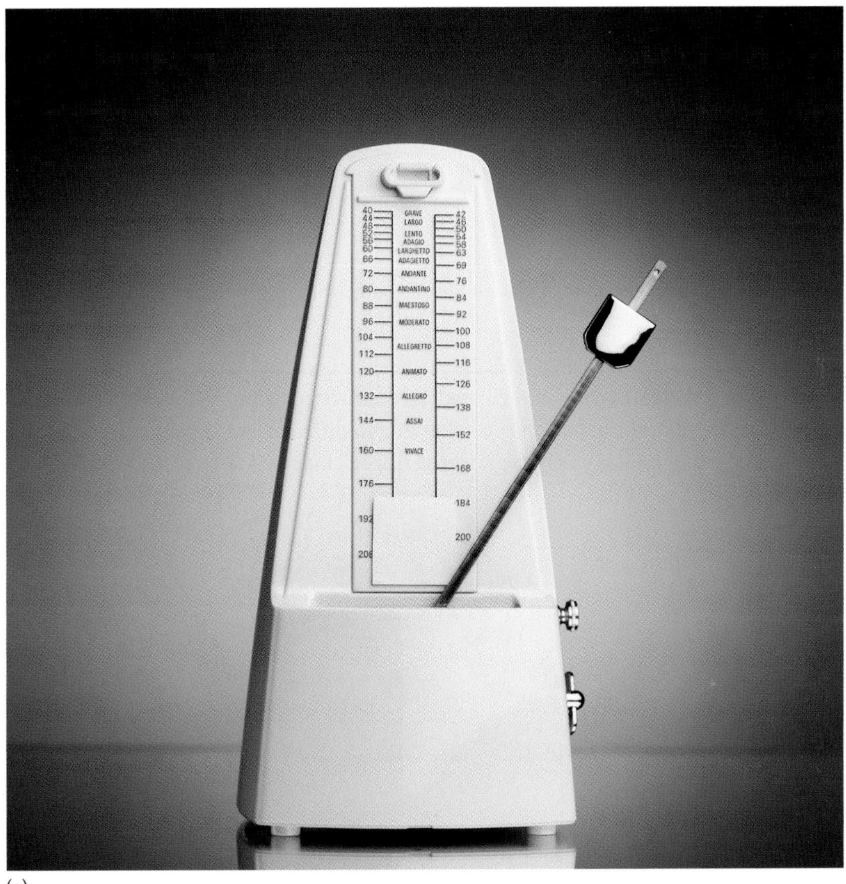

(a)

Figure N.5 (a) Metronome, used for setting the pace during a musical performance. *(Continued)*

(b)

Figure N.5 (Continued) (b) The pendulum is maintained by gears that rotate under the influence of weights.

Natural convection

[general] Fluid motion as well as HEAT TRANSFER based on thermal gradient; no active mechanism is involved. For instance, BUOYANCY forces driving the FLUID motion due to difference in density resulting from temperature gradients and variations in the fluid, for example, "warm air rise" (*also see* CONVECTION) (see Figure N.6).

Figure N.6 Natural convection of rising warm air and the ensuing wind generated based on the thermal gradient induced by the differences in specific heat (related terminology: heat capacity or thermal capacity) of land and water masses and the resulting solar heating during the day versus radiant cooling at night.

Natural frequency

[acoustics, electromagnetism, general, mechanics] Resonant phenomena of mechanical devices and electronic circuits based on their composition characteristics (*also see* **HELMHOLTZ RESONATOR**). The natural frequency (ν_0) of a single-opening design (e.g., GLASS bottle; a SOUND is generated when blowing over the open neck of the bottle) is mathematically defined by the physical characteristics including device volume V, cross-sectional area of the ORIFICE A, effective neck length, which includes a correction for the air-volume near the opening (i.e., $\delta\ell$) that flows in and out in order to generate the sound $\ell' = \ell + \delta\ell$, yielding $\nu_0 = v_s/2\pi\sqrt{A/\ell' V}$, or $\omega(\vec{r},t) = A\sqrt{E_{mech}/\rho\ell^2}$, with v_s the speed of sound, E_{mech} the Young's modules, and A is the constant. The HELMHOLTZ RESONATOR has a behavior similar to a mass-spring harmonic oscillator with mass $m = \rho A\ell'$ and spring-dashpot ELEMENT where for a volume of FLUID, the spring constant is defined by $k = \rho v_s^2(A^2/V)$. The dampener or DASHPOT will contribute a RESISTANCE R to the ENERGY equation (resulting in extinguishing the AMPLITUDE); however, generally the resonant frequency is in this case defined as $\nu_0 = 1/2\pi\sqrt{k/m}$. Analogously, the RESONANCE FREQUENCY for an electronic circuit with a RESISTOR (R), CAPACITOR (C), and INDUCTOR (L) in series is given as $\nu_0 = 1/2\pi\sqrt{1/LC}$, where the resistor will merely reduce the amplitude as a function of time (see Figure N.7).

Figure N.7 Tuning fork that will resonate at the natural frequency defined by the metal and geometrical configuration.

Natural light

[general] *See* **SUN LIGHT**.

Natural logarithm

[general] Logarithm to the base e, where $e \cong 2.718281828$, written as $\ln x$ or $\log_e x$, where $\ln a = \int_1^a (1/x)dx$, also known as "hyperbolic logarithm." The concept of the natural logarithm was documented back to 1619 in tabulated solutions by John Speidell (~1600 to ~1635?), but was officially mentioned in 1668, by the German scientist and land surveyor Nicholas (Nikolaus) Mercator (1620–1687) in his work Logarithmotechnia (*also see* **LOGARITHM**).

Natural materials

[biomedical] Materials that are biocompatible with the biological nature, can be integrated in biological units (e.g., prosthetic devices and PACEMAKER), or can degrade without release of toxic components (e.g., SCAFFOLD for tissue ENGINEERING and regenerative medicine).

Navier, Claude-Louis Marie Henri (1785–1836)

[computational, fluid dynamics, general] An engineer and scientist from France. Known for his FLUID DYNAMICS work, specifically describing the equation of MOTION behavior of an INCOMPRESSIBLE FLUID (the NAVIER–STOKES EQUATION) and the follow-up by SIR GEORGE GABRIEL STOKES (1819–1903), and in MECHANICS defining the general theory of ELASTICITY in a convenient mathematical form in 1821. In 1826, Claude Navier defined the ELASTIC MODULUS as a material property (see Figure N.8).

Figure N.8 Claude-Louis Marie Henri Navier (1785–1836): bust erected at the École Nationale des Ponts et Chaussées in Paris, France.

Navier–Stokes equation, viscous fluid

[energy, fluid dynamics, general] Equation of MOTION, specifically for FLUID behavior, defined by the work of CLAUDE-LOUIS NAVIER (1785–1836) in 1822, and later refined by SIR GEORGE GABRIEL STOKES (1819–1903). The following definitions are used in the description of the Navier–Stokes equations for FLOW: the three-dimensional flow velocity is defined by $\vec{u} = (u, v, w)$, Cartesian coordinate system $\vec{x} = (x, y, z)$, ∇ is the Laplace operator, P the pressure, Q *resp.* q the heat flux, $\vec{g} = (g_x, g_y, g_z)$ gravitational orientation with respect to flow ELEMENT, E_t the total ENERGY of the system, Pr is the Prandtl number, Re is the REYNOLDS NUMBER, ρ is the density of the fluid,

$$\tau = \begin{matrix} \sigma_{xx} & \tau_{xy} & \tau_{xz} \\ \tau_{yx} & \sigma_{yy} & \tau_{x} \\ \tau_{zx} & \tau_{zy} & \sigma_{zz} \end{matrix}$$

defines shear stress, with σ the normal stress: for example, $\sigma_{xx} = (F_x / A_x)$, Fx the force $(\vec{F})$ acting in the x direction over a presumed contact surface: A_x μ the dynamic VISCOSITY, and λ the secondary viscosity (which is zero for incompressible flow) The following Navier–Stokes equations are available to describe three-dimensional UNSTEADY FLOW phenomena. The EQUATION OF CONTINUITY reads $\partial\rho/\partial t+\partial(\rho u)/\partial x+\partial(\rho v)/\partial y+\partial(\rho z)/\partial y=0$. The momentum equations (in CARTESIAN COORDINATES) for incompressible fluids are as follows:

$$\rho g_x-\frac{\partial P}{\partial x}+\frac{\partial}{\partial x}\left[2\mu\frac{\partial u}{\partial x}+\lambda\nabla\cdot\vec{u}\right]+\frac{\partial}{\partial y}\left[\mu\left(\frac{\partial u}{\partial y}+\frac{\partial v}{\partial x}\right)\right]+\frac{\partial}{\partial z}\left[\mu\left(\frac{\partial w}{\partial x}+\frac{\partial u}{\partial z}\right)\right]$$

$$=\rho\left[\frac{\partial u}{\partial t}+u\frac{\partial u}{\partial x}+v\frac{\partial u}{\partial y}+w\frac{\partial u}{\partial z}\right],$$

respectively

$$\rho g_y-\frac{\partial P}{\partial y}+\frac{\partial}{\partial y}\left[2\mu\frac{\partial v}{\partial y}+\lambda\nabla\cdot\vec{u}\right]+\frac{\partial}{\partial z}\left[\mu\left(\frac{\partial u}{\partial z}+\frac{\partial v}{\partial y}\right)\right]+\frac{\partial}{\partial x}\left[\mu\left(\frac{\partial w}{\partial y}+\frac{\partial u}{\partial x}\right)\right]$$

$$=\rho\left[\frac{\partial v}{\partial t}+u\frac{\partial v}{\partial x}+v\frac{\partial v}{\partial y}+w\frac{\partial v}{\partial z}\right],$$

and

$$\rho g_z-\frac{\partial P}{\partial z}+\frac{\partial}{\partial z}\left[2\mu\frac{\partial v}{\partial z}+\lambda\nabla\cdot\vec{u}\right]+\frac{\partial}{\partial x}\left[\mu\left(\frac{\partial u}{\partial x}+\frac{\partial v}{\partial z}\right)\right]+\frac{\partial}{\partial y}\left[\mu\left(\frac{\partial w}{\partial z}+\frac{\partial u}{\partial y}\right)\right]$$

$$=\rho\left[\frac{\partial w}{\partial t}+u\frac{\partial w}{\partial x}+v\frac{\partial w}{\partial y}+w\frac{\partial w}{\partial z}\right].$$

The energy of the flow system is defined by

$$\partial(E_t)/\partial t+\partial(uE_t)/\partial x+\partial(vE_t)/\partial y+\partial(zE_t)/\partial y$$

$$=-\partial(uP)/\partial x-\partial(vP)/\partial y-\partial(zP)/\partial z.$$

In the case of flow around a prolate spheroid, the unsteady Navier–Stokes equations for incompressible flow at a function of TIME (t) are written as $\nabla\cdot\vec{u}=0$ and $\partial\vec{u}/\partial t+\text{ü}\cdot\nabla\vec{u}=-\nabla\vec{P}+(1/Re_\infty)\nabla^2\vec{u}$, and Re_∞ the Reynolds number based on the freestream flow velocity u_∞. A prolate spheroid is a spheroid that is narrower in the direction of flow than perpendicular to the flow, with d the diameter of the spheroid in the direction of flow; in contrast to a "squashed" spheroid, which will be wider in the direction of flow. (see Figure N.9).

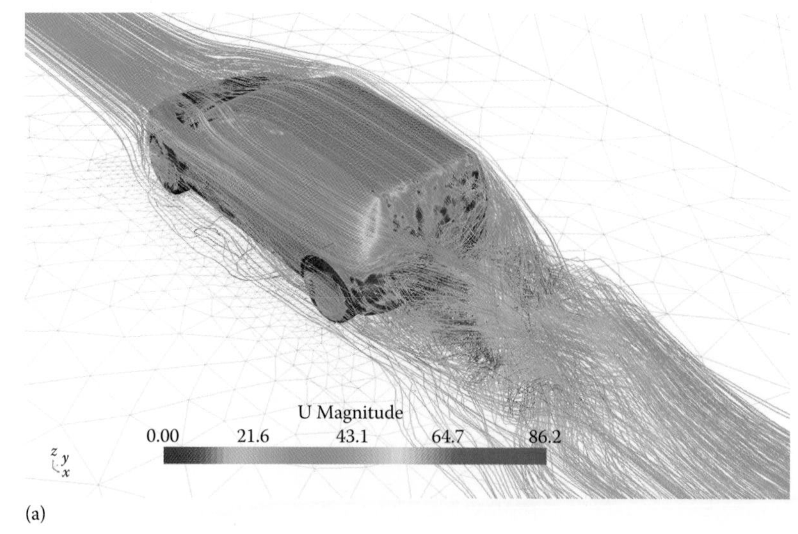

(a)

Condition	Navier–Stokes equations 3-dimensional unsteady		Glenn Research Center
Coordinates: (x,y,z) Velocity components: (u,v,w)	Time: t Density: ρ Total energy: E_t	Pressure: p Stress: τ	Heat flux: q Reynolds number: Re Prandtl number: Pr

Continuity: $$\frac{\partial \rho}{\partial t} + \frac{\partial(\rho u)}{\partial x} + \frac{\partial(\rho v)}{\partial y} + \frac{\partial(\rho w)}{\partial z} = 0$$

X-momentum: $$\frac{\partial(\rho u)}{\partial t} + \frac{\partial(\rho u^2)}{\partial x} + \frac{\partial(\rho uv)}{\partial y} + \frac{\partial(puw)}{\partial z} = -\frac{\partial p}{\partial x} + \frac{1}{Re_r}\left[\frac{\partial \tau_{xx}}{\partial x} + \frac{\partial \tau_{xy}}{\partial y} + \frac{\partial \tau_{xz}}{\partial z}\right]$$

Y-momentum: $$\frac{\partial(\rho v)}{\partial t} + \frac{\partial(puv)}{\partial x} + \frac{\partial(\rho v^2)}{\partial y} + \frac{\partial(pvw)}{\partial z} = -\frac{\partial p}{\partial y} + \frac{1}{Re_r}\left[\frac{\partial \tau_{xy}}{\partial x} + \frac{\partial \tau_{yy}}{\partial y} + \frac{\partial \tau_{yz}}{\partial z}\right]$$

Z-momentum: $$\frac{\partial(\rho w)}{\partial t} + \frac{\partial(puw)}{\partial x} + \frac{\partial(\rho vw)}{\partial y} + \frac{\partial(\rho w^2)}{\partial z} = -\frac{\partial p}{\partial z} + \frac{1}{Re_r}\left[\frac{\partial \tau_{xz}}{\partial x} + \frac{\partial \tau_{yz}}{\partial y} + \frac{\partial \tau_{zz}}{\partial z}\right]$$

Energy:

$$\frac{\partial(E_r)}{\partial t} + \frac{\partial(uE_r)}{\partial x} + \frac{\partial(vE_r)}{\partial y} + \frac{\partial(wE_r)}{\partial z} = -\frac{\partial(up)}{\partial x} - \frac{\partial(vp)}{\partial y} - \frac{\partial(wp)}{\partial z} - \frac{1}{Re_r Pr_r}\left[\frac{\partial q_x}{\partial x} + \frac{\partial q_y}{\partial y} + \frac{\partial q_z}{\partial z}\right]$$

$$+ \frac{1}{Re_r}\left[\frac{\partial}{\partial x}(u\tau_{xx} + v\tau_{xy} + w\tau_{xz}) + \frac{\partial}{\partial y}(u\tau_{xy} + v\tau_{yy} + w\tau_{yz}) + \frac{\partial}{\partial z}(u\tau_{xz} + v\tau_{yz} + w\tau_{zz})\right]$$

(b)

Figure N.9 (a) Computer simulation of flow around a car (Courtesy of Johan Hoffman and Claes Johnson and G2 FEniCS software; http://www.bodysoulmath.org/.) based on Navier–Stokes equations. (Courtesy of Johan Hoffman and Claes Johnson and G2 FEniCS software, http://www.bodysoulmath.org/.) (b) Compressible flow Navier–Stokes equations. (Courtesy of NASA.)

NDE

[acoustics, electromagnetism, general, mechanics] *See* **NONDESTRUCTIVE EVALUATION.** It is also known as "nondestructive testing in quality control".

Near point

[general, optics] The closet point to the EYE that can be observed with optimal accommodation. For the average human this point changes with AGE and is generally takes as 25 cm for a healthy young eye. By the age of 40, the near point, where a person can read comfortably at closest DISTANCE, can be increased to 40 cm (see Figure N.10).

Figure N.10 Illustration of the near-point for vision requiring corrective lenses.

Nearest-neighbor interpolation

[acoustics, computational, general] The data point closest to the requested x value data point on the phenomenological basis for a function $(f(x))$ with outcome is used to estimate the matching $f(x) = y$ value for the desired value. Interpolation is the process used to determine the missing values of a function based on the known values. There are four approximation methods available: nearest-neighbor interpolation, linear interpolation, polynomial interpolation, and spline interpolation.

Nearfield acoustic holography

[acoustics] Principle of acoustical imaging using an array of detectors to reconstruct the exact source location of an acoustic perturbation resulting from incident sound waves with respect to an acoustic discontinuity in a medium. In the near-field approach, the MICROPHONE array is placed in relative close proximity to the SOUND source array. The near field is generally defined as less than two wavelengths DISTANCE pertaining to the highest frequency used by the source. Often, this can be accomplished by using the source material as the detector, as in piezoelectric devices. This mechanism is of general application in ULTRASONIC IMAGING, specifically three-dimensional imaging. The mechanism of action is limited by the following two selection criteria, which both put requirements on the source operations and frequency band: spatial RESOLUTION, the ability to separate two sound sources, and dynamic range, sound MAGNITUDE level differences in dB between real secondary sound sources and the immediate surrounding mathematical artifacts. The imaging process is based on the following three steps: (1) transform the acoustical pressure field by spatial FOURIER TRANSFORM from the spatial domain to the WAVE number domain, (2) use the Dirichlet Green function to analyze the backpropagation of the different waves to the new defined plane, and (3) apply inverse spatial fourier transform to convert the ACOUSTICS signal from the wave number domain to the spatial domain. The imaging planes are restricted to an orientation that can only be parallel with the detection array (see Figure N.11).

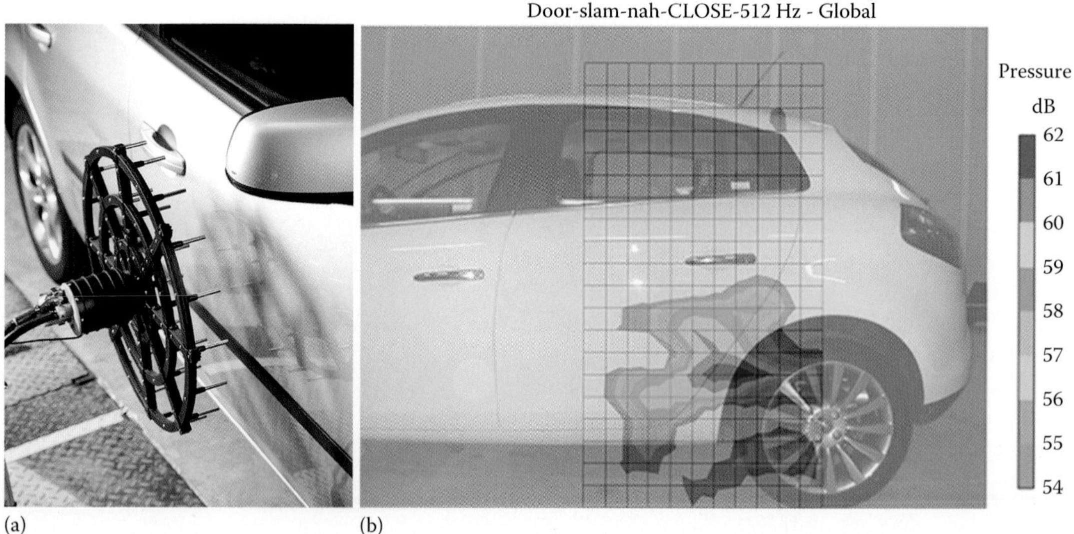

Figure N.11 (a) Illustration of a nearfield acoustic holography camera. (b) Image acquired by camera. (Courtesy of Designworld online; as produced by LMS International/Siemens.)

Near-field scanning optical microscope (NSOM)

[optics] The NSOM utilizes the fact that observations are made from a DISTANCE to the object under investigation at less than, or in the order of the interrogating wavelength. The illumination of the sample is also provided by a source with dimensions less than the wavelength. In addition, the NSOM does not provide an instantaneous global view of a section of the sample under investigation; however, the object is probed (scanned) in the near-field of the sample surface, by moving the source and/or detector across the specimen in nanometer steps, hence the name. A total IMAGE is formed with RESOLUTION less than the Abbe limit, after a series of line scans is performed, and all the intensity arrays are combined. Even though the NSOM is a relatively new instrument (inception 1982, Dieter Wolfgang Pohl and W. Denk), the concept was described in letter exchanges between Edward Hutchinson Synge and Albert Einstein in 1928. NSOM is an optical microscope that provides high spatial resolution capabilities with light sources in the visible spectrum. There is no high demand on sample preparation or confinements on working environments with NSOM. Thus far, it has been shown that working within the near field generates high spatial frequency information. However, what is needed in an optical microscope is high spatial frequency information on a subwavelength scale. Most explanations of the diffraction BARRIER on spatial resolution capabilities, take in account just the diffraction of light as it propagates through a collection LENS of a far-field optical system. Light will interact with the edges of the circular APERTURE of the lens causing the deviation of light from its initial line of travel. However, it is not just the interaction of the light with the collection lens that limits the resolution, but there exist the effects of the light interacting with detail in the sample structure. In the initial developmental stages of NSOM, the proposition was made for an optical microscope in which light would pass through a subwavelength aperture in an OPAQUE screen, illuminating an object directly below the screen. The screen would be maintained at a constant DISTANCE of a few nanometers from the sample surface, placing the sample in the near field. The idea is that the transmitted radiation would remain collimated, as it interacts with the sample. Therefore, a subwavelength beam interacts with a small volume ELEMENT of the sample, and this light that interacts with the sample is collected by an objective. The sample is basically broken into small PIXEL areas. The subwavelength LIGHT SOURCE would be scanned over

each pixel area, generating a two-dimensional intensity image. There are two theoretical parameters that give the near-field scanning optical microscope the high spatial resolution capabilities. The first theoretical boundary condition is that the sample is maintained in the near field by keeping the sub wavelength aperture a constant height above the sample surface. The second condition is that the spot size of the light that interacts with the sample is confined to the dimensions of the sub wavelength aperture. The combined effect of these two parameters yields high spatial frequency information on the sub wavelength scale. General design of NSOM microscope is as follows. The near-field scanning optical microscope can take on many different forms, depending on the user's specific application. Typically, the near-field scanning optical microscope is constructed on top of an inverted microscope. The inverted microscope allows the user to target specific areas on the sample surface before any high-resolution imaging is performed. First, laser light is passed through a bandpass filter to remove any undesirable wavelengths. The bandpass filter is followed by some wave plates, which are used to control the POLARIZATION state of the laser light. The light is then coupled into a single mode optical fiber via a launcher. The end of this single mode optical fiber is heated and pulled or chemically etched to form a subwavelength aperture. The small near-field resolution is primarily due to the tapered fiber tip design. The very end of the single mode optical fiber, where the subwavelength aperture was fabricated, is mounted to an atomic force microscope (AFM). The AFM head will be discussed in more detail, but it is part of the mechanism that is used to maintain the subwavelength light source at a constant height above the sample surface. The light is transmitted through the subwavelength aperture and impinges upon the sample that is mounted to an XYZ piezoelectric translation stage. This XYZ translation stage is used to scan the nanoscopic light source over each pixel area described earlier. The light interacts with a small volume element of the sample, and then, it is collected by the inverted microscope's objective. The collected light is optically guided out of the inverted microscope where it is sent to a detector. The type of detector that is used at the output of the NSOM depends directly on the desired application in which the system is being used. The optical information from each pixel that is measured by the output detector is sent to a computer. The computer is used to construct a high-resolution image of the sample and to run the ELECTRONICS involved in scanning.

NSOM Tip

The NSOM tip is the most essential part of the imaging device and requires that great care is taken in its preparation. NSOM tips have taken on many different shapes, sizes, and material make up. Most of the earlier NSOM tips suffered low transmission of coupled light and poor reproducibility. However, the most widely used NSOM tip design was adopted from Bell Labs. In the early 1990s, Bell Labs proposed a tapered single-mode optical fiber with a reflective metal coating as a design for an NSOM tip. These NSOM tips that are made from optical fiber are fabricated in two different ways, heating and puling or chemically etching the fiber. In heating and pulling the optical fiber, a commercial micropipette puller is used in the fabrication process. Essentially, a laser is used to heat the optical material, and the fiber is then pulled to a fine point. At the tip of this point, an APERTURE with a diameter on the order of 50–100 nm is formed. One can carefully control the heating and pulling parameters, making this method of fabrication highly reproducible. On the other hand, chemical etching utilizes a SOLUTION that consists of hydrofluoric ACID with an organic buffer layer on top to fabricate the optical fiber. One end of a single-mode optical fiber that has been stripped of its cladding is immersed into the etching solution, which consists of a buffer layer on top of hydrofluoric acid. A MENISCUS is formed in two different locations along the fiber, due to electrostatic interactions between the solution's components and the fiber. However, the etching process only occurs at the organic solvent/hydrofluoric acid interface. As the diameter of the immersed optical fiber in the HF decreases with time, the height of the meniscus formed at the solvent/HF interface decreases. Over a period of time, the etching process is terminated and a tip is formed. The conical shape of the tip can be adjusted by changing the organic SOLVENT that is used in the etching solution. Although there now is a sub-wavelength aperture formed at the end of the single-mode optical fiber, the fabrication process is not complete. There still exists the need to coat the NSOM tip with a reflective metal. The reason for this metallic coating is related to the mode-field structure that propagates through an optical fiber. The ability of a single-mode optical fiber to guide and confine one wavelength of light is directly related to the dimensions and material composition of the optical fiber. As the diameter of the single-mode optical fiber decreases in the tapered region, the ability of the fiber to confine and guide the light is lost. Therefore, the light is no longer confined to just propagate out of the subwavelength aperture; it escapes out of the sides of the tapered region. High spatial RESOLUTION capabilities of the near-field scanning optical microscope depend strongly on the fact that the beam spot size is to be confined to the subwavelength aperture. The metallic coating applied to the tapered region is required to prevent the leakage of light. This metallic coating also attenuates the light before it can escape. The NSOM tip proposed by Bell Labs, although the most widely accepted, is prone to some inefficiency problems. One such problem has to do with the amount of light that can be transmitted through the subwavelength aperture. A large quantity of light is lost by tip design itself, or the REFLECTION of the light back up through the fiber from the tapered region. Therefore, only a small fraction of the initial coupled light from the source is transmitted through the aperture. This inefficiency tends to limit the applications of NSOM. Feedback mechanisms employed to maintain a constant tip and sample separation. In order to achieve high-resolution imaging capability, an NSOM must employ another specific feature. The NSOM tip needs to be maintained at a constant height of a few nanometers from the sample surface during scanning. There are various techniques that can be employed to maintain a constant DISTANCE between the tip and the sample surface. However, only two of these techniques have become widely adopted by NSOM designers. Shear force tip feedback and tapping-mode feedback have their foundations in atomic force microscopy. These are the most reliable two methods available to maintain a constant tip and sample separation. Both methods involve the mounting of the NSOM tip to a QUARTZ tuning fork and driving the fork/tip system at mechanical resonance. However, one technique dithers the NSOM tip laterally in reference to the sample surface and the other dithers the tip perpendicularly.

Shear-force-mode tip feedback

The tuning fork uses shear-force tip feedback method, where the tip is dithered laterally in reference to the sample surface. An NSOM tip is rigidly attached to one arm of a quartz tuning fork that has a well-defined RESONANCE FREQUENCY of 32.768 kHZ and a QUALITY FACTOR, *Q*, of around 7500 in AIR. Typically, the tip is mounted to the QUARTZ tuning fork using some sort of glue or epoxy. This fork/tip system has a new resonance frequency that is slightly lower than that of the quartz tuning fork, and a quality factor, *Q*, that ranges from 150 to 300. The fork/tip system is driven at mechanical resonance either by directly applying a sinusoidal voltage to the fork or by applying a sinusoidal voltage to a piezoelectric tube that shakes the fork/tip system at resonance. However, we will only discuss the situation in which the fork/tip system is mounted to a piezoelectric tube that shakes the fork/tip system at mechanical resonance. The quartz tuning fork is piezoelectric in nature. Therefore, the shaking of the fork/tip system at mechanical resonance induces a periodic voltage across the tuning fork that can be monitored through contacts integrated in each arm of the fork. As the resonating fork/tip system approaches the sample surface within a few nanometers, the NSOM tip experiences frictional forces. These frictional forces cause the fork/tip system to become damped, and the amount of DAMPING can be measured through the integrated contacts in each arm of the fork. Essentially, this resonating fork/tip system can be used as a mechanical pick-up for the frictional forces that cause damping. This measured voltage across the quartz tuning fork can be used in a closed loop feedback mechanism, which employs a lock-in amplifier and proportional integral (P.I.) electronic circuit, to maintain the NSOM tip at a constant DISTANCE from the sample surface. As the fork/tip system is brought close to the sample surface, frictional forces interacting with the NSOM tip causes the monitored potential across the fork to decrease in AMPLITUDE and shift in PHASE, any shift from 90° out of phase with the reference, generates an output voltage from the lock-in. An active feedback voltage is sent from the lock-in to the P.I circuit. The P.I circuit sends an immediate response voltage to the XYZ piezoelectric translation stage to adjust the *z*-position of the stage, in order to maintain the monitored potential at resonance.

Tapping-mode tip feedback: Tapping-mode feedback has also been employed to maintain the NSOM tip at a constant height above the sample surface. It is a more sensitive mechanical pick-up for the frictional forces that interact with the NSOM tip. However, the bend in the tip reduces the throughput efficiency. Therefore, in certain applications that require a relatively high intensity to interact with the sample, shear-force tip feedback will be chosen over tapping-mode feedback. The fork/tip system and the piezoelectric tube form the AFM head that was mentioned earlier in the shear-force mechanism. Essentially, an atomic force MICROSCOPE has been integrated into the NSOM. The atomic force microscope consists of the lock-in amplifier, P.I circuit, and *xyz* piezoelectric stage, which are employed in a closed-loop feedback mechanism. As the tip is being scanned across the sample, that has some surface variations, the *z*-position of the piezoelectric stage is adjusted to maintain the monitored potential across the fork at resonance. A topography IMAGE can be formed serially, pixel by pixel, by monitoring *z*-voltage that has to be applied to the positioning stage. The beauty of having the atomic force microscope integrated into the NSOM is that intensity and topography images can be built simultaneously.

Intensity imaging

Most biological samples that are studied are very thin and transparent. There are not a great deal of contrast mechanism within the sample to exploit. Therefore, samples have to be treated with dyes, even in NSOM imaging. Typically, samples are stained with dyes that have specific ABSORPTION SPECTRUM. The stained samples are deposited on a piece of mica or a MICROSCOPE cover slip, and air-dried. A sample is mounted to the xyz piezoelectric stage, which scans the sample under the fixed NSOM tip. The light excites fluorescence in the sample is collected by the collection LENS of the inverted microscope. The collected light is optically guided out of the inverted microscope and is passed through a notch filter. The notch filter is used to separate the FLUORESCENCE from any laser light that may be propagating through the system. The light is sent to a high quantum efficiency detector, such as an avalanche photo DIODE operating in single PHOTON count mode. The detector measures the frequency at which photons strike the sensing ELEMENT in the detector.

Phase imaging

Additional work is being done to extend the capabilities of NSOM to include phase imaging. In order to achieve high-resolution subwavelength phase-contrast images an NSOM is integrated into an INTERFEROMETER. The ability to construct high-resolution phase images would have a huge impact in the study of biological samples. Samples would no longer need to be treated with dyes to have a contrast mechanism to exploit. This method would be one step closer to providing a system that could be used to IMAGE living cells. Since NSOM makes use of an optical fiber to achieve subwavelength RESOLUTION capabilities, a hybrid Mach–Zehnder interferometer utilizing an all fiber bidirectional coupler represents the system of choice. The Mach–Zehnder interferometer relies on the same phase sensitive information as described for the other interferometers. Only this time the recombination takes place after transmission instead of REFLECTION. (see Figure N.12).

N

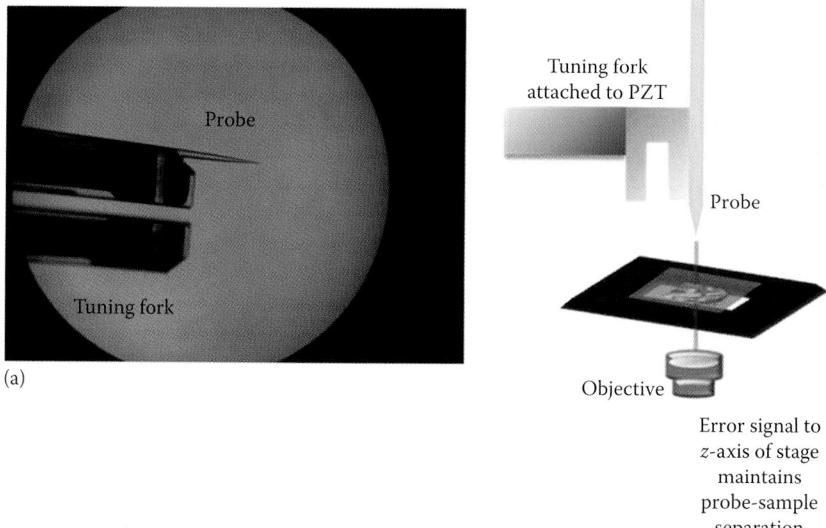

Figure N.12 (a) Nearfield scanning optical microscope. (Courtesy of Kert Edward, University of North Carolina at Charlotte, Charlotte, North Carolina.) *(Continued)*

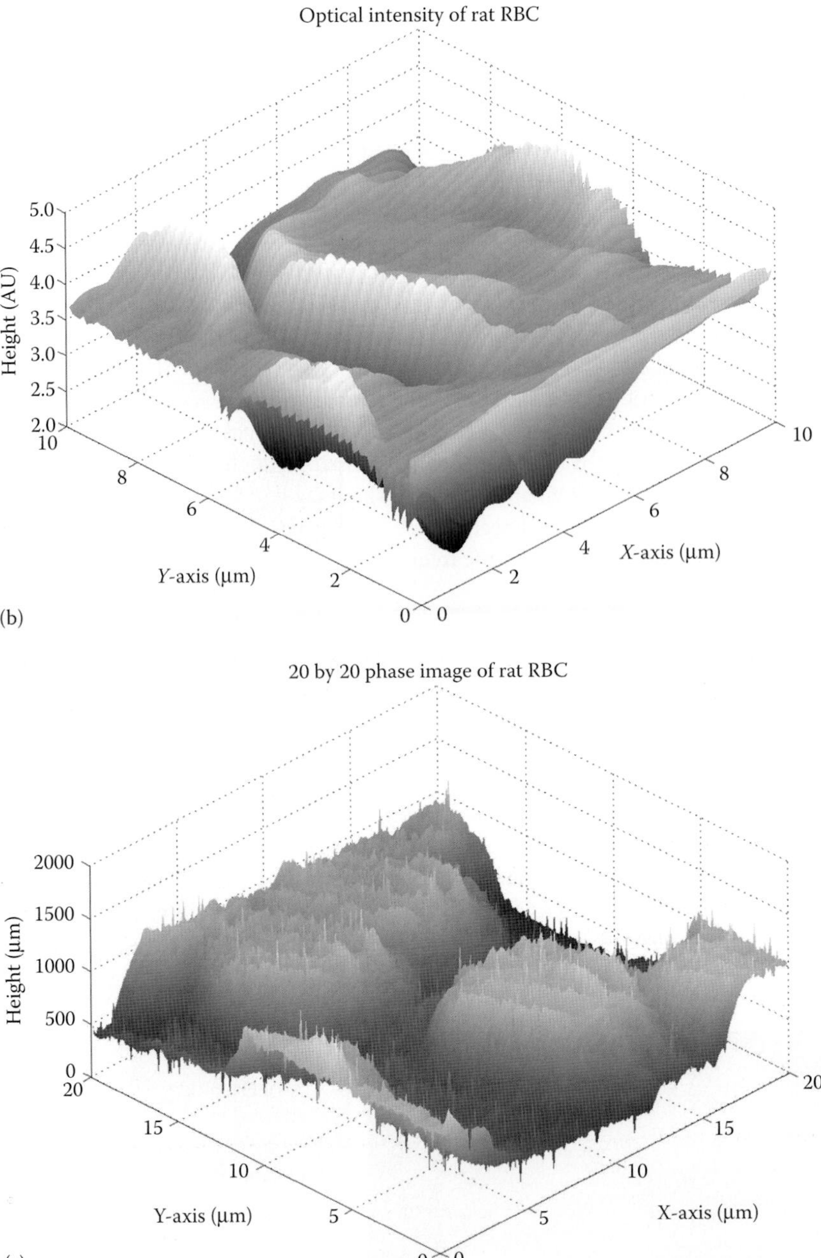

Figure N.12 (Continued) (b,c) Images acquired by means of NSOM methodology. (Courtesy of Kert Edward, University of North Carolina at Charlotte, Charlotte, North Carolina.) *(Continued)*

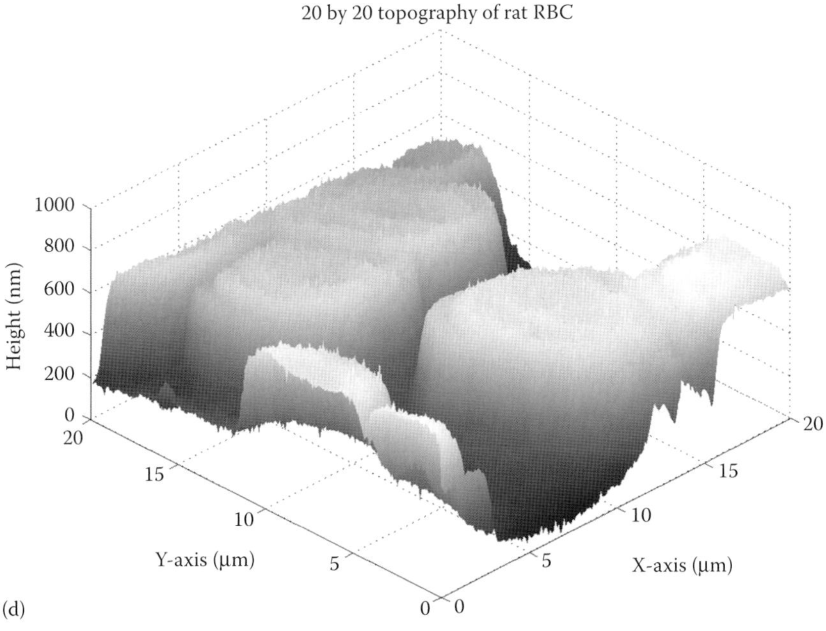

Figure N.12 (Continued) (d) Images acquired by means of NSOM methodology. (Courtesy of Kert Edward, University of North Carolina at Charlotte, Charlotte, North Carolina.)

Nearsightedness

[biomedical, general, optics] *See* MYOPIA.

Necheles, Heinrich (1897–1979)

[biomedical] A physiologist and scientist from Germany that implemented anticoagulation in the dialysis process for BLOOD filtration in people with KIDNEY malfunctions (see Figure N.13).

Figure N.13 Heinrich Necheles (1897–1979). (Courtesy of *Hektoen International Journal*, Hektoen Institute of Medicine, Chicago, IL.)

N

Necking

[general] An ENGINEERING process that deforms a ductile instrument or device by application of tensile force. Tensile deformation that induces relatively large amounts of strain are rearranged disproportionately in a small volume of the material, resulting in a slimming down process (see Figure N.14).

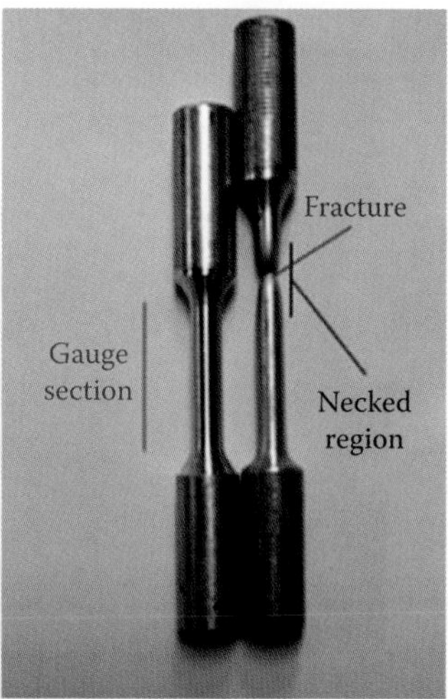

Figure N.14 The process of necking for a narrow metal rod under tensile force applied by an Instron® testing machine.

Neddermeyer, Seth Henry (1907–1988)

[atomic, nuclear] A scientist from the United States who worked on the MANHATTAN PROJECT (see Figure N.15).

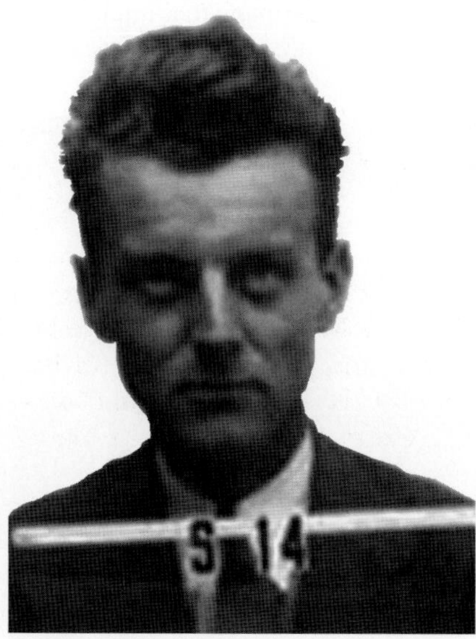

Figure N.15 Seth Henry Neddermeyer (1907–1988). (Courtesy of Los Alamos National Laboratory, Los Alamos, NM.)

Needle valve

[fluid dynamics] Valve that uses the adjustable opening from a tapered needle in an ORIFICE of FLOW for flow control. The VALVE will have a loss factor that is nonlinearly proportional to the total opening area. Additional loss in flow may result from TURBULENCE and CAVITATION (see Figure N.16).

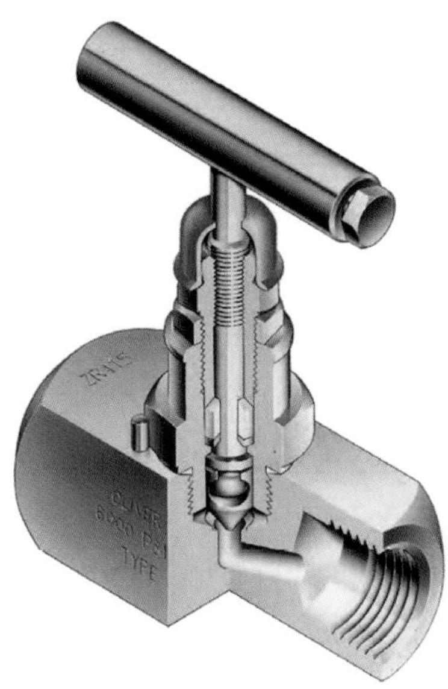

Figure N.16 Needle valve. (Courtesy of Oliver Valves.)

Negative acceleration

[general] Acceleration in direction opposite to the direction of MOTION, resulting in a reduction in velocity, for example, applying the brakes.

Negative charge

[general] Charge consisting of a collection of electrons.

Negative kinetic energy

[nuclear, quantum] In QUANTUM MECHANICS, negative kinetic energy is a SOLUTION to the SCHRÖDINGER EQUATION involving QUANTUM TUNNELING. In general, there is no real negative kinetic energy. In the process of TUNNELING the momentum (classical mechanic, nonrelativistic: $p = mv$, where v is the velocity of mass m; however, in quantum MECHANICS, the value is a solution to the Schrödinger equation) will have an imaginary value as well as an imaginary WAVE number, and hence "virtual" negative kinetic energy (since by definition $KE = p^2/2m$).

Negative lenses

[general] Lens with at least one concave surface, and hence a virtual FOCAL POINT and is diverging (*see* **LENS**).

Negative magnification

[general] Reduction in IMAGE size with respect to object (*see* **MAGNIFICATION**).

Negative temperature

[quantum, thermodynamics] Situation where electrons in a very low ENERGY state at micro Kelvin temperature that are virtually not able to move due to the fact that the POTENTIAL WELL is deep and narrow, which is inverted to a potential crest by manipulating the LATTICE. The crest is very stable and the energy cannot go down, and is hence considered "negative." This concept of temperature is directly linked to the entropy of the system in a QUANTUM STATE, not anymore to the MOTION as in classical MECHANICS.

Nephelometer

[biomedical, fluid dynamics, geophysics, thermodynamics] The stationary or portable analytical instrument that can be applied to measure and analyze the light-scattering coefficient of atmospheric and laboratory aerosols to determine the concentration of suspended particulates in a LIQUID or GAS colloid. The nephelometer specifically gauges the stray light outside the path of incidence, hence determining the scattering CROSS SECTION. Specific applications are in drug solubility screening, and other general nephelometric measurements. The biomedical use relates specifically to immunological assay analysis, the principles of nephelometry rely on the reactions between antibodies and antigens. Antibodies in this realm are specific proteins of the immune system, whereas the antigens are the foreign proteins that can be a threat. Antibodies are very specific and selective in their association with particular antigens and will bind strongly to it (see Figure N.17).

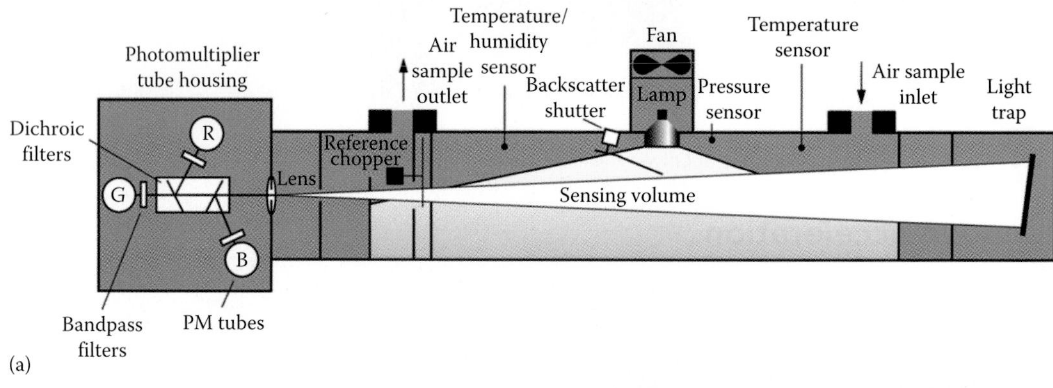

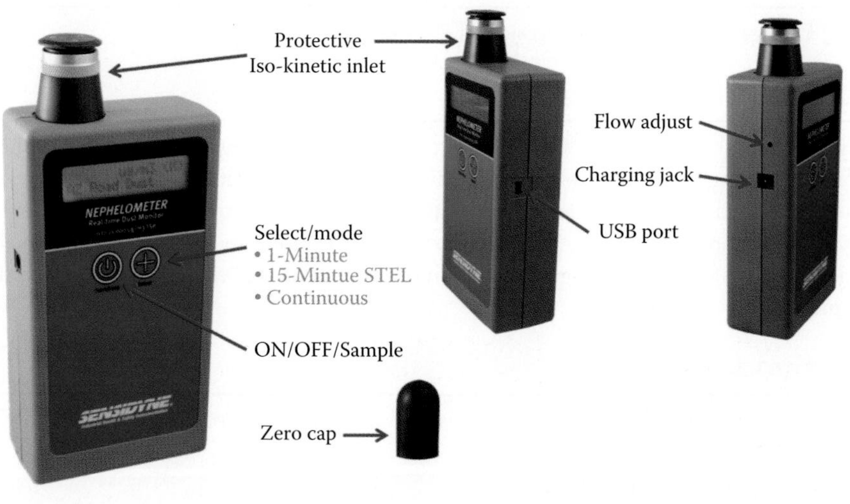

Figure N.17 (a) Outline of Nephelometer, this one in particular operating at 550 nm. (Courtesy of Lynn Russell, Princeton University, Princeton, NJ.) (b) Professional Sensidyne Nephelometer. (Image courtesy of Sensidyne, LP—www.Sensidyne.com.)

Neptunium ($^{237}_{93}Np$)

[atomic, nuclear] Metallic ELEMENT discovered in 1940. The first ISOTOPE was produced in the University of California, Berkeley by Edwin Mattison McMillian (1907–1991) and Philip Hauge Abelson (1913–2004) by bombarding uranium with slow moving neutrons, creating neptunium-239, with a half-life of approximately 2.3–2.4 days, decays to plutonium-239 by beta DECAY. The most stable configuration is neptunium-237, discovered in 1942 by A. C. Wahl and Glenn T. Seaborg, has a half-life of 2,144,000 years, decays into protactinium-233 through ALPHA DECAY and is a by-product of the production of PLUTONIUM ($^{244}_{94}Pu$).

Nernst, Walther Hermann (1864–1941)

[biomedical, chemical, energy, thermodynamics] A German physicist and chemist who contributed to the model of the electrical stimulus propagation in biological communications, on a chemical (ionic) basis. Nernst was born in Wąbrzeźno, at the time Briesen part of the Prussian ("German") Empire now Poland. Walther Nernst is best known for his work in electrochemical applications in biology. More generally, the electrochemical efforts were focused on galvanic cells, such as the BATTERY. The galvanic NERNST POTENTIAL describes the electrical potential resulting from a CHEMICAL GRADIENT. The Nernst potential is the pivotal instrument in the HODGKIN–HUXLEY MODEL of propagation of electrical DEPOLARIZATION along the length of a nerve CELL. The electrical gradient across the cellular membrane is directly related to the VAN'T HOFF EQUATION or with respect to the OSMOTIC PRESSURE across a SEMIPERMEABLE MEMBRANE. Nernst received the Nobel Prize (1920) for his contributions to the chemical embodiment of the THIRD LAW OF THERMODYNAMICS applied to chemical affinity (see Figure N.18).

Figure N.18 Walther Hermann Nernst (1864–1941).

Nernst equation

[biomedical, chemical, thermodynamics] The electrical transmembrane potential resulting from a ION gradient expressed by Walter Nernst (1864–1941) as $\Delta V = \Delta V^{\circ} - (RT/nF_{far})\ln Q_r$, where $R = 8.3144621(75)$ J/Mmol is the GAS constant, T is the (absolute) temperature, n is the number of transferred charges, Q_r is the reaction quotient, $F_{far} = 96485$ C/mol is the FARADAY CONSTANT, and ΔV is the maximum POTENTIAL DIFFERENCE due to the MOTION of charges at normal conditions (temperature and pressure). The biological membrane potential was later defined more rigorously by the Goldman voltage equation.

Nernst potential

[biochemical, chemical, thermodynamics] *See* **NERNST EQUATION**.

Nernst principle

[thermodynamics] Theory of the electromotive force that defines the electrical potential of the voltaic CELL (i.e., BATTERY) developed by Walter Nernst (1864–1941) in 1888. The principle describes the change in free ENERGY from the chemical reaction that leads to the current produced. The GIBBS FREE ENERGY (G) is the energy that determines whether a reaction will be spontaneous or not. It is defined as the change in ENTHALPY (H) minus the TEMPERATURE (T) times the ENTROPY (S): $\Delta G = \Delta H - T\Delta S = \Delta U + P\Delta V - T\Delta S = \Delta G_0 + RT \ln Q_r$, where P is the pressure, U is the internal energy, V is the volume, $R = 8.3144621(75)$ J/Kmol is the GAS constant, and Q_r is the reaction quotient. Later this was summarized in the NERNST EQUATION.

Nernst–Planck diffusion equation

[biomedical, chemical, thermodynamics] The FLUX of ions across a membrane $\overrightarrow{J_K}$ [current/area] is calculated as a function of the concentration of the species of interest $[C_K]$, the DIFFUSION constant D_K: $\overrightarrow{J_K} = -D_K\left(\nabla[C_K] + ([C_K]/\alpha_K)\nabla V\right)$, where $\alpha_K = RT/F_{far}Z_K$ is the ION transfer rate, Z_K is the VALENCE of the ionic constituents in the diffusion process, $F_{far} = 96{,}485$ C/mol is the FARADAY CONSTANT, $R = 8.3144621(75)$ J/Kmol is the GAS constant, and T is the (absolute) temperature. It was described by WALTER NERNST (1864–1941) and ERNST PLANCK (1858–1947).

Neumann, Carl (Karl) Gottfried (1832–1925)

[computational, material] Scientist and mathematician from Prussia (now Germany). Neumann is best known for his pioneering work in the development of integral equations, as well as the NEUMANN SERIES. In 1875, Neumann also introduced the notation $\bar{d}$, representing an "inexact" differentiation associated predominantly with heat and work that depend on the path in which the differentiation is taken, later replaced by the symbol δ by James Riddick Parlington (1886–1965) in 1924, a chemist and thermodynamic physicist from Great Britain (*Note*: James Parlington worked under Walther Nernst [1864–1941]) (see Figure N.19).

Figure N.19 Carl (Karl) Gottfried Neumann (1832–1925).

Neumann boundary condition

[computational, thermodynamics] Specification of the derivatives of a function at a boundary of the vector domain, introduced by CARL NEUMANN (1832–1925). In thermodynamic applications, this defines the first order derivative conditions for the differential equation $f'' + f = 0$ over the interval $[x_1, x_2]$ as $f'(x_1) = A_1$

and $f'(x_2) = A_2$, where A_1 and A_2 are real numbers, or multidimensionally $\nabla^2 f + f = 0$, where ∇^2 is the Laplace operator, with on the boundary of the vector space $[\partial f(\vec{x})]/\partial\vec{n} = \varphi(\vec{x})$, with $\varphi(\vec{x})$ being a SCALAR function and $\vec{n}$ the normal to the boundary. In comparison, the Cauchy boundary condition is a combination of the Neumann boundary condition and the Dirichlet conditions and forms a mixed boundary condition.

Neumann function

[computational] Cylinder function of the second kind $N_p(x) = \lim_{k\to p}\left(J_k(x)\cos(k\pi) - J_{-k}(x)\right)/\sin(k\pi)$, where $J_k(x)$ and $J_{-k}(x)$ are BESSEL FUNCTIONS, named after CARL NEUMANN (1832–1925). The asymptotic value for large x yields $N_p(x) \approx \sqrt{(2/\pi x)}\sin\left(x - (p\pi/2) - (\pi/4)\right)$. A special occasion is the radial equation, an specifically the Bessel equation of order ℓ yielding $\left\{\rho^2(d^2/d\rho^2) + 2\rho(d/d\rho) + \left[\rho^2 - \ell(\ell+1)\right]\right\} f_\ell$, using $U_\ell(\rho) = \rho f_\ell(\rho)$. Solution to the Bessel equation of order ℓ (which is, for instance, an EIGENFUNCTION for the HYDROGEN ATOM $\left(-(d^2/d\rho^2) + [\ell(\ell+1)/\rho^2]\right)U_\ell(\rho) = U_\ell(\rho)$, with $U_\ell(\rho) = U_\ell(k\vec{r})$, k the wavenumber), with Neumann solution: $N_p(x)$ (*also see* **GREEN'S FUNCTION**).

Neumann series

[computational] Analytical series developed by CARL NEUMANN (1832–1925) in 1877 defined as $\sum_{n=0}^{\infty} \urcorner_n = (Id - \urcorner)^{-1}$, where $\urcorner$ is an operator and Id and identity operator. Where the sum has analogies to the special case geometric series: $x/(1-x) = 1 + x + x^2 + \cdots$. The identity operator, in the vector space X, defines the asymptotic behavior of the operator. The Neumann series has special implication for potential theory.

Neural network

[computational] Artificial network of information processing that is mirrored after how the biological nervous system processes information. The processing resembles cluster computer system, in a manner that processing ELEMENTS work in parallel to solve one specific complex problem. The artificial neural network learns as it processes, mimicking adjusting synaptic connections in the brain. The concept of neural networks predates the introduction of the personal computer. The first rudimentary artificial NEURON was produced by the neurophysiologist and analyst Warren McCulloch (1898–1969) and the logician and cognitive psychologist Walter Harry Pitts (1923–1969) in 1943. The neural network's learning aspect is represented as follows: the network adapts as follows: change the weight of an input by an amount proportional to the difference between the desired output and the actual output: $w_i = \eta * (D - Y)\cdot I_i$, where w_i is the weight of the "decision"/conclusion, η is the learning rate, I_i is the perception/input, D is the desired output, and Y is the actual output. This is referred to as the "perceptron learning rule" and was introduced in the early 1960s. Still, the learning process of the brain is mostly unknown; however, the basic operations by means of neurons, synapses, axons, and dendrites is anatomically described in great detail. In the biological neural network, there is a threshold that needs to be exceeded before a pulse is sent over the dendrites, leading to the cell NUCLEUS, before passing on to the axon that splits in a multitude of branches, causing a form of SIGNAL amplification by number of branches, which is subsequently passed on by SYNAPSE that communicates with the next network of dendrites and so on. A special neural network introduced by John Joseph Hopfield (1933–) in 1982 uses a similar recurrent artificial neural network, called an "associative neural network." The associative network of John Hopfield relies on content-addressable memory systems that are equipped with binary threshold nodes (see Figure N.20).

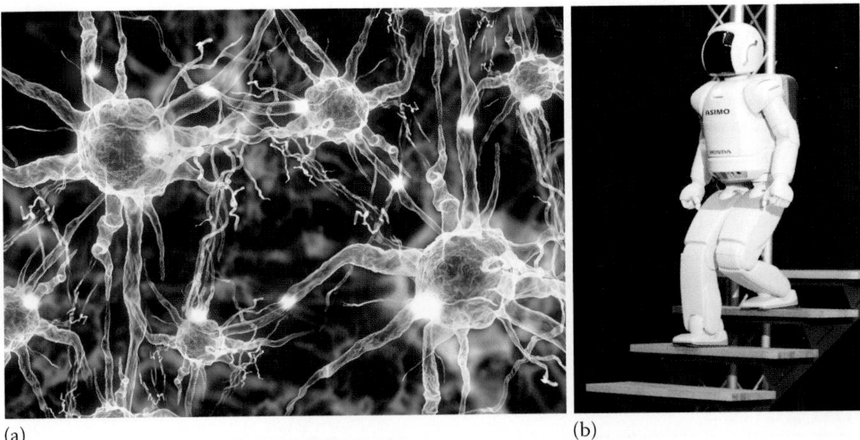

Figure N.20 (a) Advanced form of a neural network, adaption in the signal transmission, artist impression (b) robot "Asimo" developed by Honda relying on neural network.

Neuron

[biomedical, computational] Conducting and/or excitable CELL that propagates impulses based on membrane DEPOLARIZATION in binary format as pulse trains. Neurons are part of the nervous system, consisting of the autonome and parasympathic nervosystem in the spine and diffusely distributed through the body of biological beings (animals and human), the brain and the senses (HEARING, smell, taste, touch, and VISION [sight]). Specialized neurons are found for muscular ACTIVITY and specific senses; they are referred to as the MOTOR neuron and sensory neuron, respectively, partially based on the specific chemical release from the SYNAPSE. Neurons are components of myelinated and nonmyelinated nerve cells, each conducting in respective fashion. MYELINATED NERVE cell are not excitable over the entire length, but only a certain point: the nodes of Ranvier. Nonmyelinated nerve cells can be excited at will at any location. The propagation process for the respective types of nerve cells is very different, the nonmyelinated neuron conducts continuously and the MEMBRANE depolarization propagation can be described by the TELEGRAPH EQUATION with respect to the SIGNAL transmission. The myelinated neuron depolarizes in jolts at the nodes of Ranvier, while the signal jumps without conduction, and propagates at least an order of MAGNITUDE faster than for the non-myelinated neuron (*see* **NERVE**) (see Figure N.21).

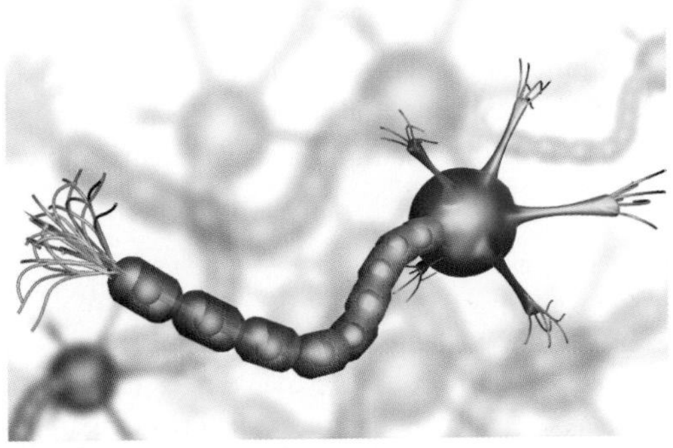

Figure N.21 Illustration of myelinated neuron.

Neurotransmitters

[biomedical, chemical, energy] Secretion of signaling molecules from the synaptic terminals of neurons (*see* NERVE) (see Figure N.22).

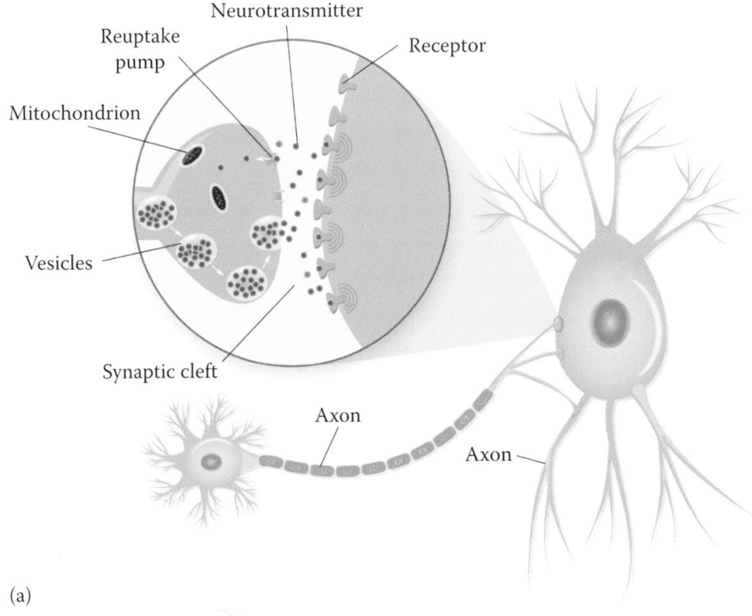

(a)

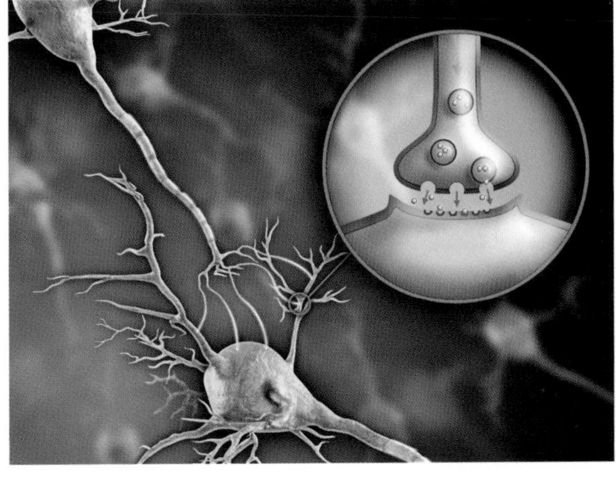

(b)

Figure N.22 (a,b) Typical structure of a chemical synapse in neural communications using neurotransmitter for signal relay between two or more nerve cells.

Neutrino

[atomic, general, high-energy, nuclear, quantum, solid-state] (ν^*), elementary PARTICLE with no CHARGE and negligible REST MASS compared to an electron is produced from the breakdown of a NEUTRON which balances its ENERGY (i.e., CONSERVATION OF ENERGY) with that of the emitted ELECTRON: $n \rightarrow p + e + \nu^*$, where n is a neutron, p is a PROTON, and e is an electron. In addition, the neutrino has a role in the CONSERVATION OF

MOMENTUM, SPIN, AND MASS. The electron and neutrino balance each other in such a way that when the electron ENERGY (i.e., KINETIC ENERGY) is high the neutrino energy is low and vice versa. The neutrino has an intrinsic ANGULAR MOMENTUM of $L = \hbar/2$, with $\hbar = h/2\pi$ the reduced PLANCK'S CONSTANT. The neutrino spins around the axis parallel to the direction of its MOTION. The rotational direction of the neutrino SPIN (clockwise/counterclockwise) is given by the RIGHT-HAND RULE. The neutrino has a counter part: the ANTI-NEUTRINO, which has the opposite spin given by the LEFT-HAND RULE (see Figure N.23).

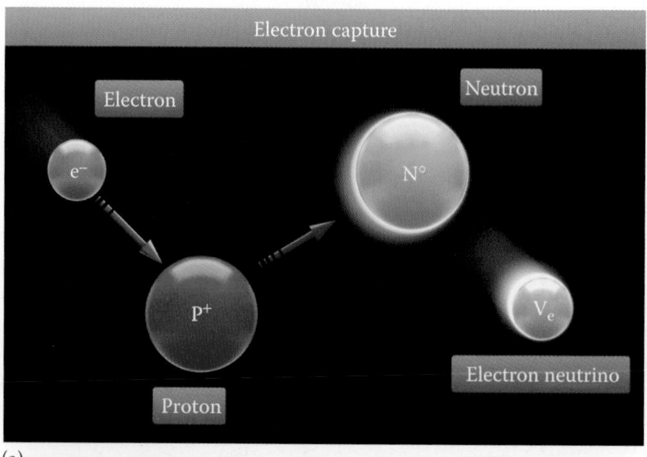

(a)

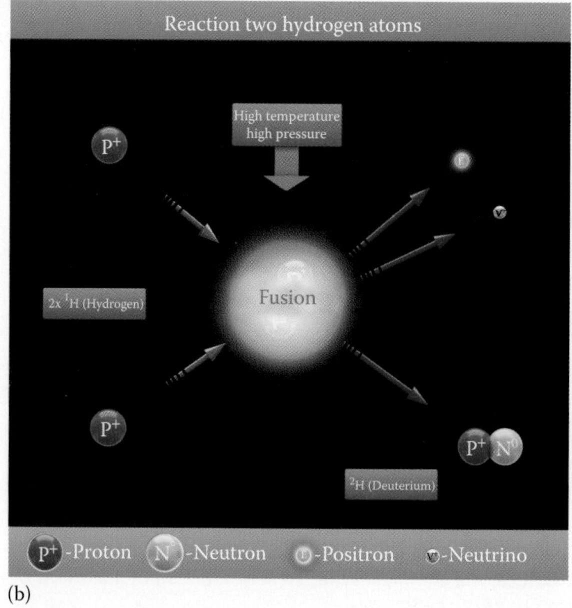

(b)

Figure N.23 (a,b) Elementary neutrino release in the formation of deuterium resulting from a collision of two hydrogen atoms under high temperature and high pressure.

Neutrino (ν)

[atomic] Elementary PARTICLE released in the dissociation of a PROTON in a NEUTRON, a positron, and a neutrino: proton $\rightarrow$ neuron $+\beta^{+}+\nu$. Introduced by WOLFGANG PAULI (1900–1958) in 1931 and named in 1934 by ENRICO FERMI (1901–1954) and experimentally verified in 1959 by Clyde Cowan (1919–1974) and FREDERICK REINES (1918–1998). Neutrinos are very similar to the electron; however, they do not carry an ELECTRIC CHARGE, and it has an anti-particle (anti-neutrino: $\overline{\nu}$) (see Figure N.24).

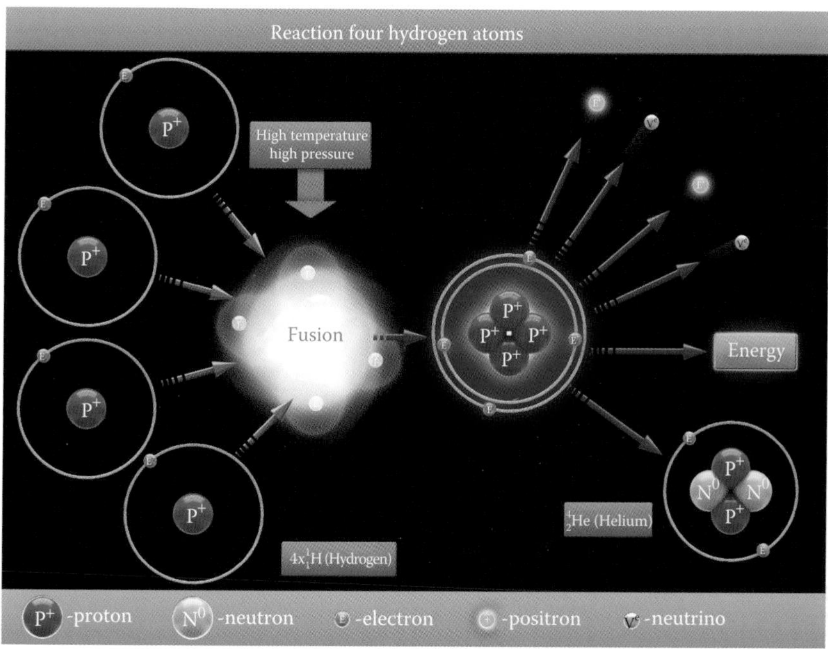

Figure N.24 The release of a neutrino during a fusion process involving four hydrogen atoms.

Neutron

[atomic] Subatomic neutral (no net ELECTRIC CHARGE) particle of the hadron class. The neutron is generally part of the atomic NUCLEUS. The neutron was experimentally verified by JAMES CHADWICK (1891–1974) in 1932, because the newly discovered RADIATION could not be explained by gamma principles or alpha

particles. The neutron is composed of three quarks: one UP QUARK and two DOWN QUARKS. The MASS OF THE NEUTRON is marginally larger than the mass of the PROTON. The lifetime of the neutron outside of the atomic nucleus is only 885 s (see Figure N.25).

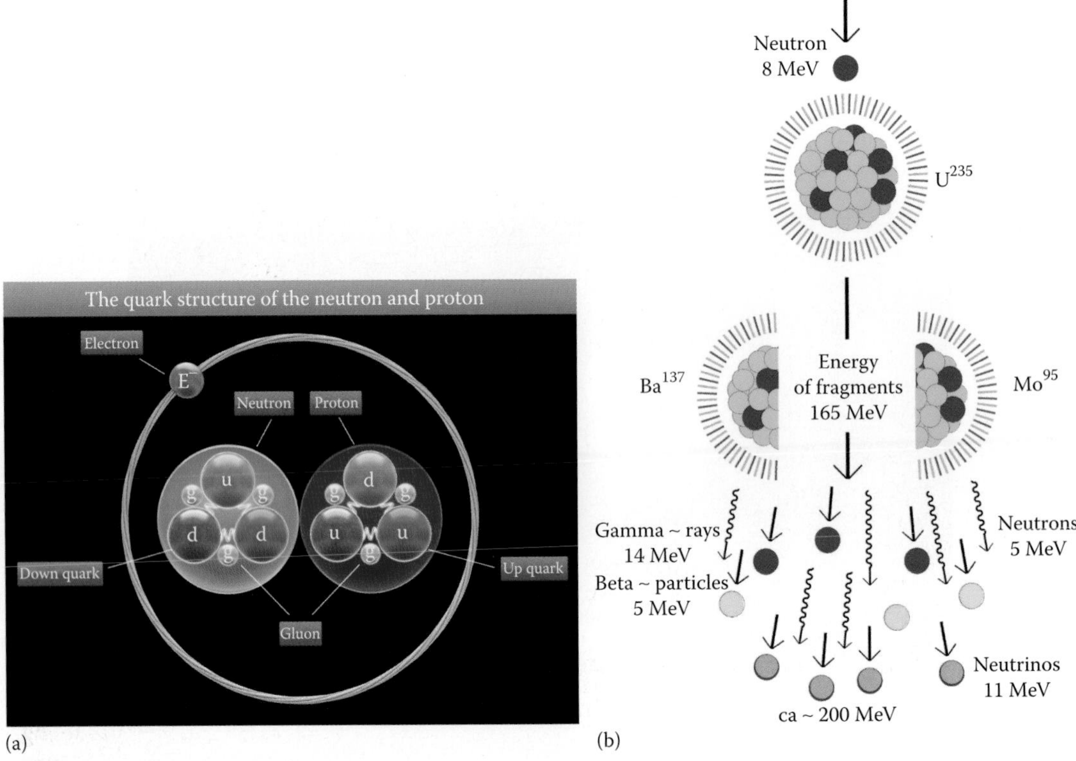

Figure N.25 (a,b) Neutrons involved in the uranium fission process.

Neutron cross section

[nuclear] Expression of the likelihood of a NUCLEON interaction, for a single collision the cross section of a neutron will depend on the PARTICLE involved in the interaction, size, charge and SPIN, and so on for nucleon-nucleon SCATTERING studies both experimental and theoretical information needs to be considered, specifically due to the Heisenberg uncertainty principles and WAVE functions involved. The cross section is a function of the "location" of the neutron (the NUCLEUS of the ELEMENT in question, type of nuclear reaction, the ENERGY (E) (including TEMPERATURE [T]), and the velocity (v) of both the incident particle and the nucleus with the imbedded neutron(s), as well as the relative ANGLE between the incident particle and the target nuclide. The standard unit for atomic, nuclear, and elementary particle cross section is the *barn* $= 10^{-28}$ m^2. The general cross section is the target area projection in the two-dimensional plane, perpendicular to the path of the incident PROJECTILE. The choice of "radius" is however not always that straightforward. One approximation would be the use of the Broglie wavelength of the neutron and the incident particle: $\lambda(E) = \hbar/\sqrt{(2mE)}$, where $\hbar = h/2\pi$ and $h = 6.62606957 \times 10^{-34}$ m^{2}kg/s is Planck's constant. Subsequently, the cross section (σ) becomes proportional to a combination of the effective radius of the physical object (R) of the size combined with the MOTION: $\sigma(E) \propto \pi(R + \lambda(E))^2$. Frequently, cross

sections are provided in tables in reference books particular to the application (e.g., NUCLEAR FISSION and scattering) (*also see* CROSS SECTION) (see Figure N.26).

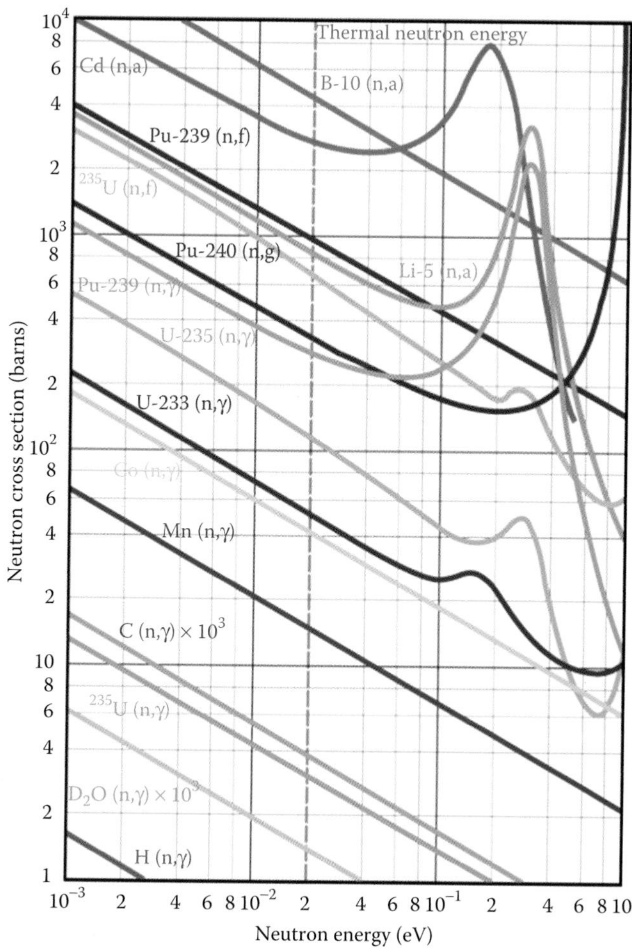

Figure N.26 Diagram of the relation between neutron cross section and neutron energy, image source: CC-BY-NC-SA—DoITPoMS, University of Cambridge (http://www.doitpoms.ac.uk/tlplib/nuclear_materials/).

Neutron detectors

[nuclear] Neutron can be detected by scintillation counters, BUBBLE-, or IONIZATION chambers and specialized semiconductor detectors, although the lack of charge presents specific limitations. Generally, neutron detectors can only detect fast NEUTRON and often require a nuclear conversion process generating a charged PARTICLE. Certain materials used for detection are boron, gadolinium, helium, and LITHIUM, connected to a photo-multiplier or photocell.

Neutron star

[astronomy/astrophysics, quantum] Compact STAR with diameter of approximately 20 km, presumably one of various mechanisms a star can terminate. As the star completes burning its nuclear fuel, it will terminate by means of a SUPERNOVA explosion. The neutron star is a condensed version of a star that originally had a mass four to eight times the mass of our Sun and concurrently has a gravitational attraction that is in the order of 2×10^{11} times the earth's GRAVITATIONAL ACCELERATION. Based on this neutron star's density a tablespoon of star MATTER would weigh in excess of 2×10^9 kg. Because of the complex charge structure, neutron stars also may carry a MAGNETIC FIELD that is in the order of 10^6 times stronger than fields experienced on EARTH (see Figure N.27).

(a) (b)

Figure N.27 (a) The core of the Crab Nebula is a strong pulsar neutron star; part of the constellation Taurus. (b) The Crab Nebula is a remnant of a supernova that exploded presumably in the year 1054 (date of origin derived from spectroscopic analysis).

Neutron–proton chart

[atomic, nuclear] Chart describing the transmutation of a NEUTRON to a PROTON for a specific atomic number ELEMENT: proton converts into a neutron, releasing both a POSITRON (β^+) and a NEUTRINO (ν): proton $\rightarrow$ neuron $+ \beta^+ + \nu$, obeying all CONSERVATION LAWS. Ultimately, heavy radioisotopes will DECAY until they attain the extreme stability of the iron NUCLEUS. Note that in IRON the nucleons are the most tightly bound of all nuclei. The chart lists the BINDING ENERGY per nucleon displayed as a function of the atomic mass number (amu).

Newcomen, Thomas (1664–1729)

[general, mechanics] An English blacksmith. He is the inventor of the atmospheric reciprocating steam ENGINE in collaboration or in parallel with the works of THOMAS SAVERY (1650–1715), DENIS PAPIN (1647–1712), and JOHN CALLEY (1663–1717) approximately in 1712 (see Figure N.28).

Figure N.28 Thomas Newcomen (1664–1729).

Newton, Isaac, Sir (1642–1727)

[fluid dynamics, general, mechanics, nuclear, solid-state] An English scientist supporting the corpuscular theory of light as proposed by the ancient Greek philosophers, also the pioneer of MECHANICS (i.e., DYNAMICS). Newton postulated three laws of motion (Newton's first, second, and third laws) and one law on GRAVITY (Newton's LAW OF UNIVERSAL GRAVITATION) that define the concepts of modern PHYSICS (nonrelativistic). NEWTON'S FIRST LAW describes that any object will remain at rest without an external perturbation or remains in constant MOTION; NEWTON'S SECOND LAW defines that an object will accelerate under the influence of a force; NEWTON'S THIRD LAW describes the equal and opposite force experienced (e.g., floor exerts a force). Sir Newton indicated, as one of the first, that SURFACE WAVES in liquids can be defined mathematically in his 1687 *Principia* (see Figure N.29).

Figure N.29 (a) Sir Isaac Newton (1642–1727) and (b) stamp with the "infamous" apple that supposedly struck Isaac Newton on the head to initiate his thought process regarding the formalization of the concept gravity.

Newton (*N*)

[general] Unit of force, expressed in International Standard System (SI), kgm/s^2. The definition was introduced based on the Newtonian system, specifically $F = ma$, force F equals the mass m multiplied by the acceleration a of that mass.

Newton's equation of motion

[general, mechanics, thermodynamics] A system of n particles, each with mass m_ζ, with representative position vector $\vec{r_\zeta}$ for the ζth paticle, and momentum $\vec{p_\zeta} = m_\zeta(dr_\zeta/dt)$ can be described with a force $(\vec{F} = m(d^2\vec{r}/dt^2))$ combining the external force on each respective particle $(\vec{F_\zeta}^{ex})$ and the internal interaction between the particles $(\vec{F_{\chi\zeta}})$ as $d\vec{p_\zeta}/dt = \vec{F_\zeta}^{ex} + \sum_{\chi\neq\zeta}\vec{F_{\chi\zeta}}$. The system is subject to all CONSERVATION LAWS, including but not limited to conservation of momentum, CONSERVATION OF MASS, and conservation of force, introduced by SIR ISAAC NEWTON (1642–1727).

Newton's first law

[biomedical, general, mechanics] A body at rest remains at rest and a body in MOTION tends to remain in uniform linear motion at constant velocity. It was introduced by SIR ISAAC NEWTON (1642–1727). This is also called the LAW OF INERTIA because the constant velocity defines constant INERTIA. Generally, this translates in the condition that when the sum of the forces on an object are zero the body is compelled to stay in constant uniform linear velocity. The "first law" also defines the concept of INERTIAL REFERENCE FRAME; the inertial reference frame can be external to the object or it can be assigned to travel with the object.

Newton's law for fluids

[fluid dynamics, mechanics, thermodynamics] For a NEWTONIAN FLUID the equation of force (F) per unit VOLUME (V) of a FLUID is defined as $\vec{F}/V=(1/V)(d\vec{p}/dt)=(1/\rho)(D\vec{v}/Dt)=(1/\rho)(\partial\vec{v}/\partial t)+\rho\vec{v}\cdot\nabla\vec{v}$, where $\vec{p}$ is the momentum vector, t the time, ρ the density, and $\vec{v}$ the velocity of FLOW as a vector field; where D/Dt represents the "substantive derivative," and $\nabla=(d/dx)+(d/dy)+(d/dz)$ the gradient. This was introduced by SIR ISAAC NEWTON (1642–1727).

Newton's law of cooling

[thermodynamics] The rate of change of the temperature of a body of material is directly proportional to the difference between the TEMPERATURE (T) of the object (T_b) and the ambient temperature (T_a): $dT/dt=k_{temp}\left(T_b-T_a\right)$, where k_{temp} is the rate of cooling, and t time (*also see* **FOURIER'S (CONDUCTION) LAW AND FICK'S LAW**). This was introduced by SIR ISAAC NEWTON (1642–1727).

Newton's law of viscosity

[biomedical] Constitutive equation (not a fundamental law though) that is used to define the MOTION of primarily Newtonian fluids, under a restricted range of conditions. This was introduced by SIR ISAAC NEWTON (1642–1727). Sometimes interpreted as the RESISTANCE to deformation of solids as the shear modulus, which is the ratio of the shear stress to the shear strain: $E_{mod}=(\text{shear}-\text{stress})/(\text{shear}-\text{strain})$, and in fluids, the ratio of the shear stress to the rate of shear is $\mu=(\text{shear}-\text{stress})/(\text{rate of shear}-\text{strain})$.

Newton's rings

[optics] Interference pattern resulting from a variable gap DISTANCE between two surfaces, specifically when a plano-convex LENS is placed on a flat window pane. The air-gap (separation: t) with distance increasing with respect to the center of the contact location provides a reflection pattern where the path length back-and-forth between the first and second surface has a difference of multiple odd number of half-wavelengths will result in amplification (*Note*: the PHASE of the WAVE changes at the REFLECTION from AIR to glass, although the GLASS to AIR reflection does not incur a phase change): $2t=\left(m+(1/2)\right)\lambda$, where λ is the wavelength of the light. When the optical path length differs by a whole number of wavelengths, the INTERFERENCE will create amplification (see Figure N.30).

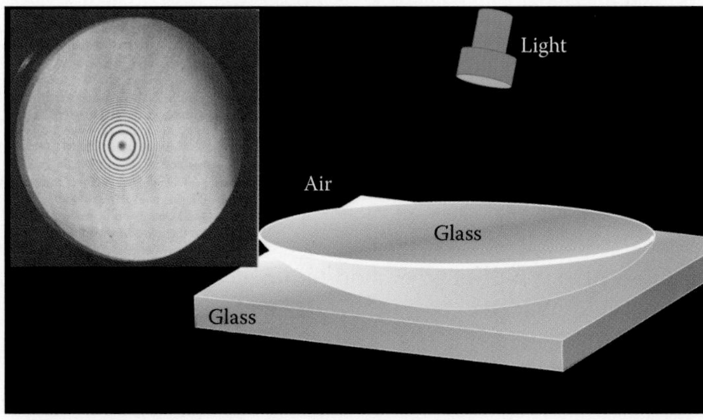

Figure N.30 How Newton's rings are formed.

Newton's second law

[biomedical, general, mechanics] Placed in an INERTIAL REFERENCE FRAME a body with mass m will accelerate (acceleration a) with a MAGNITUDE proportional to the applied net force (F), moving in the direction of the force: $\sum \vec{F} = m\vec{a}$. This was introduced by SIR ISAAC NEWTON (1642–1727).

Newton's third law

[biomedical] An object experiencing an external force from another body will in turn exert a force equal in MAGNITUDE but opposite in direction on said initial body, also called "law of reaction" or in popular science terminology: "for every action there is an equal but opposite reaction." This was introduced by SIR ISAAC NEWTON (1642–1727).

Newtonian fluid

[biomedical, fluid dynamics] Medium with linear VISCOSITY response as a function of the velocity gradient within the FLOW, that passes through the origin of the rheogram outlining velocity-gradient versus shear stress. Examples of Newtonian fluids in approximation are water and gases, while in practicality, there are no real perfect Newtonian fluids; however, under certain conditions, they are a close approximation; for instance, water will have a non-Newtonian BOUNDARY LAYER at a rigid WALL. Certain fluids may transition over into a Newtonian behavior when a shear-rate threshold is exceeded. BLOOD can act as a Newtonian liquid in the center of large vessels, while at low flow and small vessel diameter, blood is a pseudoplastic fluid. In close relation to the Newtonian fluid is the Bingham fluid, which has an offset from the origin, a flow-initiation threshold at minimum shear stress, a concept introduced by SIR ISAAC NEWTON (1642–1727) (*also see* VISCOSITY) (see Figure N.31).

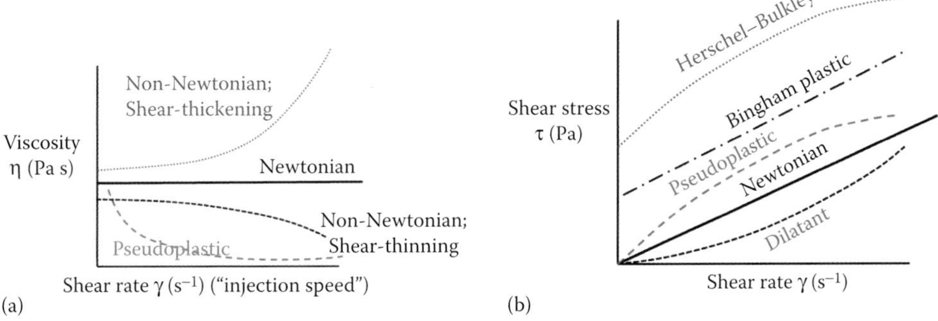

Figure N.31 (a,b) Graphical representations of the concept of Newtonian liquid, with perfectly linear viscosity.

Newton–Cotes methods

[computational] Quadrature rule used to interpret the trapezoidal rule and can be generalized to represent higher degree polynomial interpolants. A function $f(x)$ in the domain $\{a,b\}$ can be developed in a series of polynomials and can be integrated precisely with the help of the Newton–Cotes quadrature rule. The function is developed as $f(x) = \sum_{j=0}^{n} f(x_j)\ell_j(t)$, where $\ell_j(t) = \prod_{i=0,i\neq j}^{n}(t-x_i)/(x_j-x_i)$, with $j = 0,1,\ldots,n$ being the Legrange polynomial, where all data points are given nodes within the domain. The accuracy has a degree of at least n and the integral $\int_a^b f(t)\,dt$ is solved numerically. Newton number ($\mathrm{Ne} = F_{\mathrm{drag}}/\rho_f v^2 \ell^2$), dimensionless number representing the ratio of resistive (hydrodynamic DRAG $F_{\mathrm{drag}} = mL/t^2$) to the net INERTIA force, where ρ_f is the density of the FLUID, v is the characteristic velocity, L is the characteristic length, m is the mass, and t is the characteristic time.

Newtonian mechanics

[general] Under nonrelativistic conditions MECHANICS has a straightforward correlation between space and time. Newtonian mechanics describes the classical mechanics of MOTION with all CONSERVATION LAWS intact as well as the three laws of Newton apply. These are concepts related to the work of SIR ISAAC NEWTON (1642–1727).

Newtonian reflecting telescope

[general, optics] Optical device designed by SIR ISAAC NEWTON (1642–1727) that relies on REFLECTION of light combined with REFRACTION of light to avoid the DISPERSION and CHROMATIC ABERRATION obtained from diffracting optical ELEMENTS (e.g., PRISM and lens) (see Figure N.32).

Figure N.32 Newtonian reflector telescope.

Newtonian theory of gravity

[general] *See* LAW OF UNIVERSAL GRAVITATION.

Nicholson, John Williams (1881–1955)

[astrophysics/astronomy, computational, general] A mathematician and astronomer from the United Kingdom/Great Britain who obtained astronomical SPECTROSCOPY and based on the observations of certain nebulae, in particular the CRAB NEBULA, proposed the existence of several ELEMENTS in 1911 that were at the time still undiscovered. However, his hypothesis was somewhat unfounded and the proposed "proto-elements" were never confirmed. The unconventional methods and bad results from Nicholson were however the lead for several confirmed discoveries and theoretical derivations on spectral line patterns.

Nier, Alfred Otto Carl (1911–1994)

[astrophysics/astronomy, atomic, nuclear] A physicist from the United States, and a pioneer in mass-spectroscopy device development and experimental observation. Nier designed the mass spectrometers used on the MARS space travel by Viking spaceships, in a miniaturized form (see Figure N.33).

Figure N.33 Alfred Otto Carl Nier (1911–1994) in 1940. (Courtesy of Elmer Anderson Library of the University of Minnesota, Minnesota, Minneapolis, MN.)

Niobium

[acoustics] Chemical ELEMENT, metal: $^{41}_{93}\mathrm{Nb}$, formerly known as columbium. Niobium is widely used in superconducting alloys, which may also contain TITANIUM and tin. Specifically found in superconducting magnets used in MRI scanners.

Nipkow, Paul Gottlieb (1860–1940)

[general, nuclear] An engineer from Poland/Germany (Prussian Empire). He is the discoverer of the principle of television transmission in 1884 (see Figure N.34).

Figure N.34 Paul Gottlieb Nipkow (1860–1940) in 1884.

Nipkow disk

[general, nuclear] Spiral perforated disk used to display a sequence of images imbedded in a perforated disk that is illuminated by a lamp for projection on a WALL designed by PAUL GOTTLIEB NIPKOW (1860–1940) in 1884. The concept of the Nipkow disk was used in 1928 by Scottish (Great Britain) engineer John Logie Baird (1888–1946) at the Baird Television Company based on the, by then, expired Nipkow patent in "emchanica" television transmission. The Nipkow disks were a popular pass-time for handheld IMAGE sequence viewing. Predating the Nipkow disk is the phenakistoscope (or "spindle viewer"), introduced in 1832 by physicist Joseph Antoine Ferdinand Plateau (1801–1883) from Belgium in collaboration with his sons. Coincidentally and independently, a similar device was introduced in the same year by Simon Ritter von Stampfer (1792–1864) from Austria, who had named his invention a stroboscope and the zoetrope (also named Daedaleum) by William George Horner (1786–1837) from Great Britain introduced in 1834. Prior to Plateau, MICHAEL FARADAY (1791–1867) and Peter Mark Roget (1779–1869) had designed a device called the "Michael Faraday's Wheel," consisting of two discs spinning in opposite directions. Even farther back, there is documented evidence that EUCLID (~300 BC) also described the same or similar concepts (see Figure N.35).

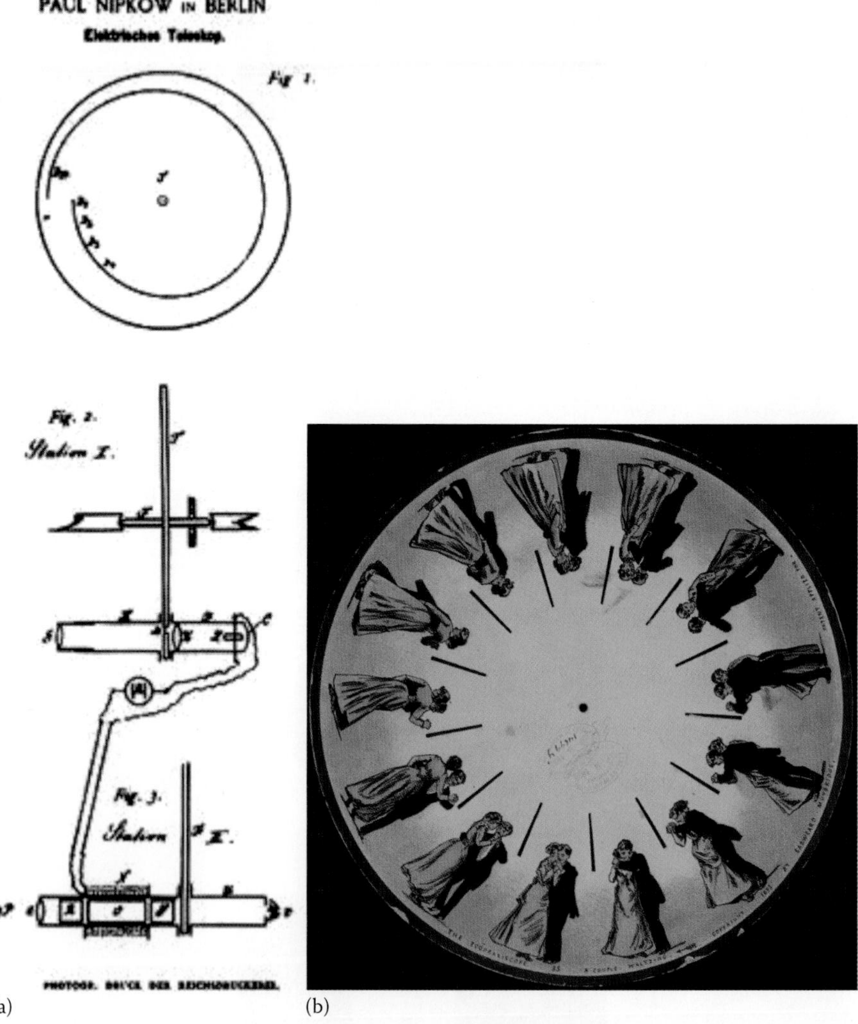

Figure N.35 (a) Nipkow disk patent application 1884 and (b) phenakistoscope disk by Eadweard Muybridge (1830–1904) in 1893.

Nitinol

[biomedical, solid-state] Metal alloy of equal portions of nickel and TITANIUM. Metallic compound that is sensitive to thermal stress and strain, providing a mechanism for flexible but sturdy structural support due to the difference in RESISTANCE to longitudinal and lateral strain. Nitinol alloys have the following unique properties: shape memory (return to the original shape after applying a specific elevated temperature) and superelasticity (10–30 times the ELASTICITY of the original metallic components). One specific application of nitinol is in vascular stents, to enlarge the vascular lumen under atherosclerosis, implemented under balloon angioplasty (see Figure N.36).

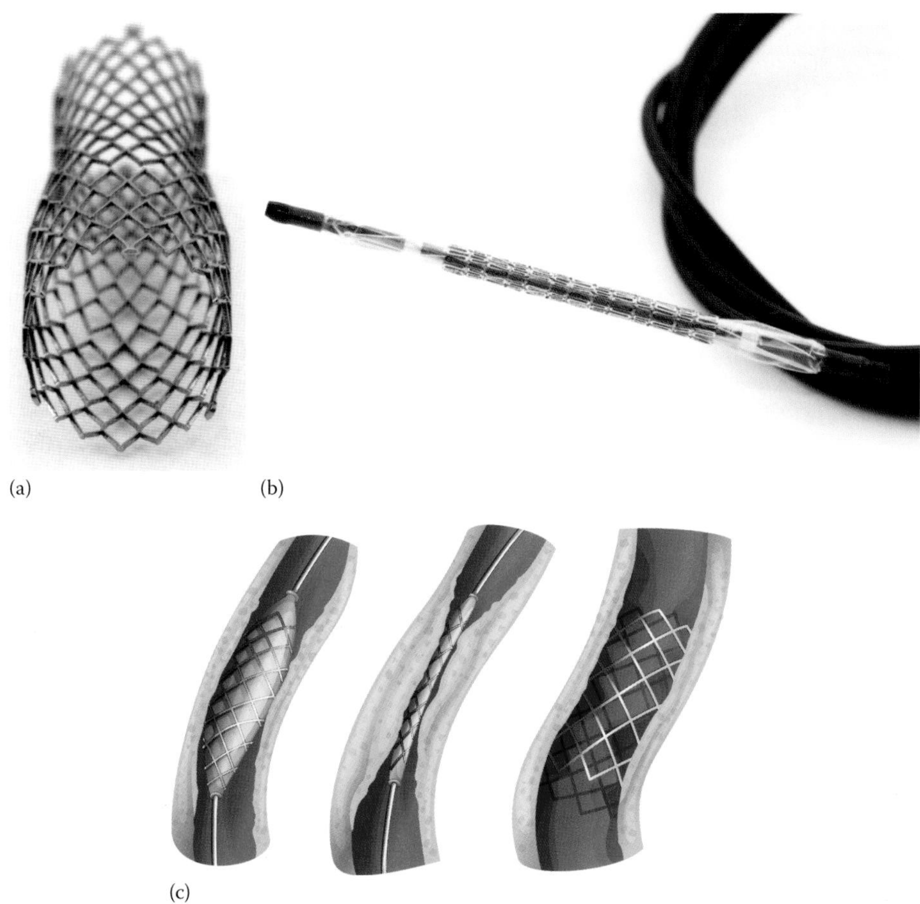

Figure N.36 (a,b) Nitinol stent concept used to expand the vessel lumen. (c) Nitinol stent maintains a flexible and wide pipe diameter.

Nitrocellulose

[biomedical, solid-state] Highly flammable mixture of nitric esters made by nitrating CELLULOSE. The nitrating process is mediated through exposure under nitric ACID or other nitrating agents. It is originally known as guncotton (because of its cotton-like POLYMER appearance), the main ingredient in gun powder. Nitrocellulose was used historically as an explosive (starter) or propellant. Additional applications are found as plasticizer in recording film strip (e.g., PHOTOGRAPHY and film), introduced by Kodak in 1889 (see Figure N.37).

Figure N.37 Strip of photographic film negatives on Nitrocellulose base.

Nitrogen (N_2)

[biomedical, general, geophysics, thermodynamics] Chemical ELEMENT, diatomic MOLECULE, gaseous under standard conditions: ${}^{14}_{7}N$, MELTING POINT: $-210°C = 63K$. Nitrogen is the main component of the Earth's ATMOSPHERE, at approximately 78% of the total balance of gases. It was discovered by Daniel Rutherford (1749–1819) in 1772. Nitrogen is very versatile and is essential in the following: fertilizers, ammonia (NH_3), "super-glue" (cyanoacrylate), is part of Kevlar fabric, and is found in amino acids; it is also crucial component in nitroglycerin as an explosive LIQUID, which is additionally used as vasodilator (i.e., the chemical interaction will make the vessel WALL extend by releasing the muscular constraint in the medial layer in the vessel wall and smooth MUSCLE, increasing the BLOOD flow) medication for HEART problems and other vascular concerns (*see* **N**[14]) (see Figure N.38).

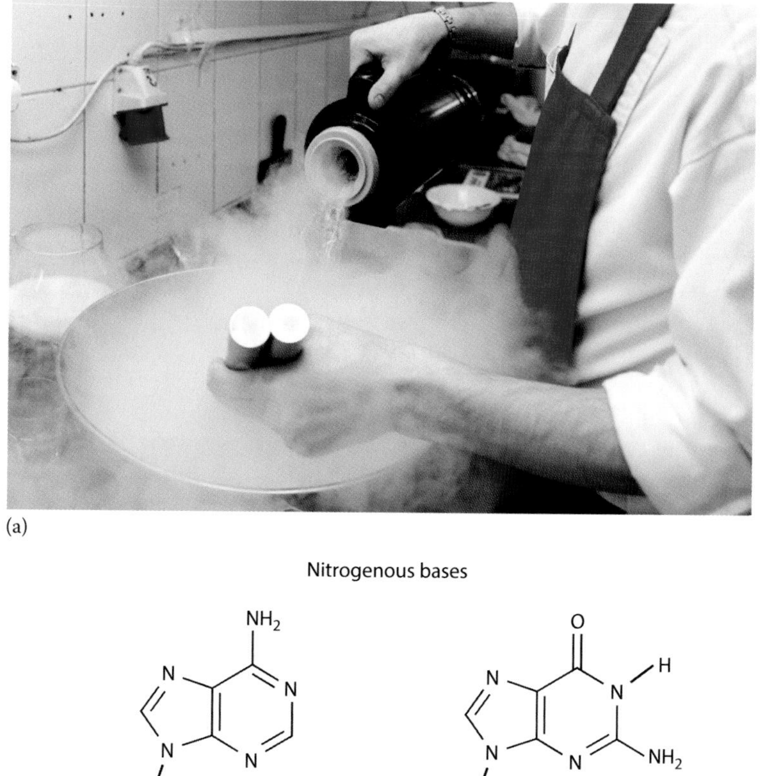

(a)

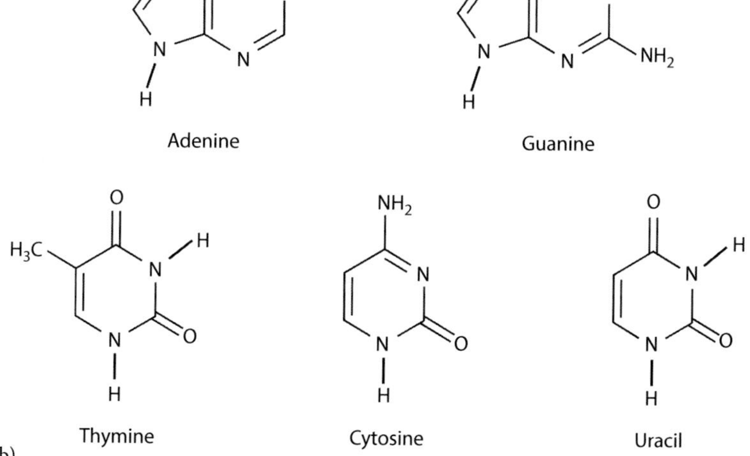

(b)

Figure N.38 (a) Nitrogen is used for rapid cooling and maintaining at low temperature and (b) nitrogen used in chemical compounds; examples of nitrogen bonds in DNA constituents.

Noble gas

[atomic, general] Monatomic ELEMENTS that were originally considered to be inert due to the OXIDATION number of zero (0). The six noble gases, all in group 18 (VIIIa) of the PERIODIC TABLE OF ELEMENTS are as follows: helium, neon, argon, krypton, xenon, and radon, all odorless and colorless with minimal chemical reactivity. In the 1960s, there were new discoveries that indicated the potential for chemical links with noble gases; in 1962, the first CHEMICAL COMPOUND of a noble gas was uncovered: xenon hexafluoroplatinate, by Neil Bartlett (1932–2008), and more thereafter. In the outer shell, all noble gases have the maximum number of electrons allowed: two for Helium, and eight for all the remaining five elements, which is what makes these elements so stable. The term is an English translation from the German word "Edelgas," introduced by Hugo Erdmann (1862–1910) in 1898 (see Figure N.39).

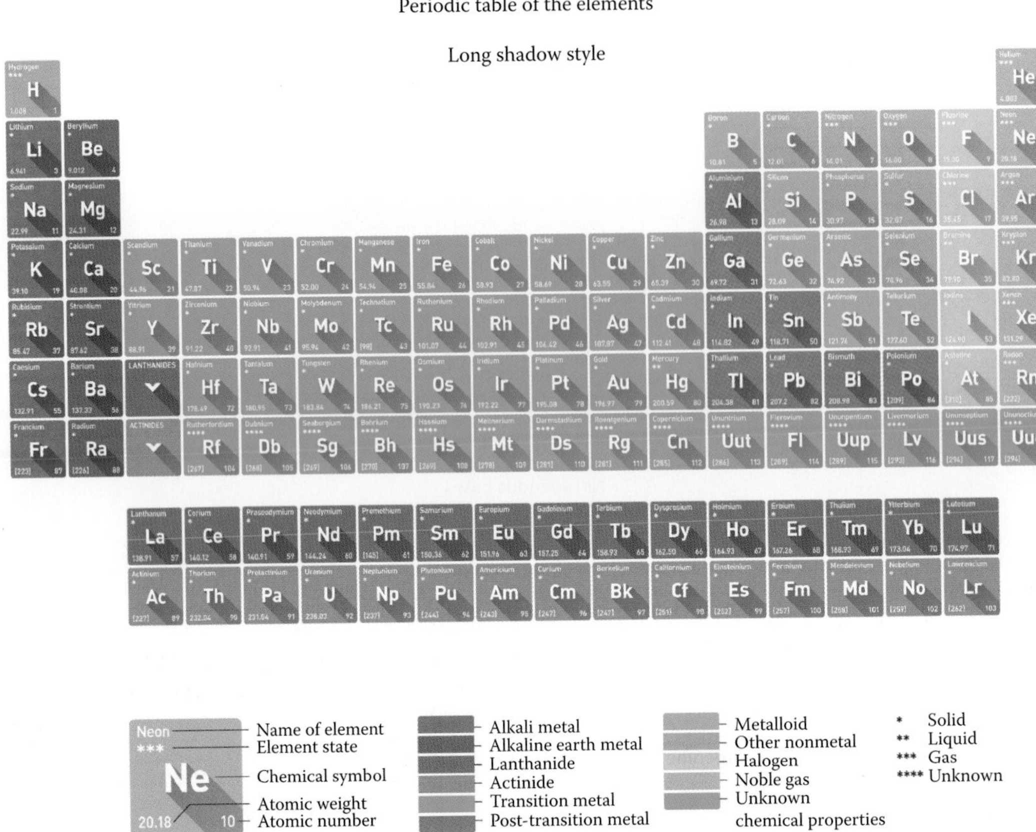

Figure N.39 Periodic table of elements highlighting the Noble gases in light green.

Nodal precession

[mechanics] Orbital precession of the rotation axis of a PLANET or moon. This phenomenon is responsible of the climatological changes on EARTH where the northern and southern hemispheres alternate in proximity to the Sun over the span of the conveniently chosen timescale of 1 year. The earth's MOON has two precession motions: the first along the long axis precesses "eastward" just under 9 years (presumably caused by the solar "tide"), whereas the second precession is the orientation of lunar orbit inclination, which is the track along which the plane of the earth's orbit intersects with the moon's orbit. The first precession pertains to the respective line of the apsides: perigee and apogee. The second, turning of the lunar orbit, has a period of approximately 18.6 years (see Figure N.40).

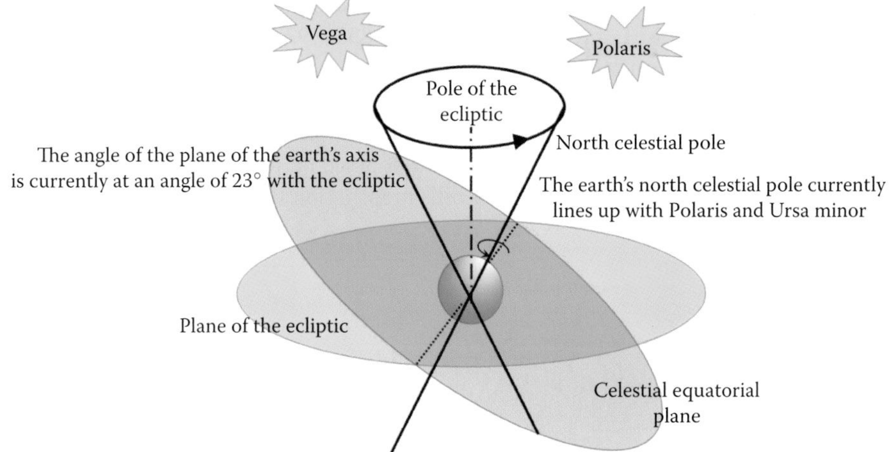

Figure N.40 Nodal precession.

Noddack, Ida Eva (1896–1978) (maiden name: Ida Eva Tacke)

[energy, general] A scientist from Germany. In 1935, Ida Tacke published the first work on the concept of ENERGY generation by NUCLEAR FISSION, while in 1925, she and her team uncovered two missing ELEMENTS in Mendeleev's periodic table of elements; ELEMENT 75: rhenium and element 43: masurium (rejected by the scientific community for unknown reasons, and later attributed to Carlo Perrier (1886–1948) and EMILIO GINO SEGRE (1905–1989) as technetium, current name). Her discoveries were based on spectroscopic X-RAY using the equation from the work by HENRY GWYN JEFFREYS MOSELEY (1887–1915) for identification: $\nu = (3/4)R_y\left(Z-1\right)^2$, where ν represents the frequency, $R_y = 10973731.6\ \mathrm{m}^{-1}$ is the RYDBERG CONSTANT, and Z is the atomic number (see Figure N.41).

Figure N.41 Ida Eva Noddack (maiden name: Ida Eva Tacke) (1896–1978).

Node of Ranvier

[biomedical, electromagnetism] Ionically permeable section in the WALL of MYELINATED NERVE cells between impermeable isolated segments, wrapped by Schwann cells. This anatomical phenomenon was described by the French histologist Louis Antoine Ranvier (1835–1922). The amount of ION exchange during DEPOLARIZATION is substantially less at the node of Ranvier than for a full length membrane depolarization under nonmyelinated nerve-cell activation pulse propagation, in the order of 200 times less. The reduced ion exchange provides one of the advantages in pulse propagation, next to the fact that a depolarization pulse "jumps" from node to node, instead of based on priming of the neighboring wall segment for nonmyelinated cells. Myelinated nerve cells propagation is at least an order of MAGNITUDE greater (*see* NERVE *and* MYELIN) (see Figure N.42).

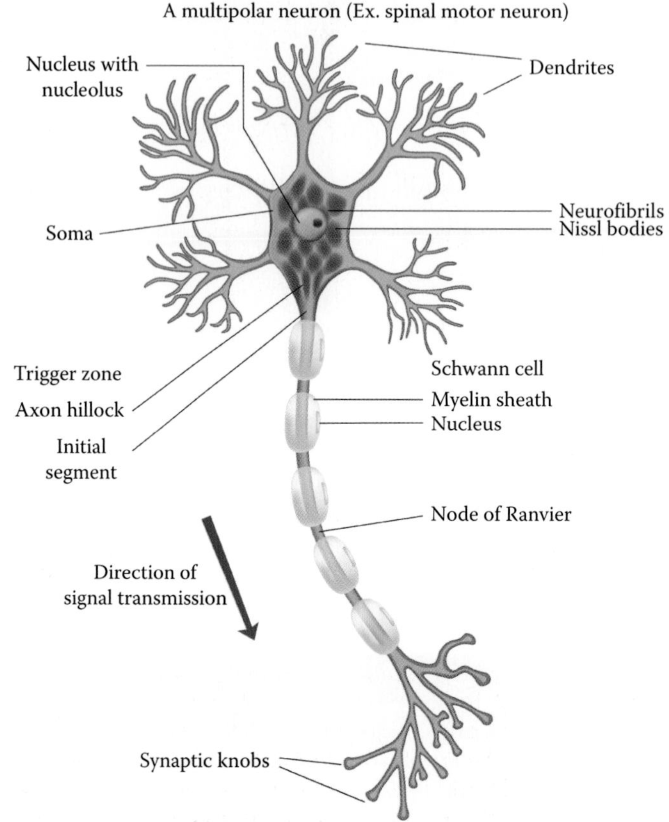

Figure N.42 Node of Ranvier.

Noether, Amalie (Emmy) (1882–1935)

[computational, general] A mathematician and scientist from the Prussian Empire, Germany. The work of Amalie Noether involved the definition of the following three concepts: associative law (mathematical grouping can be interchanged, in rudimentary format: $(a+b)+c=a+(b+c)$ and $(a*b)*c=a*(b*c)$), commutative law (finding association between phenomena and functions characterized by substitution, interchange, or exchange: $a+b=b+a$ and $a*b=b*a$), and the distributive law (captured in essence as $a*((b+c)=(a*b)+(a*c))$. Her work was far reaching and influential and she was commended by ALBERT EINSTEIN (1879–1955) for her mathematical contributions to his efforts. Noether created a theorem that united the symmetry in nature and the universal laws of conservation: Noether's theorem, or NOETHER'S PRINCIPLE. Her mathematical efforts were influential in the uncovering of the HIGGS BOSON (see Figure N.43).

Figure N.43 Amalie (Emmy) Noether (1882–1935).

Noether's principle

[computational, energy, general, thermodynamics] For every conservation law, there is a continuous symmetry and alternatively for every continuous system, there is a symmetry that correlates to a corresponding conservation law. It was introduced by AMALIE NOETHER (1882–1935), also known as "Noether's theorem."

Noise

[acoustics, general, optics, theoretical] Random fluctuations in the AMPLITUDE and/or frequency pattern resulting from characteristics of the phenomenon, such as temperature, external forces, external RADIATION, as well as other changing boundary conditions such as perturbation of reflective/SCATTERING media. Additional noise factors may come from the fact that the sensing mechanism used for QUANTIFICATION of the phenomena (providing the "SIGNAL") is not able to remain in one single location. In certain cases, the measurements on an active system, biological or physical, will have changes in chemical equilibrium and chemical constituents due to METABOLIC ACTIVITY (biological) or due to forced or passive DIFFUSION. The changes in chemical configuration can influence the accuracy of the measurement of another event/phenomenon due to the electrical interaction with the device or the wired or wireless communications of these observations. One significant noise factor in measurements on various levels are solar flares, which may even interact with the semiconductor materials used in a device. Acoustic noise can change the FREQUENCY SPECTRUM as, for instance, resulting from dust on a vinyl recording album played over STEREO equipment for reproduction of the authentic event. Optical noise can result from density changes as well as from thermal collisions and thermal emissions. Measurement of the brain's activities by electroencephalogram electrodes on the SKIN can be influenced by MOTION or sweat, and other MUSCLE activity such as EYE motion, as well as MACHINES switching in neighboring rooms (creating inductive INTERFERENCE). An indication of the stability of an event, measurement, phenomenon, or equipment is usually indicated by the signal-to-noise ratio, the higher the better. Noise in FLOW systems can result from unexpected TURBULENCE (see Figure N.44).

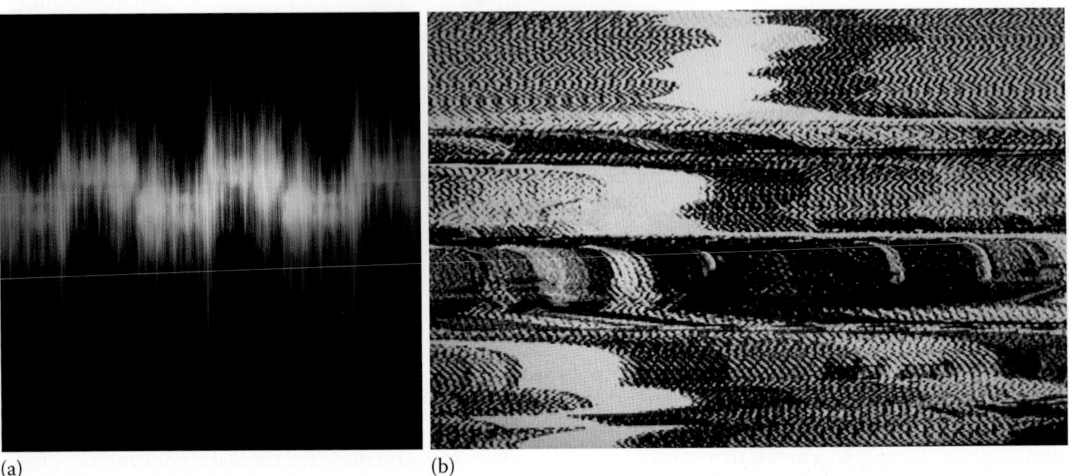

(a) (b)

Figure N.44 (a,b) Television image distorted by electronic noise resulting from the interference in the line of transmission (primarily affecting analog signal only), or thermal effects in the processing electronics. During analog signal transmission moving conductive objects will reflect the signal stream of electromagnetic radiation, which in turn will also be captured by the antenna of the receiving instrument. Old-fashioned "rabbit-ear" antennas sitting on top of the television where notorious for interference noise, either induced by people walking through the room or a plane passing over the volume of air where the electromagnetic television wave transmission passed from transmitter to receiver station.

Nollet, Jean-Antoine (Abbé) (1700–1770)

[energy] A physicist from France. Nollet is most known for his invention of a device to measure (static) ELECTRIC CHARGE the ELECTROSCOPE. His work involved the use of the LEYDEN JAR as well, electrifying a group of 180 soldiers on display for King Louis XV. Abbé Nollet also phenomenological described the phenomenon that the sharper an object, the greater the charge stream, that is, the electric field is a function of the radius of curvature of a CONDUCTOR in his attempts to describe the rudimentary principles of FLOW of electric MATTER and forces between electrically charged bodies in 1745, predating the fundamental work of his fellow countryman CHARLES AUGUSTIN DE COULOMB (1736–1806). His work coincided with the efforts of the American statesman and scientist BENJAMIN FRANKLIN (1706–1790), demonstrating LIGHTNING as a form of ELECTRICITY. Additional work of Jean-Antoine Nollet provided insight in the concepts of OSMOSIS,

illustrating how a SOLVENT passed selectively through a MEMBRANE, providing the foundation for the work by JACOBUS HENRICUS VAN'T HOFF (1852–1911) (see Figure N.45).

Figure N.45 Jean-Antoine (Abbé) Nollet (1700–1770).

Nomarski, Georges (Jerzy) (1919–1997)

[optics] An optical scientist and theoretician from Poland. Nomarski developed a special INTERFERENCE microscope, the "differential interference contrast (DIC) microscope," using polarized light that is split in two perpendicularly POLARIZATION directions for enhanced contrast, split and recombined by an optical configuration of two Wollaston prisms. The Nomarski MICROSCOPE is a special form of PHASE contrast microscopy (see Figure N.46).

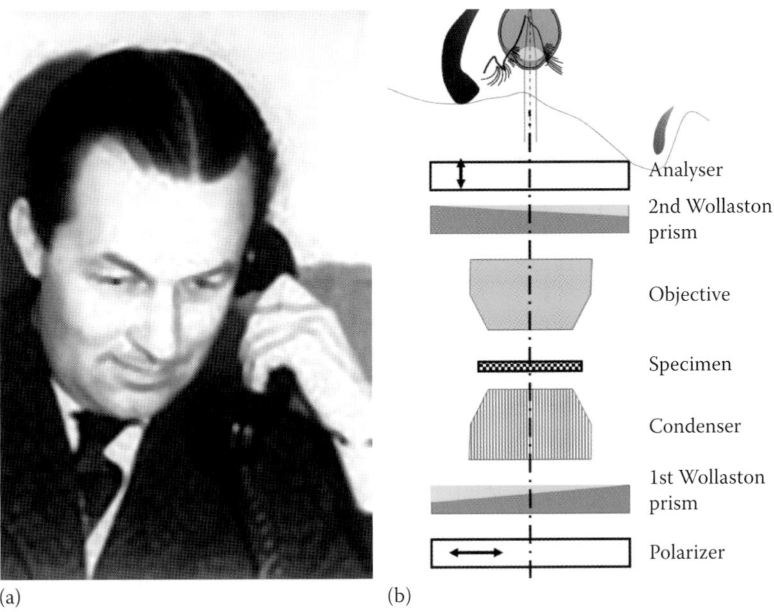

Figure N.46 (a) Georges (Jerzy) Nomarski (1919–1997) and (b) diagram of the differential interference contrast (DIC) microscope.

Nomenclature for nuclear reactions

[nuclear] A form of shorthand for the process of a nuclear reaction. For instance, the interaction of nitrogen with a NEUTRON forming radioactive carbon and PROTON in the Earth's ATMOSPHERE under cosmic radiation as ${}^{1}_{0}n + {}^{14}_{7}\mathrm{N} \rightarrow {}^{14}_{6}\mathrm{C} + {}^{1}_{1}p + \text{energy}$, or in "shorthand": ${}^{14}\mathrm{N}(n, p)\,{}^{14}\mathrm{C}$ ("transfer reaction"), where the first item in brackets refers to the PROJECTILE. Note that ${}^{14}\mathrm{C}$ can be used for radioactive dating, due to its integral incorporation in all biological media. The nomenclature for the interaction process has the following classifications: compound reaction, direct reaction, INELASTIC SCATTERING, knock-out reaction, nuclear photoeffect, nuclear scattering, RADIATIVE CAPTURE, resonance reaction, RUTHERFORD SCATTERING, and transfer reaction.

Nonadiabatic process

[atomic, solid-state, thermodynamics] A process in theoretical chemistry that involves the interaction in a molecule that hold the exchange between electronic and nuclear vibrational MOTION, referred to as "vibronic coupling." Vibronic coupling pertains to the MIXING of electronic states of the MOLECULE as a result of small vibrations and is tied to the derivative of the WAVE function for the configuration. Nonadiabatic chemical processes occur at the conical interactions. In a molecular ENERGY configuration when two potential energy surfaces are degenerate and intersect the energy state in conical intersect. At this point the nonadiabatic coupling between these two energy states is also nonvanishing. The energetic BOUNDARY LAYER surrounding the conical intersect no longer obeys the BORN–OPPENHEIMER APPROXIMATION, supporting the nonadiabatic conditions. Nonadiabatic effects, specifically involve the splitting and SCATTERING of the wave packet (QUANTUM effect dominated solution to the time-dependent SCHRÖDINGER EQUATION) at potential energy surface crossings, such as associated with TUNNELING. Chemical interactions that can be described by the conical intersection are photoelectric reactions, combustion, and explosion, for instance. One specific example of the conical intersect is the stability of DNA (DNA molecule encoded with a range of biological properties: genetic structure) under irradiation by ULTRAVIOLET light, where the "excited" electrovibrational state of the molecular wave packet will "roll-back" to the electronic GROUND STATE on the conically curve potential energy surface of the molecular binding. The number of vibrational DEGREES OF FREEDOM is directly related to the number of atoms making up the molecule; for instance, a diatomic molecule has two degrees and consequently progressively upward. On a nuclear level, similar principles will apply; only in this case, the energy potentials are outlined by the PROTON and neutron interactions (see Figure N.47).

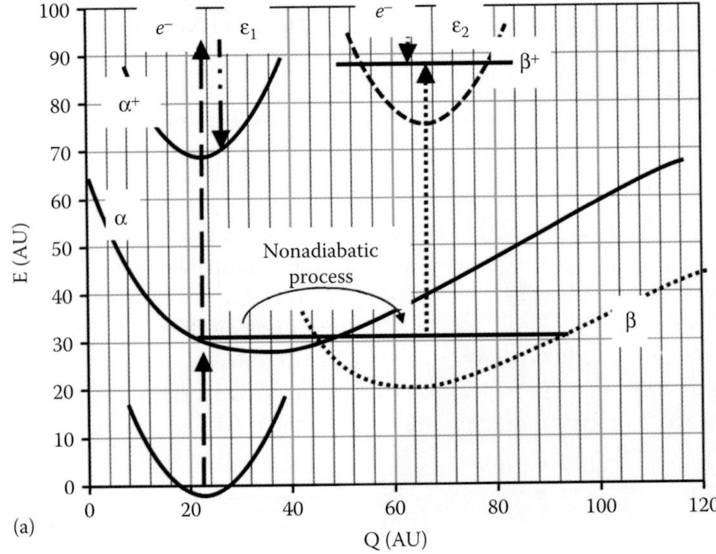

Figure N.47 Nonadiabatic processes occur on electronic and macroscopic scale: (a) nuclear vibration energy diagram. *(Continued)*

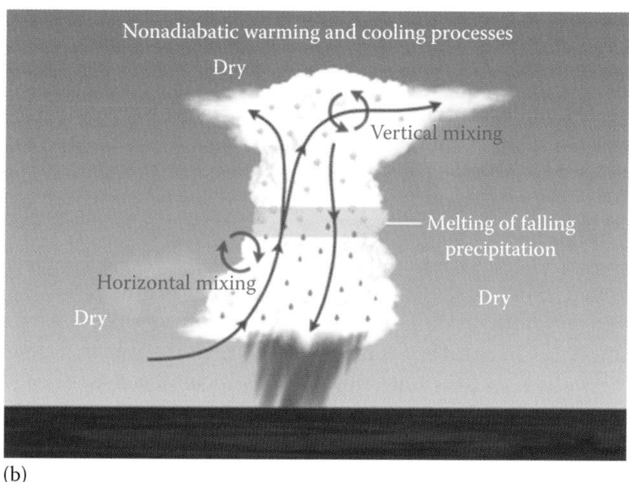

(b)

Figure N.47 (Continued) Nonadiabatic processes occur on electronic and macroscopic scale: (b) atmospheric nonadiabatic thermal inversion.

Nonconductor

[general] *See* INSULATOR.

Nondegenerate ground-energy value

[quantum, thermodynamics] Ground state of a quantum-mechanical energy system. A quantum MECHANICAL ENERGY level is said to be degenerate if two or more different measurable states exist simultaneously, where the number of corresponding states indicates the degree of DEGENERACY for a specific energy level. This is represented by a single EIGENVALUE solution for the Hamiltonian of several independent eigenstates. For a nondegenerate state, the condition is that the eigenvalue in its eigenspace is one dimensional. By definition, the GROUND STATE is the only energy state that can be nondegenerate, because there is no change in conditions at this energy, but this not exclude degenerate ground states from occurring. Theoretically, this can be illustrated by the density functional theory, which provides the electronic structure of atoms, molecules, and solids in their ground states. The electronic density distribution plays a central role, defining the degenerate ground states, SPIN density (describing spin-up and spin-down densities as well as PARAMAGNETISM or cooperative MAGNETISM), as well as multicomponent systems (e.g., nuclei and electron–hole assemblies in semiconductor).

Nondimensional groups

[computational, fluid dynamics, thermodynamics] Dimensionless analysis is a mathematical technique used to determine the relationships between several variables and hence predict physical parameters that influence the fluid FLOW, HEAT TRANSFER, and other transfer process. By converging to the basic MLT units (kg, m, s), the elementary concepts become dimensionless. The LAW OF SIMILARITY allows the principles to be applied in analogy between FLUID DYNAMICS, THERMODYNAMICS, or various other aspects of engineering and physics. Examples of dimensionless parameters are the REYNOLDS NUMBER, Froude number, Weber number, and MACH NUMBER.

Nondispersive component

[biomedical, solid-state] The free ENERGY at the interface surface of a medium with another medium. The nondispersive free energy is the geometric mean of the free energy of medium 1 (for instance, a solid) and medium 2 (for instance, a LIQUID). The free energy can, for instance, be derived from Fowkes' expression and the Young's equation for the respective medium.

Nondispersive wave

[acoustics, mechanics, optics] Wave propagation in a nondispersive medium, with no inherent deformation. DISPERSION stands for the variability in propagation velocity with respect to direction of propagation, governed by the WAVE EQUATION in one dimensional: $(\partial^2\chi(x,t)/\partial t^2) - v^2(\partial^2\chi(x,t)/\partial x^2) = 0$, or multidimensional: $\partial^2\vec{\chi}/\partial t^2 - v^2\nabla^2\vec{\chi} = 0$ for a wave phenomenon χ with (PHASE) velocity of propagation v, where the velocity is independent of the wavelength. The wave equation is generally solved by SEPARATION OF VARIABLES, taking the real part $\chi(x,t) = Re\left[x(x)*t(t)\right]$. Nondispersive waves maintain both the spectral and temporal information (see Figure N.48).

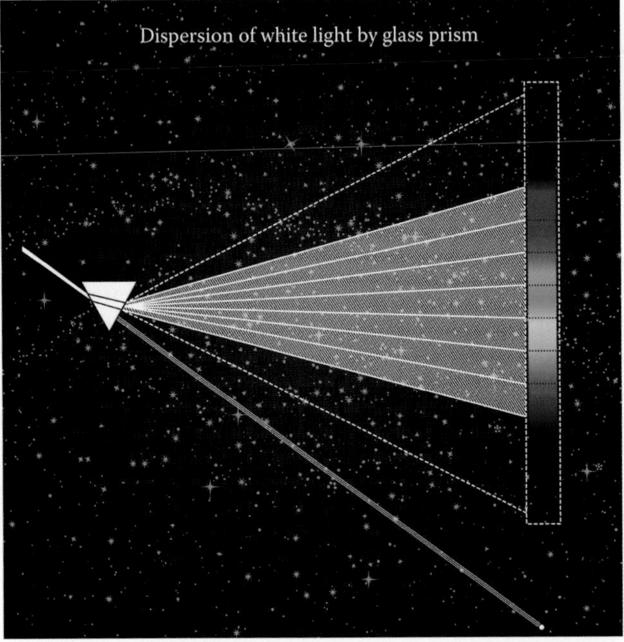

Figure N.48 A nondispersive wave can be generated by a single wavelength emitter, such as a laser; in contrast to broad band emitters which will be subject to dispersion at certain gradients or discontinuities with the medium of transmission. Dispersion of white light from a prism. In contrast a laser beam can hold its coherence for light years, spanning across the galaxy, as used in remote sensing, collecting the returning signal from great distances with embedded encoding that can be resolved by interferometric analysis. Certain mechanical waves can be nondispersive, under well-defined boundary conditions, for instance, in a perfectly homogeneous medium (free-space [atmospheric], at uniform temperature and pressure) or single wavelength acoustical sensing.

Nonelastic

[biomedical, mechanics, nuclear] Rigid material that will have a yield strength at which it will break without deformation. In nuclear collision, the nonelastic CROSS SECTION refers to the steady-state target cross section of nuclides solely based on the physical size and interactions with inherent loss of kinetic ENERGY (i.e., inelastic) (*see* **COMPTON SCATTER**) (see Figure N.49).

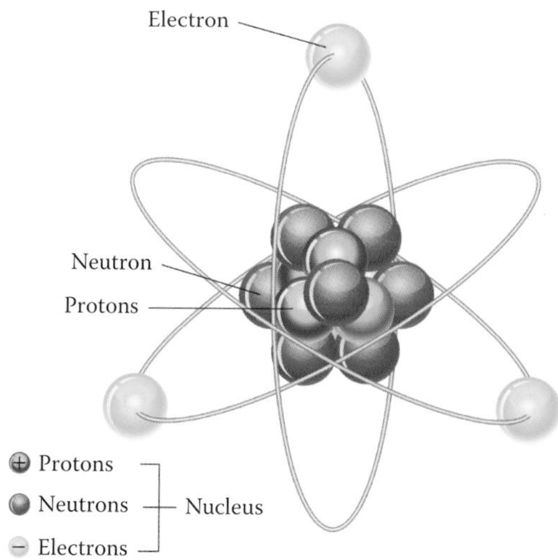

Figure N.49 Rigid, nonelastic hard-shell model of the atom, specifically the nucleus.

Nonequilibrium state

[thermodynamics] The broad range of conditions defining chemical reactions and transport processes (e.g., ENERGY and material).

Nonideal mixture

[thermodynamics] Mixture composed of components that do not behave as an IDEAL GAS or operate at PHASE transitions. According to the ideal GAS LAW, the pressure of the constituents of a mixture should change linearly with temperature and volume, assuming a fixed quantity. In parallel, for liquids, an ideal liquid obeys RAOULT'S LAW, linking the VAPOR PRESSURE to the individual contributions of the respective components. For liquids, the PHASE DIAGRAM of nonideal mixtures introduces the concept of an azeotropic mixture. In an azeotropic mixture, the vapor state has the exact same composition as the LIQUID state, so that the components cannot be extracted by simple DISTILLATION.

Non-Newtonian fluids

[fluid dynamics] Every fluid, the NEWTONIAN FLUID is a theoretical idealistic condition, specifically pertaining to the VISCOSITY aspects (*see* **NEWTONIAN FLUID** *and* **VISCOSITY**).

Nonohmic electrical devices

[general] Devices that do not obey OHM'S LAW: $V = IR$, where the voltage drop (V) is directly linked to the CURRENT (I) through a RESISTANCE (R). Example of a nonohmic device is a doped silicon DIODE; the voltage current diagram is not linear, but has a logarithmic correlation and specifically, the resistance is

not a constant. For a DIODE, the resistance is generally different for the direction of current, sometimes by orders of MAGNITUDE.

Nonpolar nature of a medium

[biomedical, chemical, fluid dynamics, mechanics, thermodynamics] Materials (especially liquids) can on a molecular level be electronically inert with neutral charge across the MOLECULE. Oil is a clear example of the natural nonpolarity. Water is a polar liquid. Detergents have a polar and a nonpolar side to the molecule, making them ideal for acting as a degreaser while dissolved in water.

Nonrelativistic energy

[nuclear] Even for nuclear events, a range of ENERGY can be identified for which a nonrelativistic approach will yield only a small error, in the order of 1%. This generally applies to ALPHA DECAY, which is nonrelativistic for the momentum; however, beta DECAY is relativistic for the momentum. On the energy level, electrons operate nonrelativistically when $KE < 20.7$ keV, and for protons, the phenomena can be treated nonrelativistic when $KE < 38$ MeV (*also see* **ENERGY**). The nonrelativistic prediction of the DIRAC EQUATION for the nonrelativistic coulomb problem has the following expression, using a SCALAR potential resulting from the NUCLEUS ($\phi = A_0$): $\left((p^2/2m)-(Ze^2/4\pi r)-(p^4/8m^3c^2)+(Ze^2\{\vec{L}\cdot\vec{S}\}/8\pi m^2c^2r^3)+(Ze^2\hbar^2/8m^2c^2)\delta^3(\vec{r})\right)\Psi = E^{nr}\Psi$, where $E^{nr} = E - mc^2$ is the nonrelativistic energy, $p = mv$ is the momentum, m is the mass of the PARTICLE, v is the velocity, Z is the charge number, $e = 1.60217657 \times 10^{-19}\,C$ is the coulomb charge, r is the separation DISTANCE, $\vec{L}$ is the ORBITAL ANGULAR MOMENTUM, $\vec{S}$ is the spin, $c = 2.99792458 \times 10^8$ m/s is the speed of light, $Ze\delta^3(\vec{r}) = \nabla\cdot\vec{E}$, $\hbar = h/2\pi$ with $h = 6.62606957 \times 10^{-34}$ m^{2}kg/s Planck's constant, and Ψ the "Schrödinger" wavefunction. The phenomena are determined by the fact that nonrelativistic particles have continuous and discrete DEGREES OF FREEDOM (with respect to momentum, for instance, as a continuous reference frame and SPIN component for the discrete reference frame).

Normal compressive strain (ε_{nc})

[general, mechanics] Strain of an object under compression, in contrast to TENSILE STRAIN, but no difference in expression (*see* **NORMAL STRAIN**) (see Figure N.50).

Figure N.50 Vice applying normal compressive strain.

Normal distribution

[atomic, computational] Probability density function for events and measured values: $f_{\text{normal}}(x) = 1/(\sigma_{\text{stat}}\sqrt{2\pi})\exp\left[-(21/2\sigma_{\text{stat}}^2)(x-\mu_{\text{stat}})^2\right]$; where μ_{stat} is the mean value of the observation x and σ_{stat} is the statistical variance. Generally, the variance can be derived as follows:

$\sigma_{stat}{}^2 = 1/(n-1)\sum_{i=1}^{n}(x_i - \mu_{stat})^2$, with n values. This is closely linked to the GAUSSIAN DISTRIBUTION. The standard normal distribution has as conditions $\sigma_{stat}{}^2 = 1$ and $\mu_{stat} = 0$ (see Figure N.51).

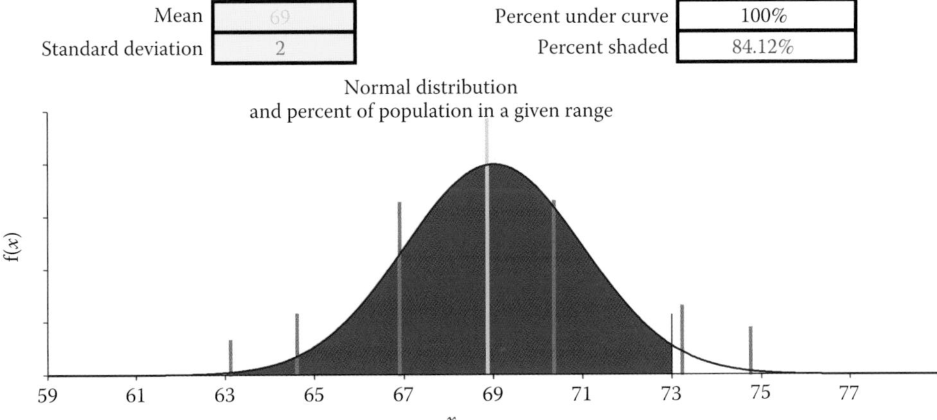

Figure N.51 Plot of the normal distribution, plotting the function f(x) as a function of a variable "x" around the center point "69".

Normal force (F_n)

[biomedical, general, mechanics] Resiprocating force in response to an applied force, normal to the surface; perpendicular to the surface. The force of a table top in response to a object resting on the table yields the normal force in equivalence to NEWTON'S THIRD LAW. Friction is a direct function of the normal force: $f_K = \mu_K F_n$, where μ_K represents the KINETIC FRICTION coefficient for kinetic friction force f_K (see Figure N.52).

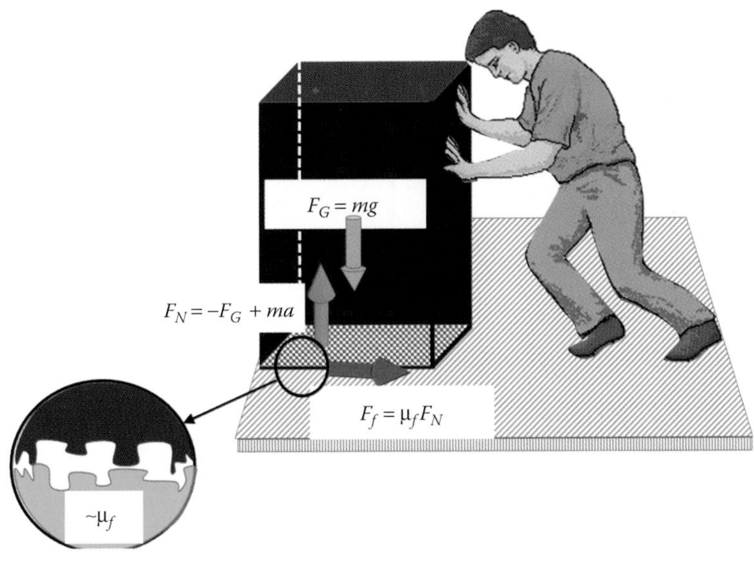

Figure N.52 Normal force.

Normal strain (ε_n)

[biomedical, mechanics] Fractional change in body length (ℓ) as a result of an applied normal STRESS: $\varepsilon_n = \Delta\ell/\ell$, a rod under tension is under TENSILE STRAIN while a rod under compression is under compressive strain (see Figure N.53).

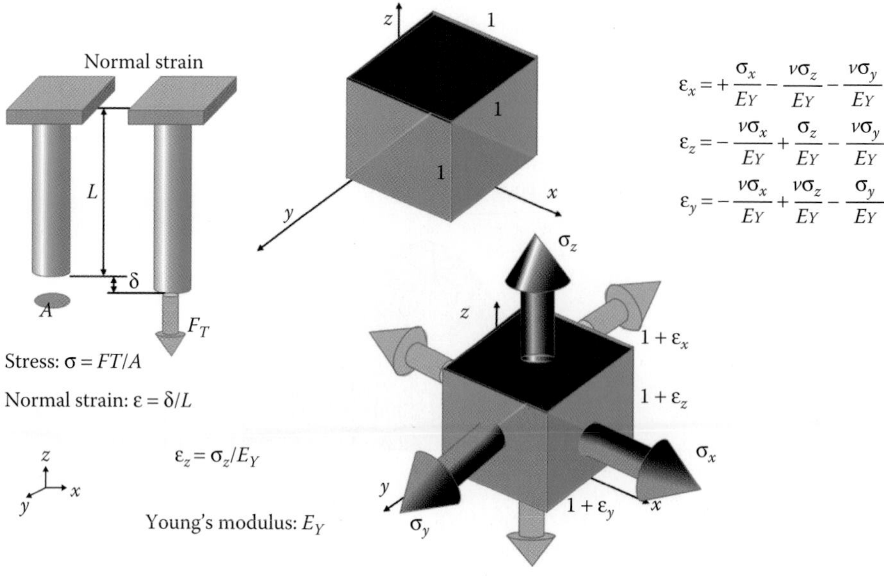

Figure N.53 Normal strain.

Normal stress (σ_n)

[biomedical, mechanics] Ratio of normal force (F_n) applied on a body and in the cross-sectional area (A) the applied force is normal to $\sigma_n = F_n/A$, when the body is under tensile force the stress is considered TENSILE STRESS, and alternatively under compression compressive stress. The difference between pressure and stress is in the fact that pressure is a SCALAR quantity and stress is a TENSOR (see Figure N.54).

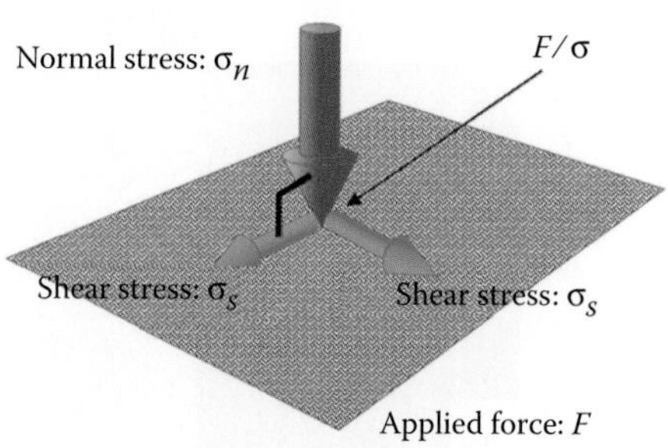

Figure N.54 Normal stress.

Normal Zeeman effect

[atomic, nuclear, quantum] *See* **ZEEMAN EFFECT, NORMAL.**

Normalization

[atomic, computational, general] Process of unification of the combined results by incorporation of a coefficient that renders a peak of the PROBABILITY distribution of an event or the range of data to unity.

Norman, Robert (1550–1600)

[general] A seaman and maritime scientist from Great Britain who invented the concept of navigation by means of a magnetic compass in 1581, describing the LODESTONE (also found as "loadstone," a MAGNET) and ensuing practical applications to navigation. Note that the magnetic properties were known to the ancient Greek, well before the introduction in seafaring navigation. Robert Norman discovered the fact that the compass needle is influenced by the fact that the earth's MAGNETIC FIELD does not run parallel to the earth's surface, causing a deviation called "magnetic inclination." The MAGNETIC inclination is the ANGLE that the magnetic field makes with the horizontal as a function of the LATITUDE (see Figure N.55).

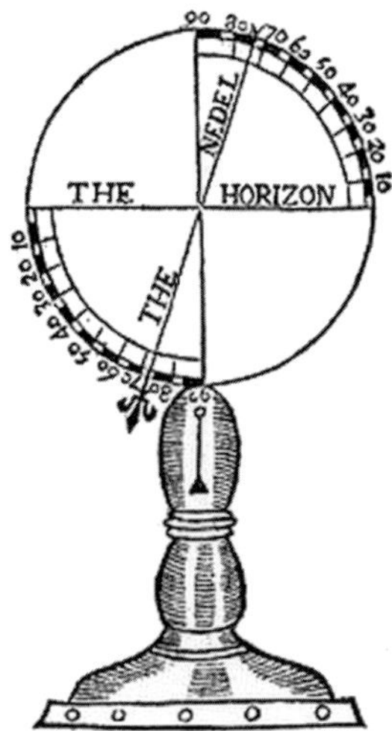

Figure N.55 Magnetic dip as outlined and described by Robert Norman (1550–1600).

North

[electromagnetism, general, geophysics] Colloquial reference to the direction indicated by the compass needle. (*see* MAGNETIC NORTH POLE). In MAGNETIC devices, this indicates the location of the device where the MAGNETIC FIELD lines emerge to loop around in three-dimensional space to terminate on the South Pole of the device (see Figure N.56).

(a)

(b)

Figure N.56 (a) A compass pointing north and (b) ice-field found at the north-pole. There is no lands at the north pole, in contrast to the land found at the south-pole.

North geographic pole

[general] *See* GEOGRAPHIC NORTH POLE.

North magnetic pole

[general] *See* MAGNETIC NORTH POLE.

Northern Light

[astrophysics, atomic, energy, geophysics] *See* AURORA *and* AURORA BOREALIS.

Nozzle

[fluid dynamics, mechanics, thermodynamics] A duct with a variable CROSS SECTION. Because of the change in the cross-sectional area (A) as a function of location in the FLOW of a fluid, the flow can be regulated and directed, achieving, under certain conditions, acceleration and forming a high-velocity (v) stream. The FLUID velocity distribution can be explained by the principles of CONSERVATION OF MASS (m), more specifically for an INCOMPRESSIBLE FLUID: $dm/dt = \rho vA$. A nozzle converts potential ENERGY confined by the work performed under PV, where P is the pressure and V the volume, into kinetic energy. Nozzle provides flow that is nearly adiabatic and result in little or no change in potential energy and require no shaft to convey the work. The change in ENTHALPY (H) across the nozzle is $\Delta H = (v_0^2 - v_1^2)/2g$, where v_0 is the exit flow velocity, v_1 is the flow velocity before the nozzle, and g is the GRAVITATIONAL ACCELERATION. The throat is the narrow section of the nozzle, after which it may expand or not. Under certain conditions, the outflow from the nozzle may reach Mach conditions, specifically when: $P_0/P_1 \cong \left(1+0.2Ma_e^2\right)^{-3.5}$, where P_1 is the pressure in the reservoir leading to the nozzle, P_0 is the external pressure, and Ma_e is the MACH NUMBER on exit from the nozzle. The maximum flow rate is achieved when the velocity in the throat, with cross section A_t reaches sonic speed, providing: $(dm/dt)_{max} = 0.0404(p_1/\sqrt{T_1})A_t$, where T_1 is the ABSOLUTE TEMPERATURE in the reservoir. The ISENTROPIC efficiency of a nozzle, if defined by the difference between the actual velocity (v_a) and the isentropic velocity (v_{is}, presumed constant ENTROPY [S]) on exit is $\eta_{nozzle,is} = (v_{a,0}^2/2g)/(v_{is,0}^2/2g) = v_{a,0}^2/v_{is,0}^2$, where the isentropic velocity follows from the entropy (S) versus enthalpy (H) diagram for the flow. The adiabatic efficiency is defined as $\eta_{nozzle,adiabatic} = (H_{is,0} - H_{is,1})/(H_{a,0} - H_{is,1})$. ADIABATIC COMPRESSION is exemplified by TEMPERATURE (T) versus entropy (S) diagram, respectively entalphy (H) versus entropy diagrams (see Figure N.57).

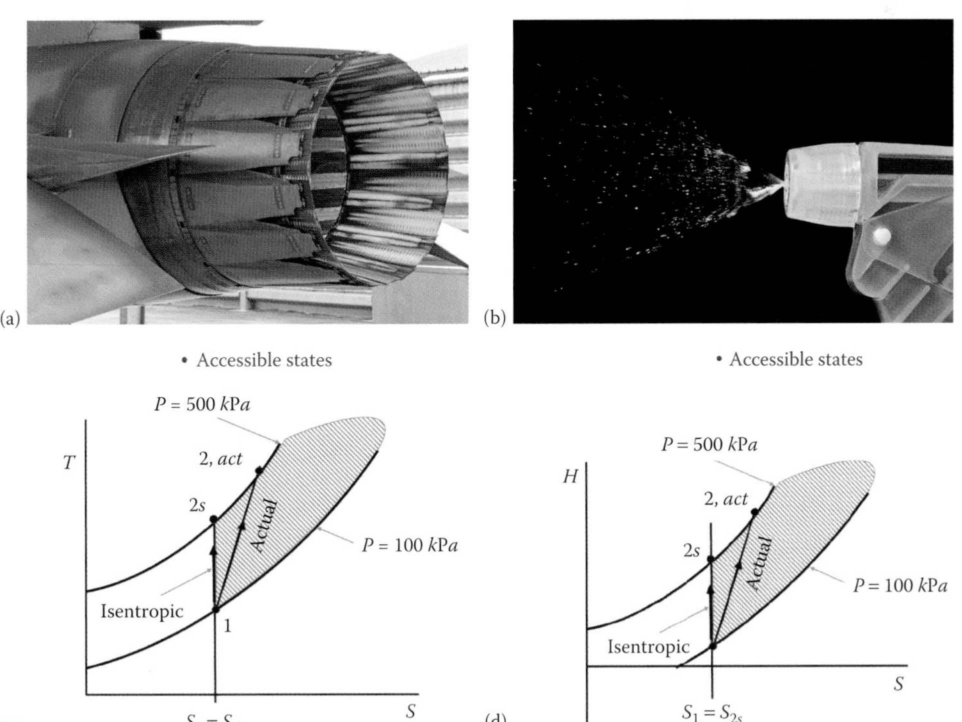

Figure N.57 (a) Jet engine nozzle, (b) adiabatic compression at the nozzle described by a TS phase diagram, (c) HS diagram, and (d) TS diagram for adiabatic compression processes.

npn transistor

[electronics, general] Standard design semiconductor TRANSISTOR that has a P-TYPE SEMICONDUCTOR (electron deficit, holes) material sandwiched between two electronegative semiconductor materials, with excess electrons (predominantly silicon or germanium). The segments of the npn transistor are collector, base, and emitter, in sequence of current FLOW, where the base is controlled by an externally applied electrical potential and regulates the current flow from the collector to emitter. The current flow is regulated by the Fermi levels at the respective *pn*-junctions for the lightly doped collector and heavily doped emitter. The lesser used PNP TRANSISTOR is the alternative (see Figure N.58).

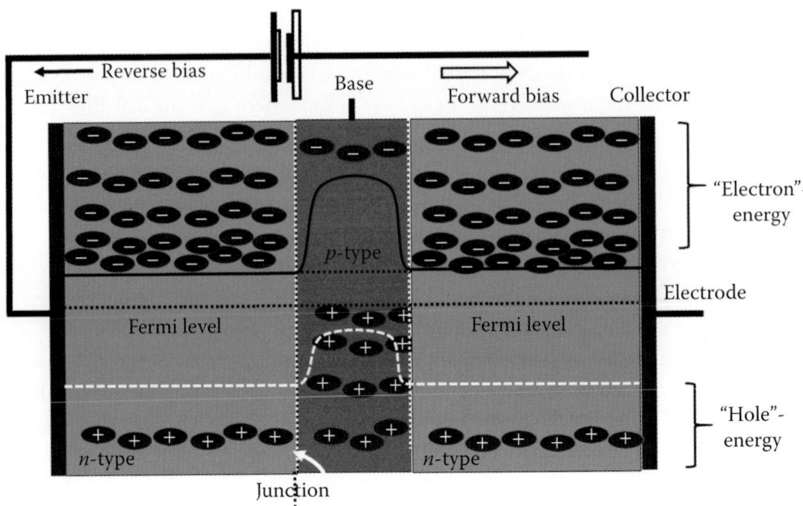

Figure N.58 Transistor, functional diagram.

NSOM

[optics] *See* **NEARFIELD SCANNING OPTICAL MICROSCOPE.**

n-type doping

[atomic, electronics, general] The process of administering an excess amount negative ions in a semiconductor matrix. The process changes the ENERGY bands (e.g., FERMI LEVEL) of the medium, in particular at the boundary with a *p*-type doped medium in a DIODE or TRANSISTOR configuration (*also see* ***pn*-JUNCTION**) (see Figure N.59).

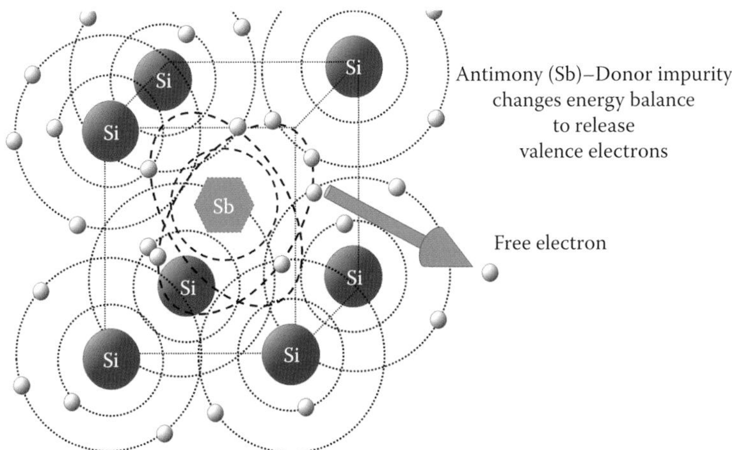

Figure N.59 *N*-type semiconductor, doped with antimony as electron-donor.

n-type semiconductor

[electronics, general] Electronegative semiconductor materials, with excess electrons (base predominantly silicon or germanium) achieved by DOPING with phosphorus (P), arsenic (As), or antimony (Sb) (*see* ***pn*-JUNCTION**, ***npn* TRANSISTOR**, *and* **SEMICONDUCTOR**).

Nuclear adiabatic (de-)magnetization

[atomic, nuclear] A procedure that is used to change the temperature of a system by changing the local absolute value of the MAGNETIC FIELD strength. This process was discovered independently by both PETER DEBYE (1884–1966) in 1926 and William Francis Giauque (1895–1982) in 1927. The nuclear ADIABATIC DEMAGNETIZATION provided a tool to lower the temperature well in the decimal numbers below 1 K near the ABSOLUTE ZERO. In this situation, the mechanism of action relies on the existence of some form of disorder that can be organized by configuring MAGNETIC DIPOLE seeds. The magnetization M of a medium results from circulating electric (eddy) currents on a MACROSCOPIC scale or on an atomic level by elementary atomic magnetic moments. Magnetization is defined as the magnetic moment per unit volume of these collective currents or moments. The units are gauss in the electromagnetic system of units (emu) and weber per square meter in the mks system, respectively: $1\,(\text{weber/m}^2) = (1/4\pi)10^4$ gauss.

Nuclear angular momentum

[nuclear] *See* **ANGULAR MOMENTUM, SPIN.**

Nuclear atom

[general] Atomic model developed in 1911 by ERNEST RUTHERFORD (1871–1937) based on a small NUCLEUS with POSITIVE CHARGE surrounded by an orbiting cloud of electrons. This model is primarily based on phenomenological observations and data and was a marked improvement on the "plum pudding model" introduced in 1904 by JOSEPH JOHN THOMSON (1856–1940), of whom Rutherford was a student.

This is different from the Bohr model, which has more theoretical and far-reaching implications. The Rutherford model was based on the scattering CROSS SECTION of a thin sheet of METAL (e.g., gold) bombarded by alpha particles. The RUTHERFORD SCATTERING cross section for the nuclear atom is as follows: $d\sigma_{Ruth}/d\Omega = \left(Z_1 Z_2 e^2/8\pi\epsilon_0 m v_0^{\,2}\right)^2 \csc^4(\theta/2)$, where σ_{Ruth} is the SCATTERING cross section as a function of the SOLID ANGLE of PERCEPTION Ω for a target with charge number Z_2 and incident ballistic charge number Z_1 for electron charge $e = 1.60217657 \times 10^{-19}\,C$ and ballistic mass m, measured with angle θ under PROJECTILE velocity v_0, with ϵ_0 being the permittivity of free space (see Figure N.60).

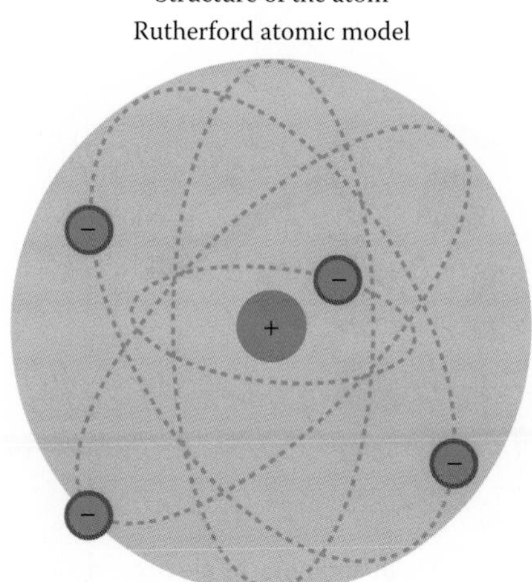

Figure N.60 Rutherford's atomic model of the nuclear atom, solid nucleus with no distinguishable constituents.

Nuclear binding energy

[atomic, nuclear] The nucleus contains approximately 99.975% of the total mass of an ATOM and hence the ENERGY requirements for dissociation are very high. The NUCLEAR BINDING ENERGY is the energy contained by holding the appropriate number of protons and neutrons together, and the energy released when a grouping of protons and neutrons is split off from the NUCLEUS. The total binding energy (BE) can be derived from the MASS ENERGY equivalence: $BE = \left[Zm_p + (A - Z)m_n - {}_Z m^A\right]c^2$, where Z is the number of protons (the atomic number) with m_p being the respective mass, A the atomic mass (with $A - Z$ the number of neutrons, with mass m_n), c the speed of light, and ${}_Z m^A$ the sum of the rest of the masses of the respective protons, neutrons, and remaining nucleus.

Nuclear bomb

[nuclear] An explosive device that releases nuclear ENERGY based on nuclear reactions of either fission or FUSION. The first fission bomb experimentally tested in 1945 (also referred to "ATOMIC BOMB") released approximately 20 kton (kilo-ton) of TNT (the explosive energy yield equivalent to the detonation of 20,000 ton {metric ton} of TNT); where 1 ton TNT = 4.184 GJ. The most popular isotopes used in the fission process are uranium-235 (enriched uranium) and plutonium-239. The first fusion bomb ignited in 1952, also referred to as "thermonuclear bomb" (the "hydrogen" bomb, which is actually a fission–fusion mechanism) released approximately 10 Mton TNT. The HYDROGEN BOMB uses uranium fission as the "detonator" for the hydrogen fusion process. The use of the description "atomic bomb" (A-BOMB) is a misnomer because the energy comes from the NUCLEUS. The FISSION process becomes self-sustaining when a critical mass of unstable medium is exceeded, slightly more than 10 kg of plutonium-239 surrounded by the U-238 ISOTOPE. The H-BOMB relies on the heat and pressure of fission initiated by the uranium explosion initiating the following process. Hydrogen-2, or {deuterium (^2D)} fuses with hydrogen-3 {tritium (^3T)}and

forms helium-4 (^{4}He) as well as one neutron (n) and energy ($E \approx 17.6$ MeV $= 2.81983075 \times 10^{-12}$ J) that is converted in THERMAL EXPANSION and ELECTROMAGNETIC RADIATION: $^2D + ^3T \rightarrow ^4He + n + E$. Note that 1 kg of hydrogen contains 5.975×10^{26} atoms (see Figure N.61).

Figure N.61 Rendering of the (a) "Little Boy" atomic bomb targeted to be dropped on Hiroshima, Japan, on August 6, 1945 and (b) Boeing B-29 bomber: Enola Gay, used to deploy the "atom bomb" over Hiroshima, Japan as well as participated on the attack on Nagasaki, Japan, which resulted in the termination of the war offensive by Japan during the Second World War (1940–1945), (c) rendering of the pressure evolution, and condensation and debris "mushroom" cloud resulting from an above ground nuclear explosion.

Nuclear charge

[nuclear] Total charge resulting from the number of protons in the nucleus of an ATOM. The nuclear charge is indicated by the PROTON number Z (atomic number). This charge will affect the BINDING ENERGY of the electrons in their respective orbits. The charge configuration can be determined with the use of elastic electron SCATTERING cross sections and Bayesian probability distributions.

Nuclear coulomb barrier

[general] Because of the charge distribution of the NUCLEUS, an electric POTENTIAL BARRIER is created that can be accessed by TUNNELING or under FUSION the kinetic ENERGY of the incident PARTICLE needs to exceed the coulomb barrier. For fusion to overcome the electric repulsion, the fusing particle will need to get close enough to allow for the attractive nuclear strong force to be activated. The energy barrier is derived from the electrostatic potential energy: $U_{\text{Coulomb}} = (1/4\pi\epsilon_0)(q_1 q_2/r) = (1/4\pi\epsilon_0)(Z_1 Z_2 e^2/r)$, where

ϵ_0 is the permittivity of free space, r is the separation between the two charges q_1 and q_2, with the charge MAGNITUDE defined by the atomic number Z (*also see* QUANTUM TUNNELING).

Nuclear fission

[atomic, nuclear] Special type of nuclear transformation characterized by the splitting of a NUCLEUS into at least two other nuclei and the release of a relatively large amount of ENERGY. The most well-known FISSION process is that of uranium-235 (*see* **FISSION**) (see Figure N.62).

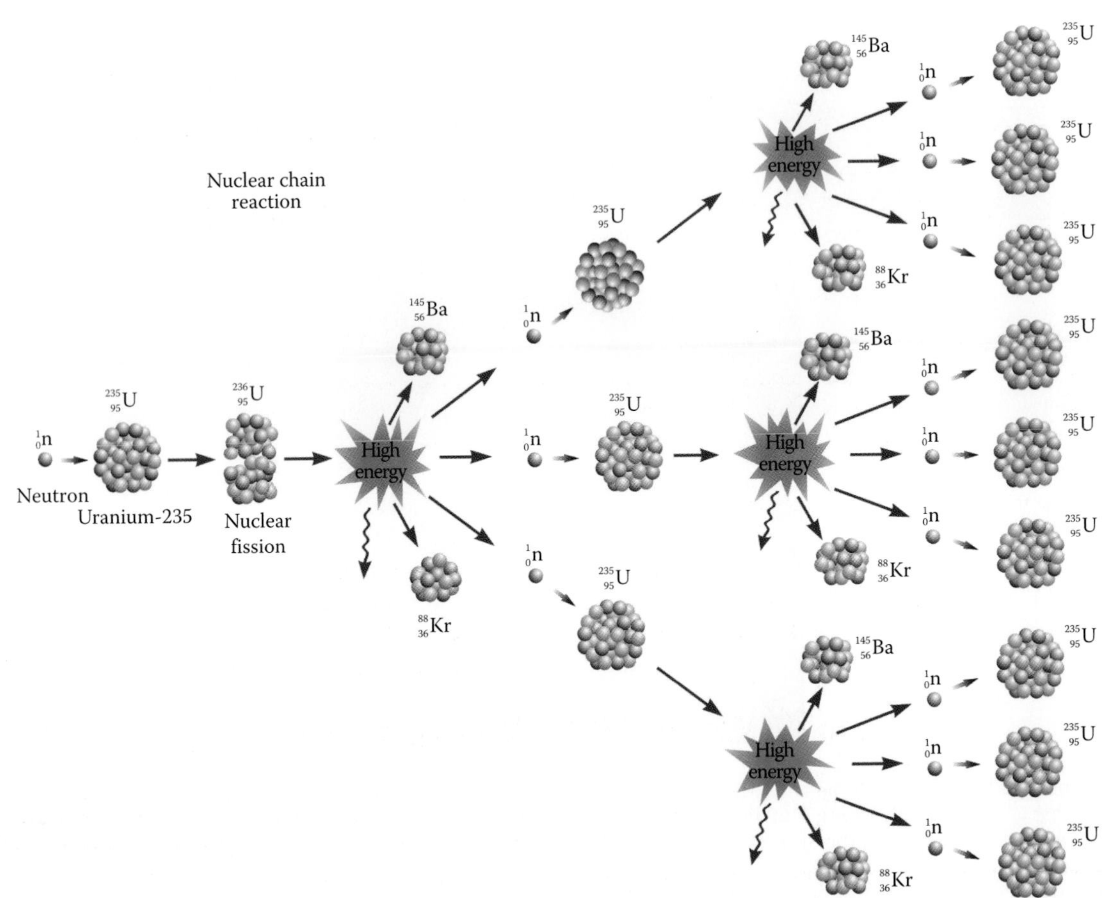

Figure N.62 Nuclear fission.

Nuclear force

[general] Nuclear forces can be distinguished as strong and weak nuclear forces, as part of the four principle force, including gravitational force and electromagnetic force. Weak nuclear force has a range of 10^{-17} m $= 10$ am (attometer) working between atomic constituents, quarks and leptons, and the strong force has a range of 10^{-15} m $= 1$ fm (femtometer), acting between subnuclear particles: quarks and gluons. Apart from the coulomb force acting between opposite and like charges, attractive and repulsive, respectively, the nucleon–nucleon force generally becomes negligible for a separation greater than 4×10^{-15} m $= 4$ fm and is generally strong at smaller DISTANCE than 1 fm, stronger than the prevailing coulomb force: $F_c = (1/4\pi\epsilon)(Z_1Z_2/r^2)$, where Z_i represents the respective charge on the two particles at distance r and $\epsilon = \epsilon_r\epsilon_0$; $\epsilon_0 = 8.85419 \times 10^{-12}$ C^2/Nm^2 the DIELECTRIC permittivity, in VACUUM: "$_0$," and ϵ_r is the relative

permittivity. The large scale nucleon–nucleon attraction between the respective neutron–neutron, neutron–proton, or proton–proton configurations can be described in first order approximation by the SCHRÖDINGER EQUATION: $-(\hbar^2/M)\nabla^2\psi + V_{elec}\psi = i\hbar(\partial\psi/\partial t)$, where ψ is the two-nucleon WAVE function, $\hbar = h/2\pi$, where $h = 6.63 \times 10^{-34}$ Js is Planck's constant, V_{elec} is the electrical potential of the BINDING ENERGY, $M = 939\ \mathrm{MeV/c^2}$ is the NUCLEON mass (with a negligible difference between the PROTON and NEUTRON mass), ∇^2 is the Laplace operator representing the second order derivative in all dimensions, and t is the time. The potential V_{elec} is a function of the nucleon separation $\vec{r}$, the orientations of the spins of the two interacting nucleons $S^{(a)} = (1/2)\hbar$ and $S^{(b)} = (1/2)\hbar$, each with a SPIN component in the z-direction $S^{(i)} = \pm(1/2)\hbar$, yielding four possible spin configurations, each resulting in a 4×4 matrix for the potential and three matrix solutions for the three nucleon interaction combinations. In molecular PHYSICS, the interaction between two nucleons with the release of a PION ("π") (i.e., π-meson), with mass m_π being represented by the potential equation: $V = \overline{\overline{\tau}}_a \cdot \overline{\overline{\tau}}_b g_\pi^{\,2}\left(m_\pi/2M\right)\left[(1/3)(e^{-\mu_c r}/r)\left(\overline{\overline{\sigma}}_a \cdot \overline{\overline{\sigma}}_b\right) + \left((1/3) + (1/\mu_c r) + (1/\mu_c^{\,2} r^2)\right)\left(e^{-\mu_c r}/r\right)S_{ab}\right]$, where $1/\mu_c = \hbar/m_\pi c = 1.4$ fm is the pion COMPTON WAVELENGTH, $\sqrt{g_\pi^{\,2}/\hbar c}$ = is the pion-nucleon coupling constant, $\hbar = h/2\pi$, where $h = 6.6260 \times 10^{-16}$ Js is Planck's constant, $\overline{\overline{\sigma}}_a$ and $\overline{\overline{\sigma}}_b$ are the PAULI SPIN MATRICES for the respective nucleons a and b, $\overline{\overline{\tau}}_a$ and $\overline{\overline{\tau}}_b$ are the respective isospin matrix in 2×2 format for nucleon a and b, r is the nucleonic interspacing distance, c is the speed of light, g_π is the pion ENERGY, and $S_{ab} = 3\left(\overline{\overline{\sigma}}_a \cdot \vec{r}\right)\left(\overline{\overline{\sigma}}_b \cdot \vec{r}\right) - \left(\overline{\overline{\sigma}}_a \cdot \overline{\overline{\sigma}}_b\right)$ is the TENSOR operator; the intrinsic spin can also be characterized as $S^{(a)} = \overline{\overline{\sigma}}_a \hbar/2$.

Nuclear fusion

[atomic, nuclear, thermodynamics] The coalescing of two or more nuclei to form a new NUCLEUS with relative stability. The FUSION process requires penetrating the NUCLEAR COULOMB BARRIER, placing a high velocity constraint on the process, hence only operational under very high temperatures. The fusion process relies on QUANTUM TUNNELING, a process discovered in 1929 by German physicist Friedrich Hund (1896–1997). In the fusion process, some of the combined mass is converted into ENERGY, yielding a high energy EXOTHERMIC REACTION. The first successful attempt in nuclear fusion was made in 1932 by Australian physicist Mark Oliphant (1901–2000) with hydrogen isotopes. Substantial focused research was initiated in the early 1940s in the United States as part of the MANHATTAN PROJECT. Additional research in the development of THERMONUCLEAR FUSION for civil purposes was initiated in the early 1950s (see Figure N.63).

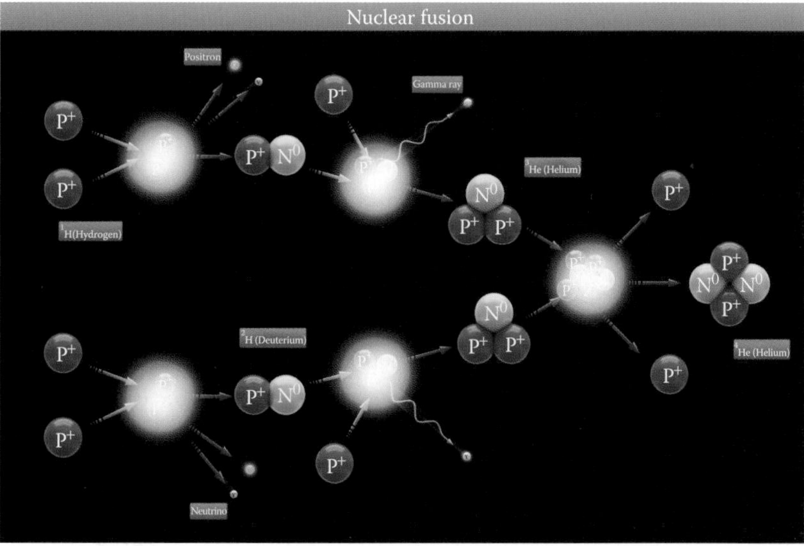

Figure N.63 Nuclear fusion.

Nuclear g-factor (g_n)

[atomic, energy, nuclear, optics] The spectral split under influence of the nuclear SPIN is determined by the influence of the nuclear spin and the interaction with the electron orbital MAGNETIC FIELD (*see* **G-FACTOR, NUCLEAR**. *Also see* **ZEEMAN EFFECT** *and* **HYPERFINE STRUCTURE**).

Nuclear magnetic moment

[atomic, nuclear] $\mu_{I_n} = g_n\left(m_e/M_n\right)\left(e/2mc\right)\vec{I}$, with g_n the nuclear g-factor, $\left(m/M\right)$ the ratio of the electron mass (m_e) over the nuclear mass (M_n) and $\vec{I}$ the nuclear SPIN.

Nuclear magnetic resonance (NMR)

[general] *See* **MAGNETIC RESONANT IMAGING (MRI)**.

Nuclear magneton (nm)

[atomic, nuclear] The MAGNETIC MOMENT (MM) associated with the intrinsic spin of nuclear particles is expressed in unit nuclear magneton: $nm = \left(e\hbar/2m_p\right) = 5.0505 \times 10^{-27}\ \mathrm{Jm^2/Wb}$; for a PROTON, this is $MM_{\mathrm{proton}} = 2.79275$ nm, and for the NEUTRON, $MM_{\mathrm{neutron}} = -1.9135$ nm.

Nuclear medicine

[atomic, biomedical, computational, general, imaging, solid-state] Therapeutic applications that use radioactive isotopes to create selective modifications to the biological DNA or cause CELL death as well as rely on the selective incorporation of radioactive isotopes in a metabolic event to be used for imaging purposes. In imaging, the use of iodine ISOTOPE is one of the mechanisms that allow for monitoring the ACTIVITY of the thyroid by means of a gamma CAMERA. Another application in positron emission TOMOGRAPHY imaging is the use of fludeoxyglucose isotope (active component: positron emitting fluorine-18), known as "fluorodeoxyglucose" as a RADIOPHARMACEUTICAL used as a GLUCOSE replacement for metabolic imaging. Cancer treatment uses radiopharmaceuticals that are designed to go directly to the organ considered for treatment, for example rhodium (^{105}Rh) and rhenium-188, mostly used as beta emitters to inflict CELL death. In therapeutic applications, the success will hinge on the target to nontarget differentiation of uptake of the peptide or other molecular structure (see Figure N.64).

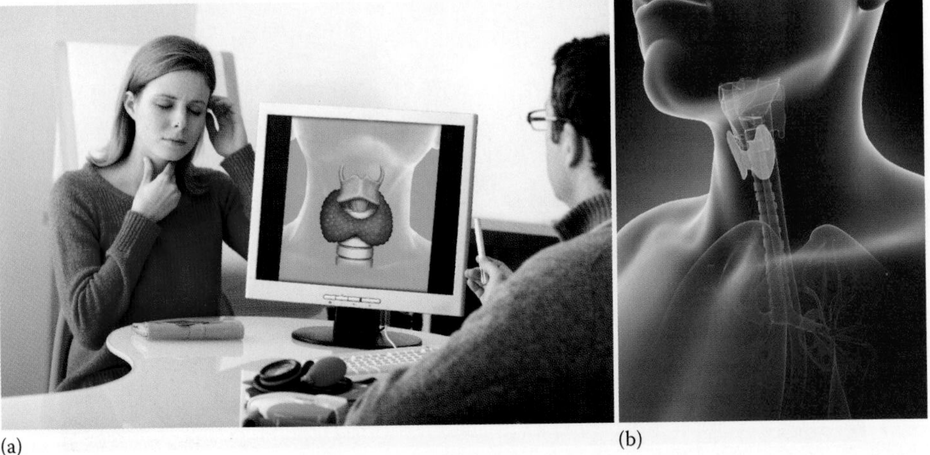

(a) (b)

Figure N.64 (a) Illustration of the thyroid gland and (b) the treatment of thyroid cancer is one application of nuclear medicine.

Nuclear microscope

[general, nuclear] Force probe microscopy on ATOM scale (*also see* **ATOMIC FORCE MICROSCOPE**).

Nuclear models

[nuclear] Various models are available to describe the nuclear structure, based on energetic configuration or resulting from historical observations. Some of the models available are collective model, compound NUCLEUS model, direct reaction model, LIQUID-DROP MODEL, Rutherford model, and Bohr SHELL MODEL.

Nuclear reactor

[atomic, nuclear] Power-generating mechanism based on NUCLEAR FISSION or FUSION, creating steam to drive turbines that generate ELECTRICITY for general consumption. The general construction of a nuclear reactor has RODS of various composition suspended in a LIQUID. The fuel rods form the principle nuclear reaction, such as uranium-235 in a FISSION reactor; balanced by control rods that can partially capture the emissions driving the nuclear reaction, hence controlling the rate of the reaction, as well as the liquid itself which is known as the MODERATOR and often consists of "HEAVY WATER," a mixture of bound oxygen molecules tied to deuterium or tritium, replacing the standard hydrogen in water. The bath is surrounded by a concrete shield for absorption of stray emissions. In the nuclear conversion process the base for the fuel is obtained from various locations, each with specific grade of purity and contamination. The mined components will require processing, that is, enrichment, before it can be used in a nuclear reactor. An additional step in the preparations before use in the power station is the fabrication of the fuel rods from the enriched uranium, for instance. The steam GENERATOR is separated from the reactor vessel to avoid contamination, and relies on a heat exchanger to transfer the heat from the REACTOR to the steam generator. The steam is maintained in a closed circuit at pressures on the order of 0.5 mPa or greater. The steam is lead through the TURBINE from where it is cooled by a CONDENSER that vents to the outside by means of the cooling towers. A different type of nuclear reactor is the breeder reactor, which produces fuel for fission in parallel with generating power, producing plutonium-239 from uranium-238. Spent fuel will remain radioactive for several hundred years, up to in excess of a thousand years (depending on the accepted cut-off emission threshold), and requires an elaborate system of waste-management. Because of the high ENERGY radiation produced during the DECAY mechanism, nuclear power plants have a high risk associated with their operation. The first fission reactor was made operational in 1951 near Arco, Idaho. Several accidents with nuclear reactors have resulted in long-term damage to the area in which the reactor was placed, for instance, Three-mile Island in Dauphin County, Pennsylvania (1979); Chernobyl in the former USSR, now Russia (1986), and the Fukushima Daiichi pant in Okuma and Futaba, Japan (2011). Additional accidents have involved the unplanned release of radioactive steam into the ATMOSPHERE and RADIATION leaks through cracks in the shielding concrete WALL of the reactor. An example of a natural FUSION REACTOR is the Sun, additional artificial fusion nuclear power plants have been created based on the tokamak principle. The first tokomak base fusion reactor was build and operated in Novosibirsk in 1968 (see Figure N.65).

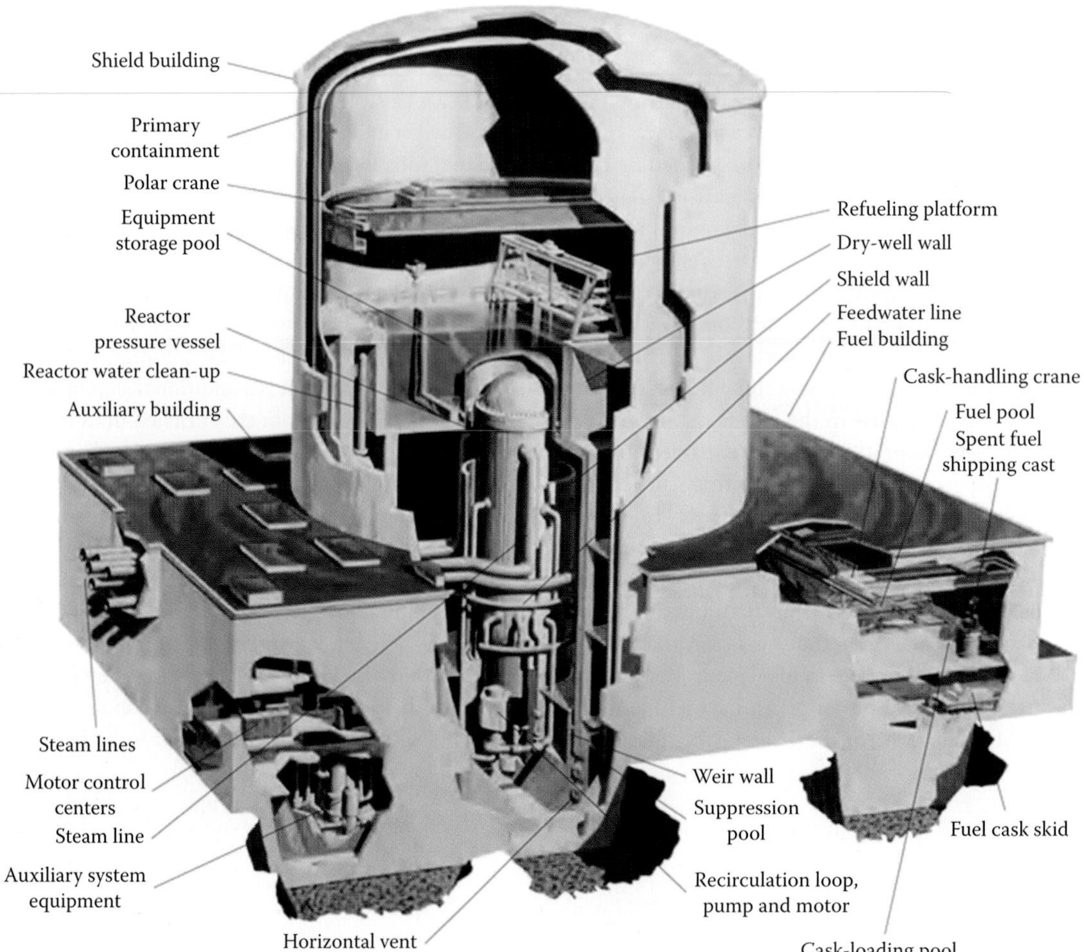

Figure N.65 Nuclear power plant reactor design. (Courtesy of General Electric Corporation [GE], Fairfield, CT.)

N

Nucleation

[fluid dynamics, general, mechanics] Process of BUBBLE formation, followed by collapse (CAVITATION). Formation of temporary voids in a LIQUID resulting from thermal agitation (i.e., boiling or PLASMA formation [the latter in the case of both solid and liquid media]), growing from MICROSCOPIC to MACROSCOPIC proportions (*see* CAVITATION) (see Figure N.66).

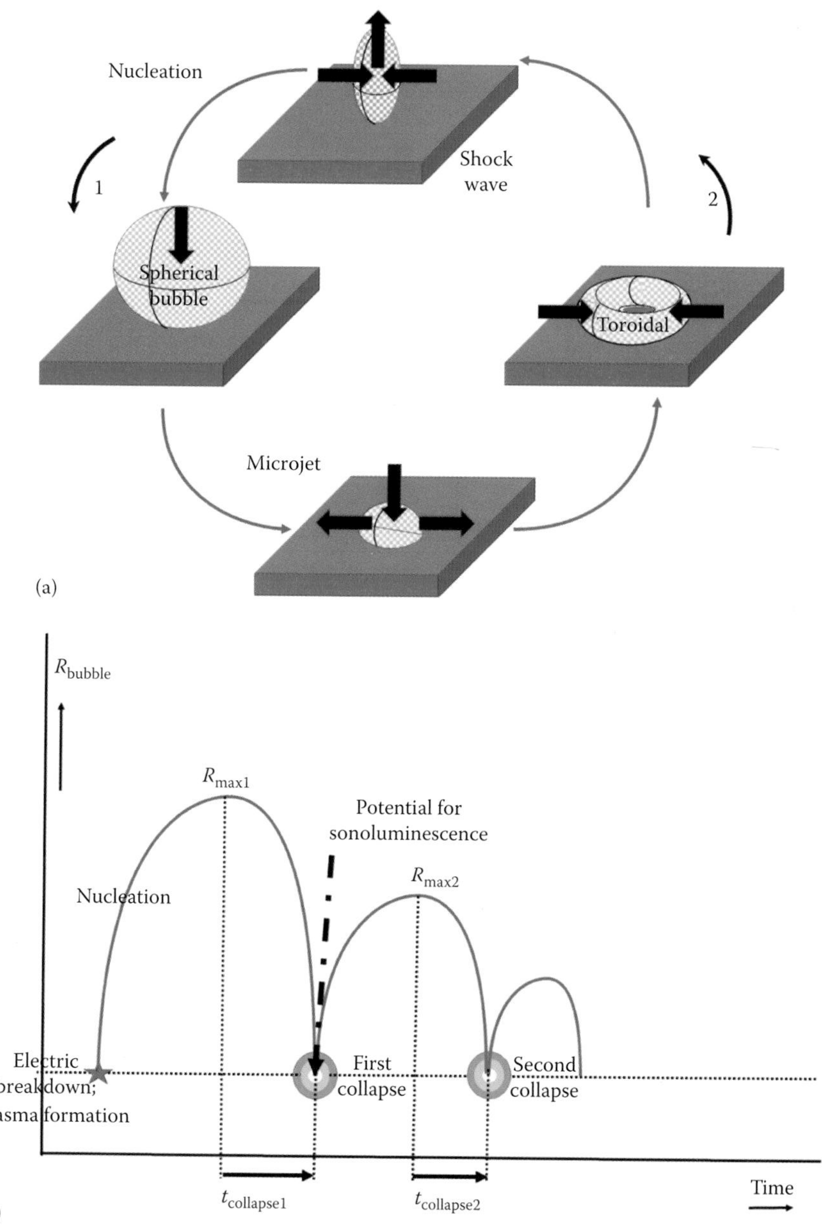

Figure N.66 (a) Progress of bubble formation and (b) nucleation.

Nucleon

[nuclear] The common name for the constituent parts of the NUCLEUS. At present applied to protons and neutrons, but will include any other PARTICLE that is found to exist in the nucleus (see Figure N.67).

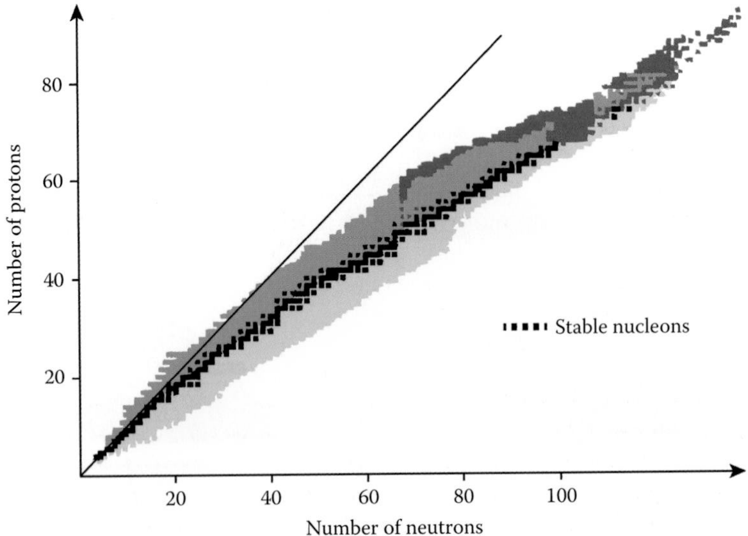

Figure N.67 Chart of nuclides. Nucleon pattern, proton versus neutron assembly.

Nucleon configuration

[atomic, nuclear] The NUCLEUS consists of protons identified by the atomic number Z and neutrons indicated in quantity by N. The following configurations for the nuclear make-up can be recognized: even proton-even neutron (even-even), odd proton-odd neutron (odd-odd), odd proton-even neutron (odd-even), even proton-odd neutron (even-odd). The even-even configuration has an even mass number ($Z + N = A$); note that the electron mass ($m_e = 0.0005446623$ amu $= 9.10938188 \times 10^{-31}$ kg) is negligible compared to the NEUTRON mass $m_n = 1.0086649156$ amu $= 1.6749 \times 10^{-27}$ kg and proton mass $m_p = 1.00727638$ amu $= 1.6726 \times 10^{-27}$ kg. The even-even configuration is the largest population of ELEMENTS with 148 stable nuclides with an additional 21 long-lived radio-active nuclides, the odd-odd group contributed only 5 stable atomic structures and 4 long-lived primordial nuclear ISOMERS, the odd-even configuration has 48 stable nucleons with an additional 5 long-lived nuclides, and the even-odd nuclei total 53 stable and 3 long-lived isotopes. All even-even nuclei have a base total nuclear SPIN of $s = 0$ in GROUND STATE, the odd-odd nuclides have integer spin; however, none has spin zero. All remaining nuclides with odd mass-number are classified as fermions, meaning that the total spin is half-integer, and have an array of spin number orientations.

Nucleus

[nuclear] The heavy central part of an ATOM in which most of the mass and the total positive ELECTRIC CHARGE are concentrated, greater than 99.975%. The charge of the NUCLEUS, an integral multiple Z of the charge of the PROTON, is the essential factor that distinguishes one ELEMENT from another. Z is the atomic number. The net POSITIVE CHARGE of the nucleus forms the attractive mechanism for orbiting electrons defined by the coulomb force.

Nuclide

[nuclear] General term referring to all nuclear species and isotopes, both stable (known so far 275) and unstable (approximately 500), of the chemical ELEMENTS known and listed in the PERIODIC TABLE OF ELEMENTS (*see* NUCLEON).

Numeric evaluation

[acoustics, computational, general, optics] Mathematical analysis based on function association, tying parameters together. When the mathematical correlation becomes too complex, the function may be solved numerically by insertion of incremental steps. One specific example of a NUMERICAL analysis is in the propagation of ELECTROMAGNETIC RADIATION through SCATTERING media, as applied to galactic dust and in biomedical applications for the EQUATION OF RADIATIVE TRANSFER. Additional numerical analyses are common in FLUID DYNAMICS due to the complex boundary conditions of a system of interest, providing a three-dimensional result that is location specific and varies with time.

Numerical

[computational, fluid dynamics, general, optics] The mathematical approach for solving equations by means of taking numerical incremental steps and solving step-wise with numerical data point solutions that are logged and graphically represented. An analytical solution stands in contrast to a numerical approach, both providing an equation all the same.

Numerical aperture

[general, optics] (NA) introduced by ERNST ABBE (1840–1905) as $NA = n\sin\theta$, with θ is the maximum half—solid-angle of the "hypothetical" cone defined at the surface of an optical device (e.g., LENS, fiber-optic face) within which light can exit or enter the optical device and n is the INDEX OF REFRACTION of the medium in which the lens is placed. Parameter for optical devices that describes the relationship between the maximum APERTURE to the focal length of, for instance, a compound lens system. The numerical aperture is defined by half the acceptance ANGLE (θ) of the device and the index of refraction of the medium (n) through which the ELECTROMAGNETIC RADIATION travels as $NA = n\sin\theta$. Hence, the numerical aperture can be increased by placing a drop of OIL between the specimen on a MICROSCOPE slide and the objective of the microscope. The numerical aperture is an indication of the light gathering capability of an optical system, the larger the better (see Figure N.68).

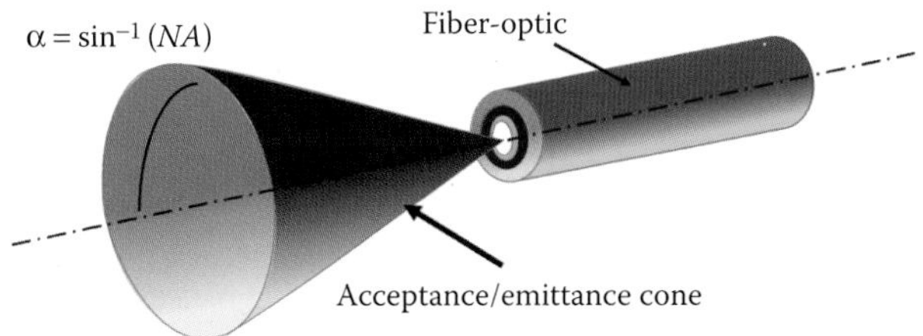

Figure N.68 Numerical aperture.

Numerical fluid mechanics

[computational, fluid dynamics] Computational techniques for solving Navier–Stokes equations as well as finite ELEMENT techniques for three-dimensional solutions. The finite element methods will generate a grid pattern that has variable RESOLUTION depending on the geometric and anticipated FLUID DYNAMICS complexity within a certain volume. The computational aspects are geared to finite differences approximations for elliptic, parabolic, and hyperbolic equations. Often, the NUMERICAL approach uses Fourier decomposition and requires error analysis to establish the validity of the SOLUTION and within what domain. In particular, the use of numerical analysis applies to turbulent flow characteristics and boundary conditions. The time-resolved assessment is also very useful for flow development and time perturbation analysis (*also see* COMPUTATIONAL FLUID DYNAMICS).

Nusselt (Nuβelt), Ernst Kraft Wilhelm (1882–1957)

[biomedical, fluid dynamics, thermodynamics] An engineer and scientist from Germany. Nusselt developed the dimensional HEAT TRANSFER analysis (see Figure N.69).

Figure N.69 Ernst Kraft Wilhelm Nusselt (Nuβelt) (1882–1957). (Courtesy of Technische Universität (TU) Desden, Dresden, Germany.)

Nusselt number (Nu = h_tL/κ)

[fluid dynamics, thermodynamics] Dimensionless number identifying the temperature gradient at a surface, for instance, under FLOW or condensation; it was introduced by ERNST KRAFT WILHELM NUSSELT (Nuβelt) (1882–1957); this surface phenomenon relates to BOUNDARY LAYER or condensate film respectively. (Note that for condensate film, $\mathrm{Nu} = \bar{h}_t L/\kappa = c\left[(\rho_\ell g(\rho_\ell - \rho_v)h_{fg}L^3)/(\eta_{\mathrm{molec}}\kappa_\ell(T_{\mathrm{sat}} - T_w))\right]$), where L is the characteristic dimension of the phenomenon, κ is the THERMAL CONDUCTIVITY, and h_t is the HEAT TRANSFER coefficient, $\bar{h}_t$ is the average heat transfer coefficient for condensation of a film respectively, ρ_ℓ is the density of the VAPOR, ρ_v is the density of the vapor, g is the GRAVITATIONAL ACCELERATION, h_{fg} is the LATENT HEAT of vaporization, η_{molec} is the molecular viscosity, κ_ℓ is the thermal conductivity of the LIQUID, T_{sat} is the SATURATION temperature of the vapor, T_{sat} is the surface temperature, and constant c is dimensionless and accounts for size and shape. From this, it becomes evident that for smaller bodies, (characteristic dimension small) the heat transfer coefficient is larger than for large bodies. The definition of the Nusselt number is the transport of THERMAL ENERGY ratio between that under forced convection to that of conduction. As with any dimensionless number, the role is to reduce the quantity of independent variables.

Nutation

[astrophysics/astronomy, biomedical, mechanics] Rocking, oscillating, swaying, or bobbing MOTION of the axis of rotation of a predominantly axially symmetric object. This MOTION may pertain to the earth's rotation, a GYROSCOPE. Additionally, certain plants have slow or fast nutation resulting from unequal rate of growth at respective different sides (sunflowers orient themselves toward the Sun as the day passes). Other examples are the sensitivity of certain plants to temperature, such as the tulip and the crocus. The crocus can distinguish a temperature change of 0.5°C and will change its orientation/inclination in response to a temperature change of 20°C within 2 min. In biology, there is the pivotal motion of the sacrum (gyration, in reference to the dance moves by Elvis Presley [1935–1977]), which is a large, triangular bone at the base where the spine meets the pelvic bone (*also see* **PRECESSION**) (see Figure N.70).

Figure N.70 Nutation spinning top stays erect, but "wobbles" about the equilibrium.

Nuttall, John Mitchell (1890–1958)

[atomic, nuclear] A physicist from Great Britain. John Nuttall discovered the regularities of DECAY rates for even-even nuclei (even number of protons [Z]; even number of neutrons [N]) and introduced the decay constant. He has been a collaborator with Hand Geiger on the detection of RADIATION. The collaborative efforts resulted in the GEIGER–NUTTALL LAW of RADIOACTIVE DECAY: $\log\lambda = a + b \log r_{range}$, where λ is the decay rate, r_{range} is the range of radiation in AIR, a is a material parameter, and b is a constant.

Nylon

[biomedical, chemistry] It is a synthetic POLYMER. Nylon is a versatile material used in many consumer and industrial applications as well as in biomedical use for prosthetic construction and reinforcement, also used as suture material and sewing wire. Nylon is a diverse family of products that were initiated at DuPont in 1935 by Wallace Carothers (1896–1937). Nylon as a generic definition is a polyamide of repeating chemical units that are linked by amide bonds. Nylon is a copolymer formed through condensation of diamine and a dicarboxylic ACID, in equal parts, forming the amide chains. Nylon was used initially in broom brushes and shortly thereafter in lady's stockings ("nylons," introduced in the 1940s). Nylon can withstand high temperatures and as a solid sheet can be press-molded into most any shape and has a MELTING POINT of

256°C. Nylon has a high tensile strength and is used as rope for a broad range of applications, including hoisting heavy equipment (see Figure N.71).

Figure N.71 (a–f) Illustrations of the use of Nylon.

Nyquist, Harry Theodor ("Nyqvist") (1889–1976)

[computational, thermodynamics] A Swedish electrical engineer and physicist. Nyqvist worked for AT&T and Bell laboratories. In 1960, Nyquist received the IRE Medal of Honor from the Institute of Radio Engineers, for his involvement in the description of "fundamental contributions to a quantitative understanding of thermal NOISE, data transmission and negative feedback." His collaborative work with CLAUDE ELWOOD SHANNON (1916–2001) led the foundations for information theory and SIGNAL sampling principles, additionally his work with Herbert Eugene Ives (1882–1953) formed the roots for feedback control theory (see Figure N.72).

Figure N.72 Harry Theodor Nyquist ("Nyqvist") (1889–1976). (Courtesy of IEEE.)

Nyquist frequency

[computational] The highest frequency component that can be distinguished at half the frequency at which data acquisition is performed. The Nyquist frequency provides a discrete data array as a function of time. This concept was proposed by HARRY THEODOR NYQUIST (1889–1976).

Nyquist rate

[computational] The minimum sampling frequency that needs to be applied to obtain the frequency resolution of the highest rate of change in an observed phenomenon, obtained at a RESOLUTION that is half the Nyquist rate sampling frequency, as a continuous-time signal. Introduced by HARRY THEODOR NYQUIST (1889–1976). Sampling at lower rates (i.e., undersampling) may result in ALIASING, where DRIFT between separate signals is not captured as individual data streams; this may be linked to two separate signal functions (separate sources) that produce similar data streams, which can be out of PHASE. Oversampling will cost in processing time and can result in missed data points or introduce NOISE.

Nyquist–Shannon sampling theory

[computational] The SAMPLING rate for data acquisition for an observation will need to be at least twice the frequency of the phenomenon under observation in order to retrieve all frequency information imbedded in the events, and subsequently separate out individual events and factors driving the manifestation of physical parameters. This principle was introduced by HARRY THEODOR NYQUIST (1889–1976) and CLAUDE ELWOOD SHANNON (1916–2001). If an observation in time $f(t)$ is confined to a maximum frequency of ν^* Hz, the phenomenon is fully determined by a data array with time spacing of samples information at $(1/\nu^*)s$ intervals (*also see* **Nyquist frequency**) (see Figure N.73).

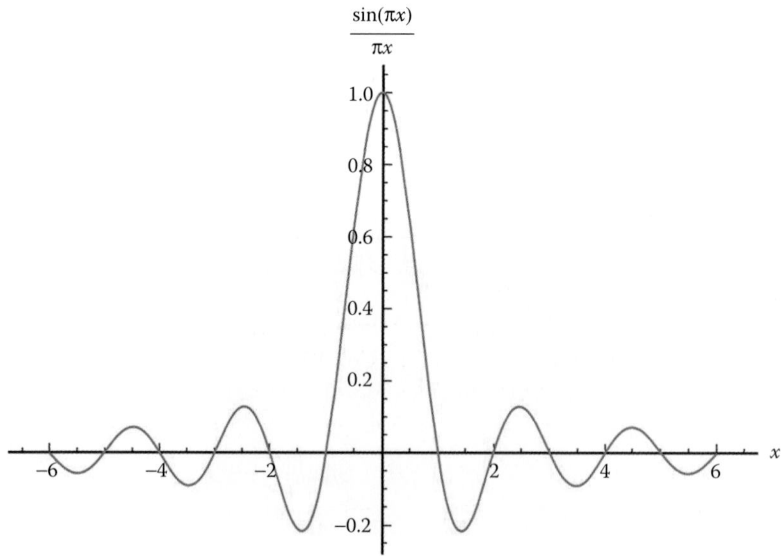

Figure N.73 Mathematical mechanism of action used to interpolate the numeric sequence during signal sampling can be described by sinc functions.

Nystagmus

[biomedical, mechanics] The locking MOTION of the eyes on a target point during rotation of the body followed by a slow tracking when the observational limit is reached. The quick reflect of the EYE followed by slow deviation tracking is nystagmus. Nystagmus can consist of rotational, horizontal, or vertical motion. In humans, the irritation of the labyrinth of the EAR used for equilibrium can cause random eye motions; one aspect is the irrigation of the ear by cold water resulting in involuntary nystagmus. Nystagmus also provides a tool for the analysis of certain brain disorders. Additionally, nystagmus can be used to describe the uncontrollable motion of the eye as a clinical condition ("dancing eye," affecting one in several thousand people) (see Figure N.74).

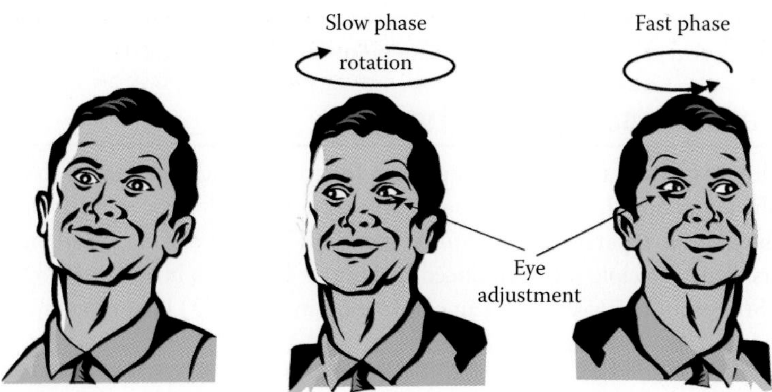

Figure N.74 Nystagmus.

Oak Ridge National Laboratory

[atomic, nuclear] Oak Ridge, Tennessee, was established in 1942 as a uranium enrichment production site for the MANHATTAN PROJECT. The city still hosts a major concentration of basic and applied research. The Oak Ridge National Laboratory and the University of Tennessee are combining their effort, supported by federal and state funding and a public research. The Oak Ridge National Laboratory is the largest US Department of Energy research facility, focusing on multifaceted and multidisciplinary science and technology research, managed by UT-Battelle, LLC (see Figure O.1).

Figure O.1 Oak Ridge National Laboratory. (Courtesy of the United States Department of Energy, Washington, DC.)

Obert, Edward F. (1910–1993)

[thermodynamics] A scientist and engineer from the United States. The work of Obert includes the published charts illustrating the "PRINCIPLE OF CORRESPONDING STATES" with L.C. Nelson in

1954, referring to the work of JOHANNES DIDERIK VAN DER WAALS (1837–1923), published in 1880 (see Figure O.2).

Figure O.2 Edward F. Obert (1910–1993) on right during the award of the Benjamin Smith Reynolds Award for outstanding contributions to the teaching of engineering students, May 4, 1973. (Courtesy of the University of Wisconsin-Madison College of Engineering, Madison, WI.)

Object wave

[general] Light incident on an object is diffracted, forming a collective WAVE front of scattered light that is subject to superposition generating a collective WAVEFRONT referred to as the "object wave" (see Figure O.3).

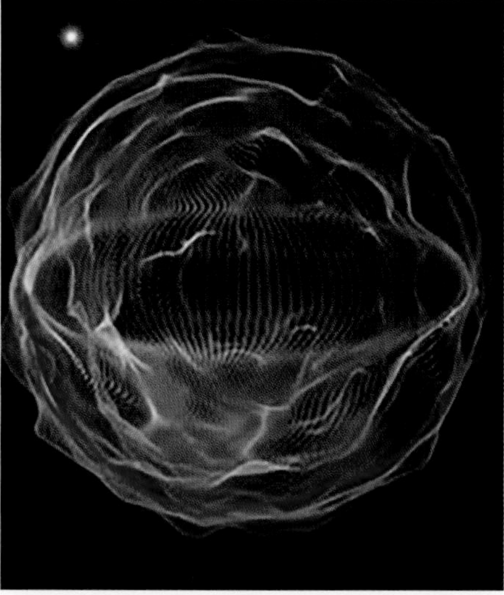

Figure O.3 Representation of the appearance of an object wave pattern.

Oblique angle scanning

[acoustics] Scanning of multilayered targets with ULTRASOUND, specifically using pulse-echo detection, yields reverberations that complicate the direct characterization of the composition of the medium. Under oblique ANGLE detection, the first order reverberant echoes are rejected, hence providing a more clearly defined ultrasound SIGNAL with greater detail. Similar principles also apply in positron emission TOMOGRAPHY imaging. The oblique angle SCATTERING brings about considerable artifacts that interfere with proper IMAGE formation (see Figure O.4).

(a)

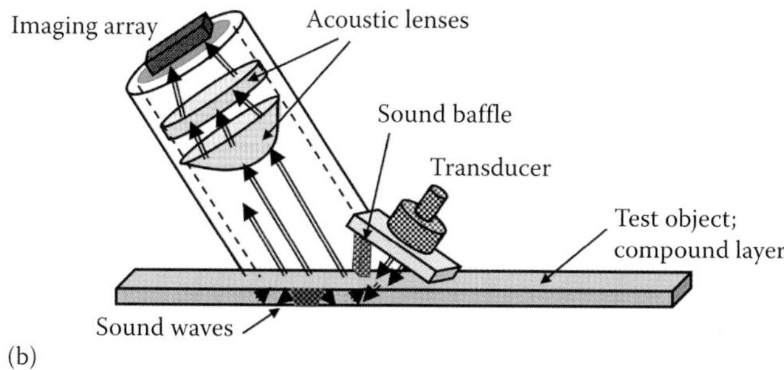

(b)

Figure O.4 (a) Oblique angle deflection providing characteristics about the structure and composition of a medium and objects within a medium. For instance, the mere visual recognition of the material (metal, plastic, ivory, or wood) in this optical scatter image of chess pieces as well as the identification of the isolated pawn. (b) Oblique detection angle for ultrasound imaging.

Oblique shock wave

[fluid dynamics] A SHOCK WAVE propagation traveling with inclination with respect to the incident upstream FLOW direction, unlike a normal shock. An oblique shock wave is generally formed at the tip (wedge) of an object in supersonic, compressible, flow. An example is the thermodynamic discontinuity at the nose of a plane approaching, and subsequently exceeding Mach velocity. The WAVE is at this point deflected at an corner angle (θ), diverting with respect to the streamlines: α, the oblique shock angle, conforming to: $\tan\theta = 2\cot\alpha[(M_1^2\sin^2\alpha - 1)/M_1^2(\gamma_{hc} + \cos 2\alpha + 2)]$, where M_1 represents the MACH NUMBER, and γ_{hc} the heat capacity ratio. The MACH WAVE itself is only an infinitesimally weak shock wave. The coalescing of a multitude of Mach waves originates an actual oblique shock wave, similar to the normal shock wave. The flow direction of the oblique shock wave is tangential to the surface of the disturbance. Similar principles also apply to NOZZLE flow (see Figure O.5).

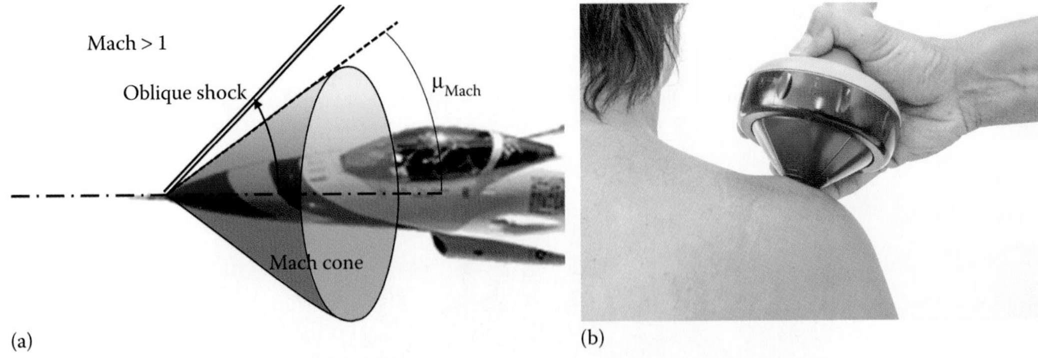

Figure O.5 (a) Principle of oblique shock wave and (b) low frequency shockwaves for joint therapy.

Occhialini, Giuseppe ("Beppo") Paolo Stanislao (1907–1993)

[astrophysics/astronomy, nuclear, thermodynamics] A geophysicist from Italy involved in the identification of COSMIC RAYS, concerning charge and ENERGY. He is a close collaborator with PATRICK BLACKETT (1897–1974). Giuseppe Occhialini also contributed to the discovery of the pi-meson (PION) in 1947, while the other associates of the research team that all received the Nobel Prize in Physics are César (Cesare) MANSUETO GIULIO LATTES (1924–2005) and CECIL FRANK POWELL (1903–1969) (see Figure O.6).

Figure O.6 Giuseppe ("Beppo") Paolo Stanislao Occhialini (1907–1993) in 1925. (Courtesy of the Università degli Studi di Milano-Bicocca, Milan, Italy.)

Oceanography

[energy, fluid dynamics, general, geophysics] A field of PHYSICS dealing with physical phenomena in the LIQUID part of EARTH'S ATMOSPHERE directly related to the FLOW and PHASE transitions of the oceans and large and small bodies of water, also referred to as "MARINE GEOPHYSICS" (*see* **HYDROLOGY**) (see Figure O.7).

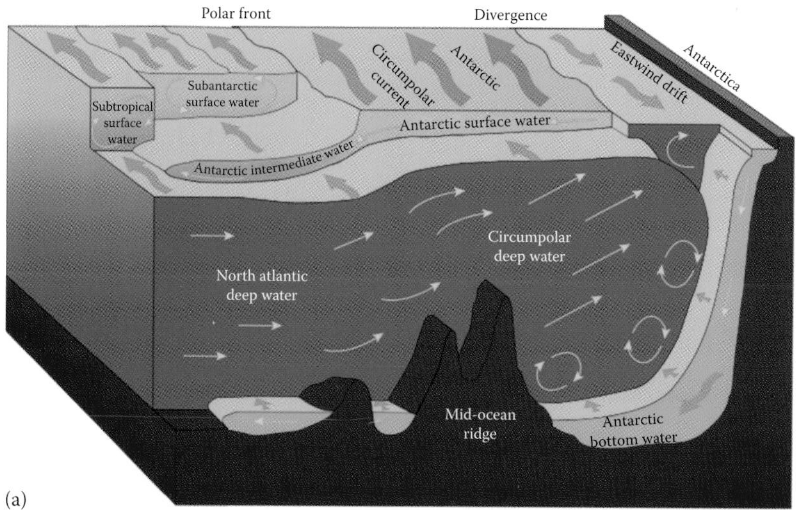

(a)

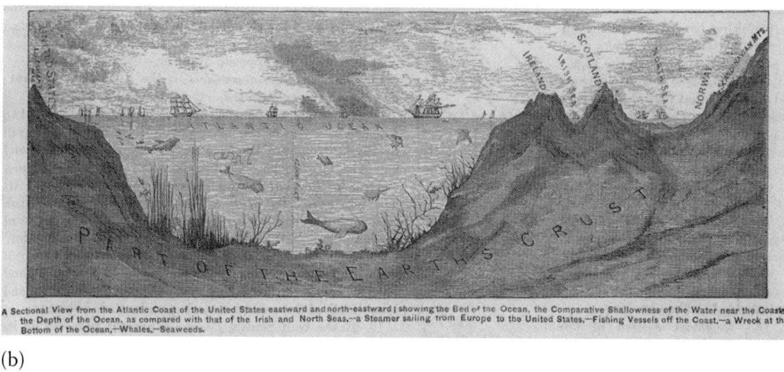

(b)

Figure O.7 (a) Geographic description of the Antarctic Ocean water composition and (b) 1872 hypothetical description of a cross section of the Atlantic Ocean, limited due to incomplete information as a result of unavailability of instrumentation.

Octane number

[chemical, mechanics] A fossil fuel standard that represents the reciprocal of the PROBABILITY that an ENGINE will have incomplete combustion as a result of spark ignition in a four-stroke engine. An octane number of 100 represents perfect combustion and is rated based on isooctane (2,2,4-trimethylpentane,

C_8H_{18}). The number will depend on the compression ratio of the piston/cylinder configuration. The octane number of a fuel is determined in the "cooperative fuel research knock-test engine," which has a variable compression ratio (see Figure O.8).

Figure O.8 Gasoline pump with octane numbers for the different grades of fuel.

Octave

[acoustics] Particular to music, the interval between one PITCH and another with double or half the respective frequency. The concept dates as far back as PYTHAGORAS (c. 570–490 BC). Musical notes that are one or several octaves apart are represented by the same letter symbol (C, D, E, etc.). In ELECTROMAGNETIC THEORY, the same applies; the best example is the visual response of the HUMAN EYE is approximately one octave: 325–650 nm, within certain luminescent boundaries. Octave equivalence denotes the fact that certain resonant frequencies share many of the same overtones. Octave equivalence refers to the format of the affinity of tones, synonymous to similarity. A concept referred to as "octave equivalence" has been observed in human infants and rats. This refers to the sensory octave affinity, which is based on commonality of multiple pitches in harmonic complex tones (see Figure O.9).

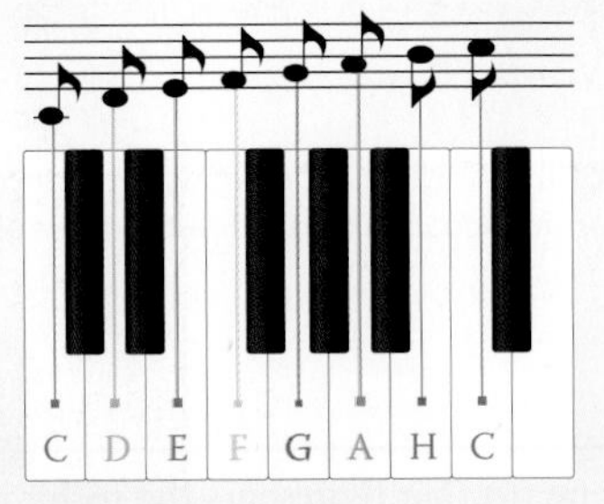

Figure O.9 Outline of piano keys over the spectral band of an octave.

Octave stretching

[acoustics, computational] The fact that octaves derived historically are not perfect 2:1 ratios. Octave stretch of tones of musical instruments was described by John F. Corso (1920–2013) in 1954.

Ohm, Georg Simon (1789–1854)

[biomedical, electronics, general, thermodynamics] A physicist and scientist from the Holy Roman Empire or Prussia, Germany. The scientific deductions of Georg Ohm while performing experimental observations with the electrochemical cell, galvanometer from Alessandro Volta (1745–1827), made him derive the relationship between current and applied electrical potential (voltage) and the associated electrical resistance known as "Ohm's law" (see Figure O.10).

Figure O.10 Georg Simon Ohm (1789–1854).

Ohm meters

[general] A portable instrument for measuring a broad range of values for electrical resistance pertaining to conductor, semiconductors, and insulating devices. The ohmmeter is an active device, working based on an applied constant current, the resistance between two points can be derived using Ohm's law. Care needs to be taken that the contact resistance is negligible, between the measuring probe and the device (see Figure O.11).

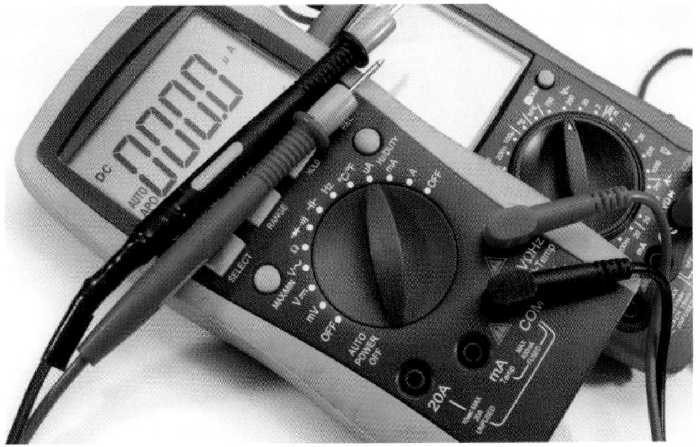

Figure O.11 Ohm meter, part of a multi-meter.

O

Ohm's law

[biomedical, electronics] A relationship derived by Georg Simon Ohm (1789–1854) describing the current through a resistor (R) resulting from an applied electrical potential across the resistor of V is defined by $I = V/R$ (see Figure O.13).

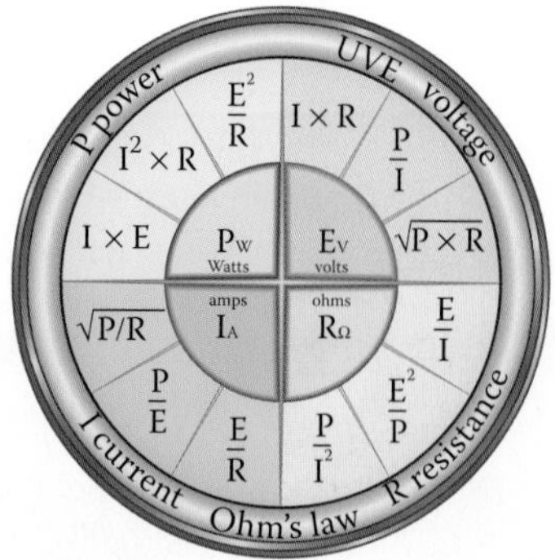

Figure O.13 Ohm's law and associated definitions.

Ohmic circuit element

[general] Electronic device that maintains a linear relationship between the applied potential and the current flow (see Figure O.12).

Figure O.12 Drawing of ohmic circuit diagram.

Ohnesorge number ($Z = \eta/(c_z\sqrt{\rho L\sigma})$)

[fluid dynamics, mechanics] A dimensionless number indicating the ratio of the net viscous force to the equalized inertial and surface forces (e.g., surface tension or friction), which is expressed as the square root of the product of the latter two forces, with η the viscosity, c_z dimensionless constant, ρ the density of the liquid, L the characteristic dimension of the phenomenon, and σ the surface tension. The Ohnesorge number is primarily used in the classification of momentum transfer, for instance, in atomization.

O

Oil

[chemical, fluid dynamics, mechanics] Fossil residue that has many chemical applications, ranging from combustible fuel to lubricants and the production of PLASTICS. Oil is neutral in charge and nonpolar. The substance is a viscous LIQUID that is hydrophobic as well as lipophilic, OIL will float on water and mix with fatty substances. Crude oil or petroleum is the most recognized base material; however, plant and seed extracts are also referred to as "oils." Next to petrochemical crude oil, we know mineral oil and sunflower oil as well as other plant products and animal oils. Chemically, oils are liquids with a high carbon and hydrogen content. Oils have applications in painting, cooking, cosmetics, LUBRICATION, base ELEMENTS for generation of chemical components, and fuels, and have attributes that make them effective HEAT TRANSFER media (e.g., high thermal conductivity, high flash point, and high vapor point). When a thin layer of oil covers a large surface of water, the mechanical properties of the water are directly affected as expressed by the modifications to the WAVE phenomena. The oil film results in a reduction of the AMPLITUDE of the water waves and also affects the Fourier spectrum of the wave phenomena, eliminating higher order frequencies (see Figure O.14).

(a)

(b)

Figure O.14 (a) Oil rig (oil platform) used for drilling for oil and (b) olive oil.

Oil-drop experiment

[atomic, nuclear] An experiment devised by ROBERT ANDREWS MILLIKAN (1868–1953) to determine the elementary ELECTRIC CHARGE (*see* **MILLIKAN OIL-DROP EXPERIMENT**).

Oil-film method

[fluid dynamics] Mechanism to provide a fast and simple approach to help validate computational FLUID DYNAMICS numerical simulations of fluid flow. Colored OIL injected in or floating on top of a fluid-dynamics process will provide a visual display of the FLOW processes, and boundary phenomena.

Old quantum theory

[general, quantum] Early theoretical results in QUANTUM MECHANICS from 1900 to 1925, based on Bohr–Sommerfeld quantization, which predate modern quantum mechanics. The original principles of QUANTUM THEORY were introduced in 1905 by ALBERT EINSTEIN (1879–1955), describing the quantum theory of light. The principles of the old quantum theory rely on the fact that MOTION in an atomic system is discrete and can be quantized. Such as system generally obeys classical mechanics with the exception that not every motion is allowed; only the motions that obey the old quantum condition are allowed: $\oint_{H(p,q)=E} p_i dq_i = n_i h$, where $H(p,q) = E$ is the Hamiltonian of the motion, p_i denotes the momentum values of the system and the q_i denotes the corresponding coordinates, n_i is the respective quantum numbers and $h = 6.62606957 \times 10^{-34}\ \mathrm{m^2kg/s}$ is PLANCK'S CONSTANT. The integral is taken over one period of motion, taken at constant ENERGY, which is defined by the Hamiltonian.

Oncotic pressure

[biomedical] A specific form of OSMOTIC PRESSURE under the Starling principle: COLLOID OSMOTIC PRESSURE, partial pressure (Π) resulting from the large protein molecular solution in BLOOD or biological PLASMA (note that the protein cannot transport through the MEMBRANE of the vessel wall): $\Pi = -(RT/V)\ln(x_{\mathrm{sol}}) \underset{\mathrm{ideal}}{\Rightarrow} iMRT$, where $R = 8.3144621(75)\ \mathrm{J/Kmol}$ is the GAS constant, T is the TEMPERATURE, V is the VOLUME, x_{sol} is the fractional MOLE solute concentration, i is the VAN'T HOFF FACTOR, and M is the molarity (see Figure O.15).

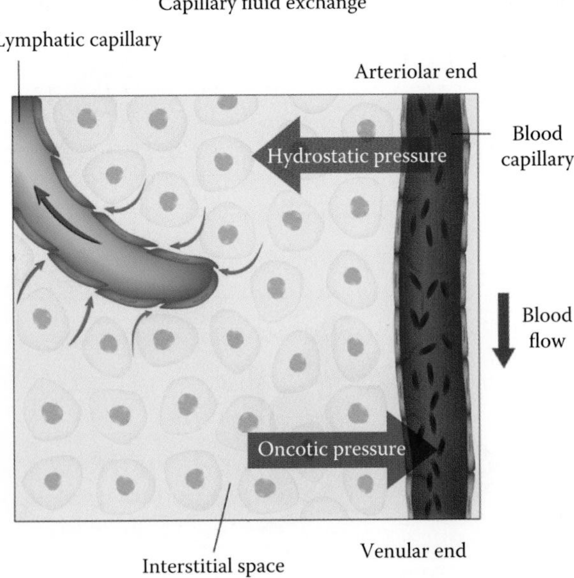

Figure O.15 Oncotic pressure resulting from interstitial fluid solution concentration.

One-dimensional compressible flow

[fluid dynamics] Many of the compressible flows can be modeled as flows through a PIPE, duct or a stream tube for which cross-sectional area changes with relatively small gradual increments in the FLOW direction, relative to the flow velocity. For one-dimensional approximation, there can be no flow components perpendicular to the streamline. Generally, the flow will be steady state. The laws of CONSERVATION OF MASS and momentum apply. The flow conditions under negligible viscous forces are described by the Euler equation: $-(dP/\rho) = vdv$, where P is the pressure, ρ the density, and v the flow velocity. The CONSERVATION OF ENERGY provides the condition that the net change in enthalpy ($H = U + PV$, where U is the internal ENERGY, P is the pressure of the system, and V is the volume) and kinetic energy (E_{kin}) must equal the heat transferred into the control volume and the work done by the FLUID (per unit mass), neglecting work yields: $c_p T + (v^2/2) + dq = c_p\left(T + dT\right) + [(v + dv)^2/2]$, where T is the system temperature, c_p is the SPECIFIC HEAT under constant pressure and $q = \dot{Q}/\dot{m}$, where $\dot{Q}$ is the rate of flow and $\dot{m}$ is the change in mass over time.

One-dimensional flow

[fluid dynamics] For incompressible flow, the conditions are very similar to the compressible flow, with the exception that the Euler equation reduces to BERNOULLI'S EQUATION: $(v^2/2) + (P/\rho) = \text{constant}$, where P is the pressure, ρ is the density, and v is the FLOW velocity.

Onnes, Heike Kamerlingh (1853–1926)

[atomic, general, material science, solid-state, thermodynamics] *See* **KAMERLINGH ONNES, HEIKE.**
A physicist from the Netherlands involved with CRYOGENIC research and the effects of cold temperatures on materials, specifically near the ABSOLUTE ZERO (0 K). Heike Kamerlingh Onnes established the LIQUEFACTION temperature of Helium ($^4_2$He) to be at 4.2 K. Kamerlingh Onnes received the Nobel Prize for Physics in 1913 for his cryogenic work. Dr. Kamerlingh Onnes was a colleague and research associate of JOHANNES DIDERIK VAN DER WAALS (1837–1923) during his appointment at the Delft University of Technology. The work of Kamerlingh Onnes provided a great deal of insight into the conditions near absolute zero, which he approached to close degree. His work on cryogenic cooling and the effect it has on materials also offered a new concept: SUPERCONDUCTIVITY.

Onsager reciprocal relations

[thermodynamics] In thermodynamic systems, the Onsager reciprocal relations are used to express the equality of particular ratios between forces and flows that are not specifically in equilibrium; however, local equilibrium may exist under strict boundary conditions. It was introduced by the Norwegian scientist Lars Onsager (1903–1976) in 1931.

Opaque

[general, solid-state] Not transparent, material property.

Open channel

[fluid dynamics] Flow conditions for a system consisting of a conduit with a free surface. A free surface is where a FLUID has zero parallel shear stress and is simultaneously subject to constant perpendicular normal stress. Examples of free surface are the boundary between two homogenous fluids, such as the liquid–water interface with the AIR in the Earth's ATMOSPHERE. This applies, for instance, to channel FLOW (see Figure O.16).

Figure O.16 Open channel.

Open channel, Bazin equation

[fluid dynamics] Equation for deriving the average flow velocity of water flowing in an OPEN CHANNEL, proposed by Henry E. Bazin (1829–1917) in 1897 (finalized after his death by his assistant Henri P. G. Darcy [1803–1858]). There is a close correlation with the CHÉZY'S FORMULA for flow in an open channel, relying on the Chézy discharge coefficient ($C_{Chézy}$), with relations to the FLOW configurations defined by the hydraulic radius (r_h) and a channel roughness coefficient (k_1), expressed as $C_{Chézy} = 157.6/[1+(k_1/(1/2)r_h)]$. This yields the average velocity (v_{avg}) as $v_{avg} = C_{Chézy}\sqrt{(i_{slope} r_h)}$, where i_{slope} is the slope of the bedding of the flow system (e.g., the bottom of the river) (see Figure O.17).

Figure O.17 Open channel flow, wide canal flowing out into the North Sea.

Open channel, Chézy's formula

[fluid dynamics] An empirical formula designed by the French HYDRAULICS engineer ANTOINE DE CHÉZY (1718–1798) in 1775 that relates river flow (Q) to the dimensions of the channel (i.e., the hydraulic radius, r_h) and slope of the water surface ($s_{surface}$) as $Q = AC_{Chézy}\sqrt{r_h s_{surface}}$, where A is the cross-sectional area of the river, and $C_{Chézy} = 157.6/\{1+[k_1/(r(1/2))]\}$ is the Chézy discharge coefficient.

Open channel, Ganguillet–Kutter equation

[fluid dynamics] An empirical formula designed by the Swiss HYDRAULICS engineers Emile Oscar Ganguillet (1818–1894) and Wilhelm Ruldoph Kutter (1818–1888) in 1869 that relates average river flow velocity (v) to the dimensions of the channel (i.e., the hydraulic radius, r_h) and slope of the water surface ($s_{surface}$, representing the ENERGY drop) as

$$v = \left\{ \frac{\left(a + (b/n_K) + (P/s_{surface})\right)}{\left[1 + (n_K/\sqrt{r_h})\left(a + (P/s_{surface})\right)\right]} \right\} \sqrt{r_h s_{surface}},$$

where n_K is the Kutter roughness factor, which is generally between 0.01 and 0.035 for the usual channel bottom surfaces; the value of Kutter's C, to be used with Chézy's formula, ranged from 22 to 220, where $a \sim 41.66$ for uniform channel and $b \sim 1.811$ for uniform channel are coefficients based on the work of Henri E. Bazin (1829–1917) and P represents the hydrostatic pressure. For values of $s_{surface} > 0.0005$ the term $P/s_{surface}$ can generally be neglected.

Open channel, hydraulic mean depth

[fluid dynamics] The ratio of the cross-sectional area to the surface width. Channels can have many different contour configurations based on the methods in which the channel was dug-out, primarily a V-shape is found (such as the Suez Canal), but over time the shape can change. Other digging mechanism require a more rectangular shape, such as the Panama Canal (see Figure O.18).

Figure O.18 Locks for the Panama Canal.

Open channel, Manning equation

[fluid dynamics] An empirical formula derived by the Irish engineer Robert Manning (1816–1897) in 1851, that relates river flow (Q) to the dimensions of the channel (i.e., hydraulic radius: r_h) and slope of the water surface ($s_{surface}$) $Q = (C_{Chézy}/n)Ar_h^{2/3}i_{slope}^{1/2}$, where n is Manning's coefficient (accounting for flow bed roughness), $C_{Chézy} = 157.6/\{1+[k_1/(r(1/2))]\}$ is the Chézy discharge coefficient, i_{slope} is the slope of the bedding of the flow system (e.g., the bottom of the river), A is the cross-sectional area of the river; which translates to an average velocity: $v_{avg} = (C/n)r_h^{2/3}i_{slope}^{1/2}$.

Open cycle

[fluid dynamics, thermodynamics] The concept of the open cycle relates to thermodynamic processes but has no physical thermodynamic meaning. The concept refers to the external energy supply to, for instance, an engine in the form of fossil fuel and that the remaining, unconverted portion of energy embedded in the spent combustion mixture, is expelled as exhaust to the environment. Thermodynamics cycles can be divided in two categories: power cycles and heat-pump cycles. The power cycle produces power output while the heat-pump cycle has a net power consumption. Gas turbines fall under the power cycle and have an open cycle, representing the intake of fresh air and the exhaust. Other open-cycle dives are combustion engines. This is different from refrigeration, which is a closed cycle, or cyclic system (see Figure O.19).

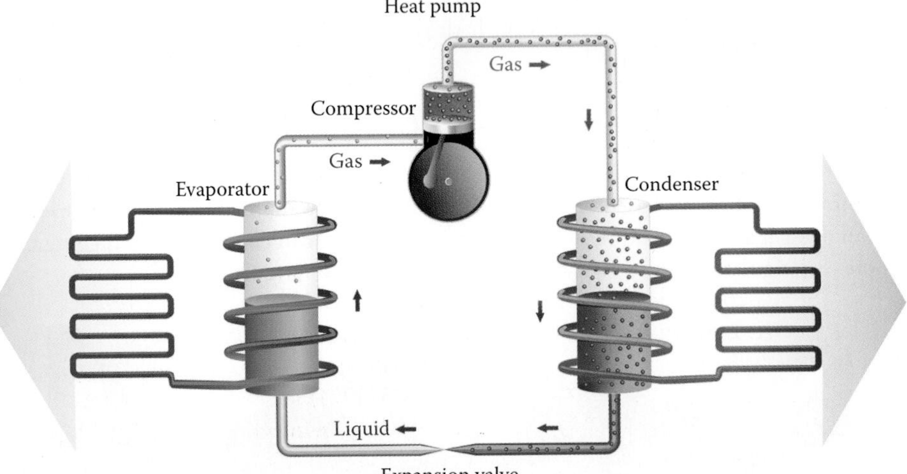

Figure O.19 Example of an open-cycle process: Heat pump cycle diagram.

Open Joule–Brayton cycle

[thermodynamics] A thermodynamic process of combustion, heat engine, or boiler that is per definition open, involving intake and exhaust. The Joule–Brayton cycle is a constant-pressure cycle that defines the operation of the gas turbine engine (e.g., jet engine and electric power generation). It is named after American engineer George Brayton (1830–1892), although it was originally proposed and patented by English engineer John Barber (1734–1801) in 1791. The involvement of English physicist James Prescott Joule (1818–1889) added his name to the process. The Joule–Brayton cycle applies to gas turbines only when both the compression and expansion processes take place in rotating process (machine). The Joule–Brayton cycle is a sequence of an isentropic compression and isentropic turbine. The useful power generated by the turbine is the difference between the compression ($P_T = mc_pT_i(1-(1/\delta)^{(\kappa-1)/\kappa})$, where κ is the specific heat ratio, δ is the pressure drop at the outlet, m is the mass of the combustible, c_p is the specific heat under constant pressure, and T is the temperature) and turbine ($P_T = m\Delta h = mc_p\Delta T$, where h the specific enthalpy): $P = P_T - P_C$, also known as either "Brayton cycle" or "Joule cycle."

Open MRI

[biomedical, imaging] Magnetic RESONANCE imaging system that has a configuration with large bore access, in contrast to the traditional MRI machines that have a narrow cylinder through which the patient is transported on a sliding table during the image-slicing process. Open MRI uses permanent magnets and have lower NOISE than the traditional MRI (see Figure O.20).

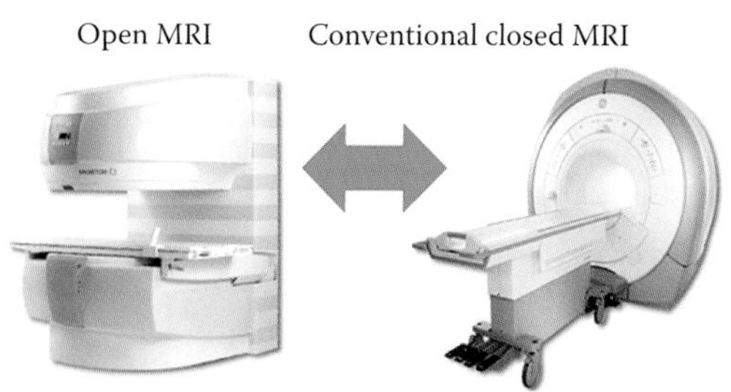

Figure O.20 Comparison of open-design MRI machine versus the conventional closed MRI.

Operational amplifier (OpAmp)

[electronics] A differential input high-gain electronic voltage amplifier, using DC coupling, with usually a single-ended output. By configuring the power supply and the termination impedance ratio across the specific POLES, an output potential can be generated that is hundreds of thousands of times larger than the POTENTIAL DIFFERENCE between the input terminals, the gain, while simultaneously maximizing the signal-to-noise ratio. In contrast, a simple resister, TRANSISTOR, CAPACITOR, and INDUCTOR circuit can generate amplification, but the NOISE follows suit to the SIGNAL. OpAmps were initially used in analog computers. OpAmps can perform basic mathematical operations, such as multiply, differentiate, integrate, and in turn provide filtering opportunities. The mathematical operations are selected based on the configuration of the electronic peripheral components, a capacitor will provide the basic tools for integration. OpAmps are some of the most widely used electronic devices. OpAmps are found in various and vast amounts of consumer devices as well as industrial and scientific devices. OpAmps are generally based on semiconductor materials; however, George A. Philbrick (1913–1974) introduced a VACUUM tube OpAmp in 1948. Following the birth of the transistor in 1947, the first discrete integrated circuit (IC) OpAmp was introduced in 1961 (see Figure O.21).

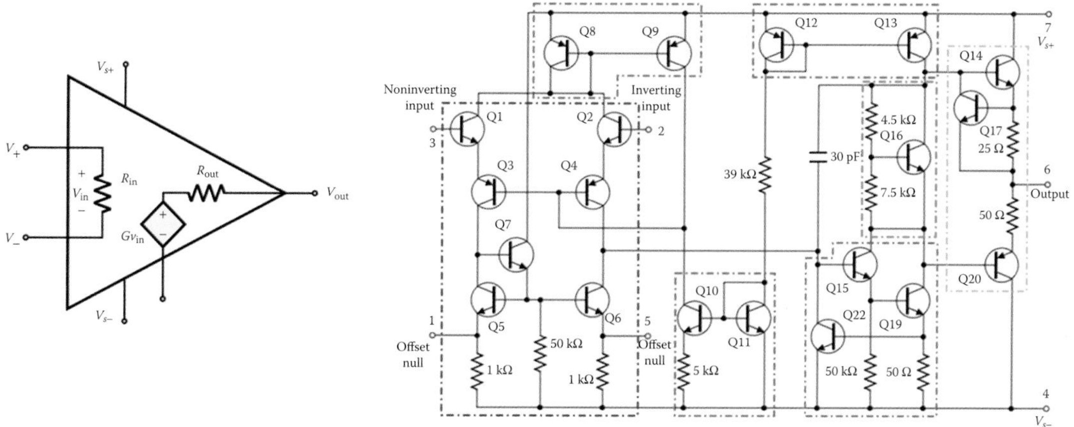

Figure O.21 Diagram of operational amplifier.

Ophthalmology

[biomedical] Medical specialty that focuses on all aspects of the EYE, including but not limited to the ANATOMY, PHYSIOLOGY, and diseases of the eye. This branch of MEDICINE provides support for restoration or enhancement of VISUAL ACUITY. The specific anatomical components of the eye of interest are the LENS shape and functionality, the RETINA, signal communications (e.g., optic nerve), and the pathology of the lens, such as cataract, next to diseases to the optic nerve such as glaucoma (see Figure O.22).

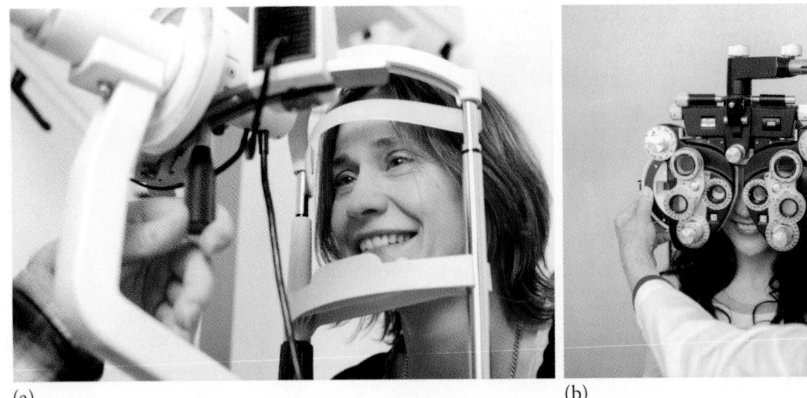

(a) (b)

Figure O.22 (a,b) Ophthalmologic eye exam.

Oppenheimer, Julius Robert (1904–1967)

[energy, general, nuclear, quantum] A theoretical physicist from the United States. President Roosevelt established the MANHATTAN PROJECT in 1941 and appointed Robert Oppenheimer as director in June 1942. The resulting first ATOMIC BOMB was detonated in new Mexico under his guidance on July 16, 1945, followed by two atomic bomb drops on Japan in July and August. Oppenheimer was one of the first scientist to predict the existence of ANTIMATTER based on theoretical analysis (see Figure O.23).

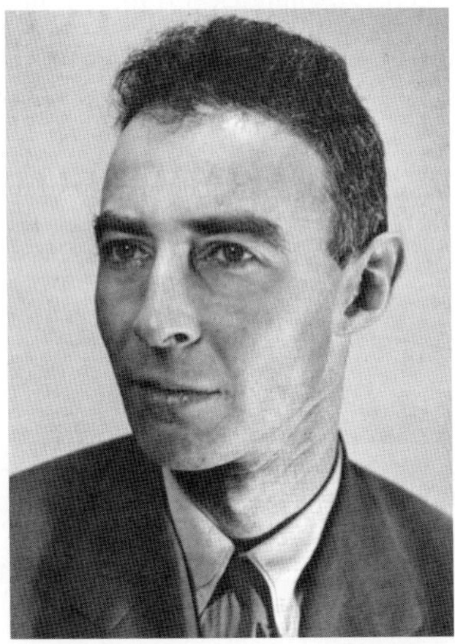

Figure O.23 Julius Robert Oppenheimer (1904–1967). (Courtesy of the Los Alamos National Laboratory, Los Alamos, NM, in 1943.)

Optical activity

[biomedical, chemical, optics] Rotation of polarization ANGLE of ELECTROMAGNETIC RADIATION induced by large complex molecules (chiral molecule), first observed in liquids and gases by JEAN-BAPTISTE BIOT (1774–1862). Two kinds of rotation can be distinguished: dextrorotary (clockwise rotation) designated as (+) and levorotary (rotate counterclockwise) designated as (–). Dextrose will generally rotate the polarized light clockwise, whereas fructose is a levorotary solution. Naturally occurring in milk, dextro-lactic ACID is a food, whereas artificially produced laevo-lactic acid is a poison (in actuality, left-turning lactic acid does occur in natural form however in extremely small percentage). The rotation of linearly polarized light by solid media was first observed by French physicist FRANÇOIS JEAN DOMINIQUE ARAGO (1786–1853) in 1811 in QUARTZ (see Figure O.24).

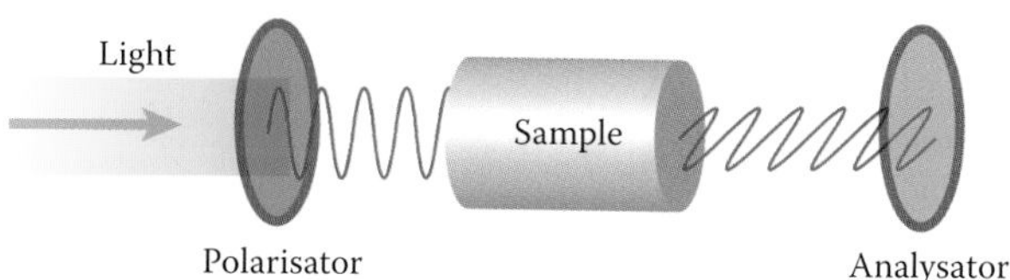

Figure O.24 Optical activity, such as would be experienced with glucose solution.

Optical attenuation screening for concentration

[biomedical, imaging, optics] Optical attenuation imaging method for determination of molecular separation while applying the ULTRACENTRIFUGE principle. The chromophores in the SOLUTE will absorb the incident ULTRAVIOLET or visible light and the density of chromophores is a direct indication of concentration due to the symmetric outline of the sample cell/ampule. The concentration is plotted as a function of location in the vial (also *see* **CHROMATOGRAPHY** *and* **GAS CHROMATOGRAPH**) (see Figure O.25).

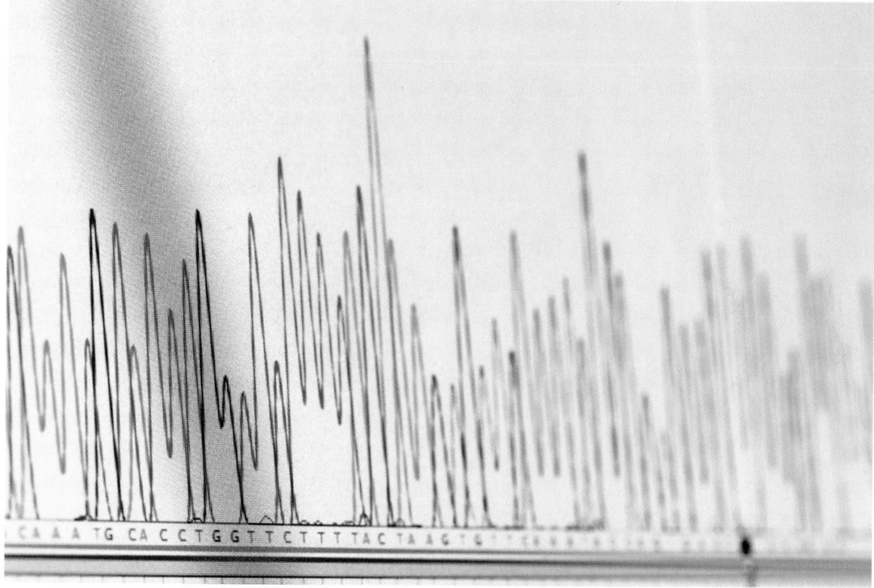

Figure O.25 Chromatography spectral representation of chemical composition for DNA (deoxyribonucleic acid).

Optical biosensor

[biomedical, optics] Biometric sensors that rely on optical interrogation the determination of physiological parameters. One specific example is the attenuation determination of a minimum of two wavelengths for

BLOOD oxygen saturation in the application pulse oximetry. In pulse oximetry, the use of additional wavelengths can eliminate errors resulting from biological variability in blood or surrounding tissues. Additionally, use of OPTICAL ACTIVITY has been applied to the determination of blood GLUCOSE levels with respect to diabetic patients, measured in the EYE (*also see* **PULSE OXIMETRY**) (see Figure O.26).

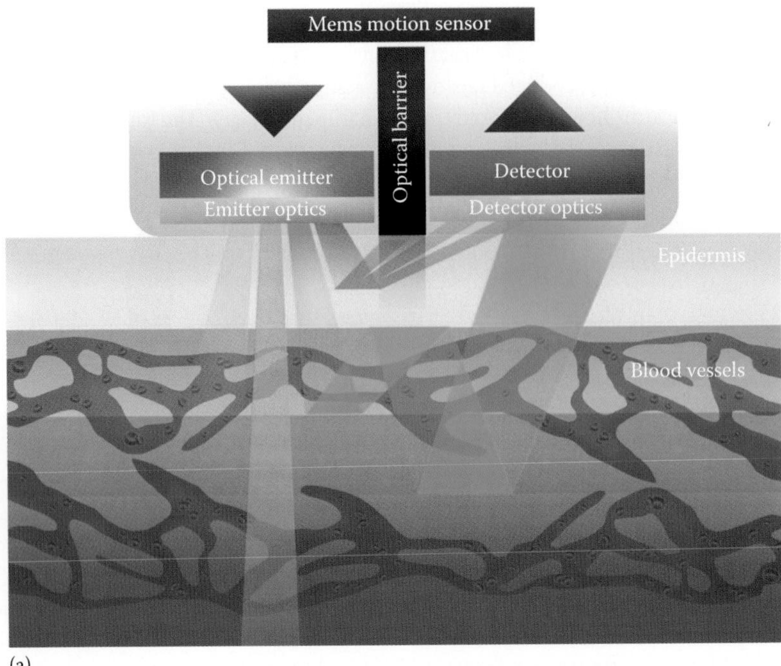

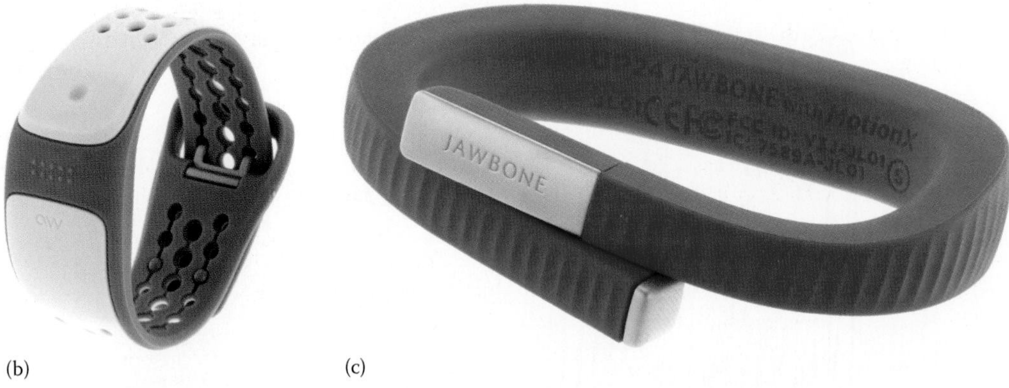

Figure O.26 (a) Optical biosensor using the back-scattered light to gain information about spectral signatures of chemical constituents (e.g., pulse oximetry [b]) and periodically changing events such as blood flow associated with heart pump rate (i.e., heart rate [c]).

Optical coherence tomography

[imaging, optics] Optical scanning imaging technique using interferometry to selectively collect light from axial locations at various depths from the surface used for tomographic IMAGE reconstruction. The general concept of optical coherence tomography (OCT) is very similar to B-SCAN ultrasound in the fact that point-by-point "intensity" data is collected for within a three-dimensional structure. The imaging principles of OCT rely on scanning the device across the surface of the volume of interest, without actually requiring contact, as well as probing the surface location by changing the boundary conditions for the scanning device by optical and mechanical means. A two- or three-dimensional image reconstruction follows after all the required data points within the medium under investigation are collected, stored in a location specific matrix and processed for specific electromagnetic features contained in the optical signal. The main electromagnetic features are AMPLITUDE of the electric and MAGNETIC FIELD, the PHASE of the wave, the orientation of the electric field (POLARIZATION) as well as wavelength specific information. Since the wavelength of light is very small with respect to the scanning range, the phase of the WAVE becomes essential in isolating the relevant information in radiance with respect to the location of interest. Interference will provide a maximum intensity in the SIGNAL collected by a PHOTODETECTOR when the phase of the wave returning from an object under investigation matches the phase of a wave returning from a reference MIRROR in the balancing arm of the INTERFEROMETER. Consider a MICHELSON INTERFEROMETER, with a probing arm and reference arm that are the result of splitting the light from a source in two directions. Once the light returns from the probing arm and reference arm, it is recombined and the superposition principle applies to the two wave-phenomena that is measured by the photocell in the measurement arm. The INTERFERENCE signal in the measurement arm is maximal when the probing arm length matches the reference arm length. This interference pattern is repetitive in increments of the wavelength of the incident light from the source. For a MONOCHROMATIC LIGHT source, this makes the identification of the secondary source location inside the medium being investigated not uniquely defined, because the interference will occur at every wavelength DISTANCE with equal MAGNITUDE. When a broadband source is used, rather than a laser, the interference pattern of all the wavelengths in the spectral distribution of the source will need to coincide for maximal signal magnitude in the measurement arm. The use of a broadband optical source provides the critical aspect for depth resolved imaging under OCT. The advantage of optical imaging is that it can provide high RESOLUTION media-interrogating imaging (better than X-RAY, magnetic RESONANCE imaging, or ULTRASOUND) and it can be performed in situ using hand-held devices, specifically under in vivo conditions for biological imaging. The use of optical imaging also has no concerns for side effects, and light can penetrate deep into turbid media. The concept of OCT was developed at the Massachusetts Institute of Technology (MIT) under the lead of Dr. James G. Fujimoto (mid twentieth century), with team members Carmen A. Pulliafito (mid twentieth century), Eric A. Swanson (mid twentieth century), and David Huang (mid twentieth century) in the late 1980s. The fact that most media and solid objects have light SCATTERING properties, the loss of light due to scattering before returning to the point of introduction at the surface for collection and process provides significant reduction in signal strength. The impact of scattering on the signal quality in the optical interrogation of turbid media places significant constraints on the imaging modality. On the positive side, the in-site high-resolution imaging can be performed under relatively low instrument cost. The OCT technology does not require expensive high-powered laser sources and can be used in FIBER-OPTIC mode or free-space. OCT has an axial resolution of better than 3 μm and lateral in the order of μ, with depth of probing exceeding 3 mm. The depth resolution is a function of the coherence length of the broadband source. The LATERAL RESOLUTION is a function of the device dimensions, specifically the tip diameter of the fiber-optic probe. The depth resolution is directly proportional to the coherence length, where the coherence length (L_c) is defined by the bandwidth ($\Delta\lambda$) of the source with respect to the central wavelength (λ_0): $L_c = (2\log 2/\pi)(\lambda_0^{\,2}/\Delta\lambda)$. For a super-luminescent DIODE, the bandwidth is in the order of $\Delta\lambda = 32$ nm with inherent resolution $\mathrm{Res}_{ax} = 10\ \mu\mathrm{m}$, alternatively a MODE-LOCKED LASER will provide $\Delta\lambda = 350$ nm with inherent resolution $\mathrm{Res}_{ax} = 1.5/n\ \mu\mathrm{m}$, n the index of REFRACTION of the medium. The bandwidth of the pulse laser is defined by the pulse width (Δt) as $\Delta\nu\Delta t \geq 1/(4\pi)$, $\nu = c/\lambda$ the frequency of the ELECTROMAGNETIC RADIATION and c the speed of light. The probing mechanism of the OCT is not a stationary process. In order to provide accuracy about the true maximum signal strength at the balance interferometer depth in the medium a process called "heterodyning" is applied, providing a perturbation around the equilibrium position. Heterodyning ensures the isolation of the exact magnitude of positive interference for all wavelengths in the wave package from the broadband source. By changing the length in the reference arm on a fixed periodic interval (with angular frequency ω_h; frequency ν_h), the acquired signal from the equilibrium depth will fluctuate over time in depth. The source signal is modulated by frequency $\nu_{h,1}$ and the detected signal will be modulated at frequency $\nu_{h,2}$ which yields the interference signal at the detector: $\Psi(t) \propto A^2(t) = \left(A_{1,0}^{\,2}/2\right) + \left(A_{2,0}^{\,2}/2\right) + A_{1,0}A_{2,0}\cos\left(2\pi\left[\nu_{h,1} - \nu_{h,2}\right]t\right) \propto \mathrm{Voltage}(t)$ with $A_{i,0}$ the respective electric field amplitude in the reference signal and sample signal. The modulation of the detection (sample) signal provides a mechanism of phase-locked detection (similar to what is applied in RADIO receivers). This interference signal fluctuates with the BEAT FREQUENCY (ν_b) with respect to the two modulations. The heterodyning provides a significant increase in the signal-to-noise ratio, better than 140 dB. The envelope of this signal contains the information pertaining to the three-dimensionally defined location inside the medium to be used for tomographic image reconstruction. Additionally, the path-difference between the reference arm of the interferometer and the sample arm introduces a time delay: $\tau_{\text{interferometer}} = (L_1 - L_2)/c = (d_{\text{diff}}/c)$ which influences the "visibility" of the interference fringe. The fringe "intensity" is a function of the spectral bandwidth and the path difference as $S(\tau_{\text{interferometer}}) = \int_{\nu_{\min}}^{\nu_{\max}} S(\nu)\left[1+\cos(2\pi\nu\tau_{\text{interferometer}})\right]d\nu$. This in turn translates into a visibility function for the fringe that is the relative difference between the minimum intensity and the maximum intensity: $V_{\text{vis}}(\tau) = \left[(S(\tau)_{\max} - S(\tau)_{\min})/(S(\tau)_{\max} + S(\tau)_{\min})\right] = S_0\left\{1+U(\tau)\cos\left[2\pi\nu_0\tau + \phi(\tau)\right]\right\}$, where $\phi(\tau)$ is the phase shift, and $U(\tau) = \exp\left(-(d_{\text{diff}}/L_c)\right)$ is the envelope of the heterodyne function. With this algorithm, very accurate and sensitive measurements of the localized optical parameters can be performed, thus identifying the medium based on documented reference table of optical parameters and optical effects. Using all the electromagnetic properties various types of OCT devices have been developed, in combination with specific computational techniques: POLARIZATION sensitive, phase resolved, spectroscopic, time-domain, DOPPLER, and Fourier domain. Each respective technique can provide certain particulars about the medium under optical interrogation. The most well-known imaging applications for OCT are for the RETINA of the EYE. Additional application are also found in the intestines by means of endoscopic probing, as well as the investigations of SKIN with respect to for instance stage and spread of cancer growth. The imaging modalities are still relatively confined to surface applications (see Figure O.27).

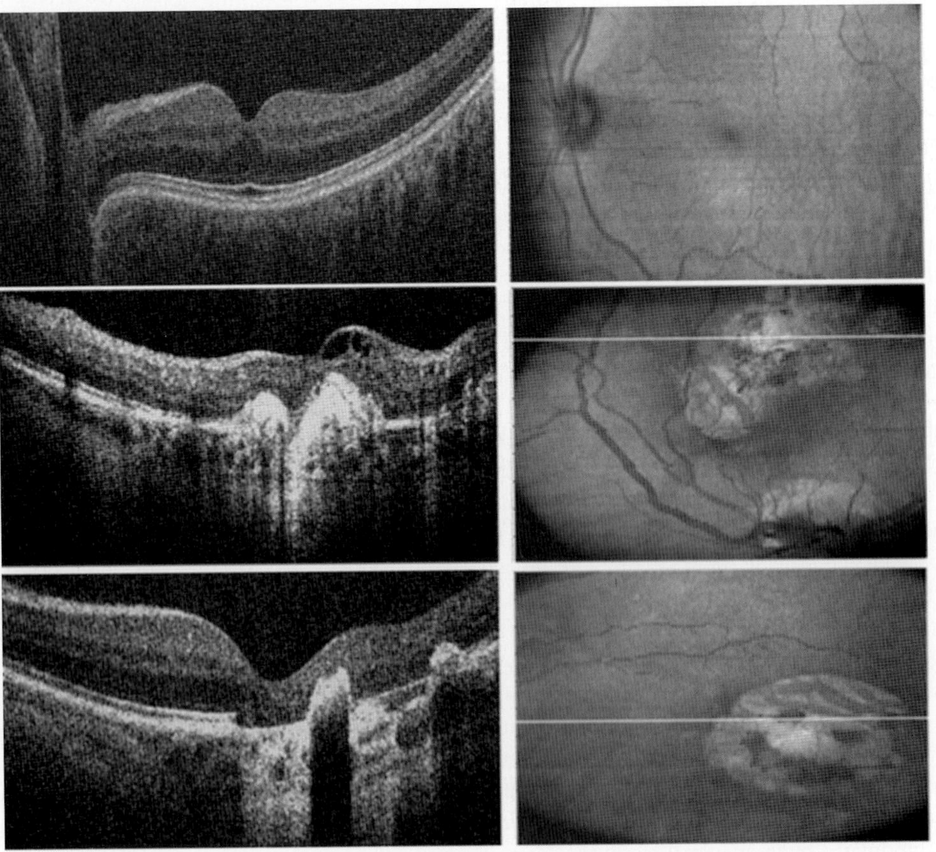

Figure O.27 Optical coherence tomography image. (Courtesy of the Bioptigen, Raleigh, North Carolina.)

Optical density (OD)

[general, optics] Optical attenuation quantity that uses the LOGARITHM of the value for the attenuated radiance with respect to the incident light for a specific optical component and is not referenced against the thickness of the medium: $OD = -\log_{10} T$, where T represents the transmission of light in standard units, usually determined in derived unit of "voltage" based on the sensor unit, detection mechanism and SIGNAL acquisition. The optical density of a medium will be a function of wavelength and has no units.

Optical magnification

[biomedical, engineering, general, optics] Two types of magnification can be distinguished: angular magnification and lateral magnification. Lateral magnification is the ratio of the size of the IMAGE (i) to the object size (o): $M_{mag} = -(i/o)$, where the sign indicates the relative orientation of the image with respect to the object. Angular magnification indicates the observed size by the EYE based on the ANGLE that the object subtends to the eye, where the angle is measured with respect to the optical axis: $M_{mag} = \theta/\theta_N$, where θ_N is the relative angle from the NEAR-POINT of the eye $(\sim 0.25m)$: $\theta_N = h/0.25m$, with h the "height" (vertical length) of the object, and θ the angle at which light rays enter the eye (using the rays originating from the edges for maximum value) (see Figure O.28).

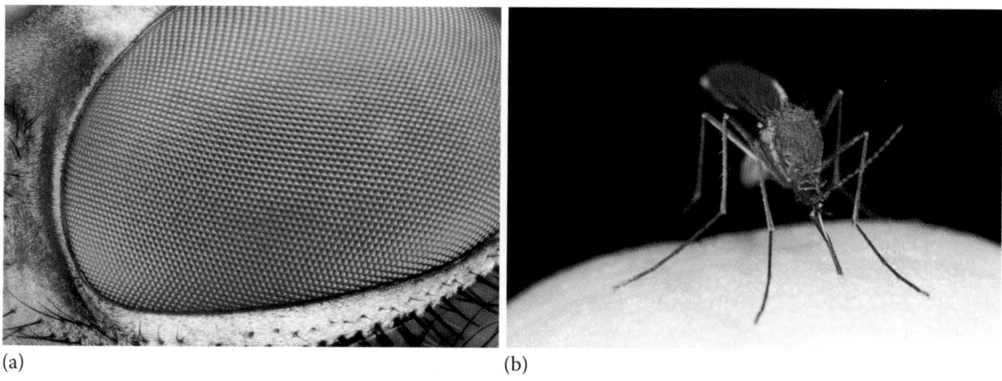

(a) (b)

Figure O.28 (a,b) Magnified view of insect compound eye.

Optical path length (O.P.L.; *D*)

[biomedical, general, optics] The average DISTANCE light can travel in a turbid medium before it is annihilated between SCATTERING interaction and absorption, based on a PROBABILITY distribution of the relative proportions for both events: $D = 1/[\mu_a + (1-g)\mu_s]$, where μ_a is the ABSORPTION COEFFICIENT, μ_s is the SCATTERING coefficient, and g is the scattering anisotropy factor (see Figure O.29).

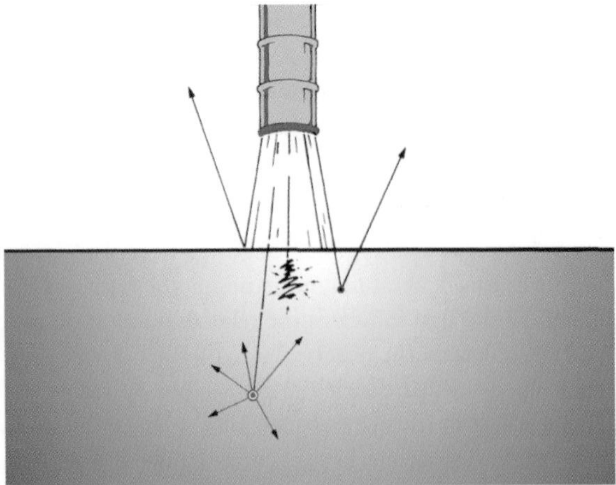

Figure O.29 Representation of five photons traveling in a turbid medium until each respective photon is finally absorbed or leaves the medium through backscatter. The optical free path for air is virtually infinite, providing blue-skies and red sunsets.

Optical sensing

[electromagnetism, optics, theoretical] Any mechanism that relies on light or ELECTROMAGNETIC RADIATION as the means to derive a physical property of a medium or a biological specimen. The detection mechanism will use a sensor unit that converts the quantity of light (i.e., fluence or radiance) in an electric SIGNAL for further processing. Detection can be performed by a variety of photoelectric devices; pin diodes, solar CELL, PHOTOMULTIPLIER TUBE, DIODE as well as chemical and mechanical devices such as the ELASTOMER polydimethylsiloxane (PDMS, a pressure sensor polymer). One specific application of optical sensing is in character recognition, retinal scans and the like, based on a two-dimensional pattern of light and dark (see Figure O.30).

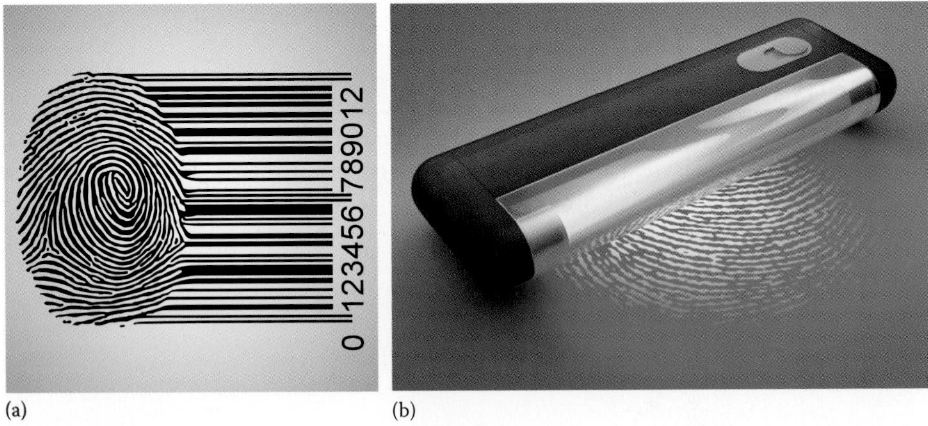

Figure O.30 (a) Optical fingerprint recognition using ultraviolet light and (b) to detect the greasy imprint of the pattern of ridges on the fingertip.

Optical spectra

[optics] The wavelength content of the collected light after interaction with a medium, generally resulting from a broadband LIGHT SOURCE. There are several kinds of spectra that can be distinguished based on the manner it is created or the mechanism of action involved in the formation of the emitted LIGHT. Two kinds of spectra are recognized: ABSORPTION and EMISSION. The emission spectra, for instance, is the creation of light from a high TEMPERATURE SOLID, liquid, or dense gas, which will be continuous, whereas a low pressure GAS will emit a LINE or BAND spectrum. An ABSORPTION SPECTRUM will display gaps representative of the ELEMENTS in the exposed medium. Specific spectral analysis techniques are available to retrieve specific details about the light-matter interaction. The specific light interaction on a molecular or atomic level can provide identification mechanisms for the presence and volumetric MAGNITUDE of chemical constituents. Molecular spectra can be recognized based on ELECTRON SPIN states (specifically electron paramagnetic resonance), molecular VIBRATION, molecular rotation, atomic scissor-action within the MOLECULE, as well as electronic states. Specific spectroscopic analyses include, for instance, Raman spectroscopy, vibrational circular dichroism spectroscopy, hyperspectral imaging, and laser-induced breakdown spectroscopy (see Figure O.31).

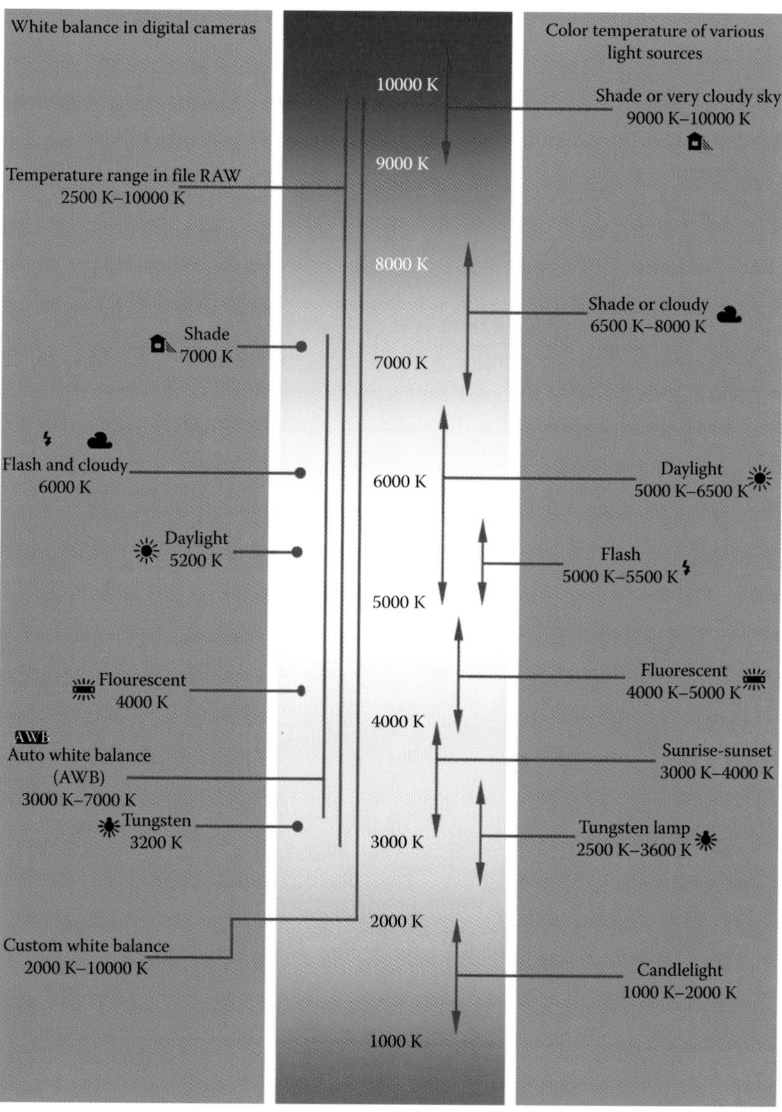

Figure O.31 Chart representing color temperature, broad spectral emission from solids.

O

Optically dense

[optics, solid-state] Solid, liquid, or GAS that has a molecular separation that is smaller than the wavelength of the light incident on the medium. For both solids and liquids, the molecular spacing is of the order of 20–30 nm. For gases, the conditions under standard temperature and pressure yield on average a separation of 300 nm. Under all of these circumstances, the internal electric field may be associated with a DIPOLE. The molecules in suspension experience an electric external field, such as the ELECTROMAGNETIC RADIATION, as well as a secondary field produced by neighboring molecular dipoles. The external field produce an OSCILLATING DIPOLE moment with associated RADIATION. This entails that the molecules in an optically dense medium will be coupled. The net result of electromagnetic (EM) radiation interaction with an optically dense medium is a superposition of the molecular interaction with the incident WAVE. The re-emitted wave can in bulk be described by either Mie or RAYLEIGH SCATTERING theory, depending on the respective wavelength ranges. At the interface between two media with a large quantity of homogeneously distributed molecules, the presumably randomly re-emitted light converts on average into SNELL'S LAW for the refracted light.

Optics

[general] Scientific discipline that investigates and utilizes ELECTROMAGNETIC RADIATION, primarily the visible spectrum, but not limited to that. Optics deals with REFRACTION, diffraction, reflection, IMAGE formation, LENS design, spectral analysis and general ENERGY transfer, FLUORESCENCE, as well as general atomic and molecular interactions. Optics investigates both the PARTICLE aspect of photons as well as the WAVE property. Optics is also engaged with the design and development of physical detection mechanisms available for diagnosing and quantifying electromagnetic radiation and its sources. Most optical interactions can be described on a rigorous level with MAXWELL EQUATIONS. The interaction of light rays at an interface can be described by geometric optics, applying laws of refraction and reflection on rays representing the path of photons. Physical optics applies to a more comprehensive model of light, including the wave phenomena, explain experiences such as diffraction and INTERFERENCE that cannot be accounted for using geometric optics. Most optical phenomena can be accounted for using a classical electromagnetic description, however, phenomena that rely on both the wave and particle properties requires a QUANTUM mechanical approach. Historically optics can be traced back as far as the ancient Egyptians and Mesopotamians in 700 BC, for their use of lenses made from polished crystal, often QUARTZ. The development of the MICROSCOPE formed an important breakthrough in 1595 by HANS JANSEN (sixteenth century, no exact dates), next to the design of the refracting TELESCOPE in 1608 by HANS LIPPERSHEY (1570–1619). Up to the proposition of the wave

theory of light by CHRISTIAAN HUYGENS (1629–1695) in 1690, the ray (corpuscular) theory of light prevailed. Visual perception (VISION) forms a small but important aspect of optics (see Figure O.32).

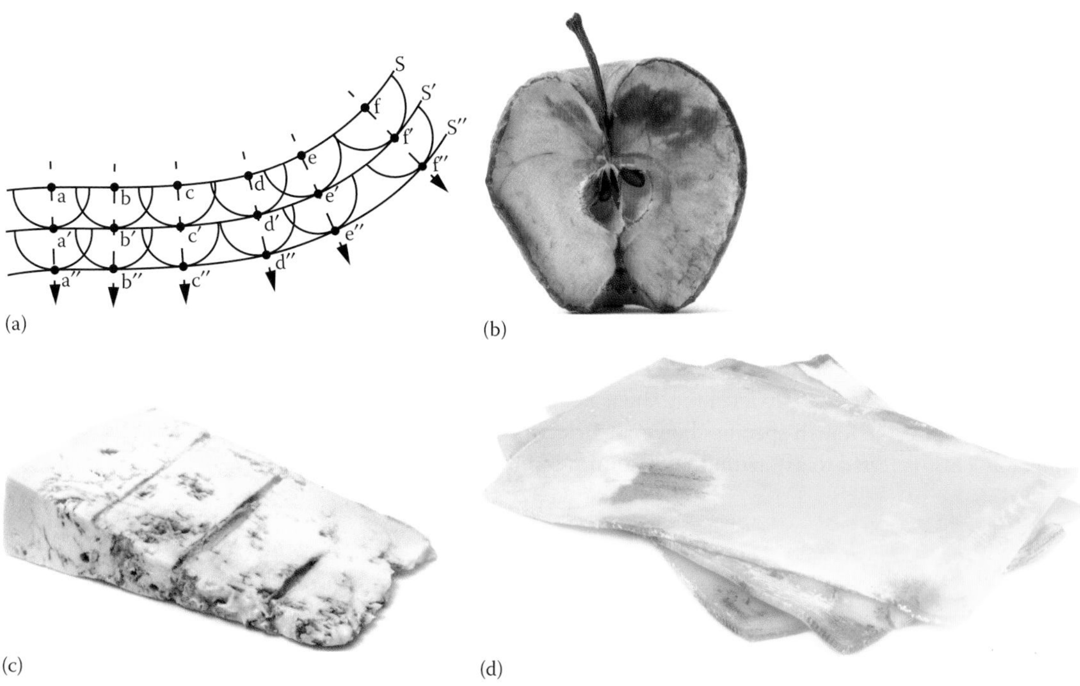

Figure O.32 (a) Huygens wavefront. The eye also performs an optical inspection, which is spectrally interpreted by the brain, warning the consumer about (b) rotten fruit or (c,d) moldy cheese.

Optoacoustic imaging

[optics, thermodynamics] *See* **PHOTO-ACOUSTIC IMAGING.**

Orbital angular momentum

[atomic, nuclear] Property that may refer to either electromagnetic waves or a QUANTUM MECHANICS angular momentum operator. In general classical mechanics, the operator for the angular momentum is the cross product of the direction ($\vec{r}$) and the moment ($\vec{p} = m\vec{v}$): $\vec{L} = \vec{r} \times \vec{p}$. For a body (of any shape) rotating around a central axis the body will be constructed of a finite number of mass ELEMENTS with respective angular momenta that are linked to the MOMENT OF INERTIA of these respective elements (combining to the rigid body): I, as $L = M_0 v_t r$, with v_t the tangential component of the velocity, M_0 the mass of the PARTICLE at orbit radius r. Under the condition of no torque resulting from central force, alternatively: $L = I\omega$, where ω is the ANGULAR VELOCITY. On an atomic level, the angular momentum will describe the orbits of ELEMENTARY PARTICLES and the description will require a quantum mechanical approach. In case the potential ENERGY for the atomic structure depends only on the DISTANCE $\vec{r}$, the WAVE EQUATION can ultimately be solved and separated to yield the angular component. In classical mechanics, the angular momentum will always be conserved due to the absence of external torque. Under quantum-mechanical approach the orbital angular momentum for a particle subject to a central potential will have EIGENVALUE solutions. In a spherical coordinate system (r, θ, ϕ), the various components of the orbital angular momentum can be derived from the respective operator; $L_{\text{op}}{}^2 = L_{x,\text{op}}{}^2 + L_{y,\text{op}}{}^2 + L_{z,\text{op}}{}^2 = -\hbar^2\left[(1/\sin\theta)(\partial/\partial\theta)\big(\sin\theta(\partial/\partial\theta)\big) + (1/\sin^2\theta)(\partial^2/\partial\phi^2)\right]$, which does not depend on r; where $\hbar = h/2\pi$, $h = 6.62606957 \times 10^{-34}$ m^{2}kg/s Planck's constant. The z-component: $L_{z,\text{op}} = (\hbar/i)(\partial/\partial\phi)$. The ensuing angular momentum now becomes: $L = \hbar\sqrt{\ell(\ell+1)}$, where ℓ is the orbital angular momentum quantum number, which stands in contrast to the classical mechanics Bohr angular momentum: $L = n\hbar$, now obsolete for atomic MOTION. Note that the z-component still satisfies the Bohr equivalent as $L_z = m\hbar$, where m is other quantum number characterizing the spherical harmonic functions as solutions to the SCHRÖDINGER EQUATION with wavefunction $\psi_{n,\ell,m}$, where n is the primary quantum number. The PARITY of the wavefunction is dependent only on the angular part of the function. The parity of the harmonic oscillator indicates the symmetry or antisymmetry of the WAVEFUNCTION: $\psi_{n,\ell,m} = \psi_{n,\ell,m}(-x)$, or respectively $\psi_{n,\ell,m} = -\psi_{n,\ell,m}(-x)$, and is defined by the ORBITAL ANGULAR MOMENTUM QUANTUM NUMBER (ℓ) as $Parity = (-1)^{\ell}$.

Orbital angular momentum quantum number (ℓ)

[atomic, general, nuclear] Integer characterizing the spherical harmonic functions of the atomic wavefunction, defined as one of the QUANTUM numbers. In solutions to the SCHRÖDINGER EQUATION ($H\psi = E\psi$), the wave functions ψ are obtained, which describes the PROBABILITY of finding electrons at certain ENERGY levels within an ATOM. The WAVE functions for the electrons are called "atomic orbitals." The electrons in an atom are described by four quantum numbers. The first three quantum number are specifying the particular orbital of interest (PRINCIPAL QUANTUM NUMBER n, angula quantum number ℓ, and MAGNETIC QUANTUM NUMBER m_ℓ), while the fourth specifies how many electrons can occupy that orbital (spin quantum number m_s), also referred to as "azimuthal quantum number" (see Figure O.33).

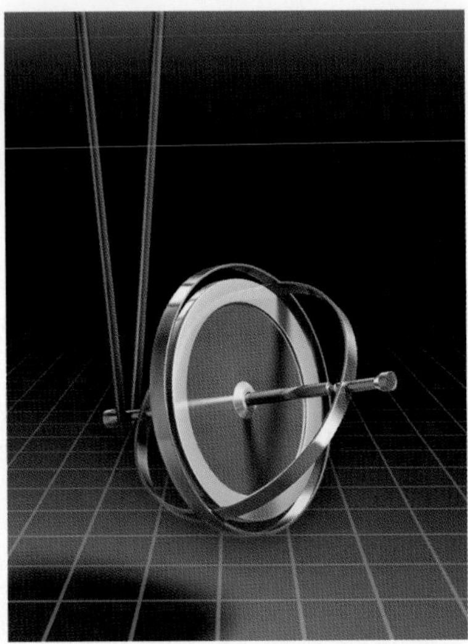

Figure O.33 Orbital angular momentum of a spinning top providing the torque to allow the top to hang at an angle with a suspension sling (i.e., gyroscope effect).

Orbital magnetic moment

[atomic, nuclear] Quantum number used to define the orientation in space of an electron orbit of a given ENERGY (n) and shape (ℓ). The QUANTUM number subdivides the SUBSHELL into individual orbitals; each subshell holds respective electrons, with $2\ell + 1$ orbitals in each subshell.

Orbital magnetic quantum number (m_ℓ)

[general] Quantum number defining the orientation in space of an orbital for a given ENERGY (n) and shape (ℓ); $m_\ell = -\ell, \ldots, 0, \ldots \ell$. A sphere ($\ell = 0$) can only be oriented in one way in space. On the other hand, orbitals that have different shapes, such as polar ($\ell = 1$) or cloverleaf ($\ell = 2$), can have an orientation in different directions. A third quantum number is therefore needed to define the orientation in space of the orbital. The MAGNETIC QUANTUM NUMBER is named this way since the different orientations of orbitals were first observed under the influence of an external magnetic field. This QUANTUM NUMBER is one of three

coordinates that result from solving the Schrödinger wave equations, providing the principal (n), angular (ℓ), and magnetic (m_ℓ) quantum numbers. These quantum numbers describe the size, shape, and orientation in space of the orbitals on an ATOM. In contrast to the Bohr model, which is a one-dimensional model that only uses one quantum number to describe the size with respect to the distribution of electrons in the atom. This quantum number subdivides the SUBSHELL into individual orbitals which hold the electrons; there are $2\ell+1$ orbitals in each subshell. In this light, the s subshell has only one orbital, subsequently the p subshell has three orbitals, ensuing for the following ELECTRON SHELLS.

Orbital quantum number, (ℓ)

[high-energy, nuclear, quantum, solid-state] *See* **ORBITAL ANGULAR MOMENTUM QUANTUM NUMBER.**

Orbital velocity

[computational, fluid dynamics, mechanics, thermodynamics] There are three specific cases of orbital velocity: the speed of a body in orbital under the influence of a GRAVITATIONAL FIELD; the velocity pattern of MOTION of particles in WAVE MOTION, in particular in water and wind waves; the equivalent SCHRÖDINGER WAVE EQUATION velocity of a bound electron required to maintain its orbital kinetic ENERGY. Generally, the orbital velocity describes a balance in two forces, yielding a tangential velocity, and angular velocity (*see* **ANGULAR VELOCITY**) (see Figure O.34).

Figure O.34 Concept of orbital velocity for geosynchronous telecommunication satellite.

Orbits

[general] Revolution of an object (man-made or natural) moving in a pattern around another celestial body. The EARTH is in orbit around the Sun. Near-circular orbits are called "Keplerian." Satellites revolve by remaining in a fixed location with respect to the earth's geometry, so that we do not have to adjust the (dish-) ANTENNA aimed at the SATELLITE used for television reception. The fixed location with respect to Earth refers to the fact that the satellite is in the GEOSYNCHRONOUS ORBIT or GEOSTATIONARY ORBIT. Spy satellites and weather satellites, on the other hand, are moving around in variable or predetermined patterns, scanning the surface in a grit-pattern. Other forms of orbital motion are equatorial orbit,

graveyard orbit, low Earth orbit, medium Earth orbit, MOLNIYA ORBIT, polar orbit, subsynchronous orbit, and supersynchronous orbit (*also see* **EARTH SATELLITE**) (see Figure O.35).

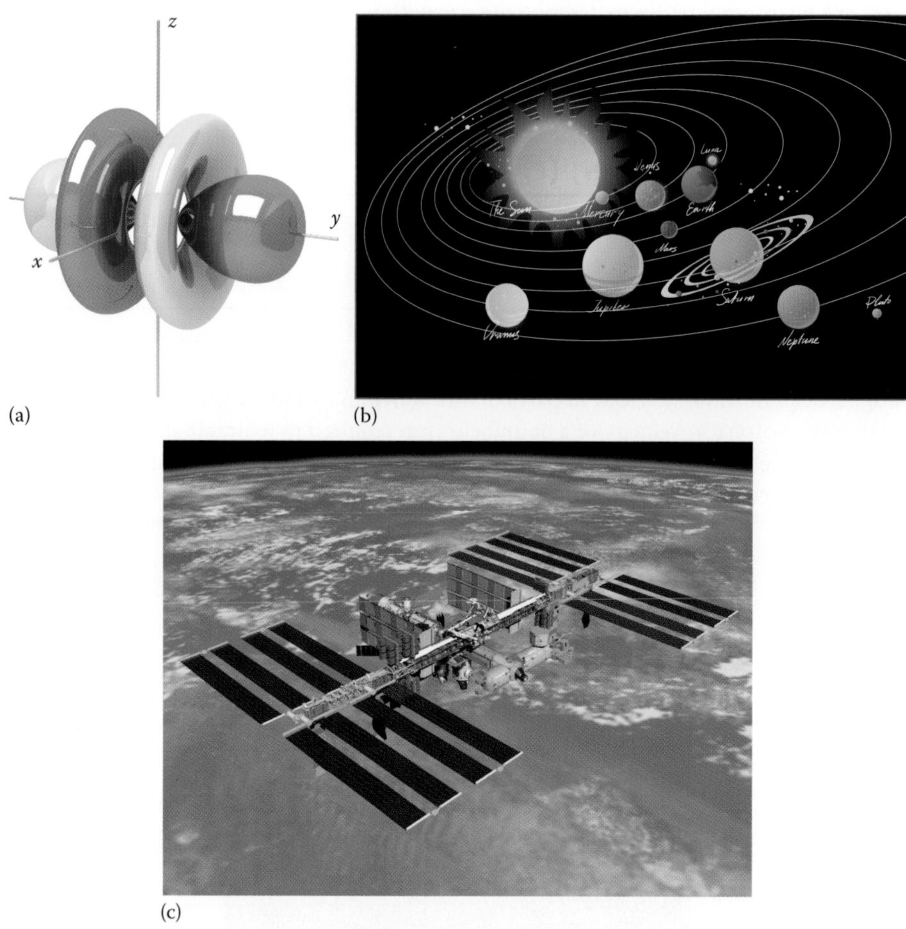

Figure O.35 Examples of orbit: (a) atomic orbit diagram, (b) planetary orbits in our solar system, and (c) a space station in orbit with an approaching space shuttle. (Courtesy of NASA)

Orbits in hydrogen atom

[atomic, nuclear] The COULOMB POTENTIAL for the HYDROGEN ATOM is primarily spherically symmetric and can be defined as a radially dependent function: $V = V(r) = -(Ze^2/4\pi\varepsilon_0 r)$, where Z is the charge number, $e = 1.60217657 \times 10^{-19}\,C$ the electron charge, r the DISTANCE to the core, and $\varepsilon_0 = 8.85419 \times 10^{-12}\ \mathrm{C^2/Nm^2}$ the permittivity of free space. The angular momentum operator applied to the WAVEFUNCTION yields a description that is only a function of the radius ($R(r)$): $(1/r^2)(d/dr)[r^2(dR(r)/dr)] + (2\mu_m/\hbar)[E + (Ze^2/4\pi\varepsilon_0 r) - (\ell(1+\ell)\hbar^2/2\mu_m r^2)]R(r) = 0$, with SOLUTION $R(r) = G(r)e^{-(r/a_0)}$, where $G(r)$ is the GREEN'S FUNCTION power series truncated to a polynomial (if not, the solution will diverge), $a_0 = 4\pi\varepsilon_0\hbar^2/Z\mu_m e^2$ the Bohr first radius ($a_n = n(a_0/Z)$), $\mu_m = m_1 m_2/(m_1 + m_2)$ the REDUCED MASS, m_i the respective masses of the system, $E_n = -(\mu_m Z^2 e^4 / 32\pi^2 \varepsilon_0^2 \hbar^2 n^2)$, where n is an integer that is greater than the angular quantum number ℓ, $\hbar = h/2\pi$, $h = 6.62606957 \times 10^{-34}$ m^{2}kg/s Planck's constant (see Figure O.36).

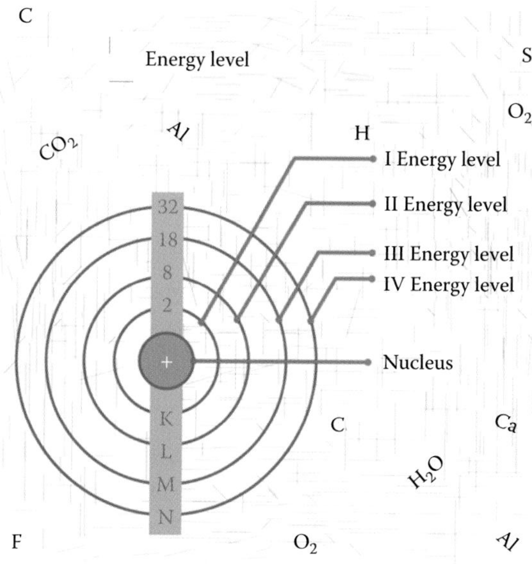

Figure O.36 Energy levels for orbital electron in atoms, including hydrogen.

Orbits of particles in water waves

[fluid dynamics] The WAVE-MOTION of the water surface can in principle be described as a circular MOTION of the individual water molecules (see Figure O.37).

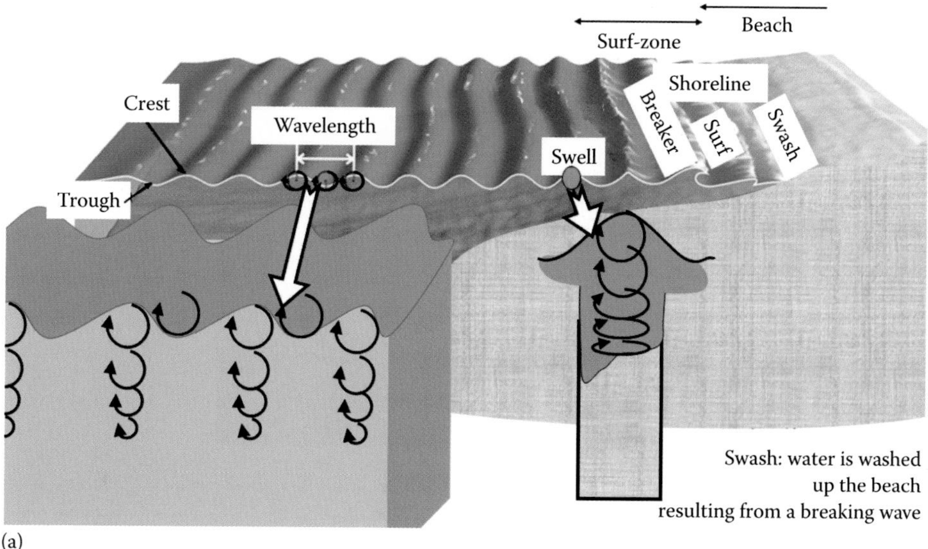

Figure O.37 (a) Diagram of water segments performing orbital motion, with the greatest "amplitude" at the surface.
(Continued)

(b) (c)

Figure O.37 (Continued) (b) "surf" wave, used for "surfing", and (c) types of waves.

Ordinary differential equations

[computational] Mathematical expression describing a function of one single independent variable and the respective derivatives of this variable in various orders, for instance $[dy(t)/dt] = f\left(t, y(t)\right)$. This stands in contrast to a "partial differential equation," which may include terms with respect to more than one independent variable.

Oresme, Nicolas (1320–1382)

[computational, general] Scientist and philosopher from France, also known as Nicole Oresme, Nicolas d'Oresme, or Nicholas Oresme. Oresme's work provided elementary foundations for the development of advanced mathematics as well as his contributions on the mathematical definitions in science. Oresme is also respected as the greatest medieval economist. Most of his scientific and economic work was based on the elementary work of Aristotle (384–322 BC) (see Figure O.38).

Figure O.38 Nicolas Oresme (1320–1382).

Organ of Corti

[acoustics, biomedical, electronics, general] Auditory ELEMENT in the cochlea of the INNER EAR. The cochlea has a spiral shape, resembling a snail shell. The organ of Corti is found on the scala-media side on the BASILAR MEMBRANE. The Organ of Corti derived its name from the pathologist Marquis Alfonso Giacomo Gaspare Corti (1822–1876) from Italy who described it. The receptor aspect of the organ of Corti has two types of receptor cells: the inner hair CELL and the outer hair cell. Each of these hair cells have different functions. The organ of Corti contains two rows of rod cells, arranged on the MEMBRANE in the form of a minute arch. To the arch, four rows of hair cells are fixed, consisting of one row on the inner side and three on the outer side. The function of the Organ of Corti is the conversion of SOUND vibrations into nerve pulses. The sound waves are transmitted along the cochlear duct, which form a LONGITUDINAL WAVE that results in the displacement of the tips of the hair, and as such flexing the hair which in turn generates an action-potential. These action-potential impulses are transmitted by the auditory nerve, or cochlear nerve, to the brain, at which location they are interpreted as sound with the frequency associated with the location on the basilar membrane. The detection of long wavelengths are farther into the cochlea (toward the apex), whereas the high frequency are detected close to the entry point at the oval membrane (the base) (see Figure O.39).

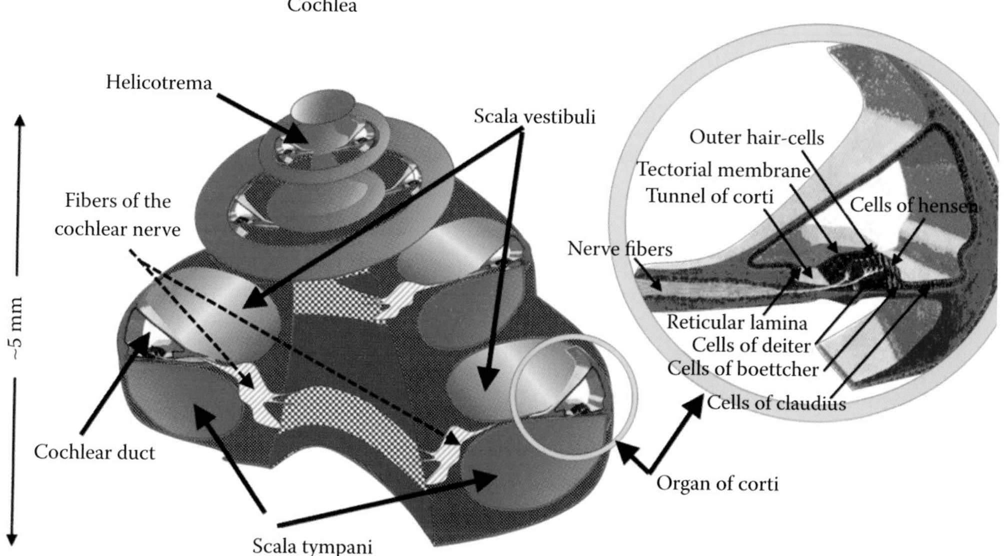

Figure O.39 Organ of Corti, as part of the cochlea, part of the "inner-ear".

Organic scintillator

[nuclear] In NUCLEAR MEDICINE generally there are three types of scintillators: inorganic crystals and organic scintillators next to photomultiplier tubes. Each type of scintillator has the general function of converting ionizing radiation (short wavelength X-RAY; high ENERGY particles), as well as NEUTRON rays, in lower energy photons that can be detected with photocells, photographic film, or the HUMAN EYE. The electronic detection will allow for digital storage, as provided by charge-coupled device array detectors. In inorganic or crystalline detectors, the scintillation mechanism is a direct function of the structure of the crystal LATTICE, using the IONIZATION aspects of energy transfer between selected energy bands. Organic scintillators provide

detection based on the FLUORESCENCE mechanism arises from transitions in the energy levels of a single molecule due to the incident ionizing radiation, no crystalline structure required. Fluorescence is as such detected independently of the physical state of the medium. Organic scintillators are generally composed of aromatic hydrocarbons. An example of an organic scintillator is anthracene as a fluorescent medium. Scintillators are used for X-ray detection (e.g., computed TOMOGRAPHY scan), GAMMA RAY detection, as well as high energy particle PHYSICS. Organic scintillators are generally more useful in high energy X-ray detection and have limited spectroscopic application, depending on the design; primarily, in PARTICLE spectroscopy (neutrons and charged particles). Plasticized organic scintillators have superior response time of a few nanoseconds (see Figure O.40).

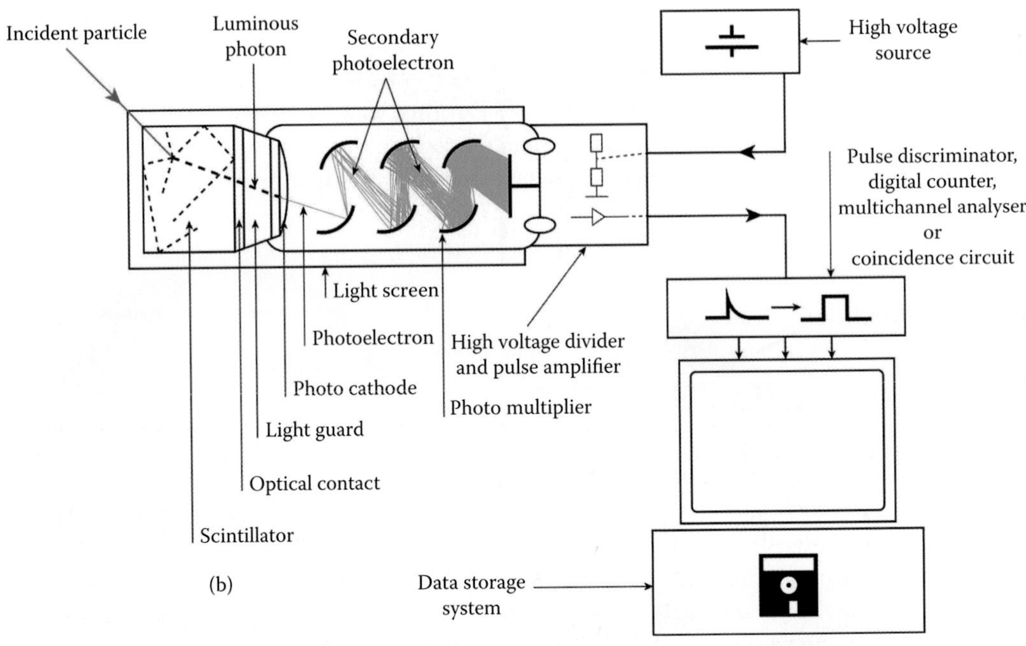

Figure O.40 (a) Principle of organic scintillator and (b) Photomultiplier tube.

Orifice

[fluid dynamics, thermodynamics] An opening, puncture, hole, exhaust, vent, void, or mouth, such as those found in a tube, PIPE, conduit, plate, or a body of material (organic or inorganic). An ORIFICE plate is a tool designed to measure FLOW rate, and can be used to reduce pressure or restrict flow.

Orifice, flow restrictions

[fluid dynamics] In any FLOW system, there is often the desire to control either or the flow and pressure pertaining to that LIQUID. Pressure and flow are interdependent yet different. Controlling the flow or pressure can affect to other and the mechanism of control can lead to unexpected, inconsistent, or even "disastrous" results. Both pressure and flow control can be achieved, under the proper conditions, using a restriction in the plumbing line. Common tools are manual valves and fixed orifices of varying dimensions. Examples are found kitchen and bathroom faucets, also known as "restrictive flow orifices."

Ørsted, Hans Christian (Oersted) (1777–1851)

[energy, general, optics] A Danish scientist. Together with ANDRE-MARIE AMPÈRE (1775–1836) their groundbreaking work led to the revelation of the link between ELECTRICITY and MAGNETISM in 1819, resulting in an upsurge in the theoretical and experimental efforts in this field (see Figure O.41).

Figure O.41 Hans Christian Ørsted (1777–1851) (Oersted).

Orthogonal function

[atomic, computational] Functions that are perpendicular to each other, as considered a generalized version of vectors. The analysis of periodic functions with FOURIER ANALYSIS yields orthogonal functions. Two functions (ϕ) are orthogonal within a segment (a, b) if the dyadic expression yields: $\int_a^b \phi_m{}^* \phi_n dx = 0$, where $\phi_m{}^*$ is the complex conjugate. Examples of orthogonal functions are BESSEL FUNCTIONS, Chebyshev polynomials, Hermite polynomials, Legendre polynomials, sine and cosine, Spherical harmonics, Walsh functions, and Zernike polynomials, and generally EIGENFUNCTION with different eigenvalues are also orthogonal (e.g., Hamiltonian). One specific example of orthogonality applies to the Legendre polynomials, also referred to as "Legendre functions of the first kind," or "zonal harmonics," which are solutions to the LEGENDRE DIFFERENTIAL EQUATION. The Legendre polynomials are orthogonal over the segment $(-1, 1)$ as defined $\int_{-1}^{1} \phi_m(x)\phi_n(x)dx = [2/(2n+1)]\delta_{mn}$, where δ_{mn} is the Kronecker delta.

Oscillating dipole

[general] Dipoles can be electronic, MAGNETIC, or mechanical (ACOUSTICS, FLUID DYNAMICS). A DIPOLE source consists of two monopole sources of equal strength but opposite PHASE (mechanical, acoustic) or opposite charge (atomic/molecular), separated by a small DISTANCE in relation to the wavelength of emission. Molecular dipoles are the most common and reveal information about material properties. Molecular dipoles were studied in great detail by PETER J. W. DEBYE (1884–1966), a chemist from the Netherlands. As a consequence, dipole moments are measured in "debye" units in his honor. Oscillating dipoles will produce some form of radiating ENERGY,

electromagnetic, and mechanical. An example of the electronic dipole is an analog ANTENNA. When the dipole is much shorter in length than the wavelength of the emitted radiation, the emitted POWER (P) at specific oscillation FREQUENCY ($\nu = \omega/2\pi$, ω the ANGULAR VELOCITY) as a function of the SOLID ANGLE (Ω) of the antenna can be defined as $dP/d\Omega = (\omega^4 P_o^2/32\pi^2\varepsilon_0 c^3)\sin\theta$, where P_0 is the power at the source, $\varepsilon_0 = 8.85419\times10^{-12}$ C^2/Nm^2 is the permittivity of free space, and $c = 2.99792458\times10^8$ m/s is the speed of light.
Mechanical examples are an unboxed SPEAKER or a two-beater kitchen mixer in a highly viscous medium (e.g., dough), generates a dipole FLOW field, with an acoustic dipole as the oscillating representative model. On more simplified terms, the oscillating acoustic dipole generates a convolution of "BUBBLE flow." Both pressure and velocity distributions have to be of the form of a SPHERICAL WAVE. The VELOCITY POTENTIAL (Φ_{bubble}) of a single oscillating bubble is described as $\Phi_{bubble} = (1/2)A(t)r^2\left(3\cos^2\theta - 1\right)$, where $A(t)$ is the periodic AMPLITUDE (generally expressed as pressure P or displacement), r is the radius to the source, and θ is the angle with the axis. The acoustic radiation field of a dipole (bipole), pair of two identical monopoles separated by a distance d (small with respect to the wavelength), can be represented as follows: $P(r) = P_0(e^{-i(kr_1-\omega t)}/r_1) + P_0(e^{-i(kr_2-\omega t)}/r_2) \equiv 2P_0(e^{-i(kr-\omega t)}/r)\cos\left(k\sin\left(\theta d/2\right)\right)$, where P represents pressure, $k = 2\pi/\lambda$ is the wavenumber for wavelength λ, and t is the elapsed time (see Figure O.42).

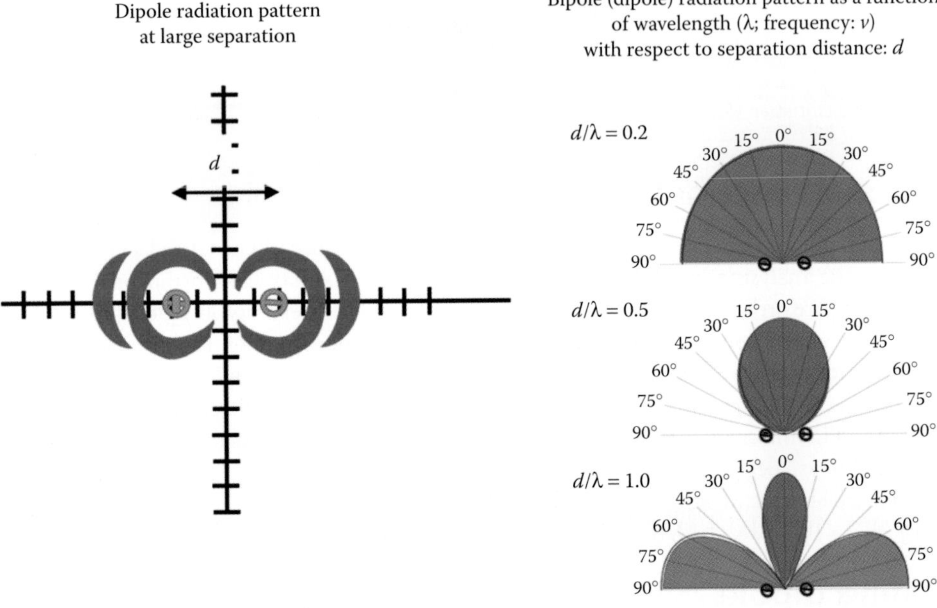

Figure O.42 Oscillating dipole.

Oscillating spring

[acoustics, electronic, fluid-dynamics, general] A MASS (m) attached to a spring that is extended by an external force (F_{ext}) will produce an OSCILLATION that can be damped (critically damped or, or under special conditions, may produce a non-damped HARMONIC OSCILLATION. The restoring force is produced by the extension and follows Hook's law: $\overrightarrow{F_{spring}} = -k\vec{x} = m(d^2/dt^2)\vec{x}$, where k is the spring constant and $\vec{x}$ is the displacement. The solution to the nondamped oscillation as a function of time (t) provides a sinusoidal OSCILLATION described as $\vec{x}(t) = A\cos(\omega t + \phi)$, where A is the AMPLITUDE of the MOTION, the length of stretch of the spring, $\omega = \sqrt{(k/m)}$, and ϕ a PHASE factor. For the damped oscillation, the amplitude will decrease with time resulting from a "frictional force" ($F_{\text{friction}} = -b\vec{v}$, proportional to the velocity $\vec{v}$, with dampening factor b) described as $-k\vec{x} - b\vec{v} = -k\vec{x} - b(d\vec{x}/dt) = m(d^2/dt^2)\vec{x}$, with solution: $\vec{x}(t) = A_0 e^{-\lambda_{\text{damp}} t}\cos(\omega t + \phi)$, where $\lambda_{\text{damp}} = -(b \pm \sqrt{b^2 - 4mk/2m})$; note there are two extreme situations next to the regular damped oscillation: overdamped $b^2 > 4mk$, and underdamped $b^2 < 4mk$. Generally, the square root will be positive with a real solution, whereas an underdamped situation may have an imaginary root solution. The DECAY time of the damped oscillation is $\tau_{\text{decay}} = 2m/b$. For the overdamped situation, the extended spring will return to the equilibrium position without oscillation, gradual exponential decay in extension only. In case a RESONANCE force is applied in a continuous fashion in a sinusoidal format, the oscillation will satisfy: $F_{\text{net}} = -k\vec{x} - b(d\vec{x}/dt) + F_0\cos(\omega' t + \vartheta) = m(d^2/dt^2)\vec{x}$, which will oscillate at the driving frequency ω' and driving amplitude (see Figure O.43).

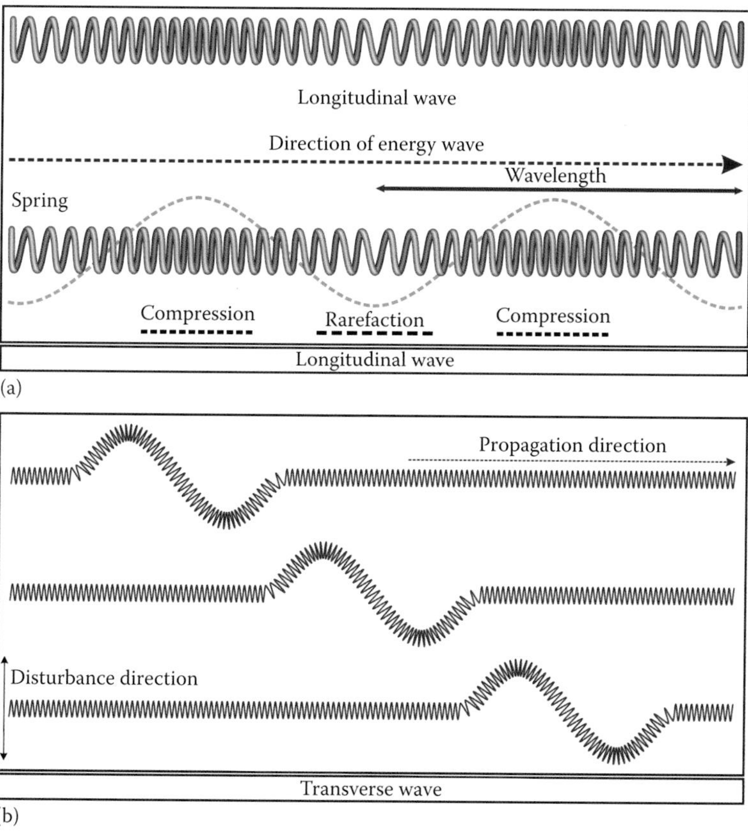

Figure O.43 (a) Oscillating spring. A spring can oscillate in transverse and longitudinal direction, the most common transverse spring oscillation is a vibrating string such as one found on a (b) guitar. *(Continued)*

Figure O.43 (Continued) (c–e) A trampoline is a complex spring, with stretch of material and suspension springs. Additional attractions are in bungee jumps.

Oscillation

[electromagnetism, general, mechanics] Periodic MOTION, repeatedly fluctuating above and below an arbitrary mean value. Examples are the pressure pattern in SOUND waves, electromagnetic signals as well as periodic solutions to mathematical equations (*also see* **SIMPLE HARMONIC OSCILLATION**). Oscillations can be driven by various sources and have external influences. A natural oscillation will require a start-up force and may remain in harmonic displacement (displacement distance: $s(t)$) as a function of TIME (t) indefinitely (i.e., free oscillation, without continuous driving force or undamped oscillation with continuous driving force); however, most oscillations require a continuous driving force or OSCILLATOR (e.g., FORCED OSCILLATION) or will eventually extinguish due to frictional or dampening forces (e.g., damped oscillation). A forced oscillation will result in RESONANCE as a function of time (t), under an external harmonic driving force ($F_{ext} = F_{e0}\sin(\omega_{ext}t)$, with ω_{ext} being the external oscillation angular frequency) to obey the WAVE EQUATION: $m(d^2x/dt^2) + b(dx/dt) + kx = F_{e0}\sin(\omega_{ext}t)$, where b is the dampening coefficient and k is the spring constant. Damped oscillation is the oscillation dampened by external frictional force (F_E)

with steady-state solution: $x = A\cos(\omega_{ext}t + \phi)$, where $A = (F_{e0}/m)/\sqrt{([\omega_0^2 - \omega_{ext}^2]^2 + b^2(\omega_{ext}^2/m^2))}$, and $\omega_0 = \sqrt{(k/m)}$. An example of a frictional force while the body with mass m in motion with displacement $s(t)$ is submerged in a LIQUID is defined proportional to the velocity (v) as $F_E = -b\vec{v} = -b[d\vec{s}(t)/dt]$, where b is the dampening constant and v is the velocity of motion, which yields NEWTON'S SECOND LAW as follows: $\sum F = ma = -ks - b[ds(t)/dt] = m[d^2s(t)/dt^2]$, where $a = [d^2s(t)/dt^2]$ is the acceleration experienced by the body in linear motion. Forced oscillation happens when a sinusoidal force is applied continuously and there will be three forces operating: a restoring SPRING FORCE, a frictional force, and an external oscillating driving force (F_E) with its own operating frequency (ω_E), yielding under Newton's second law: $\sum F = ma = -ks - b[ds(t)/dt] + F_E\sin(\omega_E t) = m[d^2s(t)/dt^2]$. Generally, an oscillation can reach a very high AMPLITUDE under resonance conditions, and in this case, the driving frequency matches the NATURAL FREQUENCY of the harmonic oscillator in one of the harmonic states, the resonant angular frequency: $\omega_R = \sqrt{\omega_0^2 - (b^2/2m^2)}$, which reduces to the NATURAL ANGULAR FREQUENCY ($\omega_0 = \sqrt{k/m}$) when the dampening is negligibly small (*also see* **MASS–SPRING SYSTEM**). In an electric system consisting of capacitors, inductors and resistors with a driving harmonic voltage source the equations are as follows. The sine-wave oscillator voltage source (V) is defined by both an INDUCTOR and a CAPACITOR with current (i) and inductance (L): $V = L(di/dt)$ and capacitance C, yielding $i = C(dV/dt)$. Combining both components gives $i + LC(d^2i/dt^2) = 0$, with undamped resonance ANGULAR-FREQUENCY $\omega = 1/\sqrt{LC}$ or frequency $\nu = 1/(2\pi\sqrt{LC})$ and solution $i = A\sin(\omega t + \phi)$, where ϕ is an undefined phase constant and A is a boundary condition dependent constant; this frequency has significant similarity to the PENDULUM frequency described by Galileo. When adding a dampener such as a RESISTOR (R) to the circuit, the differential equation becomes $i + RC(di/dt) + LC(d^2i/dt^2) = 0$, with an exponentially decaying solution: $i = Ae^{-(t/\tau)}\sin(\omega t + \phi)$, where τ is a factor indicating the DECAY time. Generally, the voltage output of the current driven oscillator is defined as $V_{out} = R_A i_{in}$, where R_A is the gain of the oscillator (technically a negative value with units of RESISTANCE [Ω]). In case the gain could be matched to a physical resistance, then the oscillator would be described by the undamped equation; however, there are many factors in the gain that cannot be matched by a linear resistance (e.g., phase shift and other nonlinear properties), which requires the introduction of a nonlinear amplifier that has a higher gain at low voltages and a low gain at a high voltage. This nonlinearity changes the format and the amplifier can, for instance, be CUBIC, which allows it to be described by the VAN DER POL EQUATION: $(d^2\xi/dt^2) + \epsilon(\xi^2 - 1)(d\xi/dt) + x = 0$, where ξ is an electronic identity (current or potential) that varies with time t, whereas ϵ is a coefficient indicating dampening and attenuation in combination with COMPLIANCE, including system nonlinearities. Another form of oscillation is in RESONANCE. Mechanical resonance can be achieved by means of a PIEZOELECTRIC actuator. The piezoelectric oscillation has both mechanical and electrical influences, where the electric part can be represented by a Colpitts oscillator operating with frequency: $\nu = \left(2\pi\sqrt{L[C_1C_2/(C_1 + C_2)]}\right)^{-1}$, where the inductor is represented by the piezoelectric crystal. (*also see* **RESONANCE** *and* **PIEZOELECTRIC RESONANCE**). An entirely different type of oscillation is in chemical binding where the chemical reaction changes periodically in time or location toward a higher entropy or a lower state of Gibbs free ENERGY. The increase in entropy is represented by an increase of product with an associated decrease in reactants through an intermediate reaction product. The rate of formation and destruction of intermediate dictates the chemical component oscillation process in both time and space. This process is referred to as OSCILLATORY REACTION (see Figure O.44).

O

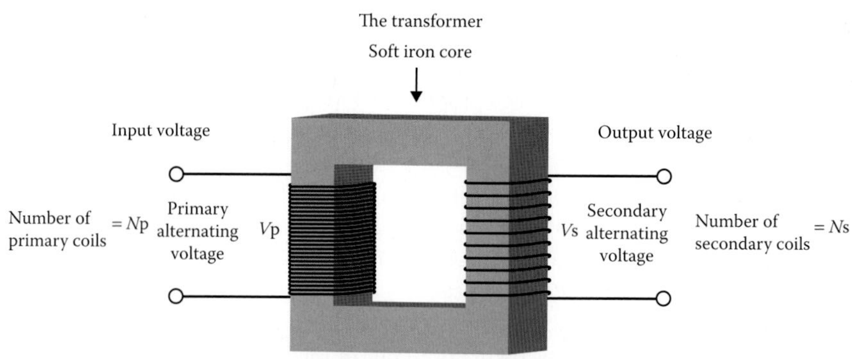

Step-up transformer: Secondary voltage Vs > Primary voltage Vp

Step-down transformer: Secondary voltage Vs < Primary voltage Vp

Formula for calculating voltages: $\frac{Vp}{Vs} = \frac{Np}{Ns}$

Step-down transformer

Primary voltage

Secondary voltage

Alternating voltage

+ 0 −

Time

Step-up transformer

Secondary voltage

Primary voltage

Alternating voltage

+ 0 −

Time

(a)

Electro-magnetic induction

S N

Insulated tube

Magnet moves into and out of the coil, generating a magnetic field opposing the motion.

An induced alternating current and voltage is generated.

S N

Insulated tube

Oscillating magnet movement

Magnet at peak of motion

Magnet is stationary

Alternating voltage and current

+ 0 −

Time

Magnet motion is reversed

(b)

L

(c)

Figure O.44 (a,b) Generalized oscillation and (c) mass oscillating between elastic barriers.

Oscillator

[general] Mechanical or electronic mechanism of action resulting in a HARMONIC OSCILLATION of a specific medium including but not limited to electromagnetic (e.g., light and radio), electric (e.g., alternating current [AC] voltage), spring (e.g., tuning fork), molecular (i.e., temperature), and SOUND (e.g., vocal cords, drum, whistle, and woofer) (*also see* MASS–SPRING SYSTEM) (see Figure O.45).

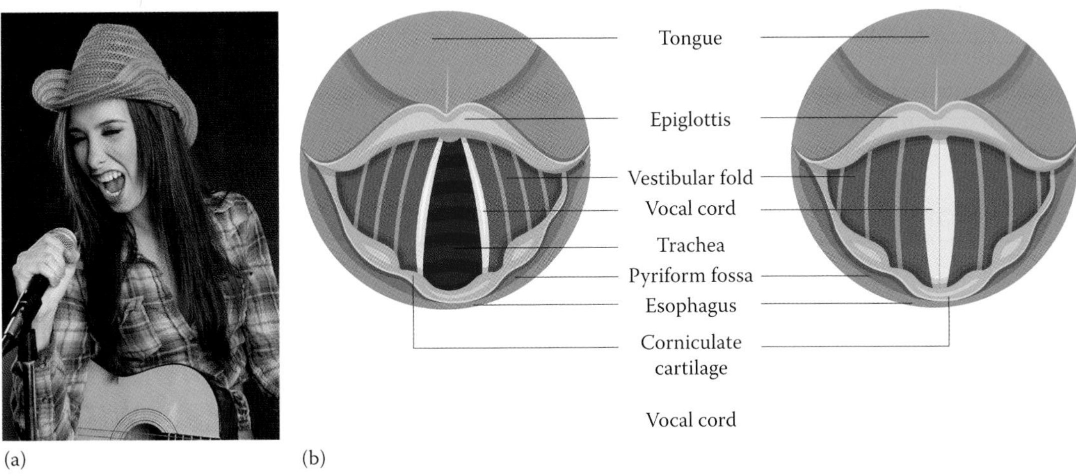

Figure O.45 (a,b) Vocal cords oscillator.

Oscillator quantum number

[nuclear] In atomic PHYSICS, the particle MOTION becomes subject to the SCHRÖDINGER EQUATION due to fact that the QUANTUM harmonic oscillator is the quantum-mechanical equivalent to the classical harmonic oscillator. The application of an arbitrary electrical potential (i.e., COULOMB POTENTIAL) considered in the vicinity of a stable equilibrium point can generally be approximated as a harmonic potential. The quantum harmonic oscillator is one of the most significant mathematical systems in QUANTUM MECHANICS. The quantum harmonic oscillator can be described by the Hamiltonian of the oscillating PARTICLE (e.g., electron) with mass m as $H_{opp} = (p_{opp}{}^2/2m) + (1/2)m\omega^2 x_{opp}{}^2$, where $p_{opp} = i\hbar(\partial/\partial x)$ is the momentum operator, $\hbar = h/2\pi$, $h = 6.62606957 \times 10^{-34}\ \mathrm{m^2kg/s}$ is the Planck's constant, $\omega = 2\pi\nu$ is the ANGULAR VELOCITY, ν is the frequency of motion, and x_{opp} is the position operator. The Schrödinger equation now becomes $H_{opp}\Psi = E\Psi$ (this corresponds to $-(\hbar^2/2m)(d^2/dx^2)\Psi(x) + U(x)\Psi(x) = E\Psi(x)$, where $U(x)$ is the potential ENERGY EIGENFUNCTION, which can be represented for the quantum harmonic oscillator as $U(x) = (1/2)k_{spring}x^2$), with eigenvalues solutions $|\Psi$ for the WAVEFUNCTION at the energy states E, under boundary conditions described by de Broglie relationship. The SOLUTION series are $\Psi_n(x) = \left(1/\sqrt{2^n n!}\right)(m\omega/\pi\hbar)^{1/4} e^{-(m\omega x^2/2\hbar)} H_n\left(\sqrt{(m\omega/\hbar)}x\right)$, where $n = 0, 1, \ldots$ is the oscillatory quantum number with corresponding eigenvalues for the energy levels $E_n = \hbar\omega[n + (1/2)] = [n + (1/2)]h\nu$ and $H_n = (-1)^n e^{x^2}(d^n/dx^n)(e^{-x^2})$, which are Hermite polynomials.

Oscillatory flow

[biomedical, fluid dynamics] Biological flow can be oscillatory or pulsatile, as can be system flow (e.g., piston flow or the FLOW from a water pump in an automobile). In biological systems, the RESPIRATION, vascular, and auditory flow is oscillatory pulsatile. Oscillatory flow has, for instance, the Womersley $\left(\alpha_{Wo} = r\sqrt{\rho\omega/\eta}\right.$, where r is the radius of the conduit, ω is the angular velocity FREQUENCY (ν) of the OSCILLATION ($\omega = 2\pi\nu$), ρ is the fluid density, and η is the VISCOSITY and Strouhal ($Sr = \nu L/v_{\nu}$, where ν_{v} is the frequency of VORTEX SHEDDING, L is the characteristic length, and v is the velocity of flow) number as boundary conditions. Small Strouhal number will represent LAMINAR FLOW. The PULSATILE FLOW obeys the Navier–Stokes equation, and has WAVE pattern characteristics. Because of INERTIA as well as viscosity and strain, the wave movement for a FLUID in oscillatory flow will be out-of-phase over the radial velocity distribution at any location along the length of flow (*see* **BLOOD FLOW**).

Oscillatory reaction

[chemical, energy, quantum] A chemical binding reaction where the chemical reaction changes periodically in time or location toward a higher entropy or a lower state of Gibbs free ENERGY. The increase in entropy is represented by an increase of product with an associated decrease in reactants through an intermediate reaction product. The rate of formation and destruction of intermediate dictates the chemical component OSCILLATION process in both time and space. One example is the Belousov–Zhabotinsky reaction, a competing effort between two reagents: bromide (Br) and cerium (Ce). The process involves the reactive oxidation of an organic substrate by the highly reactive bromate ion (BrO_3^-), in the presence of bromide ions (Br^-) and the reaction is catalyzed by a metal ION such as the constituent ion of cerium (Ce^{3+}), which has two potential states of oxidation. The bromide ion is oxidized by bromate until the concentration drops below a threshold value when the process is replaced by the OXIDATION of the cerium ion, both reactions represented as follows: $BrO_3^- + 2Br^- + 3H^+ \rightarrow 3HOBr$ (slow) and $BrO_3^- + 4Ce^{3+} + 5H^+ \rightarrow HOBr + 4Ce^{4+} + 2H_2O$ (fast). The cerium ion reduction is in fact inhibited by the presence of the bromide ion creating the environment for a cyclic reaction. In this cyclic reaction, the bromide will be reduced in quantity until the Cesium reaction takes over again. Both the products of the bromate reaction forming a bromide hydroxyl (HOBr) as hypobromous ACID and the cesium reaction will now interact intermittently with the organic MATTER, which in turn creates the bromide ion needed to shut down the Cesium reaction in the format: $\text{Organic Matter} + Ce^{4+} + HOBr \rightarrow Br^- + Ce^{3+} + \text{Bromated Organic Matter} + \text{Oxidized Organic Matter}$, which in turn will refuel the Bromide reaction. This oscillatory reaction process may also create an analyte migratory WAVE pattern (i.e., periodic mass-transport). Additionally, the exothermic portion of the described reactions will in turn also describe a temporal and spatial oscillatory process, called a THERMOKINETIC OSCILLATOR. Metabolic processes such as the formation of ATP and concurrent depletion of ADP are spatially confined by the MEMBRANE processes, imposing spatial constraints on the reaction process, which in turn leads to oscillatory reaction processes in time as well as space.

Oscilloscope

[general] Device used to display time-varying signals by diverting an electron beam (CATHODE ray) in the vertical direction based on the MAGNITUDE of the SIGNAL strength, while the horizontal axis is a time frame reference. The oscilloscope uses a VACUUM tube with a cathode-based electron gun and horizontal and vertical deflection plates that are electrically charged by external potentials. The electron beam is targeting a fluorescent screen that writes the time-dependent AMPLITUDE for visual interpretation (see Figure O.46).

O

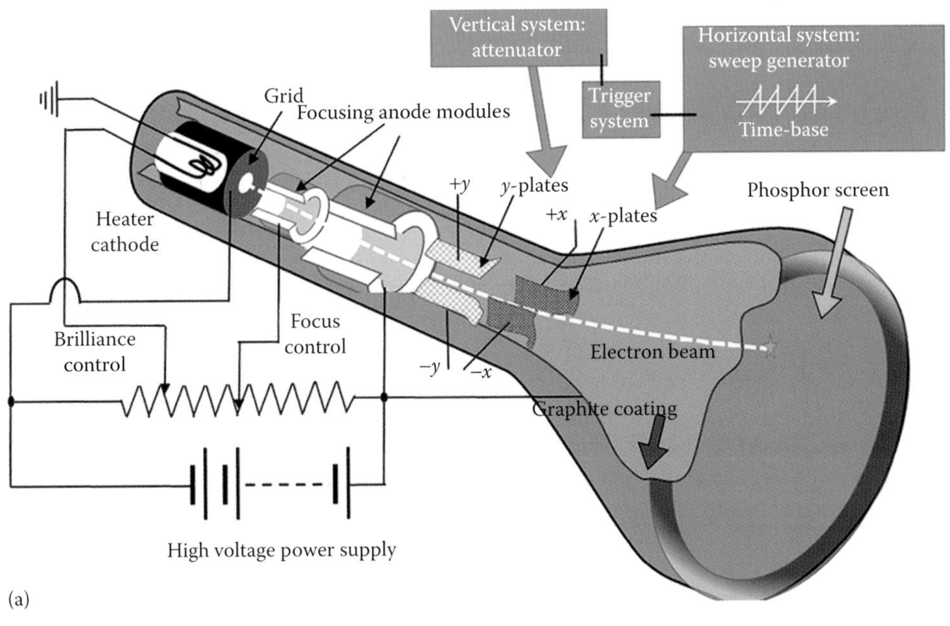

(a)

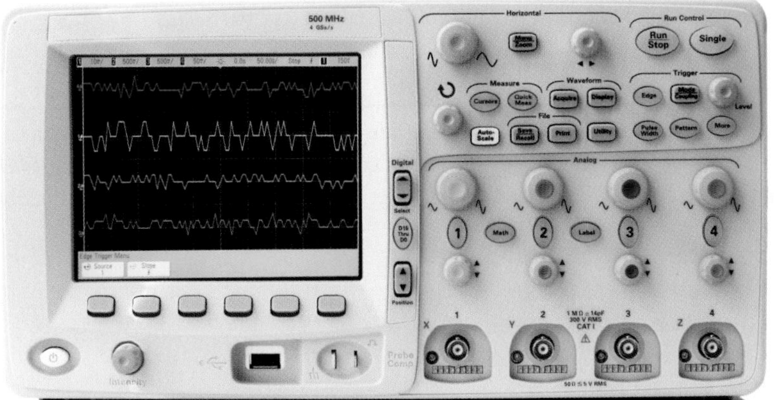

(b)

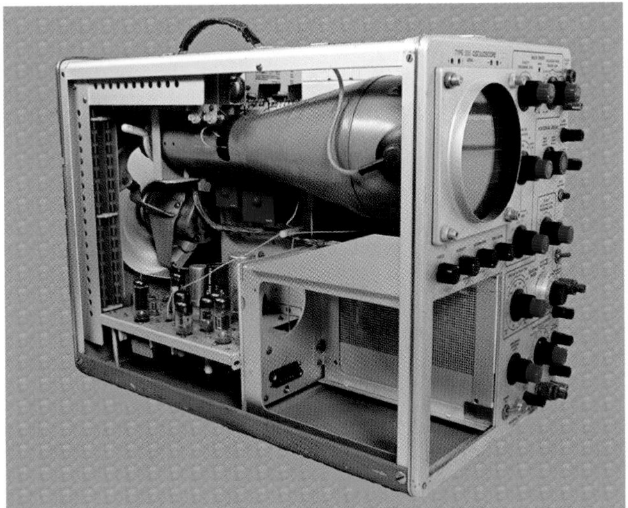

(c)

Figure O.46 (a–c) Oscilloscope.

Osmolality

[biomedical, chemical] Measure of the moles or osmoles (molar concentration of individual SOLUTE particles) of constituent solute per kilogram of SOLVENT medium expressed as (mol/kg, or molal). Note this compares to osmolarity by conversion of kilograms to liters.

Osmolarity ($\Sigma[C_i]$)

[biomedical, chemical] Sum of the molar concentrations ($[C_i]$) of dissolved solutes (measure of osmoles of solute per liter of SOLVENT medium), considering the partial pressures of the individual constituents: $\Sigma\left[C_i\right]$. When the solute concentration exceeds the EQUILIBRIUM STATE or the concentration assessed at the starting point, the FLUID becomes hyperosmotic. When the loss of electrolytes exceeds the loss of solvent, the SOLUTION becomes hypoosmotic. When the situation at the beginning and end are equal in osmotic value, although the absolute quantity need not be preserved, the solution is isosmotic or ISOTONIC. This also applies to two solutions in equilibrium across a SEMIPERMEABLE MEMBRANE. Ionic compounds, such as salts, in solution will generally dissociate into their constituent ions, thus giving the osmolarity of the two dissolved constituent. In contrast, the molarity of the solution is based on the base compound, the joint components of the dissociated solute.

Osmole

[biomedical, chemical] Molar concentration of individual SOLUTE particles.

Osmosis

[biomedical, chemical, thermodynamics] "Active" transfer of SOLVENT through a MEMBRANE (most notably SEMIPERMEABLE MEMBRANE) based on a difference in concentration of a variety of solutes. The FLUID transfer (FLOW and FLUX) for osmosis is generally faster than regular DIFFUSION. Specifically in biological applications, the osmotic transfer of interstitial fluid across the CELL MEMBRANE relies on gates that will open, or open wider under the influence of a CHEMICAL GRADIENT across the BARRIER (see Figure O.47).

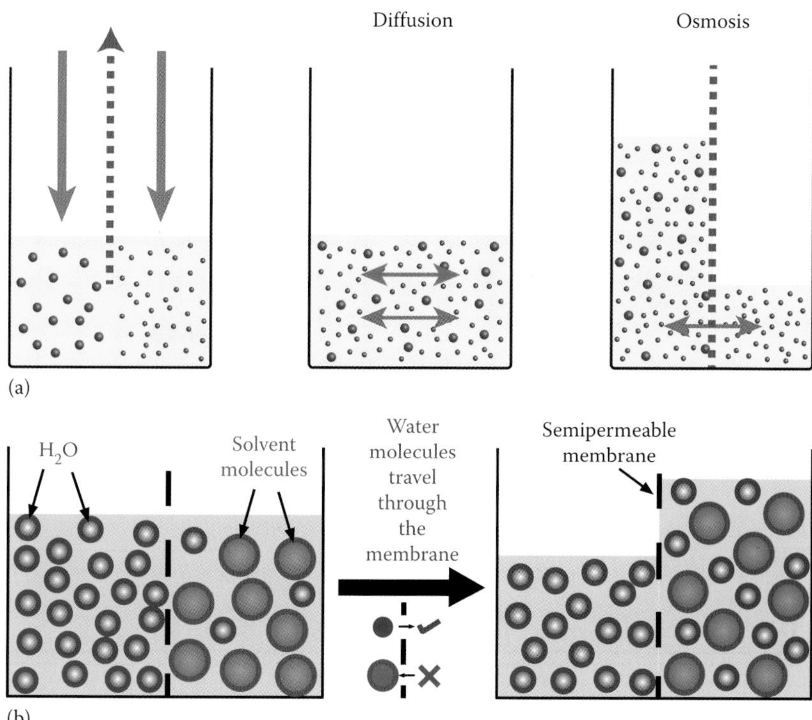

Figure O.47 (a,b) Osmosis.

Osmotic coefficient (Φ_{osm})

[biomedical, fluid dynamics] Quantity that provides a characterization of the deviation from ideal behavior for a SOLVENT, as defined by RAOULT'S LAW, defined with respect to OSMOLALITY as $\Phi_{osm} = (\mu_A^* - \mu_A)/(RTM_A\Sigma[C_i])$, where μ_A is the chemical potential of the solvent in the SOLUTION, μ_A^* is the chemical potential of the solvent, M_A is the MOLAR MASS, $R = 8.3144621(75)$ J/Kmol is the GAS constant, $\Sigma[C_i]$ is the osmolarity, and T is the temperature (in Kelvin). The osmotic coefficient (based on molality) is related to the Gibbs free ENERGY ($G(T,V,N)$), in this case available in excess to a stationary (ideal solvent) condition, as $RT(1-\Phi_{osm}) = G_{excess} - \sum[C_i](dG_{excess}/d[C_i])$.

Osmotic pressure

[thermodynamics] Solute pressure that is a direct function of the OSMOLARITY ($\Sigma[C_i]$) of a solution: $\Pi = \Sigma[C_i]RT$, where T is the TEMPERATURE and $R = 8.3144621(75)$ J/Kmol the GAS constant.

The net osmotic pressure across a SEMIPERMEABLE MEMBRANE will directly depend on the net cumulative concentration difference across the MEMBRANE (see Figure O.48).

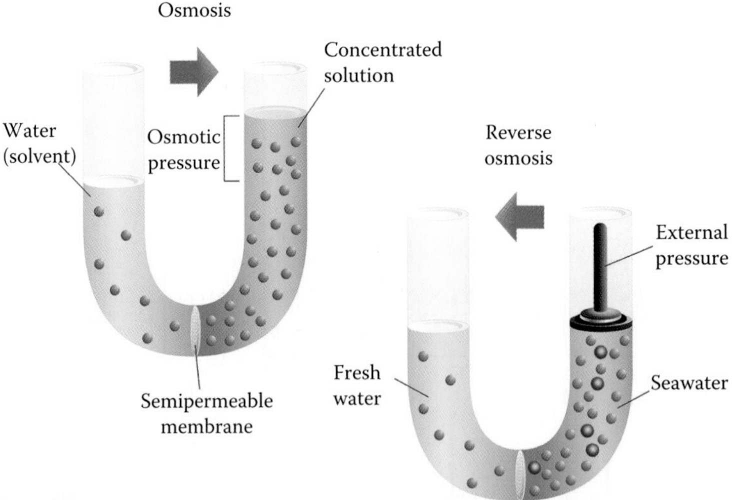

Figure O.48 Osmotic pressure.

Osmotic pressure (Π_{osm}), Van't Hoff relation for

[fluid dynamics, thermodynamics] Chemical pressure associated with the concentration of a SOLUTE in a SOLVENT, with respect to the individual solutes, each providing a partial pressure that resembles the partial pressure for a GAS. The osmotic pressure (Π_{osm}) is a function of the number of ions that result from the dissociation of the solute (i), the concentration of the SOLUTE ([Solute]), and the OSMOTIC COEFFICIENT (ϕ_{osm}) indicating the mobility of the solute: $\Pi_{osm} = i\phi_{osm}\left[\text{Solute}\right]RT$, where T is the ABSOLUTE TEMPERATURE and $R = 8.3144621(75)$ J/Kmol is the universal gas constant. Osmotic pressure influences the boiling point of a LIQUID as well as the FREEZING point. The osmotic pressure of a SOLUTION can be derived from the freezing point depression (ΔT_f) based on $i\phi_{osm}\left[\text{Solute}\right] = \Delta T_f/1.86$. When two solutions are separated by a SEMIPERMEABLE MEMBRANE, the balance can be iso-osmotic for identical osmotic pressure and hence no DIFFUSION, or alternatively higher on side 1 (arbitrary, generally outside, vs. inside [2]): hyperosmotic, or reduced pressure on the outside: hypoosmotic.

Ossicles

[biomedical] The three critical mechanical components in the human MIDDLE EAR responsible for the HEARING process, connecting the tympanic MEMBRANE to the oval membrane on the cholea by means of the hammer (malleus), anvil (incus), and stirrup (stapes) (see Figure O.49).

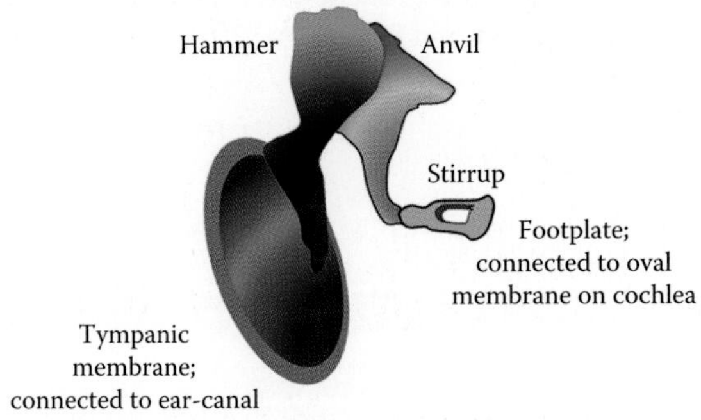

Figure O.49 The ossicles of the middle ear.

O

Osteoblast

[biomedical, mechanics] Large cell in bone responsible for the synthesis and mineralization of bone formation. The function of the OSTEOBLAST persist from initial bone formation to bone remodeling in regenerative processes. Osteoblats are part of a closely packed sheet of cells close to the external surface of the bone. Osteoblast are "activated" by mechanical strain. The osteoblast will attempt to reinforce the bone where the strain may have the highest risk for crack formation (i.e. mechanical healing action) (see Figure O.50).

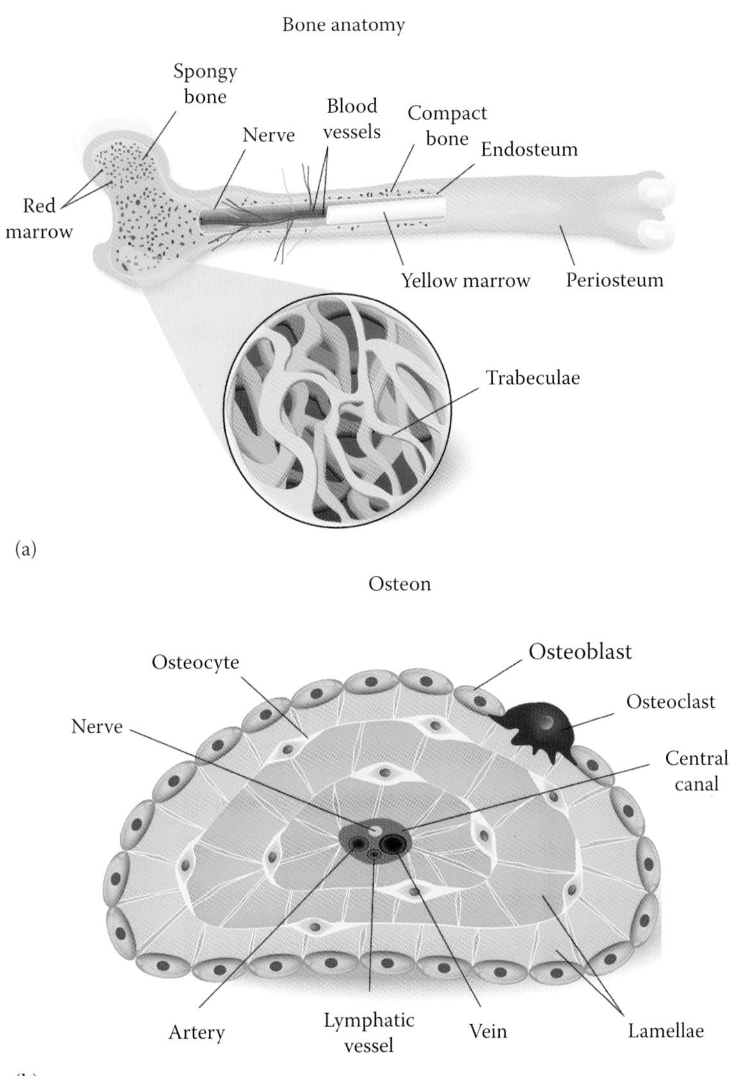

Figure O.50 (a) Osteoblast in osteon of (b) bone formation.

Osteoclast

[biomedical] Large cell in bone that is responsible for the resorbtion of bone cells that are nearing the end of their useful life span as part of the continuous regeneration process. Osteoclasts are spread throughout the bone. An osteoclast performs a function in bone remodeling in response to applied strain Osteoclasts are descended from stem cells (see Figure O.51).

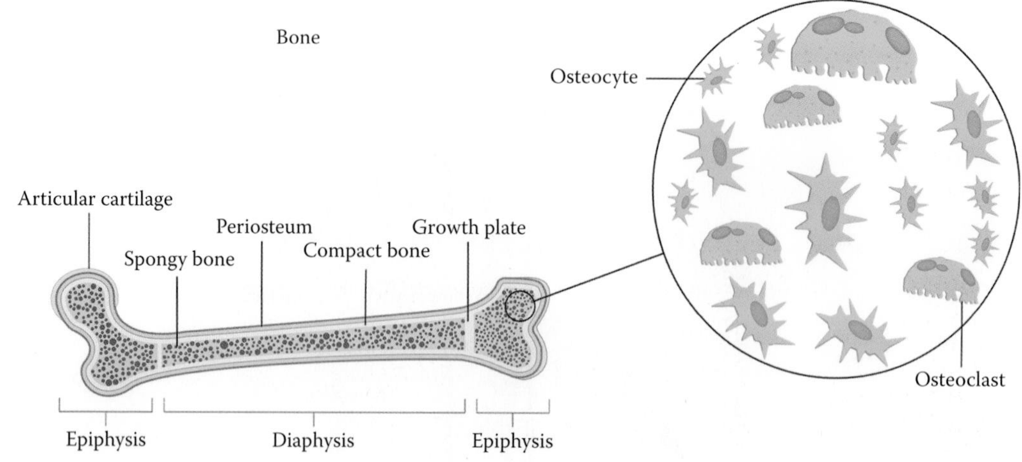

Figure O.51 Osteoclast.

Ostwald, Dilution law

[atomic, general, quantum] *See* **Dilution law of Ostwald.**

Ostwald, Wilhelm (1853–1932)

[chemical, solid-state, quantum] A chemist from Germany whose work contributed to the ion-theory published by Svante August Arrhenius (1859–1927) (see Figure O.52).

Figure O.52 Wilhelm Ostwald (1853–1932).

Otto, Nikolaus August (1832–1891)

[mechanics, thermodynamics] An engineer from Germany, or the Prussian Empire at the time. He is the inventor of the first INTERNAL-COMBUSTION ENGINE using the four-stroke mechanism of intake through the intake VALVE (increasing volume), compression, combustion with the use of a spark-plug—followed by EXPANSION and forced movement of the piston, and the final stroke pushing the exhaust fumes out through the exit valve) with the use of a piston transferring the ENERGY into work (see Figure O.53).

Figure O.53 (a) Nikolaus August Otto (1832–1891) and (b,c) Otto internal combustion principle for a V-8 engine.

Otto cycle

[thermodynamics] Idealized thermodynamic cycle representing the mechanism of action of a four-stroke INTERNAL COMBUSTION ENGINE, operating by means of spark ignition, as found in a reciprocating piston engine. The importance of the Otto cycle is the prevalence of this thermodynamic cycle in automobile engines. The process is named after NIKOLAUS AUGUST OTTO (1832–1891), who described the operations of the four-stroke engine in 1876. The efficiency of an ideal Otto cycle is described by the ratio of work performed to the heat input: $\eta_{eff} = (\text{work/heat input}) = (Q_H + Q_L)/Q_H = 1 + (1/r_{comp}{}^{\gamma_{PV}-1})$, where Q_L is the loss of heat due to the exhaust of warm fluid, Q_H is the combustion heat, $r_{comp} = V_1/V_2$ is the compression ratio comparing the cylinder volume at the end of intake (V_1) to the volume under compression (reached primarily just after combustion; combustion in modern engines is several degrees before the top position of the cylinder), and the coefficient γ_{PV} represents the abiabatic process in the PV diagram: $T_4V_1{}^{\gamma_{PV}-1} = T_3V_2{}^{\gamma_{PV}-1}$ and $T_1V_1{}^{\gamma_{PV}-1} = T_2V_2{}^{\gamma_{PV}-1}$ (see Figure O.54).

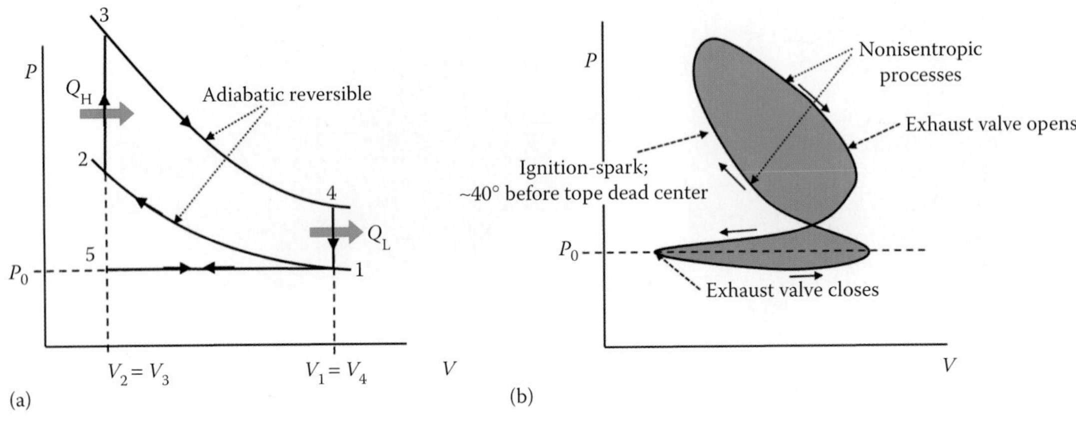

Figure O.54 Otto cycle: (a) ideal and (b) actual.

Outer ear

[general] The EAR canal extending to the open AIR along with the external ear shell, connecting with the MIDDLE EAR at the tympanic MEMBRANE, further transferring the mechanical (acoustic) ENERGY by means of the OSSICLES to the INNER EAR (see Figure O.55).

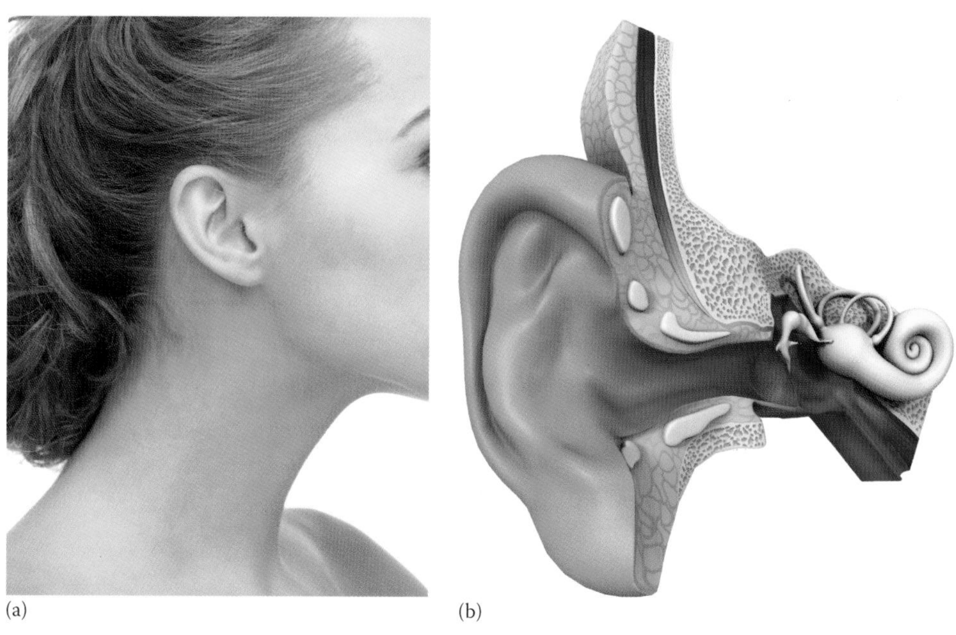

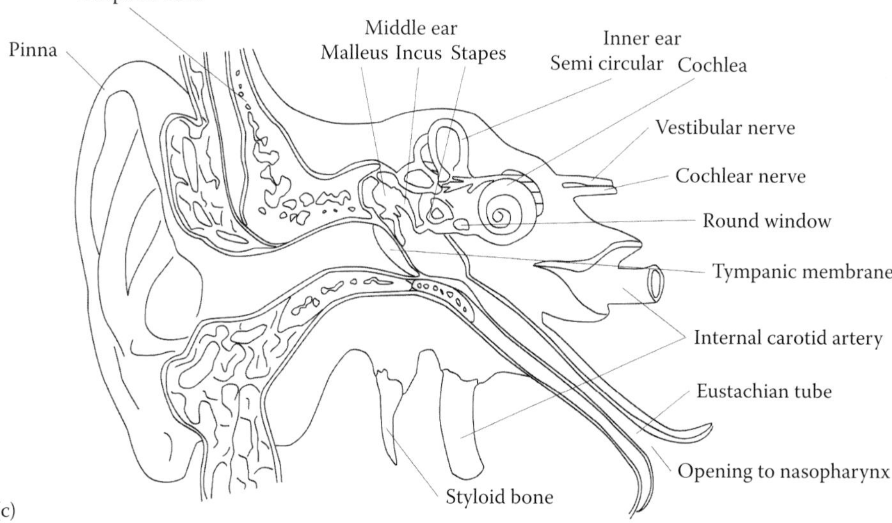

Figure O.55 (a,b) Outer ear anatomy and (c) reference to middle and inner ear. *(Continued)*

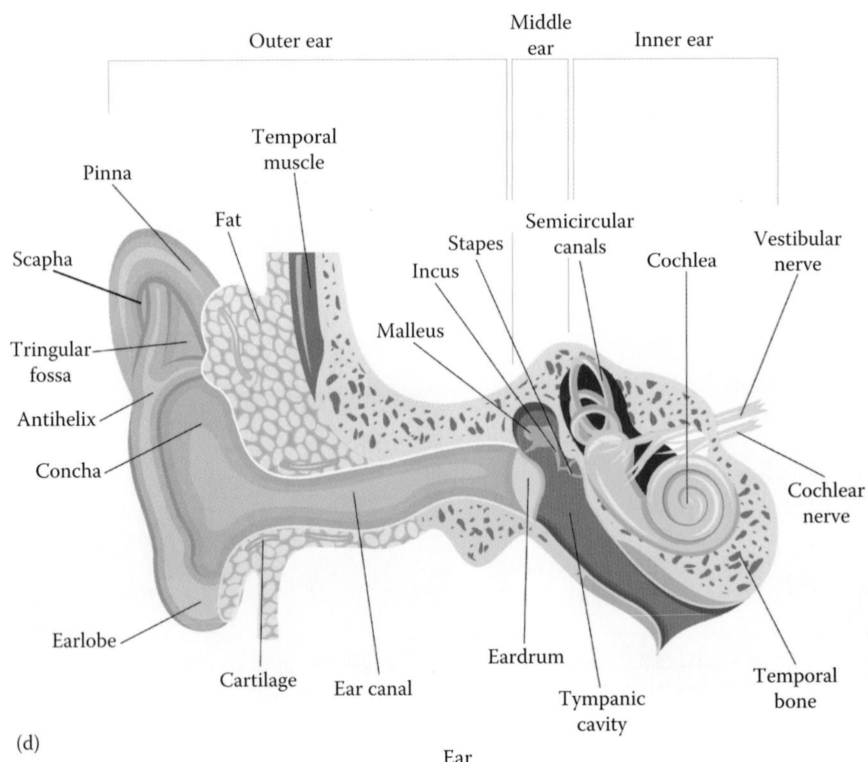

Figure O.55 (Continued) (d) reference to middle and inner ear.

Overtone

[acoustics, general] Waves emitted in addition to the FUNDAMENTAL FREQUENCY; the first overtone equates to the second harmonic (*see* **HARMONICS**).

Oxidation

[biomedical, chemical] EXOTHERMIC REACTION that combines (oxidation) oxygen with respect to another CHEMICAL COMPOUND. The process of oxygen removal is generally endothermic and is referred to as "reduction." Oxidation of carbohydrates and fossil fuels will generally result in the formation of water and carbon dioxide under the oxidation and combustion processes. A chemical reaction that involves changing the oxygen binding (oxidation) process is referred to as a "REDOX REACTION." More generally, a redox reaction pertains to the electron transfer between species. For example, combining oxygen and hydrogen forming water pertains to the fact that oxygen is reduced and hydrogen is oxidized. Another example of an oxidation reaction is the combining of hydrogen and fluorine: $H_2 + F_2 \rightarrow 2HF$.

Oximeter

[biomedical, optics] *See* **PULSE OXIMETER**.

Oxygen [$^{16}_{8}O$, O_2]

[biomedical, chemical, general] Chemical ELEMENT that is used in conversion of chemical elements to form ENERGY. The Earth's ATMOSPHERE consists of approximately 20.95% oxygen at sea level, less at greater altitudes. Oxygen in the UNIVERSE as we currently know is presumably the third most prevalent chemical, after hydrogen and helium. In biological units, oxygen forms a significant component of the following chemical compounds: carbohydrates, fats, nucleic acids, and proteins. In inorganic media, oxygen is part of the following chemical structures: silicon dioxide (silica, found most prominently as quartz), water, and many oxides. Note that most METAL oxides are transparent, whereas under environmental conditions generally a hydroxide is formed, including both hydrogen and oxygen. Oxygen was discovered around 1773 by Swedish chemist CARL WILHELM SCHEELE (1742–1786), and independently by English theologian and chemist JOSEPH PRIESTLEY (1733–1804) in 1774, and potentially by French chemist ANTOINE-LAURENT DE LAVOISIER (1743–1794) in 1778, who ultimately named it. Oxygen liquefies at 90.20 K and turns solid at 54.36 K (see Figure O.56).

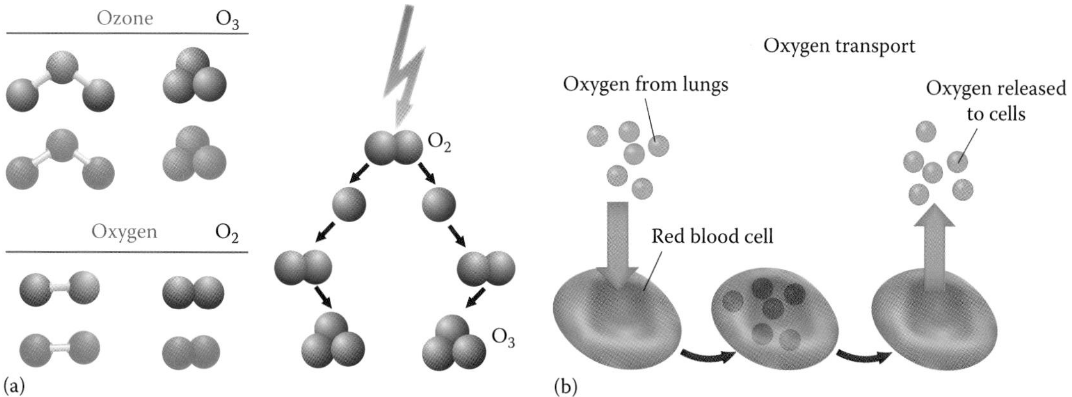

Figure O.56 (a) Oxygen and its relation to ozone and (b) biological oxygen transportation through uptake by hemoglobin in the lung and release in tissue partially regulated by osmotic pressure.

Oxygen sensor

[biomedical, chemical] A sensor that measures the quantity of oxygen as either relative or absolute. Oxygen sensors are used to measure the reaction process of chemical events. A specific application is found in automobiles to regulate the fuel-oxygen mixture for high efficiency combustion, also referred to as "Lambda sensor."

Ozone, [O_3]

[biomedical, chemical, general] Inorganic molecule with scientific name: $1\lambda^1, 3\lambda^1$ – trioxidane, also named μ – oxidodioxygen. Unstable allotrope of the ELEMENT oxygen, compared to the diatomic allotrope O_2, discovered in 1865 by Swiss chemist JACQUES-LOUIS SORET (1827–1890). Condensation point is 161 K and MELTING POINT is 80 K (see Figure O.57).

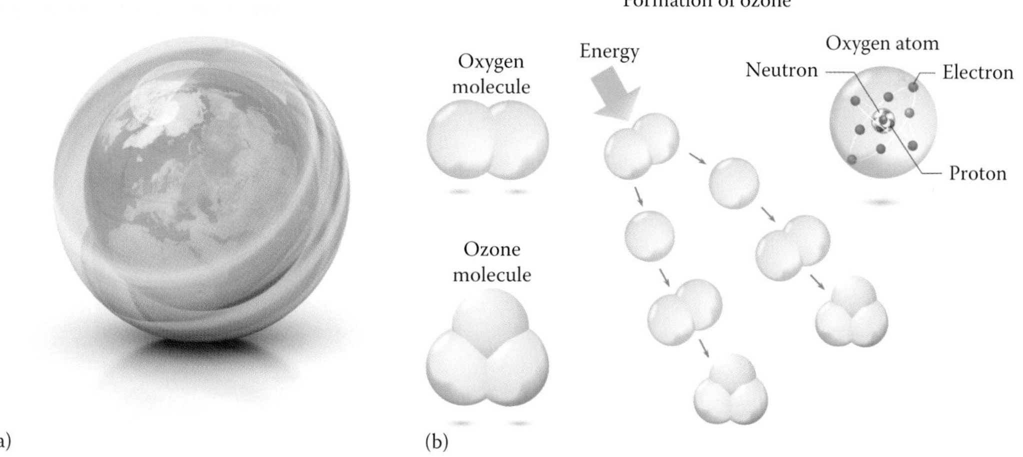

Figure O.57 (a) Ozone gas (NPT, normal pressure and normal temperature) and (b) formation process.

Index of Names

Note: Names are arranged in chronological order by date of birth. Page numbers followed by f refer to images.

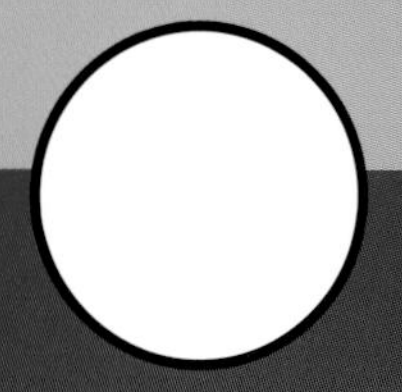

Index of Subjects

Note: Page numbers followed by f and t refer to figures and tables, respectively.